Wholes 2024 Eq
Fallon

MW00658571

MIND DYNAMICS

IN SPACE AND TIME

A PHYSICIST'S EXPLORATION OF THE NATURE AND PROPERTIES OF CONSCIOUSNESS

By
Elizabeth A. Rauscher, Ph.D.
and
Prof. J.J. Hurtak, Ph.D., Ph.D.
& Desiree Hurtak, Ph.D.

Drs. James and Desiree Hurtak, Editors

THE ACADEMY FOR
FUTURE SCIENCE

Academy For Future Science
P.O. Box FE
Los Gatos, CA 95031
www.futurescience.org

Copyright © 2016 Elizabeth Rauscher,
James J. Hurtak and Desiree Hurtak

All rights reserved. This book is fully protected by copyright and no part of it may be reproduced in any form or by any means, including photocopying, computers, audio, visual or any electronic devices for information storage and retrieval systems, the internet, the world wide web or any other system without written permission from the copyright owners.

Cover Design:
Desiree Hurtak

Additional thanks to:
Janet Phares and *Trish Roberson*

Printed in the USA

ISBN: 978-1-892139-44-3

Table of Contents

Dedication 5

Acknowledgement 7

Uncertainty II 9

Foreword by Drs. James and Desiree Hurtak 11

Introduction: The Role of Consciousness in
Modern Physical Theories 17

Chapter 1: Criterion and Evidence for
the Existence of Anomalous Phenomena 27

Chapter 2: The Remote Perception Phenomena:
A Doorway To Expanded Consciousness Awareness 63

Chapter 3: The Reality of Remote Perception, Local,
Long Distance, and Precognitive Experiments 107

Chapter 4: Los Angeles Area To San Francisco Bay Area
Remote Perception Experiment 217

Chapter 5: The Physics of PSI Phenomena in Space and Time .. 277

Chapter 6: Nonlocality as a Fundamental Principle of Reality:
Bell's Theorem, Space-Like Interconnectedness 377

Chapter 7: Quantum Mechanics and
The Observer as a Participator 419

Chapter 8: The Relationship of Complex Eight Space, The Kaluza-Klein Model and The Properties of PSI to The Current Physics and Unified Theories 479

Chapter 9: Concluding Remarks 507

Chapter 10: Mind Dynamics Unfolded 543

Chapter 11: Experimental Programs in Paraphysical Communication and Remote Viewing with Dr. A. Puharich at Lab Nine, Ossining, New York 1974-1975 557

Chapter 12: Remote Viewing Experiments Between Dr. Elizabeth Rauscher and Drs. J.J. and Desiree Hurtak 591

Chapter 13: The Nature and Properties of Consciousness 653

DEDICATION

**To all those who are awakening
to the Great Discovery of sharing life with
Life beyond Earth.**

This book is dedicated to one of those people whose life on this planet has touched so many in a positive manner with his special and unique knowledge and gifts, Ingo Swann. His passing in 2013 touched me deeply and I learned so much from him as he changed my life for the better. I remember camping in Yosemite National Park with him and friends, as well as staying at his loft in the Bowery of New York City. I sometimes note the smell of turpentine in places whenever there is none, and think of Ingo and his artwork in New York.

Ingo said I did the best of anyone in his psi tests and I had great undeveloped psychic abilities. He was real enthusiastic and showed Hal Puthoff and Russell Targ my results. Ed May said I should get a job as a psychic. I thought that all sounded good, but maybe it was just good luck, or is good luck really what is behind psi functioning?

— Dr. Elizabeth A. Rauscher

A DEDICATION TO INGO SWANN

We salute you who painted the universe with different colors and opened our world to the importance of whirling galaxies in the mind. You who are a witness to the opening of new pages of existence.

You introduced a greater space of reflection and a world of higher consciousness, providing us with a greater understanding of the Universal Mind. You, and those who have been pioneers in the field of consciousness studies, have helped humanity strip away the limited concepts of life and opened the perception of people everywhere. As we now begin to participate in the quantum leap of consciousness, let us hope that we all can find a greater awareness of Life as we help humanity discover its true higher destiny.

— Drs. J. J. and Desiree Hurtak

ACKNOWLEDGEMENT

I, Elizabeth, wish to thank the Parapsychology Foundation of New York, the Orb Foundation of London, England, Essentia Research Associates of Amherst, Wisconsin, The Academy For Future Science, and SRI International of California for their support. I also wish to acknowledge the assistance of the Lawrence Berkeley National Laboratory in supplying facilities for the operation of my "Fundamental "Fysiks" Group" during part of my employment at Lawrence Berkeley National Laboratory and University of California Berkeley.

— Dr. Elizabeth A. Rauscher

UNCERTAINTY II
by E. A. Rauscher, Ph.D.

Waves crash, roar —
foam and fly
to Ocean's golden glow.
Cliffs rise to Cobalt sky —
Sand Pipers darting
at the rolling edge of foam.
The waves
in unpredictable habits
rush in ever unforetold patterns
Laughing at me in their joy.

The water's (ever changing) path
creates waves and wrinkles
in the sand.
Where each drop and where
each grain shall
travel and rest
No one knows.

The verse of time is sung
and the Creator's Eye sees —
But who knows each atom's path or where
each one shall be?
Uncertainty rules
a world 'beyond our ken'
and chaos and order interweave in the
dance of Life.

I and the Un(I)verse
are one but
No "I" knows the
unfolding path
Laying before Us
like a great mirage.
Know uncertainty reigns
and adventure rules Supreme
Only change is a certainty
and Now is Every time.

FOREWORD

by J.J. Hurtak, Ph.D., Ph.D.

and Desiree Hurtak, Ph.D.

Mind Dynamics in Space and Time, involves an immense *summa* by E. A. Rauscher, one of the leading physicists in the 20th Century. Her research into the study of the mind, pushes the envelop of discovery and provides a striking new picture of science through her work with quantum mechanics, spacetime physics, brain function, and consciousness.

Amidst the vast number of topics and research in which she has been involved over the length of her career, Dr. Rauscher has addressed a new discipline that brings together aspects of psychology and physics, called Remote Viewing (RV). This study involves new relationships of mind-body, mind-consciousness, and nonlocal mind-mind communications that questions the very limitations of space and time and, of course, the old paradigms of scientific reductionism. In the fields of physics and parapsychology, her results have been overwhelmingly strong in the successful applications of quantum theory and extended spacetime models which she has expanded to include the powers of the mind.

In this book, we concentrate both on Rauscher's theory, as well as her direct work on Remote Viewing with colleagues and with ourselves—or as she prefers to call it "Remote Perception (RP)." The goal is to discover unknown possibilities through trained conscious and mental aptitudes that can reach around the globe to see objects at vast distances, and maybe also forward in time.

Specifically, Dr. Elizabeth Rauscher and her associates in the early 1970's established Remote Perception, obtaining data from distant and unknown targets. Her explanation for this phenomena is that it lies beyond the local activity of the frontal cortex and beyond the use of any known technology. Generally, an "outbound team" was trained to focus on a physical object while at a geographic location. An "inbound" perceiver closeted in the laboratory, then draws what was perceived from the "outbound team" without having any direct physical connection with the outbound target. Except for a specified 'time of day,' no other contact was established. The "outbound" experimental team worked generally with a camera while the "inbound" perceiver used an audio tape recorder and "human monitor". Only after the experiment was completed was the remote viewed data confirmed or not.

In studying psi research in this book, the reader is asked to bear in mind that what follows are both working models based on collected data, personal concepts we have investigated and Rauscher's proposed theory. Specifically, her theory is connected with the power of consciousness, quantum mechanics, the mathematical structure of relativity and nonlocality. Nonlocal activity is the ability for objects to react or sense one another at a distance. When the phenomena as a communication process is applied to anywhere in the world, accurate detailed descriptions can occur.

We contend that the accuracy of Remote Viewing may be explained by new, yet realistic implementations of quantum physics and relativity regarding the "observer" using nonlocal mind dynamics. In physics, when a set of expected facts is discovered, new models must be derived. We clearly have these facts from multiple well-controlled experiments. The model of why it works, however, is still simply a proposal of how best to describe the necessary conditions in which a holistic mind can encompass the true nature of reality. We are asserting that it is based on mental activity and consciousness exploration in what can be called 'All-Space,' which is not confined to the brain structure and the synaptic regulation of neural impulses.

Consequently, Rauscher's theory provides the premise of nonlocal consciousness working and functioning without the use of telecommunication devices or sophisticated technical media in our spacetime reality that is not limited to the third or fourth dimension. In fact, her work explores these unique powers of the human mind which are able to acquire "data" beyond the five senses through what she considers occurs in "Complex Eight-Space."

From direct subjective insight, Rauscher has created an advanced mathematics which calculates objective communication over great distances. The evidence of such crucial experiments as noted here in this book, needs to be looked upon as advances that can transform the standard theories of science. The reality of this nonlocal consciousness that we all share in, is truly a new revolution in twentieth-first century scientific thought.

Dr. Rauscher is not alone in her research. In addition to the research and ideas we share later in this book, her background includes experiments with other pioneering thinkers working in the field of "Remote Viewing," such as Russell Targ and Harold Puthoff (1976) at Stanford Research Institute (SRI), and leading thinkers in the sciences and humanities including Nobel Prize winner, Eugene Wigner. It was Wigner, in his stringent analysis of the consequences of measurements in a Stern-Gerlach experiment, who first speculated that the von Neumann collapse of the wave function actually occurs by an act of consciousness in the human brain which he associated with the influence of the observer in quantum mechanics (Wigner, 1967).

Russell Targ and Harold Puthoff (1976) introduced the term "Remote Viewing" to the SRI scientific community in the early 1970's which was defined as the ability to gather information about a distant or unseen target using paranormal means. Their research met the best scientific standards and serves as a benchmark for the confirmation of psi and its potential.

Most Remote Viewing experiments, as detailed in this book, involve a randomly selected target, derived from a pool of unknown targets locations locked in a safe until used in the experiment. Targets varied from being local, only four to six kilometers from the laboratory, to great distances, on the other side of the globe (e.g., San Andreas, Colombia, or Russia). Remarkable details, however, were acquired within seconds. The conclusion is that the accuracy of remote perception was the same whether it was a local object or some totally unknown structure on the other side of the planet. In short, accurate information of "mental pictures" was generated and acquired remotely by a consciousness "flow" between outbound and inbound participants working with a great variety of targets.

More uniquely, sometimes no "outbound" personnel were present at the site and only latitude and longitude coordinates were given. Correct information could still be acquired, whereby scientists could count the results as accurate "hits."

As selected engineers and research scientists worked in tandem in various locations to study Remote Viewing, Rauscher and her colleagues, such as those at SRI, built the first major database for a worldwide demonstration of nonlocality, some associate with the quantum potential and the famous Einstein-Podolsky-Rosen paradox (Rauscher and Amoroso, 2011). The brain is beginning to be seen as the transducer for consciousness and not the other way around.

There is an excitement of life when one discovers the expanded abilities of the mind from the very best research communities. Dr. Elizabeth Rauscher, herself, has worked for more than 50 years at major universities and research institutes in such areas as astrophysics, plasma physics, nuclear physics, electromagnetic effects on human systems, environmental studies, mathematics, geology, and planetary science. In addition, she was involved with highly specialized forecasting on seismic studies of earthquake profiling with her husband, William van Bise (1994). Elizabeth was also a delegate to the United Nations, discussing long-term energy strategies for renewable energy resources and worked on some aspects of the design of the NASA Space Shuttle. She has also done considerable work in developing an advanced cosmology involving Einstein's field equations, in complex geometry, nonlinear soliton coherent states and S-matrix theory.

The following chapters in addition to ours, detail Rauscher's work, in conjunction with not only SRI scientists, but also with other colleagues at her Fundamental "Fysiks" Group (F"F"G), and the Berkeley Research Group (BRG). Research scientists in these three groups were continually amazed at the accurate results of the Remote Viewing experiments.

All of the ongoing information in consciousness studies has raised new considerations among university researchers looking deeper for answers to our human identity. Fortunately, amongst many who have been successful in pursuing research careers in the most prestigious institutions, a new roadmap for humanity is appearing. This allows all of us to begin to see ourselves as cosmo-planetary-quantum beings.

The work of Remote Viewing advances the remarkable conclusion that the human mind has the triggering mechanisms for an uninhibited global mind reach in nonlocal worldwide correspondence. Elizabeth Rauscher has helped to explain acceptably how this works in areas of physics, philosophy, psychology, biology, relativity and electromagnetic theory, and related disciplines by putting forward a quantum mechanical description of the inductive processes.

Scientists, themselves, are clearly transcending the normal human skepticism as they examine the ongoing research. This includes sophisticated government funded projects which originally took place at SRI International. There Rauscher along with other research colleagues demonstrated many successful experiments of remote perception activity. Skeptical governmental scientists, including down-to-earth engineers and researchers, who reluctantly supported some of the research came to acknowledge the qualified results.

Mind Dynamics in Space and Time points to something very profound, that there is an influential consciousness reality for everything in life. We are living at a time of globalization through the Internet, where our thinking processes are being expanded into global parameters. However, the research presented here is without machines and technology, using only the science of the mind, in the hope of bringing us one step closer to rediscovering ourselves. This consciousness information revolution creates a sense of endless frontiers of the human mind, and of our human aspirations which are rethinking the roles of science and spirituality in an ever-shrinking world.

At this historic point of global consciousness awareness and development through the "remote information" revolution, the possibility of training tens of thousands of people to remote view or use the power of the mind in unique ways of awareness assumes a deeper significance. Many can now learn about their higher selves.

We are on the verge of a great mental liberation, that can lead to global stability, as well as personal balance and a more complete range of consciousness understanding. Good reading in your Becoming!

References

Puthoff, H. and Targ, R. (1976), "A perceptual Channel for Information Transfer over Kilometer Distances: Historical perspective and recent research," *Proceedings IEEE* 64, 3, pp. 224-254.

Rauscher, E.A. and R.L. Amoroso (2011) *Orbiting the Moons of Pluto: Complex Solution to Einstein, Maxwell, Schrödinger, and Dirac Equations,* World Scientific.

van Bise, William and E.A. Rauscher, (1994), "Ambient Electromagnetic Fields as Possible Seismic and Volcanic Precursors," *J. Atmo. Terr. Phys.,* Eds. M. Hayakawa and Y. Fujinawa, Terra Sci. Pub. Co., (TERRAPUB), Tokyo, pp. 221-242.

Wigner, E.P., (1967), *Symmetries and Reflections* (Indiana Univ, Press, Bloomington, IN, pp. 153-184.

Introduction
by
Elizabeth Rauscher, Ph.D.

"We must continually count on the appearance of new facts, the inclusion of which within the compass of our earlier experience may require a revision of our fundamental concepts."

— Niels Bohr

Left: Self portrait drawn by Elizabeth Rauscher, 1965.

Below: Rauscher in 1975 during her research at Lawrence Berkeley National Laboratory.

The Role of Consciousness in Modern Physical Theories by Elizabeth Rauscher, Ph.D.

We in our Western scientific culture have just begun, *en mass*, to explore our inner cosmos. Inner exploration in the past has been an intellectual activity, e.g. psychotherapy. Now it is beginning to enter the domain of emotional and spiritual development as well. Certainly the nature of our inner being, the nature and structure of our consciousness, shapes and determines our concept of reality. This realization is having a vast impact on our society and us, as individuals.

Techniques such as yoga and meditation have opened the horizons to the consideration of the expanded attributes of consciousness. There also appear to be clues as to the nature of consciousness in the structure of physical theory. In fact, the so-called internal journey and external validation system of science may be leading us onto a similar path of knowing.

The ultimate instrument for doing science, art, philosophy and all human endeavors is the "human mind and beyond," or CONSCIOUSNESS. This is the true essence of being and becoming! It is not limited to the known and has a fundamental property of nonlocality. We term some of the nonlocal attributes of consciousness: Remote Viewing, Remote Perception, and, in general, psi phenomena. Within this context are also such abilities as remote influences such as in psychic healing and psychosenses (remote mental influence on matter) and precognition (acquiring relevant information from the future).

It is not as if psi is not as old as humankind, but then gravity is older and it took Newton, Einstein and others to realize it existed and to describe the phenomena in a coherent and describable manner. The study of the properties of consciousness then, too, may bring about a new era in human concepts; a deeper understanding of the fundamental nature of reality in which we utilize the scientific method to study, analyze and comprehend psi.

We have a unique opportunity to utilize the tools of current science to study consciousness. These tools or instruments are generators, oscilloscopes, spectrum analyzers, computers, chart recorders and refined metallurgical materials. The current formulations in mathematics, which are used for the descriptive method in physics, is also a valuable tool to describe the fundamental relationship of events in space and time. Through the use of experimental methodologies and instruments and powerful theoretical formalisms, we can utilize the scientific method and tools to better understand psi and consciousness, in general, and ourselves in particular, including our significant role in existence.

In this treatise, formal studies are presented with a few spontaneous or single session experiments. We detail the protocol and give a statistical analysis of the "bit-rate" for formal studies and present extensive scientific tests. We are also able to examine the conceptual framework of Remote Perception and precognition through the verified awareness of the human mind to perceive remote spacetime events, occurrences, locations, etc., that are blocked from ordinary physical perception.

Russell Targ, formerly at SRI International, Menlo Park and Lockheed Martin, Sunnyvale, in commenting on his research, this author's work and other researchers taking part in remote viewing experiments conducted under controlled conditions stated, "It appears that about 66-70% of the Remote Viewing experiments are successful with good correspondence between the target and the remote viewer's perception, and gets better with experience." Personally, I have also found there is a learning curve; one gets better at the task with practice as in so many areas of life. The more care taken in conducting psi research the better the results!

The fundamental property of consciousness which we explore in this book and in my theoretical works is relating the psi database to the main tenants of the physics of nonlocality.

The concept of nonlocality or action at a distance has caused controversy in the past and current era. When Johann Kepler drew a radius vector from the Earth to the Sun and laid out the foundations for planetary motion around the Sun in elliptical orbits, the Church's thinking at the time was, "you can't draw a radius vector from an archangel to God—there is no nonlocality!"

Nonlocality, however, has become a conventional concept in modern physics. In the 1930's the community of physicists was quite small compared to now. With science, one explores how events, occurrences and existing things are correlated in space and time. At the turn of the last century until the late 1930's, the exciting new developments of quantum theory and relativity began to take hold. Discussions ensued as to what these concepts meant, their interpretations and what these developments implied for the future. It was an exciting time for many concepts!

The discussions were about: "What does the Heisenberg uncertainty principle tell us about determinism, choice and free will?" What do special and general relativity tell us about the relative and the absolute? Has the absolute lost its meaning? Is there a fundamental nonlocality built into the very structure of reality at the microcosm of quantum theory and the macrocosm. Some of these debates, particularly between Albert Einstein and Niels Bohr led to the famous 1935 paper by Einstein, Podolsky, and Rosen (EPR) on this paradox (Einstein, Podolsky and Rosen, 1935). Their paper laid out the foundations of quantum theory and discussed its implications for the existence of a fundamental nonlocality.

Essentially, Einstein's philosophy was one in which determinism rules and nonlocal consequences did not occur. He wanted to find every law of physics and where every particle is located in space and its momentum. Conversely, his 1905 paper on the photoelectric effect and those quantum physicists that developed the quantum theory from a vast set of experiments, points us directly towards a path of indeterminism and nonlocal-

Lawrence Berkeley Laboratory
University of California
Berkeley, California 94720
Telephone 415/843-2740

Prof. Elizabeth Rauscher teaching at the Lawrence Berkeley National Laboratory in association with the University of California in the early 1970's.

ity! Hence the principles of nonlocality in the physical universe and the psychic universe prevail. Through formalism, J. S. Bell (1964) and the test of Bell's theorem in the early 1970's by John Clauser, *et. al.* (1974) made it critically apparent that nonlocality is a physical reality and that quantum theory is a complete theory. This work was replicated and expanded on by Aspect, *et. al.* (1992) and Gisin (Gisin and Zbinden, 1999).

The path was set: it is a nonlocal universe in which events remain correlated over space and time. It is also a participatory universe as presented by John A. Wheeler (1962) and Eugene Wigner (1972). The fundamental issues of relativity, quantum theory, and macro and micro nonlocality are detailed in our book, *Orbiting the Moons of Pluto: Complex Solutions to the Einstein, Maxwell, Schrödinger, and Dirac Equations* (Rauscher and Amoroso, 2011).

The debate about the EPR paradox came about from the discussion about the interpretation of the wave function (termed the psi function) in the quantum wave equations. Does the wave function directly relate to a particular particle in the universe or the probability that a particle is at a specific location with a particular momentum? The dominant viewpoint became the Copenhagen Interpretation (where Niels Bohr was living) and became, what I experienced in my quantum mechanics classes at UC Berkeley, "don't ask questions about the foundations of quantum mechanics, just shut up and calculate." But I wanted to know why, as well as what and maybe a little bit of who (and where). I wanted to understand the philosophical basis of physics and science, in general, because I think of my self primarily as a philosopher, asking "What does Quantum Mechanics mean?" It didn't work out so well in my classes at UC Berkeley, but I still got the highest A!

So later, I started the Fundamental "Fysiks" Group (F"F"G) at the Lawrence Berkeley National Laboratory, and chaired it for over three years with up to forty physicists who examined various theories. We explored the foundations and meaning of consciousness, relativity, quantum theory, non locality and Remote Viewing. A good summation of the adventures of my group is in the book, *"How the Hippies Saved Physics,"* by David Kaiser (2011).

Fundamental to our discussion was the interpretation of the wave function (ψ, psi) and consciousness (psi) and micro and macro nonlocality of what is termed quantum entanglement. Revisiting these issues in the F"F"G (which I had named) has led to a revival of the consideration of the role of quantum entanglement and its possible application to quantum computing. There are even patents on this stuff!

Even though writing $F = ma$ on the side of a bus does not make it run, the language of physical science is in mathematics and we can use it to describe, formulate and predict useful things about the universe. The body of the psychic database is not denied by physics, it appears to be a part of physics and may even be predicted by current physicists!

I am also an open minded skeptic and this is my approach to accepted ideas, as well as non-accepted ideas. There is some accepted knowledge that is valid, however, there are some accepted ideas that in my investigation are not valid. There are some non-accepted ideas, that with extensive research, are valid and some non-accepted ideas that are false or invalid. It takes a great deal of work to sort these concepts out; in fact a lifetime of work.

Psi, which I started out as a skeptic about, turns out to be true! I had to change my thinking, my philosophy to accommodate it, but it is truth that matters. In technological societies where sophisticated testing is possible, the fundamental nature and properties of consciousness, its understanding and consideration can yield a better philosophy of life and a new world view. Thoughts are real and have real consequences. Ethics require one to be responsible not only for actions but for thoughts and the domain of active consciousness; intent and action gives us a greater access to solve world problems and become a whole being in mind, body and spirit.

The path to knowledge is sometimes difficult and fraught

with danger, but the rewards are great. The goals are to be good humans and to benefit all of reality and all existence. Have fun reading this book.

References:

Aspect, A., P. Grangier and G. Roger (1992) "Experimental Tests of Bell's inequality using time-varying analizers," Phys. *Rev. Lett.* 49, p. 1804 .

Bell, J.S. (1964) "On the Einstein Podolsky Rosen paradox," *Physics* 1, 195.

Clauser, J.F. and W.A. Horne (1974) "Experimental consequences of objective local theories," *Phys. Rev.* 10D, p. 526, and private conversations.

Einstein, A., B. Podolsky, and N. Rosen (1935) "Can quantum-mechanical descriptions of physical reality be considered complete?" *Physical Review* 47, p. 777.

Gisin, N., and H. Zbinden (1999) ''Bell inequality and the locality loophole: active versus passive switches,'' *Phys. Lett.* A264, pp. 103–107.

Kaiser, D. (2011) *How the Hippies Saved Physics*, New York: W.W. Norton.

Rauscher, E.A. and R.L. Amoroso (2011) *Orbiting the Moons of Pluto: Complex Solution to Einstein, Maxwell, Schrödinger, and Dirac Equations*, World Scientific.

Wheeler, J.A. (1962) *Geometrodynamics*, New York: Academic Press and Private conversations.

Wigner, E.P. (1972) "The place of consciousness in modern physics," in *Consciousness and Reality*, C. Muses and A. Young, Eds., New York: Outerbridge and Lazard.

Chapter 1
Criterion and Evidence for the Existence of Anomalous Phenomena
by
Elizabeth Rauscher, Ph.D.

He liked watching the glorious stars, thinking "there must be myriads of worlds out there." Then one night he shifted his awareness toward and into himself. "By God," he whispered, but only to himself, "there are myriads of worlds there, too!"

— Ingo Swann, *To Kiss the Earth Goodbye*, 1975

Table of Contents

Introduction 29
1. The Role of Consciousness in Philosophy and Modern Physical Theory 31
2. Some Basic Tenets of Science and the Western View: Duality, Causality and Object Grouping 35
3. Physical Models of Interconnectedness 40
4. Observer/Participant and Schrödinger's Cat 48
5. Particle and Processes, Geometry and the Spacetime Independence of Consciousness 51
   A. Particle and Process, Logic and Reason 51
   B. Intrinsic and Extrinsic Geometry, Mind and the Universe 53
   C. Spacetime Independence in Physics and Psychic Phenomena 53
Conclusion 56
References 58

List of Tables

Table 1: The Tenants of Science and Mysticism as related to each other 32
Table 2: Change can be Local or Nonlocal 34
Table 3: Categorization of Fields of Knowledge 36
Table 4: Some Western Philosophers and their Concepts 38
Table 5: Existence, Reality, Meaning of Truth 39
Table 6: Objectivity, Subjectivity and Reality: Contour Integral Model 46

List of Figures

Figure 1a The Eyes of the Observer Perceive the Universe 40
Figure 1b The Scale from the smallest thing in the Universe...... 45

Introduction

In investigating what is considered to be a controversial phenomena, such as what is termed "anomalous" phenomena, we must apply the rigor of science with extreme care in order to determine the weight of evidence that implies whether it exists or does not exist. Although one cannot mathematically prove non-existence, the body of science is built on reasonable experimental evidence, theoretical predictive descriptors, and consensus reality, but it cannot be used to prove something does not exist. In this presentation the application of the scientific method, research procedures and tools will be explored with regard to apparent anomalous phenomena, in particular "Remote Perception" or what is more popularly called "Remote Viewing." Discussion of the issues pertaining to the differences between anomalous research and normal or ordinary research will be given in terms of the scientific context of a database and theoretical models.

Also included will be a brief discussion on the relationship between scientific research and possible contextual influences from society at large, comprised of non-scientists. It is interesting how some areas of phenomena which were previously considered mystical were later brought under the domain of science. For example, comets were once thought to be "the hand of God;" later scientists said comets are a ball of rock and ice with a gas cloud. (Perhaps the latter does not preclude the former.) As the scientific method became a more dominant method in history for the search for truth in the western world, more phenomena previously considered mystical was explained by the methodology of science.

We will further explore in this book the detailed nature of the scientific method and its application. We will, more specifically, explore the nature and properties of consciousness and the manner in which they are compatible with the main body of physics. If one claims that what one is studying is a science, then the critical test of the scientific method must be applied. It is only through this approach that the validity of a phenomenon is determined and a scientific phenomena is confirmed. Other domains of human endeavor may yet remain in the domain of the mystical or other areas, such as art, music and poetry, to be experienced outside the realm of science. Some unusual or possible new phenomena will meet the rigorous tests of the scientific method and will be found to be experimentally reproducible and consistent with scientific theory; others will not, but we must all explore and proceed with care in order to develop a body of useful data and human knowledge.

Current science is often driven by the spotlight effect; it is easier to search where the search is well illuminated, but there may be some really good stuff where the light is dimmer and sometimes it is more meaningful and fun to search there. There may be areas of research of global and personal importance that we can only examine at the edge of the light beam and can shine additional light on them. One is the area of psi phenomena and particularly, for this book, the experimental evidence and theoretical formulation that brings to light the nature of consciousness beyond space and time limitations or the nonlocal mind! (Tart, 1972, 1975).

I have examined those aspects of human perception that appear to fall outside the range of well understood perceptual processing capabilities in our current scientific world view. Of particular interest is a human information accessing "channel" I call "Remote Perception." This phenomenon pertains to the ability to access and describe, by means of direct mental processes, information sources blocked from ordinary perception and which have been secured against such access (as explained in the Foreword).

The phenomenon, I and my colleagues, such as Russell Targ and Hal Puthoff (1976) from SRI International, investigated is the ability of a person (subject) to "view" or perceive geographical locations from several kilometers up to several thousand kilometers distant from the subject's actual physical location. The subject is given a known person or sometimes only a coordinate upon which to target. This approach has been an extremely fruitful area to research the nonlocal remote connectedness properties of psi. As in other complex scientific experiments, the experimenters may undergo a learning process and appear to be capable of learning to develop and improve the access of their remote perception capabilities.

As a researcher and theoretical physicist, I also conducted extensive work on theoretical models of the remote perception phenomena, as well as other forms of psi. I have demonstrated a method to reconcile psi with the main body of physics, as well as to better describe the manner in which mind interacts and "moves" in space and time. It is demonstrated that such a model must be hyperdimensional or multidimensional, having greater than the four dimensions of space and time, $N > 4$. In this book we describe the protocol for the remote perception experiments, present some of our data, and give the statistical analysis and a description of the theoretical models.

1. The Role of Consciousness in Philosophy and Modern Physical Theory

Let us start our discussion with the possible relationship between states of consciousness and modern physics and begin with a concept so well expressed by Sir Arthur Eddington (astrophysicist and one of the early researchers in relativity) that, "Physics is the study of the structure of consciousness," (Eddington, 1922, 1946). It is the mind that is the ultimate instrument for "doing" physics or doing anything! Not only do concepts in philosophy and psychology, but also neurophysiology lead us to the conclusion that the structure and content of physics may depend deeply on the relationship between physical theory and the structure of consciousness. In this book we speak of the concepts that have always been considered external to the body of science, but now are ready to be incorporated into modern physics based on data derived from experiments on the properties of consciousness.

Table 1

THE TENANTS OF SCIENCE AND MYSTICISM AS RELATED TO EACH OTHER

1. *duality,* or a paired concept yin-yang (mysticism) or canonically conjugate variables (science),
2. *experience,* sense detection,
3. *intuition,* direct knowing,
4. *constancy and change,* Three Gunas (mysticism), sattva (growth), rajas (maintaining), tamas (decay) and scientific law,
5. *causality,* the cause and effect relationship (Law of Karma (mystical), and Law of Causality (science),
6. *Law* or rule relationship,
7. *pattern, repeatability* and *harmony,*
8. *categorization* or object grouping (although mysticism does discuss categories of existence, this method is much more the preoccupation of the scientific method—Darwin classification of species, etc.),
9. *symbolic representation,* symbolism and language (written in symbols or spoken) is fundamental to the communication of information (science), or is a trigger to experience (mandala).

One of the deepest, most profound discoveries for the western mind is induced meditative and "altered" states introduced mainly by indigenous and eastern practitioners. These altered states of consciousness may hold great clues to resolving conceptual paradoxes in science and life. We define an altered state of consciousness as an extension of the usual three states of awake, sleeping and dreaming.

A paradox resolved leads to a new level of awareness and understanding. Perhaps current events are leading to the Kuhnian revelation, (Kuhn, 1970) referred to as a paradigm shift which may involve a shift in knowledge that expands our understanding of consciousness.

What are some of the differences between the scientific and mystical methodology? Upon observation of these methods in action in the search for truth, we "picture" the scientist in the laboratory, writing equations on the board, or with flasks of boiling liquids over Bunsen burners, racks of electronics, etc. We "picture" the mystic in quiet contemplation or meditation. Consequently, although the actual experience of science (as theory and experiments in a laboratory, with dials, chemicals, etc.) may appear different compared to mysticism (direct inspired experience, say, in meditation), there are numerous common concepts. Some of these are listed in Table 1.

Regardless, discoveries, and/or creations of new concepts in physics can lead to a greater understanding of the observer/participant issue. Quantum mechanics, the theory of the atomic microcosm, is a description that may imply that the observer may have an effect on what is observed in order to observe, and does so locally and remotely. Relativity theory implies that the relative physical state of the observer affects his interpretation of what he sees. In the context of quantum theory and relativity, we may be able to shed light on the further discovery and validation of the properties of an external, multidimensional reality.

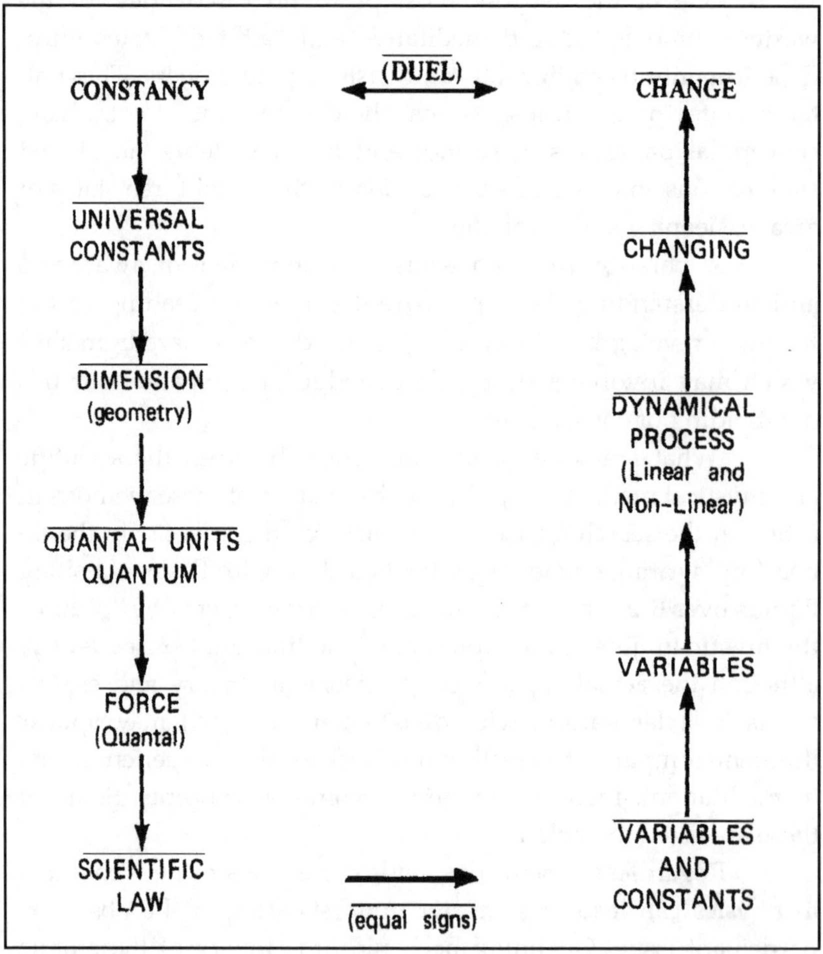

Table 2 Change can be local or nonlocal and is a function of space and time. Constancy is global and absolute and is not a function of space and time and is therefore universal.

2. Some Basic Tenets of Science and the Western View: Duality, Causality and Object Grouping

The conceptual framework of *duality* (or parts) and *unity* (or whole) has been debated in many world religions and philosophies. Central to the conceptual struggle is the attempt to understand one's connection to the whole of the Universe. In physics, we examine the possible relationship of the observer and the observed. Often, when the dualistic view is historically conceived, there is an attempt to overcome it and reunite that which has been conceptually divided. (See Table 2).

Socrates, via Plato's dialogues, suggests his own dualistic model of reality consisting of physical objects and another world, a perfect world filled with objects, such as a perfect chair or table. The perfect-image world of images also contains a representation of perfect love, or perfect good, in which it is said the modern day thinker might associate with the concept of God.

Immanuel Kant suggested that the mental attribute to categorize objects or concepts (for example, to identify and distinguish chairs from tables or love from hate) is an inborn characteristic of the human mind as is the concept of causal relationships of these objects. These are, in essence, dualistic models, and the concept of categorization, or object identification and grouping, is also a key tenet of science. (See Table 2).

Kant's view also coincides with the multiplicity of objects. A predominant concept of western scientific knowledge is that of causality or cause and effect relationships. The description of causal relationships is the way in which causes and effects are related and is certainly another dualistic model. Immanuel Kant suggests that causality, like categorization, is also an innate construct of the human mind. (See Table 3). Immanuel Kant (1997) discussed the concept that the ability to define and categorize concepts and objects is innate. This concept has given impetus to the analytical

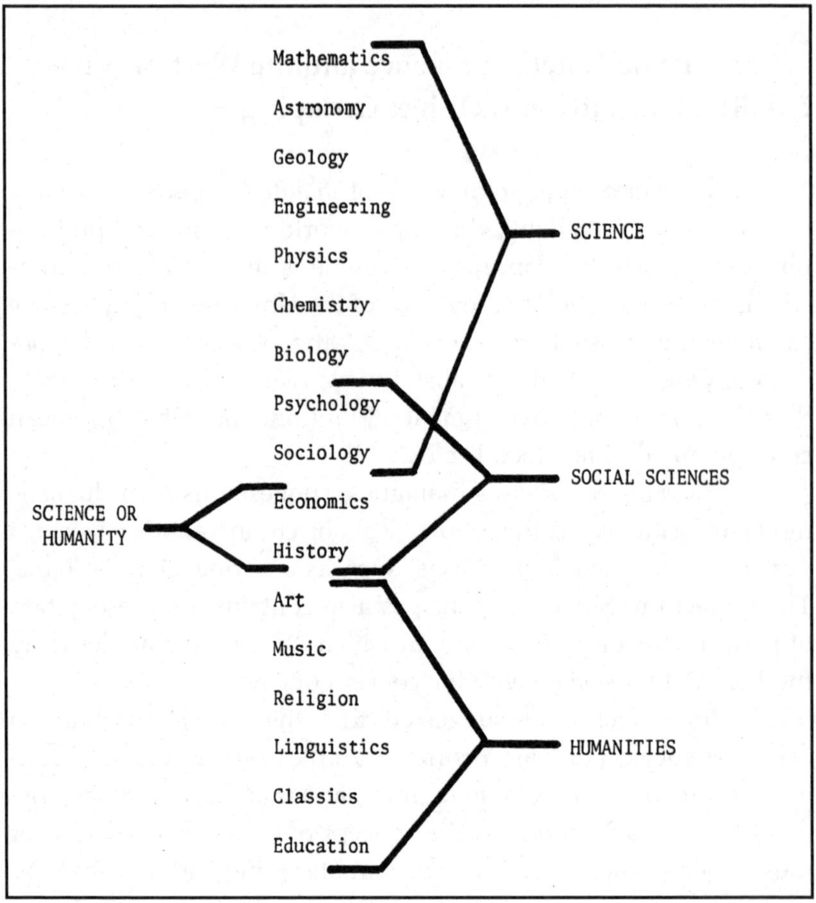

Table 3 Categorization of Fields of Knowledge

Immanuel Kant discussed the concept that the ability to define and categorize concepts and objects is innate. There have been a number of attempts to reconcile this multiplicity model with the concept of the Universal. Here for example is the current categorization of fields of knowledge. Kant also hypothesized an innate sense of causality.

method, which is a very useful but not the only method of analysis. There is also the view of synthesis. There have been a number of attempts to reconcile this categorized multiplicity with the concept of the Universal model (Rauscher, 1971b).

In the 17th century, Gottfried Leibniz (Rescher, 1991) hypothesized the existence of monads in an attempt to reconcile the Greek mind/body dualism. Monads are the true atoms of nature that have no parts and cannot be separated. Like mind and matter, they are all interconnected. This notion further states that every motion has an effect upon local and distant bodies in such a manner that can correlate one's intentions with one's actions throughout life. If one intends to raise one's arm, it will move up, not because one directly wills it to do so, but because at one's birth, the mind/matter monads were set up to produce this coincidence. (Enter the debate over free will *vs.* determinism). In this view, all events are now definable in terms of acausal terms. (See Table 4).

Besides Leibniz's theory, in which he attempts to reconcile the mind-body duality by introducing the system of monad synchronicity, is the synchronicity theory of Carl Jung. After Carl Jung's break with Freud, Jung suggested an acausal model in which events are correlated by meaningful coincidence of synchronicities (Campbell, 1971). These coincidences appear to occur "randomly". But there may be procedures that can be utilized to set up meaningful synchronicities which can yield useful information. Jung was particularly interested in the I Ching, in which information is accessed by a "random" process of a set of tosses of three coins or yarrow sticks. Jung describes a mechanism whereby the system of synchronicities is correlated by a universal or cosmic consciousness. Jung's approach is another attempt at a holistic or universal model (see Table 4 for a summary of some of the concepts of the epistemological approach of Western philosophy and science). (Duiker and Spielvogel, 2013).

A number of intellectual endeavors have been discussed that deal with dualism and try to derive or develop a concept of unity, oneness, or universality. Perhaps the duality vs. unity concepts can be further explored by understanding levels of conscious-

Philosopher	Born/Died	Some of his Major concepts
Descartes, René	(1596-1650)	1. Mechanistic View 2. Mind/body Duality 3. Importance of pineal gland 4. Acausal 5. Space-time independence 6. "What you see is what there is"
Leibniz, Gottfried Wilhelm	(1646-1716)	1. The monad as a fundamental metaphysical unity 2. Synchronistic link of mind/body division 3. Space-time independence 4. Acausal
Kant, Immanuel	(1724-1804)	1. Innate categorization 2. Causality (cause-effect) relationship
Spinoza, Benedict	(1632-1677)	1. Contingency (like monads) 2. Causality 3. One-world unity 4. Process as primary
Hegel (Georg Wilhelm Friedrich)	(1770-1831)	1. Thesis, antithesis and synthesis: analogy to yin-yang concept
Jung, Carl Gustav	(1875-1961)	1. Archetype (as in Socrates "world of images") 2. Synchronistic view (analogous to 6th century B.C. view of Lao Tze)

Table 4 Some western philosophers and their concepts. It is difficult to summarize anyone's philosophical framework in a few words. In fact, one's philosophical concepts change over time and may explore different points of view, comparing and contrasting them to others' philosophies.

EXISTENCE, REALITY, MEANING OF TRUTH

EPISTEMOLOGY (let's define existence and truth), theory of knowledge

Word		*Dictionary Definition*
Existence	→	State of being, life, duration, occurrence – having reality
Real	→	Existing as or in fact – actual, true
Reality	→	Fact, actually
Fact	→	True, reality – really true
True	→	In accord with fact
Truth	→	Reality, actual existence, correctness, exactness
Actual	→	Existing in reality, real
Correct	→	Not in error, true, fact, exact
Exact	→	Accurate, correct, precise, no error, measure, determine

ONTOLOGY ("philosophy of being")

How do we obtain truth? What is real?

Circular argument a tautology,

We need input a mega-philosophy, metaphysics or paraphysics!

Table 5 Existence, Reality, Meaning of Truth. Ontology is the "philosophy of being." How do we obtain truth? What is real? We find a circular argument or a tautology. As Webster's standard dictionary shows is that Webster does not know what reality is. We need input from a mega philosophy, metaphysics or paraphysics to address the question of what is reality.

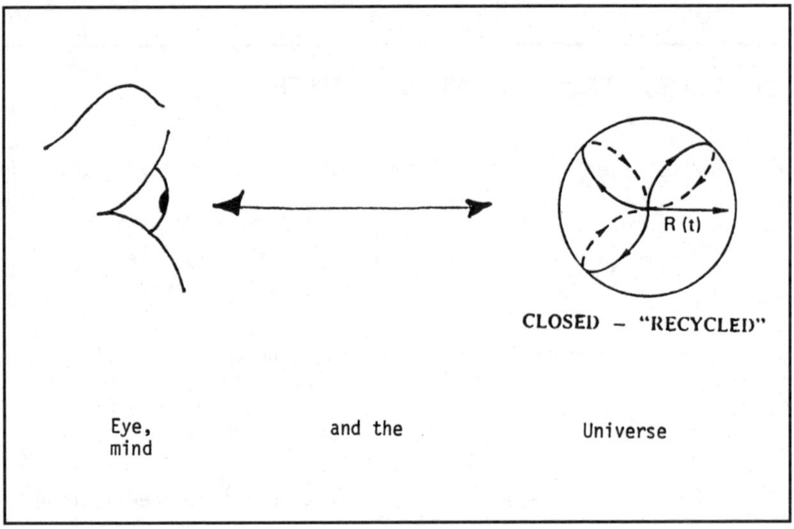

Figure 1a A modified figure from John A. Wheeler. The eyes of the observer perceive the Universe "out there" (Wheeler, 1962).

ness. Maybe new awareness states are leading us to be able to experience this resolution in modern physics! Maybe they are leading us into an awareness of the fundamental understanding of consciousness!

3. Physical Models of Interconnectedness

The observer in this world is considered a passive agent, inert with respect to the observed "reality" or what is taking place. (See Fig. 1a). Reality is defined as an external existence and although we can change it, it takes physical action. See Table 5 for the definitions of reality, truth, fact, etc.

Mysticism both from the East and the West has argued this is not the case. In fact, it make claims that the observer may not only be affecting the observed, but is linked to it in a degree. The observer is the creator of the observed reality. Science is only now beginning to comprehend the interconnection we have with the universe.

Many of the problems of our work stem from the view of

the observer and the observed as separate. This is clearly a dualistic model. Mysticism tried to re-unite the dualism through consciousness. Table 2 examines ways in which 20th century discoveries in physics may imply a link between dual pairs and the possible dissolution of them into a unity.

In science, the anthropic universe is beginning to be discussed, where observations of the universe must be compatible with conscious and sentient life. In addition to the concept of the anthropic universe, researchers who have examined Bell's theorem and the Copenhagen Interpretation have looked at the possibility that the position of particles and information about their physical properties, which we are observing and measuring, appear to be altered by our observation or simply by our measurement. It is starting to appear that we cannot "look" at the world without making an observation of it and hence produce an effect on it.

Specifically, from the macroscopic and microscopic domains, it seems that we cannot make a physical observation of the world without affecting the patterns of the observed. Somehow, "the observer is a participator; it is a participatory universe," in the words of physics professor John Wheeler (1962), formally of Princeton University. The apparent effect of the observer on the observed, in the micro domain of the atom, is termed the Heisenberg uncertainty principle.

According to Bell's theorem, microscopic quantum phenomena of systems of particles initially correlated show a connection at a remote distance. If particles, such as photons are divided that were once juxtaposed in spacetime or correlated with each other by their respective physical properties, they remain correlated even when separated by a distance of several meters to several kilometers, which is indeed large on the atomic scale (Bell, 1964; Gisin, *et. al.*, 1998, 1999). This form of interconnectedness or nonlocality was proposed by Einstein and others in the 1930's (Bell, 1964; Einstein, *et. al.*, 1935). Nonlocality relates to the formulation of the completeness of the quantum mechanical description of matter and the universal applicability of the Heisenberg uncertainty principle (Heisenberg, 1972).

Kurt Gödel (1992) also entered the search for certainty in mathematics, but demonstrated that mathematical structures (e.g., algebra) are not complete or absolute, just as Heisenberg had done for the physical sciences with his uncertainty principle (Kleene, 1950). Whereas Heisenberg demonstrated that the observer is a participator, Gödel formulated the incompleteness of mathematical systems.

John S. Bell (1964) formulated the beginnings of Bell's theorem, but left it to others to prove or disprove. His work is based on the earlier questions proposed by Einstein and others in 1935 about the nature of the incompleteness vs completeness of the quantum description of the behavior of particles. In 1973, John Clauser (Clauser and Horne, 1974) and others did put Bell's hypothesis to the test in a laboratory and found that it was valid, that mathematically certain quantum correlations do not arise from any local cause. The experiment involved the creation of a pair of photons (or quanta of light) from a single source. These two photons moved, at the velocity of light, away from each other in opposite directions. Next their relative spins were measured.

What was determined is that their spinning was correlated, i.e., they reacted to one another even when separated by several kilometers. This measurement, although somewhat complex, may indicate a faster than the speed of light signaling, and is an indication of nonlocality or fundamental interconnectedness, at least on the microscopic level (Clauser, *et. al.*, 1974; Aspect, *et. al.*, 1992 and Gisin, *et. al.*, 1998).

Bell's theorem, thus, has implications both philosophically and scientifically connected with entanglement, similar to the Heisenberg principle, but dissimilar to the idea of separation as determined by the EPR. Many philosophical discourses have been generated on the issues of observer effects, free will, quantum uncertainty and Heisenberg's uncertainty principle. To observe a table, we shine a light on it and the photons of light affect the atoms of the table.

We are proposing that the universe is constructed in such a way that what one thinks or does here on planet Earth may indeed affect conditions in the far reaches of space. David Bohm (1977) with his Implicate Order and Karl Pribram (1976) with his holonomic brain model of cognitive function as well as others, have suggested models to explain these events relating to consciousness. Our view is consistent with some of the multi-dimensional models discussed further on. (See Chapter 5 and Chapter 8).

Discoveries in physics do relate to the philosophical precepts constructed by humankind. I believe it is as if a spider in its web feels each distant disturbance of the web's far reaches as it sits at the center of the web waiting for dinner. This is sometimes termed the butterfly effect, where one may consider the flapping of a butterfly's wings in California with the formation of a tornado in Kansas. I anticipate that we have not seen an end to the volumes that will continue to be generated on Bell's "interconnectedness" theorem and its relationship not only to particles but to cognitive processes. Concepts of physics are just now being generated where implications of the theorem correlate to the visions expressed by certain mystics (Kaiser, 2011). (See Table 1).

Bell's theorem which involves nonlocality and interconnectedness appears to hold for processes at the quantum and macroscale. Are there other theories that could describe remote or nonlocal interconnectedness? There are a number of differing experiments taking place by researchers to show quantum nonlocality, and much of my work is on describing and resolving these issues. Some physical models which may answer these questions are examined in this book, as well as many other books (Ramon and Rauscher, 1980, 1982; Rauscher, 1968a; 1968b, 1981, 1982a 2010; Rauscher and Amoroso, 2008, 2011).

A physics model accommodating physical and consciousness nonlocality has been developed by this author. It is a macroscopic interconnectedness model formulated in terms of multidimensional complex geometries (Rauscher, 1979; Ramon and Rauscher, 1982; Rauscher and Amoroso, 2011; Rauscher and Targ, 2012). (See Chapter 5). Involving more than the four dimensions (three spatial dimensions and one temporal), this geometric model's construction indicates that there are conditions in which information can be accessed from remote spacetime locations so that they appear juxtaposed and not remote from each other. A set of these dimensions involves both real spacetime and imaginary dimensions which are also spacetime dimensions multiplied by the imaginary number, $i = \sqrt{-1}$.

The structure of these models in quantum physics, as well as in the structure of N-dimensional relativistic models (where N is greater than the four dimensions of spacetime) imply a fundamental remote connection of events, which can explain the possibility of how physical effects can be transmitted over a distance, while not violating our usual concept of the relationship of cause and effect (Rauscher, 2010). Thus, the property of nonlocality can be employed for experimental verification.

The important point here is that physicists are now examining the concept of remote interconnectedness and the structure of this author's geometric models in their unified four force field theories involving the fundamental intrinsic nature of nonlocality, in their Standard Model and Grand Unification Theory (Rauscher, 1968a, 1971a, 1972a, 1972b, 1973). (See Chapter 6 and 7). In systems where particles such as photons are nonlocally connected, the correlation may involve the observer and the observed. In fact, nonlocal connections demonstrate certain types of unity which have characteristics of the mystical. Physical theories may now describe how the observer's perspective determines something's appearance.

Implicit in Einstein's (1949) description of the relativity of motion is that one's perception of what one is observing is affected by one's observational vantage point. In general, the theory of relativity describes, macroscopically, the causal connections of spatial events synchronized in time. Observations in physics are that the time recorded on a chronometer or a watch depends on the relative frame of reference of the observer and the observed.

If the timepiece moves at very near the speed of light past

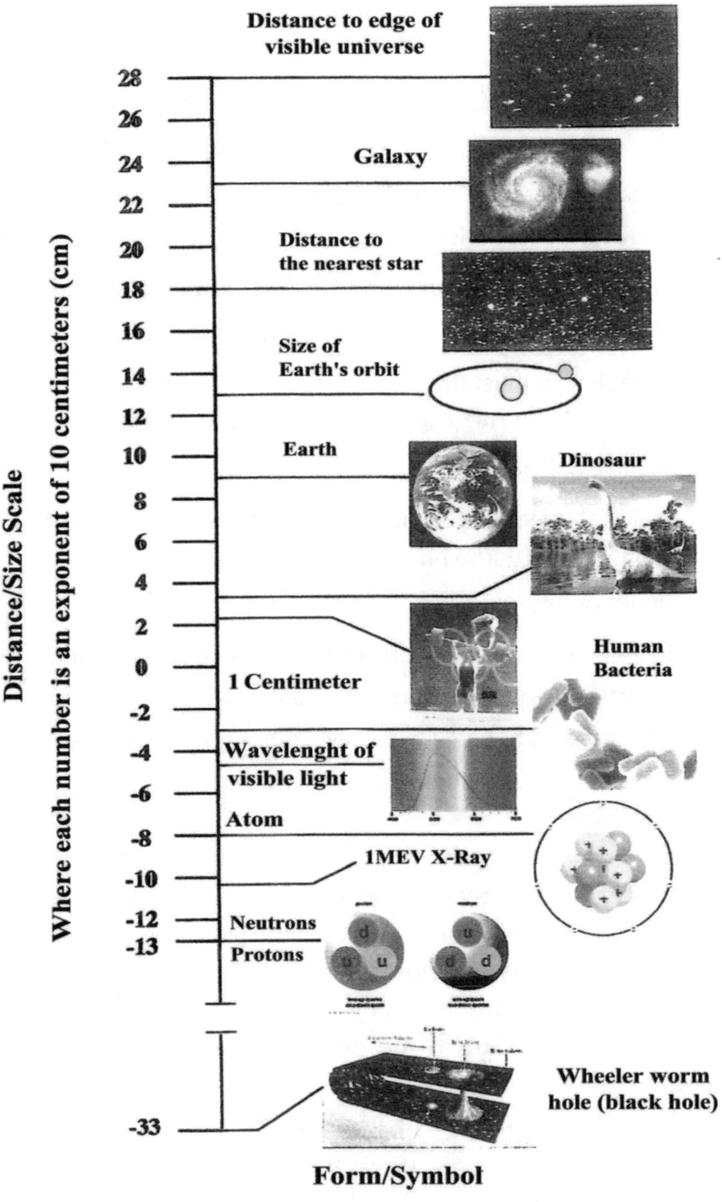

Figure 1b The scale from the smallest thing in the universe, a Planck mini-black hole, to the size of the known universe itself (Rauscher, 1971b). Artwork by Dr. Thomas Beck.

Table 6

Objectivity, Subjectivity, and Reality:

Contour Integral Model

1. What we perceive as reality depends on our assumptions and state of consciousness.
2. Barriers are useful but limited and are artificial constructs of the mind.
3. What is real must necessarily include that aspect called mind/reality as well as what is called external reality, to be complete or unified.
4. It is as though we see only the isolated islands above the sea rather than the universal of the whole of the land beneath the sea.
5. In a sense, when we include the mind's knowledge and structure in our description of reality, we find our perception appears to be dynamically "unbounded" with new aspects of possibilities.

the observer, the time reading appears to change depending on the velocity of the watch's motion (dilates or slows down as the velocity increases). The laws of physics remain unchanged according to the principle of Lorentz invariance regardless of motion, translation, rotations, etc., but to the observer things appear different, depending on the manner in which these things are observed (Rauscher, 1971a), whether it is from the macroscopic or microscopic perspective (See Fig. 1b for the size from the smallest to the largest object in the known observable universe).

Is there a difference between reality and observation? (See Table 6). Western thought, based on the logic systems developed in Greece a few centuries prior to the birth of Christ, makes the assumption that reality is external, solid, "out there" and that, in essence, this reality is immutable (Rauscher, 1971a) except for Plato's allegory of the cave. Stubbing one's toe on a hard object in the dark seems to validate this hypothesis and appears to substantiate an external reality. But is this the case? That this "reality" depends on our frame of mind, on our state of consciousness or on our "state specific science," in the words of Charles Tart, U.C. Davis, Psychology Department (Tart, 1972, 1975) is becoming clearer. If one's mood can affect how one views life, can it affect one's observation of the period of swing of a pendulum bob?

Realistic, local models of reality appear to be violated by the results of the Clauser experiment (Clauser and Horne, 1974) and other research on Bell's theorem. Because the interaction of consciousness with physical matter changes, matter is modified and can affect other consciousness, absolute "Newtonian'" objectivity is violated. The approximate objectivity of the scientific method yields results in the classical domain, but begins to break down in the quantum relativistic (DeWitt, 1970) and psi domains.

Consider again, Sir Arthur Eddington's quote that, "Physics is the study of the structure of our conscious minds!" (Eddington, 1946). Eddington's thoughts may lead us to the Buddhist (Prince Gautama, born about 550 B.C.) concept, that reality is in part, or even completely, a construct of consciousness. Not only is the universe "perturbed" by the observer consciousness, it is created by it! (Hixon, 1933). Our ultimate question thus must be: Does what we believe not only create our view of the world but determine its functioning in reality?

Scientists debate whether there is an external reality, and whether its nature and workings are created by the human mind or are discovered through individual and/or collective consciousness? Is being (or existence) created by human consciousness? It is clear that consciousness is thus an important constituent of the "equation" of reality. (See Table 6).

The epistemological approach of Western philosophy and science (See Table 4) in the discussion of the nature and structure of an external reality relies on the "discoverer" and what is "discovered." This leads necessarily to a dualistic system. How is the mind (the observer) linked to the physical reality (the observed) as the mind-body? In quantum theory, it appears that the observer is not passive or inert, but is rather an active participant. Therefore, where the observer (eye) ends and the observed (universe) begins become extremely important in quantum theories. (See Fig. 1a).

A further example of the expression of a fundamental interconnectedness is found in Ernst Mach's principle (Rauscher, 1971a) which states that a local event, such as the rotation of a bucket of water, depends on the whole fixed star system, i.e., the rest of the universe. Thus, the parabolic meniscus formed when a bucket of water is rotated rapidly depends on the existence of the universe or some fixed reference frame defined by it. (See Chapter 6).

The fixed and absolute reference frame implicit in Mach's principle may be a further clue to "connectedness" and a possible relationship to absolute "Universal Knowledge". The possibility of a fixed reference point in space is not precluded in Einstein's theory of relativity despite its axiom that states just that (Rauscher, 1971a). Bell's theorem more precisely and specifically formulates the principle of interconnectedness described by Mach, whose principle is primarily discussed in terms of astrophysics, while Bell's theorem is applied to quantum systems.

4. Observer/Participant and Schrödinger's Cat

Objectivity, one of the major foundations of scientific methodology, assumes a consensus reality about external events. Under the same conditions, if a scientist replicates his own and others' work he gets the same results. While conversely, subjectivity suggests that observations are dependent on and unique to a particular observer.

Even though internal states of reality, such as in guided meditation, have been considered subjective, we find a consensus reality here also, even though the "objects" observed are in one's head. But then where is the object of "blueness" of the sky (in our head?) and what is "out there" prompting our perception? Psychologists debate which perception is our ultimate experience, i.e., internal or external perceptions. Under certain practices such as meditation or yoga, people report similar internal perceptions.

From a physicist's point of view of the observer/observed issue: what is the definition of an external/internal boundary? What is the skin (sense), retina (sight), eardrum, anvil and stirrup (hearing)? Is this definition arbitrary?

The definition of the observer/observed link is affected by our definition of an "objective" system, indicating that the boundary between observer and observed is not arbitrary (as stated before). In the 1920's and 30's the interpretation of the newly developing description of the micro-cosmos with quantum theory led to much debate with some claiming the theory was just a pragmatic method of predicting the outcome of a specific experiment, termed the Copenhagen view, after Neils Bohr's interpretation and that one could not build a model of reality from this theory. Others said the purpose of doing physics is to comprehend reality by building testable models and, by using the scientific method and observation of nature, we must be open to both constancy and change.

A thought experiment (*gedanken*) that highlights some of the challenges of quantum theory and the observer-observed link is the "Schrödinger cat paradox," named after one of the developers of the quantum theory, Erwin Schrödinger (1926a, 1926b). A cat is locked in a box where it will eventually be killed by a poison gas pellet activated by a "random" quantum atomic decay process. Before an experimenter looks in the chamber, and after a given time interval, is the cat dead or alive? The theoretical physicist sits down with pen, paper and computer, and using the quantum theory figures out what will happen after a certain time interval. He can only calculate a probability, because the state of the cat can only be determined by observation!

The Schrödinger wave equation, used to describe the process of radioactive decay, has two solutions. In one possible universe (solution), or *eigenstate,* the cat is still alive; and in the other possible reality the cat is dead. The total solution is the sum of these two possibilities and the wave function *eigenstate* only "collapses" to the alive or dead cat *eigenstate* after the cat has been observed. In this sense the observer's consciousness participates, but then the cat knows if it is alive (and perhaps if it is dead, if there is life after death for a cat). Of the many paradoxes this famous equation focuses on is whether the physical models are objective descriptions or merely define the limits of our knowledge. (See Chapter 6 and 7).

Another way of describing the problem of where and how the observer is connected to the observed, as Evan Harris Walker (1977) states, is the problem of quantum measurement, not on the microscopic level (Schrödinger wave equation) (Rauscher and Amoroso, 2008, 2011), but the connection at the level of the macroscopic (classical) measuring device. This continues the question of how the observer is connected to the observed. This paradox may also define our lack of understanding of our connection to the universe. Does a unity exist? Maybe unity exists on a grand level and not on others? Does space and time keep us from seeing the influence we have in the universe? (Bell, 1964; Rauscher, 1979, 1981, 1982a, 1982b, 2010; Ramon and Rauscher, 1982; Rauscher and Targ, 2012). The connection path for the observer and the observed may be similar to that of the remote connection of the two photons in the experimental result of Bell's theorem.

5. Particle and Processes, Geometry and the Spacetime Independence of Consciousness

We ask what are the properties of the fundamentals of reality which appear to be rigid physical constructs and yet are transcended by consciousness. In fact, what is the fundamental building block of the Universe we live in? Some of the ancient Greeks called the fundamental construct of reality the "atom" (indivisible), the ancient Hindus called it "processes" and we may call it psi. Are there sufficient clues in nature and/or in our minds to suggest an answer? What are space and time? These basic fundamentals appear to be unraveling as we examine the elementary particles at the micro level, and perhaps even the macro level. Even the understanding of process vs. particle are being closely examined in particle physics.

A. Particle and Process, Logic and Reason

Logic and reason establish the backbone of the scientific process. The origin of these words relate directly to *logos,* "the word" (from Greek) and *ratio* or relationship (from Latin). Karl H. Pribram (1976) points out, words or "noun concepts" are the objects of scientific law (such as pressure, force, velocity and momentum, etc.) and ratios of these concepts are incorporated into scientific laws and formulations. For example, for an ideal gas we have, $P_1/P_2 = V_2/V_1$, at constant temperature, so that as the volume of the gas becomes smaller, the pressure of a fixed quantity of an ideal gas becomes larger. Scientific law is based on quantities expressing constancy and change. (See Table 2).

Western culture believes that the primary elements of the Universe are inert and immutable objects, particles, etc. which are noun terms. We need to imagine instead of just the Logos, or word, verbs or action concepts (Duiker, *et. al.* 2013). What if, as

Benedict de Spinoza suggests, God is not just Being (existing) but Becoming (process). This is closer to the Hindu Vedic concept where process is primary and not only associated with inert objects (Spinoza, 1883; Rauscher, 1971b).

We relate to conceptual frameworks with verbs as experiences—the movements of life, or the seemingly traffic jam. If we developed a physics around the concept of processes and not nouns or only objects, we would be describing the same universe but our theories would expand and become quite different!

"God does not play dice with the universe," quoting Einstein (1949) and physicists like David Finkelstein's (chairman of the Physics Department at the Georgia Institute of Technology, Atlanta) has a theory that involves "space-time codes" where he points to quantum processes that are not random (Finkelstein, 1972). Even the notion of randomness, according to Finkelstein, may not be due to some inherent property of the Universe, but rather to our ignorance of the processes behind the universe. Some experimental evidence appears to support this in that several experiments have found small (5% or so) deviation from the randomicity of radioactive decay (Rauscher, 1977, Rauscher and Amororo, 2011).

In John Archibald Wheeler's geometric model of the Universe, geometrical constructs are utilized to express the fixed, immutable, symmetric aspects of reality, an approach also taken by the "geometrizing" Greeks (Wheeler, 1962). Over the gateway to Plato's Academy were the words, "Let no one untrained in geometry enter here." The nature of and the manner in which force and dynamics originate from constant constructs in a model which assumes static geometry as primary is not well understood. Starting from dynamics to express change or process in the manifold and deriving the constant construct of geometry may be a way to proceed, or putting dynamics and process on an equal footing may lead to a new conceptual framework for physics and for science in general (Chew, 1968; Stapp, 1964, 2009; Rauscher, 1968a, 1971a, 1972a, 1972b, 1973, 1979, 1981, 1982b; Rauscher and

Amoroso, 2011; Rauscher and Targ, 2001, 2012). Geometric models are useful for expressing constant constructs in the physical universe. For scientific law to be useful (and it is) there must be constancy, which geometric models are able to express.

B. Intrinsic and Extrinsic Geometry, Mind and the Universe

Under a variety of conditions such as upon waking up, in meditation, or Kundalini yoga, in a John Lilly sensory-deprivation tank, etc, approximately one person in ten, according to Prof. Roger N. Shepard (Rauscher, 1971b), a psychologist at Stanford, has experienced "seeing" detailed and colorful geometric constructs without an external stimulus and with eyes closed in the dark. This author has noticed such a phenomenon in meditation, in a Lilly tank and while observing a variable-frequency stroboscopic flash. Many scientists and mathematicians have developed models of the universe based on geometric constraints. Perhaps there is an intrinsic structure in the mind which prompts us to describe our perceptions of reality by means of geometric structures or constraints (Rauscher, 1971a). Maybe Sir Arthur Eddington has a valid point about the study of physics divulging an aspect of the nature of consciousness (Eddington, 1946).

C. Spacetime Independence in Physics and Psychic Phenomena

Immanuel Kant formulated concepts of cause and effect. The currently defined scientific models are primarily based on space and time as independent quantities. These elements are the primary constructs of the universe. However, with recent multidimensional models in astrophysics by E.A. Rauscher (1971a, 1972a, 1972b, 1973, 1975, 1982a, 2005; Hurtak, Hurtak and Rauscher, 2013) and John Wheeler's geometric models (1962), as well as discoveries in the descriptions of elementary particle processes (Geoffrey Chew, 1968; Henry Stapp, 1964) at Lawrence Berkeley National Laboratory, spacetime, once the primary arena of physics, is no longer taking center stage nor is seen as inert.

For mystics, psychics and other self-referential experimental explorers, the subjective aspect of space and time is key. Research in Remote Perception (clairvoyance, telepathy and precognition), as well as psychic healing and psychokinesis implies that conscious perception can access remote information in space and time and transcend space and time (Rauscher, 1968a, 1979; 1982a; Ramon and Rauscher, 1980). Furthermore, in the words of Albert Einstein in his famous quote, "time and space are modes by which we think and not conditions in which we live," (Forsee, 1963) or in the words of A.S. Eddington, "time is a mental construct of our private consciousness...physicists construct the concept of a worldwide time from a string of subjective instances." (Eddington, 1922).

Since we are able to experience spacetime transcendence of consciousness, we can begin to formulate the relationship between ordinary, real spacetime and the complex multi-dimensional spacetime domain of consciousness (See Chapter 5) (Rauscher, 1981; 1982 1982a; Ramon and Rauscher, 1980, 1982). Through both particle physics and psychic phenomena, we are seeing that our present formulation of space and time is basically flawed. Thus, as an expression of event connections in space and time, the fundamental causality concept will require reformulation. This process is taking place in particle physics (for example, Chew, 1968; Rauscher, 1971b, Norsen, 2011, Kutach, 2013).

Experimental evidence has shown that the virtual energy of a vacuum (supposedly devoid of all matter and energy) affects observable physical particle processes and, therefore, in that sense, has a physical reality. This virtual energy can be seen, for example, in observable modifications of the conductivity and dielectric constant of hot fully ionized gases, called plasmas, consisting of ions and electrons. The energy of this system (of which the sun is an example) excites and polarizes the vacuum "sea" of energy which, in turn, interacts with the plasma, affecting its electrical properties (Rauscher, 1968b).

Multidimensional geometries may now allow for a form of

interconnectedness. While space and time, and matter and energy were linked by Einstein, evidence now appears to show a fundamental link between space, time, matter, energy, momentum and force. This concept is termed a Descartes geometry after René Descartes (1986, who suggested that such a geometry might be possible) (Rauscher, 1971a, 1972a, 1972b; 1973, 2005, 2013; See also John A. Wheeler's work (1962) which is an extension of the theory of relativity). In the words of Einstein (Duiker and Spielvolger, 2013), "It was formerly believed that if all material things (matter and energy) disappeared out of the Universe, time and space would be left. According to the relativity theory, however, time and space would disappear together with the things." (Einstein, 1949).

The geometrical multidimensional picture of the Universe leads us to the possible existence of a macroscopic remote connectedness which could extend from the quantum field to larger spatial disturbances. This model may be consistent with the understanding of the spacetime transcendence of consciousness tested in remote perception, at least over terrestrial distances (Rauscher, 1979, 1982a, 1982b; Rauscher and Amoroso, 2011; Ramon and Rauscher, 1979; 1982). Placing the levels of multidimensional geometries within a virtual sea of energy could possibly be the way consciousness accesses and remotely manipulates matter in the psychokinetic (mind-movement) phenomena which would truly be a measure of the connection of the observer to the observed!

"The most beautiful and most profound emotion we can experience is the sensation of the mystical. It is the sower of all true science. He to whom this emotion is a stranger, who can no longer stand rapt in awe, is as good as dead."

— Albert Einstein (1949)

Conclusion

The experience of unity is a fundamental state of consciousness. It is able to be experienced, with a universality beyond the manner in which it is achieved. While the dynamic sense of oneness with the universe, in which the observer participates and creates reality, is usually considered the subjective prattling of the few, the methodology of science, deep within its structure, yields similar concepts.

Heisenberg's uncertainty principle, nonlocality and relativity all lead us to further concepts in which the observer is a participant and the perspective from which he/she observes, determines what is seen. The concepts developed by J. S. Bell (1964) and E. Mach (Rauscher and Amoroso, 2011) lead to a universal connectedness, and recent work by this author and others indicates that some multidimensional geometries consistent with astrophysical data also lead to the concept of interconnectedness. The discussion of the completeness of physical theory (in this case quantum theory) originated from Bell's theorem.

Our current body of scientific knowledge is continuously being added to and changed, and perhaps all we know is "wrong" in the sense that it is incomplete. Tenets of science, once considered "absolute" and fixed like space and time are becoming fluid, becoming "Einsteinian flowing clocks." In particle physics, it is clear that the space and time continuum dynamically affects particles in the dynamic process of particle interaction. As Geoffrey Chew (1968), theoretical physicist from LBNL Berkeley, has said, particles are no longer isolated entities separated in spacetime, but are created out of each other and spacetime, or are "bootstrapped" from and with spacetime itself.

What one feels and how one interprets what one sees, or what one ultimately actually sees, is affected by one's state of consciousness, for observer/participant physics seems to tell us that what we see is determined by how we look at it. A test of Eddington's concept that the structure of the physical is a reflection of the structure of consciousness might be found in the examination of the question of whether our state of consciousness affects the structure of the physical theories we create (Tart, 1972).

Greater understanding of the relationship of parts to the whole may result from the recognition of the role of states of consciousness in our observations of reality. The "melting point" of the observer and the observed and the obvious connection of the two will surely lead us to a reformulation or expansion of models of physics and a new comprehension of reality.

This leads us to the question: Is the duality of the mind/body or observer/observed, etc. a fundamental property of reality? Do we only imagine a relationship between separate parts or is it real? The resolution of the universal vs. particular and the relation of parts may lie in just that—the relational description. There may be both parts and the whole, but they are related and there are methods to describe their relationship. The basic concept of universality is that, while there are in fact parts, there are no truly isolated entities or parts! Therefore, in understanding the connections of the parts to each other and to the whole lies a useful model of reality.

Mounting evidence, both physical and mystical, demonstrates the interconnection between the observer and the observed; the observer is not isolated from the world, he/she is connected to the Universe (the observed) as a participant and we need to become aware of this responsibility within existence. However, we only perceive this according to our state of awareness.

References

Aspect, A., P. Grangier and G. Roger (1992) "Experimental Tests of Bell's inequality using time-varying analizers," *Phys. Rev. Lett.* 49, 1804 and private communication with Aspect.

Bell, J.S. (1964) "On the Einstein Podolsky Rosen paradox," *Physics* 1, p. 195.

Bohm, D. (1977) "Quantum theory an indication of a new order in physics: Implicate/Explicate order in physical law," *Found. of Phys.* 3, 139 and private communication, November 1977.

Campbell, J. (1971) *The Portable Jung*. New York: Viking Press.

Chew, G. (1968) "Bootstrap: a scientific idea?" *Science* 161, 762 and private conversations.

Clauser, J.F. and W.A. Horne (1974) "Experimental consequences of objective local theories," *Phys. Rev.* 10D, 526, and private conversations.

Descartes, René (1986, original 1637 in French). *Discourse on Method and Meditations on First Philosophy*. Translated by Donald A. Cress, p. 65.

DeWitt, B.S. (1970) "Quantum mechanics and reality," Phys. *Today*, September 1970, p. 30 and private conversations.

Duiker, W. J. and J. J. Spielvogel (2013) "The Americas and Society and Culture in the West" *World History, Vol. 2, 7th Ed.: Since 1500,* Boston: Wadsworth Cengage Learning, p. 600.

Eddington, A.S. (1922) *The Mathematical Theory of Relativity*. Chelsea.

Eddington, A. S. (1946) *Fundamental Theory*. Cambridge Un. Press.

Einstein, A. (1949) *Einstein Philosopher Scientist* (P.A. Schilpp, ed.), Evanston, Illinois, *The Library of Living Philosophers,* pp. 85-683.

Einstein, A., B. Podolsky, and N. Rosen (1935) "Can quantum-mechanical descriptions of physical reality be considered complete?" *Physical Review,* 47, p. 777.

Finkelstein, D. (1972) "Space-time code," *Phys. Rev.* 5, 320 and private communications.

Forsee, A. (1963) *Einstein, Theoretical Physicist.* NY: Macmillan, p. 81.

Gisin, N., W.J. Tittel, J.H. Prendel and H. Zbinden (1998) "Violation of Bell's inequality on photons more than 10kms apart, *Phys. Rev. Lett.* 81, p. 3563.

Gisin, N., and H. Zbinden (1999) ''Bell inequality and the locality loophole: active versus passive switches,'' *Phys. Rev. Lett.* A264, pp. 103–107.

Gödel, K. (1992) *On Formally Undecidable Propositions of Principia Mathematica and Related Systems,* New York: Dover Pub.

Heisenberg, W. (1972) *Physics and Beyond: Encounters and Conversations,* New York: Harper and private communications.

Hixon, L. (1933) *Mother of Buddhists: mediation on the Prajnaparmita,* Quest Books, Wheaton, Il.

Kaiser, D., (2011) *How the Hippies Saved Physics,* New York: W.W. Norton. This book details my development of and chairing of the fundamental physics groups or "FYSIKS" which I named and started at the Lawrence Berkeley National Laboratory Theoretical Physics Group in which I was on the staff. The Fundamental "Fysiks" Group ran from 1975-1978. The purpose of this group was to explore the meanings and foundations of quantum mechanics, Bell's Nonlocality Theorem and its test, Relativity and multi-dimensional geometries and the nature and properties of consciousness. We also conducted research on remote viewing of replication studies of the SRI International, Palo Alto, CA.

Kant, I. (1997) *The Critique of Pure Reason.* Translated and ed. by P. Guyer and A. Wood, Cambridge: Cambridge University Press.

Kleene, S.C. (1950) *Intro. to Metamathematics,* NY: Van Nostrand.

Kuhn, T.S. (1970) *The Structure of Scientific Revolutions,* Chicago: University of Chicago Press.

Kutach, D. (2013) *Causation and Its Basis in Fundamental Physics.* Oxford University Press.

Norsen, T. (2011) John S. Bell's Concept of Local Causality. *American Journal of Physics.* 79, pp. 1261-75.

Pribram, K. (1976) "Problems concerning the structure of consciousness," in *Consciousness and the Brain,* G. Globus, Ed., New York: Plenum Press and private communication at Stanford University, CA.

Puthoff, H. E. and R. Targ (1976) "A Perceptual Channel for Information Transfer over Kilometer Distances," *Proceedings of the IEEE* 64, March 1976, pp. 329-354,

Ramon, C. and E.A. Rauscher (1980) "Superluminal transformations in complex Minkowski space," *Lawrence Berkeley Laboratory report* LBL-9752, Berkeley, CA, and *Found. of Phys.* 10, p. 661.

Ramon, C. and E.A. Rauscher (1982) "Remote connectedness in Complex Geometries and its Application to the Nature of the Human Mind," Vol. II, pp. 1423-1442, and Chair Women's Introduction, The ICF Press, New York, Philadelphia, PA. pp. 1405-1407.

Rauscher, E.A. (1968a) "Einstein's field equations and the quantal force," *Lawrence Livermore Laboratory report UCRL-71435,* Livermore, CA.

Rauscher, E.A. (1968b) "Electron interactions and quantum plasma physics," *J. Plasma Phys.* 2, p. 217.

Rauscher, E.A. (1971a) "A unifying theory of fundamental processes," *Bull, of Amer. Phys. Soc.,* 13, 1643 (1968); and UC/LBNL, UCRL-20808, Lawrence Berkeley Laboratory.

Rauscher, E.A. (1971b) *The Philosophy of Science.* Book and Course taught at UC Berkeley, LBNL and J.F. Kennedy University, Orinda, CA.

Rauscher, E.A. (1972a) "Closed cosmological solutions to Einstein's field equations," *Nuovo Cimento Lett.* 3, pp. 661-665.

Rauscher, E.A., (1972b) "A group-theoretical representation of the generalized Heisenberg relations," *Nuovo Cimento Lett.* 5, p. 925.

Rauscher, E.A., (1973) "The Minkowski metric for a multidimensional geometry," *Nuovo Cimento Lett.* 7, p. 361.

Rauscher, E.A. (1975) "Speculations on the Evolution of a Schwarzschild Universe," Lawrence Berkeley National Laboratory LBNL/UCB, LBL-4353, December 1975, pp. 331-333.

Rauscher, E.A. (1977) "Examination of Variation of Radio active decay rates in Si^{28}" and references therein. Our experiment involved intentional mind matter influence and some of the references involved variations in atomic structure. The experiment was conducted on the Building 70B, with a Si^{28}, calibration source with six UC Berkeley Graduate students at Lawrence Berkeley National Laboratory, in July 1976. The sessions were fifteen minutes long in which all participants concentrated on slowing the rate of radioactive decay by 4%, an interval of 15 minutes off concentration sessions were performed where the students were distracted where I ran them around the laboratory halls. The experiment was conducted over a six hour session yielding a great deal of data. See USPL-20261. The author found references to over twenty other experiments.

Rauscher, E.A. (1979) "Some physical models applicable to remote perception," in *The Iceland Papers: Frontiers of Physics.* Select papers on experimental and theoretical research on the physics of consciousness; foreword by B.D. Josephson, edited by A. Puharich. Assentia Research Associates, Amherst, Wisconsin. August, 1979, p. 50.

Rauscher, E.A. (1981) "Conceptual Changes in Reality Models from New Discoveries in Physics," Vol. II., The ICF Press, New York, Seoul, Korea, pp. 1407-1431.

Rauscher, E.A. (1982a) "Theoretical and Experimental Exploration of Remote Perception Phenomena," Vol. II, The ICF Press, New York, Philadelphia, PA., pp. 1143-1477.

Rauscher, E.A. (1982b) Solitary Waves, Coherent Non-Dispersive Solutions in Complex Minkowski Spaces," *Bull. Amer. Phys. Soc.* 27, p. 35.

Rauscher, E.A. (2005) "Cosmogenesis and Current Cosmology and the Evolution of its Physical Parameters," *The Foundation of Cosmology and Quantum Theory,* Eds. R.L. Amoroso, B. Leahnart and J.-P. Vigier, Noetic Academic Science Press, pp. 43-72.

Rauscher, E.A. (2010) "Quantum Mechanics and the Effect of Intentional Will," pp. 36-63, in *Complementarity of Mind and Body: Realizing the Dream of Descartes, Einstein and Eccles,* ed. R.L. Amoroso, Nova Science Publishing, Inc., New York.

Rauscher, E.A. and R.L. Amoroso (2008) "The Schrödinger Equation in Complex Minkowski Space, Nonlocality and Anticipatory Systems," Ed. D.M. Dubois, International Journal of Compelling Anticipatory Systems, 22, pp. 370-388.

Rauscher, E.A. and R.L. Amoroso (2011) *Orbiting the Moons of Pluto: Complex Solution to Einstein, Maxwell, Schrödinger, and Dirac Equations,* World Scientific.

Rauscher, E.A., J.J. Hurtak, D.E. Hurtak (2013) "Universal Scaling Laws in Quantum Theory and Cosmology." *The Physics of Reality: Space,*

Time, Matter, Cosmos - Proceedings of the 8th Symposium Honoring Mathematical Physicist Jean-Pierre Vigier. Edited by Amoroso Richard *et. al.* World Scientific Publishing Co. Pte. Ltd., pp. 376-387.

Rauscher, E.A. and R. Targ, (2001) "Investigation of a Complex Space-Time Metric to Describe Psychic Phenomena", *Journal of Scientific Exploration* 15, pp. 331-354.

Rauscher, E.A. and R. Targ, (2012) "Investigation of a complex Space -time metric to describe Precognition," pp. 5-26, ed. I. Fredriksson, *Aspects of Consciousness: Essays on Physics, Death and the Mind*, McFarland and Co., Inc.

Rescher, N., (1991) *G.W. Leibniz's Monadology: An Edition for Students*, Pittsburg: University of Pittsburg Press.

Sartre, John Paul (1992,) *Existentialism: Age of Reason*, New York, Vintage Press.

Schrödinger, E., (1926a) "An undulatory theory of the mechanics of atoms and molecules," *Physics Review* 6, p. 28.

Schrödinger, E., (1926b) "Quantization as an eigenvalue problem," *Ann. Physik* p. 79.

Spinoza, B., (1883) *Ethic: Demonstrated in Geometrical Order*, New York: Macmillan.

Stapp, H.P. (1964) "Space, time and elementary particles," Lawrence Berkeley Laboratory report UCRL-11688.

Stapp, H.P. (2009) *Mind, Matter and Quantum Mechanics*. 3rd edition, Berlin: Springer-Verlag, Frontiers Collection.

Swann, I. (1975) *To Kiss the Earth Goodbye*, New York: Hawthorne and private conversations.

Tart, C.T. (1972) "States of consciousness and state specific sciences," *Science* 176, p. 1203 and private conversations.

Tart, C.T. (1975,) *States of Consciousness*, New York: E. P. Dutton.

Walker, E.H. (1977) "Quantum mechanical tunneling in synaptic and ephaptic transmission," *International Jour. of Quantum Chem*. 11, p. 103.

Wheeler, J.A. (1962) *Geometrodynamics*, New York: Academic Press and Private conversations.

Chapter 2:

The Remote Perception Phenomena: A Doorway to Expanded Consciousness Awareness

by

Elizabeth Rauscher, Ph.D.

"Experiment without inspiration, or imagination without recourse to experiment, can accomplish little, but, for effective progress, a happy blend of these powers is necessary."

— Ernest Rutherford,
Father of Nuclear Physics (~1930)

Table of Contents

Introduction: 67
1. Brief Description of the Protocol of Remote Perception Experiments 69
2. The Remote Perception Protocol 73
3. Detailed Description & Analysis of Remote Perceptual Results and Protocol for Current and Future Experiments 74
4. Interviewing the Subject Participant & the Closed Laboratory Room 76
5. The Experimental Laboratory Room 78
6. Target Site Selection 80
7. The Role of the Outbound Experimenter(s) 81
8. The Role of the Coordinator 83
9. Subject Feedback and the Learning Process 84
10. Task and Procedures of the Judges or Judging Methods 85
11. PSI and Consciousness 90
12. Conclusion & Brief History of my PSI Research 92
Appendix I 94
Appendix II 95
Appendix III 98
Appendix IV 99
References 101

List of Tables

Table 1: Issues related to Human Knowledge and Consciousness 70
Table 2: Remote Perception, Experimental Design And Set up 71
Table 3: Summary of Remote Viewing Concepts 72
Table 4: Remote Perception Beyond Space and Time Questions 79
Table 5: Remote Perception: Conscious Awareness Beyond Space and Time 82
Table 6: Space-Time Properties of Consciousness and Remote Effects—Future Research 88
Table 7: Some Discoveries from General ESP Research 89
Table 8: Some Issues Related to Remote Viewing 91
Table 9: Issues Relevant to Consciousness 93

Introduction

One of the common objections to the existence of psi functioning is that it appears to be in conflict with the laws of physics. In our investigation, we attempt, first to demonstrate the possible compatibility of psychic phenomena with the laws and content of physics and then to develop a model that explains psi with predictability. It is hypothesized that we can use physical principles to assist us in understanding psi phenomena; further, that the psychic database may probably shed light on some of the current problems in physics, such as the foundations of quantum mechanics, geometrical models of spacetime, or relativity theory.

The purpose of this investigation is to make use of the remote perception experimental database to deduce the relevant physical principles and laws governing paranormal functioning and to study the psi phenomenon itself. We have considered the utilization of the constraints of the remote perception data on the structure of the spacetime metric (Ramon and Rauscher, 1980, 1982; Rauscher, 1973, 1976, 1978a, 1978b, 1978c, 1978d, 1979, 1981a, 1982a, 1982b, 1982c, 1983a, 1983b, 1983c, 1983d, 1996, 2001, Rauscher, *et. al.*, , 1975, 1975-1982; Rauscher and Amoroso, 2006, 2011; Rauscher and Targ, 2001; 2002, 2006; 2012). We will examine higher-dimensional geometries including complex coordinate geometries with regard to the possible resolution of remote viewing and precognition with causality. This helps to establish a model that not only demonstrates the constancy of precognition and causality, but may also demonstrate a fundamental relationship between Maxwell's, Schrödinger's and the Dirac equations and the structure of relativity theory in complex space (Rauscher and Amoroso, 2011; Rauscher, 2015). This leads to reconsidering the constraints of remote perception data on the structure of the spacetime metric. (See Chapter 5.)

We will also present the detailed protocol of remote viewing experiments and a discussion of experimental results of our research from 1974 to present. Strict adherence to experimental protocol is necessary for obtaining controlled and positive (statistically significant) results. We have conducted over eighty experiments with excellent results for the matching of subject mentation to geographical location. We will later also present an overview of both theoretical and experimental examination of the remote perception phenomena. The scientific method is a powerful tool in expanding our knowledge of the nature of reality.

The research reported here involves the investigation of the remote perception process, which is the ability of certain individuals to access and describe distant target locations by a mental process, although information is blocked from ordinary perception by distance, time or shielding. We can term this process Remote Perception rather than Remote Viewing, since other sensory modalities, such as smell, feeling, hearing, etc. can also be verified as being related to distant target locations. The experiments are designed to eliminate classical sensory modalities, and to enhance and investigate the phenomena.

1. A Brief Description of the Protocol of Remote Perception Experiments

As we stated, in demonstrating the possible compatibility of psi phenomena with the laws and content of physics, we have developed a model with predictability (Rauscher, 1976; Rauscher, 1996; Rauscher and Amoroso, 2011). First, in explaining the process of how this works, we need to further define the experimental protocols. While Table 1 presents some concepts related to ideas of consciousness, Table 2 begins to present the experimental design and roles of the experimental participants in real time with local and long distance remote perception experiments.

Local experiments involved target selections of geographical locations within a thirty minute drive of the laboratory while the subjects participating were sequestered so that no external means of communication (e.g., such as today's cell phones) could be used. Long distance experiments involved anywhere in the USA or in other countries. For the time sequence of a remote perception experiment, like those done at SRI or the Fundamental "Fysiks" Group, the remote perception by the subject participant is made during the time when the outbound experimenters are visiting the site. Sometimes a precognition experiment was designed where the subject remote viewed prior to the target being randomly selected and the outbound experimenters traveling to the target. Essentially the subject perceives the target location before the outbound team goes to the randomly chosen target site, the outbound experimenters use a random number generator to choose one of the targets (sealed in opaque envelopes) for real time and precognitive experiments.

We present the experimental set up in Table 2 (Rauscher, 1980). Note the subject, monitor and outbound team do not know the possible targets in the target pool ahead of the experiment. Some general concepts regarding remote viewing are presented in Table 3.

Table 1

ISSUES RELATED TO HUMAN KNOWLEDGE AND CONSCIOUSNESS:

1. What is the relationship between conception and perception? To what extent does our "mind set" limit and determine what we perceive as perception selection and "mental frame of reference?"
2. Given adequate time in a conducive civilization and knowledge dissemination from generation to generation, to what extent is the human mind capable of discerning knowledge, facts, information and truth? Can only judgmental and significant fact, etc. be known with absolute certainty?
3. Can we prove the existence of external reality? What is the relationship of perceiver and perceived? We can relate this issue to the quantum measurement issue.
4. We would like to better define and comprehend the innate constraints of the mind to expand upon and better understand such issues as defined by Immanuel Kant in regard to innate categorization and causality.
5. To what extent is human knowledge gained by the scientific methodology based on discovery of "Natural Principles" and to what extent is it based on creation of ideas and perhaps even creating external reality?
6. If perception determines to some degree what we think we perceive, and also our conscious effects on external processes which can be directly measured by Psychokine-

sis (PK), what are the implications for the scientific method as currently defined and practiced?

7. How does the possible (defined for $t > t_0$), future time relative to now time, become actualized? How do we define a causality to accommodate choice, precognition and consciousness in general?

Table 2

REMOTE PERCEPTION,
EXPERIMENTAL DESIGN AND SET UP

- Subject participant, remote perceiver
- Monitor/Recorder, pad of paper and pens
- Laboratory room
- Target selector
- Target pool (in envelopes)
- Coordinator keeps targets locked up until experiment starts, does not look inside target envelopes and chooses judges
- Random number generator for outbound experimenters
- Outbound experimental team and recorder, camera synchronized
- Monitor, subject recording
- Feedback information; post experimental time
- Judging, computer or person
- Local, non-local, precognition type of experiment

Table 3
SUMMARY OF REMOTE VIEWING CONCEPTS

A summary of some of the concepts of Remote Viewing/ Perception that goes beyond ordinary vision include:

1. Remote perception, awareness of nonlocal spatial and temporal accurate information blocked from ordinary perception, such as remote viewing and precognition.

2. Perception of internally generated states of consciousness with visual perception with no apparent external stimuli, such as the "blue pearl of spiritual wisdom", and states of consciousness.

3. Dream state, lucid dreaming, problem-solving in the dream states, dream analysis and design making based on dreams.

4. Historical, spiritual and practical use of visual perception through non-ordinary channels of perception.

5. Perception of simple visual forms through the generation of complex magnetic pulsed fields from an external antennae emitter perceived by a person whose perception is blocked from ordinary sensorial stimuli.

6. Seeing without ordinary sight, a universe of possibilities and realities.

7. An expanded view of visual perception and consciousness.

2. The Remote Perception Protocol

The proper protocol used in our remote viewing experiments generally involves pre-selected target locations, the descriptions of which are sealed in envelopes and kept under lock and key. The target locations are numbered. In an isolated laboratory room are a subject and an inbound experimenter or monitor (constituting the inbound team). At a pre-determined time, an outbound experimental team, separated from the laboratory room, randomly selects a sealed target envelope (with the aid of a random number generator chosen usually when the team is in the car ready to go to the target location). The outbound team proceeds to the denoted location in the proper predetermined allotted time, which for local experiments is about 30 minutes of driving time, to arrive at the target location.

Then the subject attempts to describe the location of the outbound experimenter's experiences and activities at the target. The time in which this process is instigated corresponds to the time set for the outbound team to arrive at their target location. The subject's information is recorded on tape, with the monitor's assistance, and also subject's drawings are made. Experimental session time usually lasts fifteen minutes at the target location.

After a series of six or so experiments are conducted, the subject's transcripts and drawing are judged by an independent experimenter who matches the subject's recorded responses (transcription descriptions) to the target locations, without prior knowledge of the correct matching. Tape or digital audio recordings of the outbound team are also made. Statistical analysis is conducted on a non-forced choice basis.

Usually a series of six remote perception experiments are considered together to be judged by an independent person who does not have any direct contact with the participants in the experiment. A intermediator person transfers the six subject mentations and six randomly chosen targets which are presented in random order to be judged, and the matching chosen. These protocols were developed by Harold Puthoff (Targ and Puthoff, 1974, 1976; Targ, Puthoff and May, 1981), Russell Targ (Targ and Haray, 1984) and Ingo Swann at SRI International, then utilized and modified by E.A. Rauscher, *et. al.* (1976) (Kaiser, 2011).

Also judging can be made using a set of seven level criteria to relate correspondence of the subject's mentation and the outbound target. Data can be digitally recorded including drawings, but paper and pen is best. Cell phones and computers are eliminated from the inbound and outbound team so that no spurious information can be transferred by other than psychic means. The judging process involves revisiting the various targets to perform the matching process (Puthoff and Targ, 1976; Rauscher, *et. al.*, 1976; Mullins and Rauscher, 1977 and 1979; Millay, 2010).

3. Detailed Description and Analysis of Remote Perceptual Results and Protocol for Current and Future Experiments

It is important to understand that the "receiver" of remote perception information who describes the target, is the one called the "subject," but the term "participant" is preferable since the word "subject" implies that this person is the only active agent in the experiment and that the other participants are passive (but we use these terms interchangeably). Therefore, the laboratory "receiver" will be called the "subject participant." There is also the "outbound experimenter(s)" or "outbound participant(s)" who can enhance the phenomena by their activities, intention, and mental set at the target.

It is critical that the outbound team concentrates on the target, because if they let their minds wander, what they are thinking too can be perceived by the subject. The inbound experimental interviewer or monitor can profoundly affect the outcome of an experiment and it also appears that the role of the judge could be dependent on such factors as training, state of mind, etc. A few experiments have shown small variances in multiple judging performances, but most have demonstrated interjudging reliability, whether they are psi acceptors or are skeptical of the phenomena. I have utilized up to five independent judges having various belief systems and they usually yield very similar results (Rauscher, *et. al.* 1976; Mullins and Rauscher, 1977 and 1979).

The essential point is that all participants need to approach this work with an open mind, and a willingness and motivation to succeed, as is true in any experimental situation. We have identified some of the factors we feel are significant to the success of this work. These include: (1) willingness to participate, (2) availability (not feeling pressed for time), (3) sincere desire to succeed, (4) open mindedness (no extreme bias pro or opposed to the existence of the phenomena nor personal investment to prove a point of view), (5) well-integrated personality, (6) honesty and a sense of integrity, and (7) a positive attitude towards life. All these factors help the accuracy of the experiment.

Other factors which we have identified as important to enhancing the success of remote perception are (1) practice and learning through doing the experiment and receiving feedback, (2) awareness, through some practice of one's subtle and internal states of consciousness, and (3) the choice of experimental participants, including the subject, on the basis of these criteria. In our early work, our subject participants were chosen on availability and willingness to participate such as the secretary or engineers down the laboratory hall. Some participants were skeptical, but open minded and some had a positive view of the existence of psi and some were meditators. As a subject perceiver, one must learn to quiet one's mind, relax and let the information come into conscious awareness.

4. Interviewing the Subject Participant and the Closed Laboratory Room

During the experimental session, a minimum of two people will be present in the laboratory room, the *subject participant* and the *inbound experimenter*. As we said, the *inbound experimenter* is a term for the interviewer or monitor, whose purpose is to solicit and record the subject's responses and assure no one enters the room before or during the subject's mentation or that anyone else makes any direct contact with the subject. We reserve the term, *coordinator*, for the person who stores and retrieves the targets and stores copies of the subject's descriptions before feedback. Sometimes this is also the role of the *inbound experimenter.*

The questioning by the *inbound experimenter,* acting as monitor, assists the subject in (1) focusing on their relevant psychic perceptions, (2) assisting the perceiver or viewer to record relevant perceptions and (3) recording them on audio tape or other media (and sometimes storing the subject participant's drawings). A number of experimenters have found that drawings can represent accurate psychic information very well. Impressions of form, shape, color, size, scale, distinct features or functions, indoor or outdoor location of the target, as well as emotions, feelings and reactions are elicited from the subject and recorded. In a sense, the inbound experimenter interviewer asks "gentle" non-intrusive "left hemisphere" questions to stimulate the subject's "right hemisphere" response.

It has been found by most researchers that impressions of form, shape, color, feelings, textures, and sounds, of course, as well as visual impressions are more accurate than attempting to identify function, location, purpose and name of the site, though both have accurately provided information by means of experienced viewers, a number of times.

However, it is important to note that the inbound experimenter has no knowledge of the target site. The inbound experimenter merely attempts to guide the subject to acquire and record detailed optimum data, as measured by judge blind matching. A quiet environment in the laboratory with a non-intrusive questioning process is of prime importance. We feel that the psychic state may be characterized by a mildly altered state of consciousness which involves the acquisition of subtle internal perceptions by the subject. We have found that meditation techniques and repeated remote perception experimental participation greatly enhances the phenomena (Mullins and Rauscher, 1977 and 1979).

We design our experiments to reduce "noise" or extraneous material in the remote viewing process. Sources of noise include: sensory intrusions, imagination, meditation imagery, guessing, other psychic impressions, and emotional distractions. Some of these sources, such as guessing are reduced by not knowing the set of possible targets, whereby the subject-inbound experimenter team is less likely to attempt to guess the target. The remote perception procedure is a free response process.

It is important to clearly specify the task to the subject. It appears that remote perception is a goal-oriented task. Time, place, "mental size" scale, and the target beacon method need to be put in perspective by the monitor, even when the monitor does not know the location. The subject can better describe the target if their perception size scale is optimum, that is, relative to their normal viewing perspective. Specifically, the subject needs to be informed whether to search for the target in the present, past or the future and its approximate size, i.e. such as a target in a small canister or a geographical location, as this also assists the remote viewing search. The subject can also change their size scale and their psychic vantage point during the experiment by the suggestions of the inbound experimenter or by their own choice.

Often when subject participants may look up to their left or right or are quiet in the beginning of the remote perception session, it is important for the inbound experimenter not to interrupt the subject's perception when they are receiving remote information. One may elicit comments after giving the subject three to five minutes to perceive the target. Some possible questions that are used by monitors are given in Table 4. Some of the methods presented enhance the phenomena.

A person can be skeptical, and not believe the phenomena exists, but be open to the possibility it does and perform well in the remote viewing task. It appears that many of the constraints on the remote perception phenomena are not "innate" physical constructs that are inherent in physical nature but are psychological biases. Such biases can be extreme, such as fear or strong beliefs that precognition does not exist, therefore the subject does not become aware of any remote perception.

It is important to set up controlled laboratory conditions which are also conducive to the relaxed but alert mental state in which psychic experiences occur. Working with people requires a warm, humanistic approach which need not, in any way, compromise the controlled conditions of the experiments. Any team of researchers, or people approaching the carrying out of a project will succeed more fully on that project with a consideration of interpersonal factors, whether related to the study of psi or other phenomena (Rauscher, 1984a).

5. The Experimental Laboratory Room

The features of the laboratory room for the subject and the inbound experimenter should first shield against inadvertent or purposeful acquisition of information about the target location, and secondly, should enhance remote perception. The first point has been already covered in the discussion of the monitor's role.

In order to enhance the quality and reliability of remote perception, as we stated the laboratory room should be very quiet and shielded against extraneous noises. The lighting should be adequate but not too intense. It is suggested that

Table 4

REMOTE PERCEPTION BEYOND
SPACE AND TIME QUESTIONS
THAT CAN BE ASKED BY THE INBOUND EXPERIMENTER:
Monitoring "The Left Hemisphere"

1. What are you feeling and what are your impressions?
2. How close are you?
3. Size comparison: How big are you relative to your impression?
4. What shapes and forms do you perceive?
5. Any associated colors with that?
6. Any associated textures or noises or smells?
7. Can you move in closer or move back?
8. Move above and get an overview, if you would like to have another perspective?.
9. Is the predominant impression of outdoors or indoors or both?
10. Could you draw and write your impression?
11. Record shapes and forms more than function.
12. Enjoy yourself (s).

incandescent or full spectrum lighting with a dimmer rheostat be used rather than fluorescent or diode lighting.

Distracting photos or pictures should be eliminated from the room and it should be a sensory-limited, but not sensory-deprived environment, since that is also distracting. The subject participant and the inbound experimenter should have comfortable chairs, felt pens, paper, and digital tape recorders ready before the session begins. Positioning of chairs, tables, and lamps can be made at the start of the session to be psychologically pleasing and functional, as well as psychically desirable by the inbound participants.

It has also been suggested that residual thought forms from previous runs (psychometry) may remain and therefore one may wish to change the position of the chairs, etc. On the other hand, some feel that familiarity with a position of furniture may enhance the phenomena. The subject's and experimenters' beliefs are to be taken into account. The key is for the participants in the remote perception process to be open minded and "shelve their biases." (See Table 5.) I have found this to be useful in life.

6. Target Site Selection

To assist in the judging process, one needs to have distinguishable sites or what are termed "orthogonal" sites. For example, in a pool of sites, if four out of six contain water as a predominate feature, the subject may describe water, and the judges may not be able to match which transcript goes with which water site. Even though psychic functioning is occurring and the water site target is remotely perceived, the judges may match it with the incorrect water site. This is also true of computer programmed judging methods. Correct matching in this case would require a very accurate description of the form, shape and function of the water at the site.

Consequently, sites should be selected on the basis of the

following features, (1) uniqueness of site in terms of its function, shape, form and the emotional mood or response associated with the location; (2) a sufficiently simple structure and form so that one can represent the site in drawings and describe it with relative ease. In selecting a target, the "squint eye" test can be used to see if in diminished light, one can perceive the general features of the location; and (3) the site should be sufficiently interesting, so as to be psychically stimulating, in order to enhance remote perception.

The original target pool usually should consist of about twenty-four distinct sites with replacement possibilities. Their brief description, location, and name is enclosed and sealed in an opaque envelope. These envelopes are stored in a locked box or safe. Before an experiment, some of the envelopes are to be shuffled and numbered for six to eight possible targets per run. From time to time these envelopes will be shuffled again by the coordinator and no distinguishing marks or features on the envelopes are to be made. For the psychometric considerations, once an envelope is used for a target, it should be discarded as it is no longer needed and not reused for another target, but another envelope takes its place in the shuffle.

7. The Role of the Outbound Experimenter(s)

The outbound experimenter(s) acts as a "psychic beacon" for the subject to demark the target location. The outbound experimenter represents a symbol which the subject recognizes as defining the target. It is important to note that abstract coordinates, names and photos can be used to denote a target without using an outbound experimenter (Puthoff, *et. al.*, 1981). If an outbound experimenter is used, their role is to enhance the emotional impact of the site (Kane, *et. al.*, 1993; Millay, 2010). (See Table 5).

Specifically, if a target is a geographical location, the outbound experimental team increases the possible information transfer by concentrating on the target for the full fifteen

Table 5
REMOTE PERCEPTION: CONSCIOUS AWARENESS BEYOND SPACE AND TIME:
To Outbound Experimenters

1. Enjoy yourself (s).
2. Experience the site.
3. Observe form and shapes (as "primitive" perceptions).
4. Observe and experience, outdoors or indoors.
5. Note your mood and feelings associated with being at the site.
6. Quiet internal dialogue; set aside extraneous thoughts.
7. Interact with site, touch and listen.
8. Have a good day!

minutes and not letting their mind wander. They also have the ability to collect relevant information for post hoc analysis. Additionally, it is critical to have a time annotation of their distinct activities, which can be perceived by the subject. Through detailed analysis, the judge can analyze the time synchronization of the outbound experimenters' activities with the subject's responses (Rauscher, 1981b).

The outbound team must pay attention to their task, arriving at the site on time, and placing full cognitive attention on the site (Rauscher, 1976, 1981a, 1981b; Rauscher, *et. al.*, 1978b, 1978c; Gough, *et. al.*, 1981). Distracted thought may be received by the subject and introduce noise into the system as we said before. Definite activity can be recorded by an audio or audio/ visual system with time synchronization accurately recorded by both groups (i.e., the subject and the outbound team), during the outbound team's activity.

Our protocol suggests, three photographs should be made by the outbound participants in real time which are to be included with the audio transcript in the judge's packet. The photographs should not be taken with a communicator device such as a cell phone. The photographs can be utilized to capture transient phenomena, which may not otherwise be considered in the post hoc analysis. The three photographs are made to produce uniformity. A larger number of photographs makes it easier to "find" similar structures that may be "by chance" only.

Some suggest that non-psychic clues can occur in giving the judges the three photos of the target. Therefore, all experiments were conducted without the photos of the target being initially observed by the judges. Only in post hoc analysis and additional judging were they used. Consequently, statistical significance was determined when the judge visited the target site.

8. The Role of the Coordinator

The coordinator stores the target envelopes in a locked box or safe. This person also monitors, from the outside, the laboratory room where the subject and the *inbound experimenter* (or monitor/ interviewer) are positioned, so that no information will be transmitted to or from the laboratory room during the course of the experiment, which could affect the final outcome of the experiment.

Security is accomplished by the coordinator, (1) by storing in a safe, the sealed target envelopes and supplying the outbound team with the set of sealed envelopes containing the information to designate the target (the outbound team preferably uses a random number generator to determine the target envelope), (2) by allowing no person to enter or leave the subject's mentation room before or during, the experiment and (3) by allowing no phones, computers or other devices such as radio transmitters or receivers to be available in the laboratory room.

Two tapes of the subject's mentation are made at each experimental session. One of these tapes, with a photocopy of any drawing which may have been made by the subject, will be handed to the coordinator at the end of the experimental session to store in the safe before any feedback to the subject is made. The other is transcribed with the subject's drawings and used for the judging process.

9. Subject Feedback and the Learning Process

I and other researchers have found that remote perception can be enhanced by learning. We feel that the learning process involves the practice of becoming more aware of the internal psychically perceived information and screening out noise in the system by recognizing it as such.

We use this technique to enhance the phenomena but we also avoid possible clueing of subjects about potential future targets. Additionally, possible transcript clues about target order are eliminated from transcripts before the judging process takes place. With a large enough target pool, or target selection of geographical locations which are varied in function and form, the possibility of guessing by the subject even with feedback is eliminated.

The feedback procedure is conducted after the coordinator is given one copy of the tape and drawings generated by the subject. Then interaction of the outbound team can be made and the target discussed. The subject is then taken to the site location on the same day (for local, real time experiments) and a tape recorder with tape can also be taken along so they can listen again to their comments at the site. They are allowed to explore the site with little interference, as subjects will also point out areas at the target they accurately described which the outbound team may not have directly observed. Revisiting the site by the subject and others is permissible, except during the judging procedure.

Subject feedback is provided by having the subject, and sometimes the monitor and the outbound team, visit the target locations together. This is done after the experimental data of the inbound and outbound team are securely stored for later judging. We have found that feedback is extremely important for the psi reception learning process. Currently using digital cameras, information can be downloaded and stored into the coordinator's files which are computer coded.

As with many life processes, psi phenomena is directly amenable to a learning curve. In several experiments, we had the subject participants attempt to perform their own matching of their description to the target pools after the experiment was completed. In general, they found this frustrating. The important point of the feedback process definitely enhances the remote perception process. In several cases of long distance Remote Viewing, feedback occurred years later in which the subject mentation demonstrated extremely accurate remote, spatial and temporal target perception.

10. Task and Procedures of the Judges or Judging Methods

Before the judging process is begun, all materials and information is properly coded and stored. The judging process proceeds such that judges and judging procedures are conducted so that no contact with the subject perceiver, monitor and outbound experimenters occurs. As we explain in this chapter, computer matching algorithms have been developed and we show how they are utilized.

The "blind" judging process consists of one or more judges (the number determined prior to the experimental series), who are given randomly ordered material from the subject and from the target locations. The matching of subject transcripts and drawings, each sealed in separate envelopes, from each session is matched to target locations. The target site envelopes contain, (1) the name of the target, (2) the location of the target, (3) three real time photo prints, which are printed out in color, with notations of the time they were taken, and (4) a typed transcript from the audio recording by the outbound experimenter(s). This material can be given to the judges on a laptop computer, iPad or other digital format. It is felt that the use of envelopes with target descriptions, as hard copy, may enhance psi instead of using computer formatted images and data (Rauscher, 1984a).

The task of the judge(s) is to match the apparent subjective descriptive information to the target location, in an objective manner. This process has some similarities to the interviewer's process of eliciting subject's subjective impressions by asking questions which lead to information which can be analyzed.

It is extremely important for the judges to visit the sites, which is more difficult for analyzing long distance experiments. Examining the target area gives them a better overview of the moods and feelings one might receive from the location, and increases the chance that they will see features described in the subject's mentations.

Both the result of the judging procedures and detailed analysis are useful in understanding the remote perception process. There is much to understand in terms of the process of objectification of the data through the judging process. Detailed analysis of word and phase correlations and time synchronizations between the outbound experimental team and the subject gives useful information as to how to enhance the phenomena and to understand the mechanism of remote perception through detailed analysis and, perhaps, the development of computer codes for word and form analysis between the inbound and outbound teams. The role of the judges is to match one modality of perception (remote perception) with another modality (direct perception). Plans are to create a system to better analyze and understand remote perception. At the end of

Chapter 3 and Chapter 4, we utilize a partially computerized judging technique to enhance the objectification of the process.

In an ultimate sense, maybe no human endeavor can be completely objectified. We can test remote perception against direct perception in such a way as to define direct perception as correct, accurate, and reliable, yet direct perception is not always that reliable, as in the frequent disagreement among witnesses of a crime case. We have found in some cases, Remote Perception can be more accurate than direct perception. This is because Remote Perception is not limited by walls, etc. Areas at sites have been described by a remote perceiver that were inaccessible to observation by a direct outbound experimental perceiver, but were later verified. Upon feedback, subjects have pointed out such areas, which then become obvious to the outbound team.

Some judges have also been observant enough to detect areas and objects not perceived by outbound experimenters. There is a very subtle process underlying the meaning and significance of the judging comparison, including form, shape, color, function, meaning, and emotions aroused remotely, as well as directly, by a target site. To obtain numerical evaluation of the accuracy of the remote perception experiment, the experimental results are subjected to independent judging on a blind basis by people not otherwise associated with any of our experimental series or by independent computer judging methods by other research groups as before stated. Working alone, the human judge's task is to visit each target location, for example, six was the usual number of targets, placing them on a scale of 1 to 6 (best to worst match); each of the six transcripts against each target, generates a 6x6 matrix, in a blind rank order.

As a first-order evaluation of the matrix, we consider simply the number of direct matches (ones on the diagonal). The appropriate statistic is derived assuming the non-independent assignment of transcripts to target sites (as in guessing the order of a random sequence of the digits 1 - 6, each is used once). We have also the Princeton Laboratory Remote Perception judging

Table 6

SPACE-TIME PROPERTIES OF CONSCIOUSNESS AND REMOTE EFFECTS—FUTURE RESEARCH

1. Optimization in experimental design to amplify, comprehend, and utilize psi phenomena.
2. Training techniques and procedures, feedback and learning.
3. Psi amplifiers for remote viewing and psychokinesis—mental, physical, psychological and emotional.
4. Psi, healing and medicine.
5. Implications for education, health, creativity, philosophy, and society.
6. Research groups, laboratory facilities, and equipment.
7. Journal publications and relationship to the scientific community at large.
8. Adequate research funding.

questionnaire which was tested and used (Jahn, *et. al.,* 1982). In all, a detailed statistical analysis is made (Rauscher and Houck, 1985; Houck, Nelson and Rauscher, 1986; Mishlove, 1979).

In Table 6 we present the goals of future research and its application. Note that point number 8 (Table 6) is difficult for most research projects, especially involving non-mechanistic studies, such as consciousness and its applications. In Table 7, we present some interesting findings about psi in general. (See also Rauscher, 1978b, 1980, 1982b, 1984a; Rauscher *et. al.,* 1976; Millay, 2010; Rauscher and Rubik, 1980, 1983; Rauscher and van Bise, 1984, 1990, 1999 and references therein).

Table 7

SOME DISCOVERIES FROM GENERAL ESP RESEARCH

1. Remote perception ELF (extremely low frequency) model 0.005 to 1 bit/sec few decibels down at 2000 Km is not high enough.

2. Precognition occurs at about the same rate of success as real time and long distant remote perception, and may be explained by advanced potentials (Rauscher and Amoroso, 2011).

3. Remote Viewing may relate to Bell's remote connectedness theorem, $v > c$.

4. PK intervention energy bacteria experiment $\varepsilon_{\Lambda e} \sim 4 \times 10^9$ erg/gm/sec in 23 generation times, 10^2 calories/sec (Rauscher and Rubik, 1980, 1983).

5. Crystal dislocations $\varepsilon_{\Lambda e} \sim 10^9$ erg/gm/cm^3 (Rauscher, 1978b, 1984a, 1984b).

6. PK energy effects for $t \sim 1°$ K and $\Delta s \sim 0.04$ (watt/gm/sec) °K.

11. PSI and Consciousness

While some researchers hypothesize that ESP is a manifestation of a primitive modality property of consciousness, I hypothesize that ESP is a fundamental attribute of consciousness and has existed and currently exists as such. The overt manifestation of psi is primarily connected to intention by the involved individual, who utilizes an aspect of consciousness in social context and belief. It is believed by this researcher that a better understanding of psi phenomena as a physical, neurological, as well as "spiritual" or mystical process, will allow us to obtain a better understanding of the fundamental nature of consciousness itself and to better comprehend the manner in which to bring about world peace (see Chapter 11), education and prosperity.

We can form some useful analogies between remote perception phenomena and other techniques that have developed over time. For instance, we can make an analogy between the current state of remote perception and the early days of photography. Look at what happened to photography with better materials and parameters on the photographic process and digitization! Likewise, I would strongly expect that remote perception may similarly improve. Setting the parameters may involve considering many issues related to enhancing psi under various conditions. Another analogy may be of use in exploring remote perception for those who have blocked this modality from their consciousness which is like explaining sight to a congenitally blind person. Also, reeducating the use of psi to those who culturally or otherwise blocked its conscious use, would be like retraining a person into regained sight, one who had lost sight at a year of age, now as an adult can perceive and use this modality as sight is regained.

Learning to utilize psi capabilities involves bringing psi information from sublevels of perception to useful conscious

Table 8

SOME ISSUES RELATED TO REMOTE VIEWING

1. Remote perception is a very strong phenomena.

2. The main constraints on the phenomena are psychological rather than restricted by physical process.

3. It is difficult to design experiments to separate types of psychic modalities.

4. Space and time do not restrict the access of remote information.

5. Transitory motion at the site can be remotely perceived by the subject in the Laboratory Room.

6. Remote Viewing gets better with practice.

7. Various judging techniques have been utilized to achieve the most objective results.

8. We feel that learning to access one's psychic impressions has potential for improving the quality of one's life.

9. We live in a non-local world.

awareness. I feel that learning to be consciously aware of one's psychic perceptions will make us more healthy persons and will definitely lead to a much better understanding of ourselves. We can become more whole and conscious people by utilizing the fuller use of our capabilities. Hence, we can lead more meaningful lives and contribute more to society and the world as a whole.

12. Conclusion and Brief History of my PSI Research

We can conclude that some of the issues related to remote viewing are listed in Table 8. Here, I summarize some of the insights I have gained by remote viewing. I have also worked with some great remote viewing teams and have enumerated some of our acknowledgements. Giving credit to the wonderful workers in the field allows the reader further exploration, and gives credit for their work, which is important. (See Appendix I, II and III.)

Some of my early remote viewing work began informally at UC Berkeley (1971) and Stanford SLAC (1972), and later at the Eighteenth Annual Convention of the Parapsychology Association at UC Santa Barbara, August 1975 (See also Rauscher, 1978b, 1978d), where we presented our first formal study. Also, as we learned in our research, inexperienced subjects gain experience, and the learning process can continually be examined. It is felt that learning a psychic task may involve learning to translate psychic input into useful and meaningful forms. In an manner that is analogous to a child's learning, what is psychically perceived attaches meaning and function to visually perceived objects. The remote perception task appears to be of sufficient interest to subjects who wish to avoid the "decline effect" and also exhibit a positive learning curve.

Table 9

ISSUES RELEVANT TO CONSCIOUSNESS

1. Consciousness must be considered as a whole.

2. An aspect of consciousness is termed psi (General ESP (GESP) and PK).

3. Psi is intrinsic in all consciousness properties and information, and energy transfer transactions.

4. To accommodate the properties of consciousness having psi may resolve the quantum measurement issue which requires a formulation in a multidimensional model of $N > 4$ dimensions of space and time.

5. Hence, conceptual and formal problems of quantum measurements can only be resolved and formulated in a hyperdimensional geometric model.

In Chapters 3 and 4, we present some experiments to provide an indication of the general type of results achieved. Some of the general considerations relevant to "Remote Viewing" are listed in Table 9 as theoretical approaches to analyzing and exploring psi. (See also Appendixes I, II, III and IV and Rauscher, 1976, 1978a, 1979, 1981a, 1982a, 1982b, 1983a, 1983b, 1983c, 1983d, 1990, 2001; Ramon and Rauscher, 1980, 1982; Rauscher and Targ, 2001, 2002, 2006, 2012; Rauscher and Amoroso, 2006, 2011.)

Appendix I

A Brief Summary of Projects, Co-Researchers and Subjects

I initiated experiments through the "Fundamental 'Fysiks' Group" (F "F" G) at the Lawrence Berkeley Laboratory, which I started in 1974, to study remote connectedness phenomena in physics such as Bell's Theorem. Also discussed was the possible existence of psi phenomena and other "nonlocal" attributes of consciousness. I and some of the F "F" G participants set up and conducted some remote perception experiments. G. Weissman and S.P. Sirag were among these participants. This researcher developed a complex multidimensional or hyper-dimensional (N>4) geometry to reconcile psi with the main body of science. This work was later published in referred physics journals and books. The model was developed in response to a criticism against psi, i.e. that it is denied by the main body of physics. Hence, the two-fold motivation in developing a multidimensional model: (1) to reconcile the psi data base with the main body of physical theory and (2) to theoretically describe some of the space-time independent features of psi.

Local real-time remote perception experiments were conducted where target location and subject were within a half-hour drive time of each other. To further test the model, long distance (over thousands of kilometers distances) and precognitive time, experiments were undertaken. some of these experimental series were later conducted when this researcher became a consultant to the SRI International research group of R. Targ, H. Puthoff, and I. Swann. This researcher also conducted the long distance experiments, with Jack Houck.

Appendix II

History Summary of Remote Perception, General ESP Research and Co-Researchers

1. Determination of remote hidden objects by UC Berkeley, Stanford University and John F. Kennedy students and SLAC Stanford employees in my *Philosophy of Science* and *Paradigm Shift* classes taught from 1971 until 1984, with good results.
2. Remote perception accessing of information blocked from ordinary senses across space and time using local and long distance geographical targets conducted at SRI International as a consultant in which I developed additional experimental design refinements with very good results. Research was conducted with Russell Targ M.S., Hal Puthoff Ph.D., Ingo Swann, Jeff Mishlove Ph.D. , Dave Hurt and others with excellent results from 1974 to 1977.
3. Remote perception experiments, remote and long distance with the LBNL "Fundamental Fysiks Group" which I developed and chaired from 1974 to 1979 with 40 physicists including George Weismann Ph.D., S.P. Sirag, Nick Herbert, Ph.D., J. Sarfatti Ph.D., Frijov Capra, Ph.D., Gary Zukov, G. Chew, Ph.D., John Clauser Ph.D., and H. Stapp Ph.D. and others. Both theoretical and experimental work was conducted including Bell's interconnectedness theory.
4. Local remote perception experiments conducted through Tecnic Research Laboratory and E.A.R.'s Berkeley Research Group through grants from the Parapsychological Foundation of New York from 1979 to 1981 with very interesting results. Experiments were conducted with Ray Miller, Gary Langford, Beverly Rubik, Ph.D., Bob Mayfield and H.J. Mullins with statistically significant results.

5. Remote viewing in France, work with Olivier Costa de Beauregard Ph.D., and Charles Crussard on PK and visit to Orsay Laboratory and Alan Aspect Ph.D., 1977. For the summer of 1977 at the Department of Physics, Birkbeck College, University of London, England work with David Bohm Ph.D., Basil Hiley Ph.D. on quantum cosmology and Bell's theorem and John B. Hasted Ph.D. Department chairman work on remote psychokinesis experiments and LLNL crystal targets.
6. Long distance remote perception experiments conducted between the S.F. Bay areas and Los Angeles, CA with Jack Houck M.S., Shumway Poole and Roger D. Nelson Ph.D. from 1982 to 1984 with good success.
7. Remote volitional effects on LBNL Laboratory grown crystals in which control samples and samples for treatment were prepared. The purpose of this experiment was to examine microscopic effects of PK and to develop a prototype experiment using controls and electromicroscopic analysis of a unique signature of PK which was found in experiments with Uri Geller in 1974 and Steven North in 1977 and other subjects and assistants.
8. Remote volitional effects on a model bacterial system in which treated and control samples were compared in a detailed growth and mortality study with the psychic healer, Dr. Olga Worrall, Ph.D. (Hon.). Four major studies were conducted at SF State University, UC Berkeley, LBNL with Beverly Rubik Ph.D. from 1979-1982. Highly statistically significant results were found. A Holms Foundation Grant, Los Angeles, CA funded part of the research.
9. Extensive remote experiments utilizing remote shielded electrochemical and electronic sensors were conducted in part under a Buch Fine Arts grant from 1982 to 1990 with William L. van Bise M.D. (Hon.) of over 2,000 trials and analysis was made on experiments conducted from 1958

to 1982 for over 3,000 trials. Both local and long distance experiments were conducted with good statistics.

10. Observation and analysis of Brazilian Healers were made in 1982 with interesting results.
11. Recent research on remote volitional effects on new novel unique electronic sensors was conducted from 1996—2001 with William L. Bise M.D. (Hon.). Over 6,000 trials were conducted and analysis with extremely statistically significant results.
12. Brain wave changes in humans associated with specific external influences were conducted with William L. Bise M.D. (Hon.), from 1979 to 1994.
13. Work with William Tiller, Ph.D. of Stanford University and Ditron Corporation and William L. Van Bise, M.D. (Hon.) were conducted on the development and use of remote volitional detector sensors development and application, from 1996 to 2001.
14. Remote viewing experiments with Dr J.J. Hurtak and Dr. Desiree Hurtak of AFFS Corporation and observations by Drs. Hurtak in the Atlantic Ocean, Egypt and Israel with positive results. (2012-2013) (See Chapter 12).

Appendix III

We Enumerate Some of the Developments of Theoretical Research on Models Applicable to Remote Perception and Remote Volitional Effects on Inorganic and Organic Systems

1. Developed multidimensional cosmology and cosmogenesis models from 1964-1975. Books and papers published with interest and input from John A. Wheeler Ph.D., Sir Fred Hoyle Ph.D., Melton Einstein Ph.D. (Einstein's brother), G. Chew Ph.D., D. Bohm Ph.D., and P. Lieber Ph.D., and many others.
2. Developed a theoretical hyperdimensional multispace mathematical model of remote perception and precognition. A number of papers have been published; work was conducted from 1973-1983, some with C. Ramon Ph.D. Interest and discussions with Gary Feinberg Ph.D., Eugene Wigner Ph.D., Glen T. Seaborg Ph.D., and J. Charon Ph.D. were beneficial.
3. Quantum theory in four and eight space, the observer effect, collapse of the wave function, the Everett-Graham-Wheeler model and global nonlinear quantum theories in N>4 space (1975-present) with interest from John A. Wheeler Ph.D., Eugene Wigner Ph.D., William L. Van Bise M.D. (Hon.), and David Bohm Ph.D.
4. Young's Double Slit experiment, Bell's theorem and local and universal remote connectedness, the multidimensional view (1958-present) related to the work of C. Clauser Ph.D., A. Aspect Ph.D., G. Weismann Ph.D., and H. Stapp Ph.D., and others in the Fundamental Physics Group, LBNL.
5. Thermodynamics, energy, information and vertical energy state models of psychokinesis. Availability and transfer of information and energy in nonlinear equilibrium systems (1974-1985), and I. Prigogine and others.

Appendix IV

Theoretical Considerations Based on the PSI Data Base

1. Let us just mention an example of Poincaré invariance which is the statement of the independence of physical laws and generalized coordinate transformations. The Poincaré invariance of the energy Hamiltonian implies the conservation of energy. One might suggest that psychokinetic interaction (PK) violates energy conservation, thus affecting the Hamiltonian; then this Hamiltonian would no longer be Poincaré invariance. One could have to experimentally test the Poincaré invariance or energy conservation of a particular experimental system and psychokinetic interaction before one can state the conservation principle of PK (specific system interaction). It appears more fruitful to hypothesize PK energy conservation, design an experiment and test this hypothesis, than say, although PK is considered "strange" i.e., unusual, it does not necessarily violate energy conservation.
2. Einstein describes the situation of a person in a railroad station waiting for his train, while an observer on an overlooking hillside is able to directly view the approaching train which is still in the future of the man in the station. This apparent perception of the future is made possible because of the "extra-dimensional" point of view of the hillside observer.
3. Tachyons or a superluminal signal alone will not explain precognition. G. Feinberg states that tachyonic signals even at near the velocity of light will net one only a few nanoseconds/foot into the future. If we choose a light cone space like signal of $v > c$ and for 3×10^{10} cm/sec then $1/c$ $(1/3) \times 10^{-10}$ sec/cm and a nanosec $=10^{-9}$ sec so that $1/c$ nanosec x 1/30 cm. If 2.54 cm = 1 inch then 2.54 cm × 12" /ft

= 30.48 cm/ft or 30.48 cm/ft ≅ 30cm/ft therefore $1/c \approx 1$ nanosec/foot.

4. There is an implied assumption about the relevant frame of reference. For example, as the subject waits 30 minutes to observe the future event, the earth has rotated approximately 300 miles at the S.F. Bay area's latitude. Also the earth is going around the sun and the sun is moving on its own spiral of our rotating Milky Way galaxy. What frame of reference do we need to consider? It appears that the earth frame of reference will be valid at least for short precognitive times just as one assumes it is valid for one's ordinary operational mode. For example, we can plan to meet someone in London next week and even next year without worrying about the rotation rate of the Milky Way galaxy!
5. An example of casual sequencing in closed time-like loops to a past event can be given in terms of a son and his mother. The type of remote time accessing obtained by Lorentz "time travel" is a time machine which goes into the past which is usually discussed in terms of the so-called Twin Paradox. (In the usual Twin Paradox transformation, the twin accesses the future of the other twin, and because the frames of reference are non-inertial (accelerated), this is a general relativistic problem which can be approximated by the special relativity result.) Thus, as a son travels back in time before his birth and kills his mother, then we have two apparent cases, one in which the son could not be born and one in which he is born (assuming that genetically only one set of parents could produce him) which leads us to a multi-dimensional concept. It would appear that the problem of closed past time like solutions would be reconciled by considering multidimensional geometry.

References

Gough, W.C., E.A. Rauscher, J. Houck, and V. Gruye (1981) "The Status of Research on the Physics of Consciousness: Working Models and Experiments", Assessment Meeting held September 15, 1980, at SRI International, Menlo Park, Calif. entered into the Congressional Records, Survey of Science and Technology issues present and future, Staff report of the Committee on Science and Technology, U.S. House of Representatives, Ninety Seventh Congress, First Session, Serial G, June 1981.

Houck, J., R.D. Nelson and E.A. Rauscher (1986) "Addendum to 'Los Angeles area to San Francisco Bay Area remote perception experiment' A Reevaluation," *Psi Research*, p. 108.

Jahn, R.G., B.J. Dunne, T.A. Curtis, I.A. Cook, E.G. Jahn, & R. Nelson (1982) *Analytical Judging Procedure for Remote Perception Experiments-II. Ternary Coding and Generalized Descriptors, Princeton University School of Engineering/Applied Science.* Princeton, NJ: Princeton University.

Kaiser, D. (2011) *How the Hippies Saved Physics: Science, Countercultures and the Quantum Revival.* W.W. Norton and Co., New York: W.W. Norton and Co.

Kane, B., J. Millay and D. Brown, editors (1993), Silver Threads: 25 Years of Parapsychology Research, Praeger, Connecticut, London and references therein.

Millay, J. Ph.D. Editor (2010) *Radiant Minds: Scientists Explore the Dimensions of Consciousness* and references therein. J. Millay Publisher.

Mishlove, J. Ph.D. (1979) Thesis, "Interdisciplinary Sciences," University of California Berkeley, CA. on the psychology of remote viewing. I was on his dissertation committee.

Mullins, H. and E.A. Rauscher (1977 and 1979) "Mind Space: The Scientific Investigation of Direct Perception Across Space and Time." Report on Parapsychological Foundation of New York contract, November 1977 to Eileen Coly, President.

Puthoff, H.E. and R. Targ (1976) "A perceptual channel for Information Transfer over kilometer distances: Historical Perspective and recent Research," *Proc. IEEE* 64, pp. 329-254.

Puthoff, H.E., R. Targ and E.C. May (1981) "Experimental Psi Research: Implications for Physics," Ed. R. G. Jahn, *The Role of Consciousness in the Physical World,* AAAS Symposium 57, Westview Press, Boulder, CO, pp. 37-86.

Ramon, C. and E.A. Rauscher (1980) "Superluminal Transformations in Complex Minkowski Spaces," *Foundations in Physics,* 10, Nos. 7 and 8, August 1980, pp. 661-669.

Ramon, C. and E.A. Rauscher (1982) "Remote Connectedness in Complex Geometries and its application to the nature and use of the Human Mind," *Proceedings of the Eleventh International Conference on the Unity of the Science,* Vol. 2, University of Pennsylvania, Philadelphia, PA, pp. 1423-1442.

Rauscher, E.A. (1973) "Theory of Remote Viewing by use of Complex Geometries: Preprint, TRL, PSRL-7031.

Rauscher, E.A. (1976) "Some Physical Models Potentially Applicable to Observed Perception Data," *Bulletin of the American Physical Society,* Series II, Vol. 21, No. 11, December 1, 1976, pp. 1304-1306.

Rauscher, E.A. (1978a) "Complex Coordinate Geometries in General Relativity and Electromagnetism," *Bulletin of the American Physical Society,* Series II, Vol. 23, January 1978, pp. 84-85.

Rauscher, E.A. (1978b) "Remote viewing as an objective science," *HDI* 6, New York, pp. 9-13.

Rauscher, E.A. (1978c) "The perception over Distance," *Psi Realité* 9, pp. 28-30, (French).

Rauscher, E.A. (1978d) "Exploration Experiments in psychokinesis with subject Uri Geller," *Psi Realité,* **7,** (French).

Rauscher, E.A. (1978e) "Some Physical Models Potentially Applicable to Observed Remote Perception Data," *Bulletin American Physical Society,* 21, 1304, 1976, and E.A. Rauscher, "Complex Coordinate Geometries in General Relativity and Electromagnetism with Applications to Remote Perception," *Bulletin American Physical Society,* 23, p. 84.

Rauscher, E.A. (1979) "Some Physical Models Potentially Applicable to Remote Perception," *The Iceland Papers; Frontiers of Physics Conference,* pp.

50-93. Select Papers on Experimental and Theoretical Research on the Physics of Consciousness. Amherst., Wis.; Essentia Research Associates, August, 1979. Republished PACE, Ottawa, Canada, 1996.

Rauscher, E.A. (1980) "Proposal to test the temporal modality in Remote Perception Experiments with Variable Precognitive Intervals," joint TRL and Washington Research Center (S.F.) Project Report, September 1980.

Rauscher, E.A. (1981a) "Conceptual Changes in Reality Models from New Discoveries in Physics," Vol. II, the New York, Seoul, Korea: ICF Press, pp. 1407-1431.

Rauscher, E.A. (1981b)"Conceptual Changes in Reality Models from New Discoveries in Physics," PSRL-1976, Preprint, September 1981. Published in *Proceedings of the First International Symposium on Non-Conventional Energy and Technology*; p. 114, October 1981, University of Toronto, Ontario, Canada and *Bulletin American*. Physical Society, 35.

Rauscher, E.A. (1982a) "Theoretical and Experimental Exploration of the Remote Perception Phenomena," *Proceedings of the Eleventh International Conference on the Unity of the Sciences,* Vol. 2, University of Pennsylvania, Philadelphia, PA, p. 1443.

Rauscher, E.A. (1982b) "Theoretical and Experimental Exploration of Remote Perception Phenomena," Vol. II, The ICF Press, New York, Philadelphia, PA, pp. 1443-1477.

Rauscher, E.A. (1982c) "*Conceptual Changes in Reality Models from New Discoveries in Physics,*" PSRL-1976, Preprint, September 1981. Published in Proceedings of the First International Symposium on Non-Conventional Energy and Technology; pg. 114, October 1981, University of Toronto, Ontario, Canada and *Bulletin Amer. Phys., Soc.* 35, 1982.

Rauscher, E.A. (1983a) "The Physics of Psi in Space and Time, Part I: Major Principles of Physics, Psychic Phenomena, and Some Physical Models," *Psi Research* 2, p. 65.

Rauscher, E.A. (1983b) "The Physics of Psi Phenomena in Space and Time, Part II: Multidimensional Geometric Models," *Psi Research* 2, p. 93.

Rauscher, E.A. (1983c) *Electromagnetic Phenomena in Complex Geometries and Nonlinear, NonHertzian Waves.* Tesla Book Co., Millbrae, CA.

Rauscher, E.A. (1983d) "Electromagnetic phenomena in complex geometries and non-linear phenomena," PSRL-3107A and *Bulletin American Physics Society* 28, p. 351.

Rauscher, E.A. (1984a) "Psychokinetic Interaction with Laboratory Prepared Materials," *Psi Research* 3, pp. 26-41.

Rauscher, E.A. (1984b) Application of human volition mind-matter interactions. *Applied Psi,* 9, and *Archeus,* 2, pp. 71-75.

Rauscher, E.A. (1990) "Theoretical Models and Experimental Data concerning the Space-Time Properties of Consciousness and Remote Mental Influence," *TRL,* 16725.

Rauscher, E.A. (1996) "Some Physical applications to Remote Perception," pp. 50-63, The *Iceland Papers: Frontiers of Physics Conference,* eds. A. Puharich and B. Josephson, Essentia Research Associates, Amherst, WI. (1979), Second Edition, PACE, Ottawa, Canada.

Rauscher, E.A. (2001) "The Speed of Thought: Investigation of Complex Space-time metric to describe Psychic Phenomena," The International Remote Viewing Association, Remote Viewing Conference, Nevada, June 2001.

Rauscher, E.A. and R.L. Amoroso (2006) "The Physical implications of multidimensional geometries and measurement," Ed. D.M. Dubois, *International Journal of Anticipatory Computing,* pp. 161-177.

Rauscher, E.A. and R.L. Amoroso, (2011) *Orbiting the Moons of Pluto: Solving Einsteins, Maxwells, Schrodingers and Dirac Equations in Complex Space,* World Scientific.

Rauscher, E.A. and J. Houck (1985) "Los Angeles area to San Francisco Bay Area remote perception experiment." *Psi Research* 4, p. 48.

Rauscher, E.A., J. Mishlove, H.J. Mullins, M. Jackson and R. Miller (1975-1982) *The Berkeley Research Group Report,* The Parapsychology Foundation.

Rauscher E.A. and B. Rubik (1980) "Effects of motility behavior and growth rate of Salmonella typhimium in the presence of Olga Worrall." *Research in Parapsychology*. Metuchen, NJ: Scarecrow Press, pp. 140-142.

Rauscher E.A. and B. Rubik (1983) "Human volition effects on a model bacterial system." *Psi Research* 2, 1, pp. 38-40.

Rauscher, E.A. and R. Targ (2001) "The Speed of Thought: Investigation of a complex spacetime metric to describe psychic phenomena," *Journal of Scientific Explorations* 15, p. 331.

Rauscher, E.A. and R. Targ, (2002) "Why only Four dimensions will not explain nonlocality," *Journal of Sci. Exploration* 16, pp. 655-658.

Rauscher, E.A. and R. Targ (2006) "Investigation of a complex spacetime metric to describe Precognition of the Future," *Frontiers of Time: Retrocausation Experiment,* pp. 121-146, ed. D.P. Sheehan, AIP Vol. 863. AAAS of University of San Diego, American Institute of Physics, New York.

Rauscher, E.A. and R. Targ (2012) "Investigation of a complex Spacetime metric to describe Precognition," pp. 5-26, Ed. I. Fredriksson, *Aspects of Consciousness: Essays on Physics, Death and the Mind,* McFarland and Co., Inc.

Rauscher, E.A. , G. Weissman, J. Sarfatti, S.P. Sirag (1975) "Remote Perception of Natural Scenes Shielded Again Ordinary Perception" in J.D. Morris, W.G. Roll and R.L. Morris (eds) Research in Parapsychology: Metuchen, NJ: Scarecrow Press.

Rauscher E.A. and W. van Bise (1984) "The dynamics of electromagnetic healing effects on in vitro and in vivo biological systems." *Preprint PSRL -10796.*

Rauscher E.A. and W. van Bise (1990) "Theoretical Models and Experimental Data Concerning the space-time properties of Consciousness and Remote Mental Influence, " *PSRL-60788,* Buck Fine Arts Grant, San Leandro, CA, pp. 1-220.

Rauscher E.A. and W. van Bise (1999) "Experimental Detection and Determination of the Properties and Characteristics of Human Remote Volitional Intentional Psychokinetic Effects on a Remote Electronic sensor System," Grant from Ditron, LLC., Tenic Research Laboratory, Apache Junction, AZ, Rev. I, 2000.

Targ, R. and K. Haray (1984) The Mind Race: Understanding and Using Psychic Abilities. New York: Random House Inc.

Targ, R. and H. Puthoff (1974) "Inbound transfer under conditions of sensory Shielding," *Nature* 251, pp. 602-607.

Targ, R. and H. Puthoff (1976) *Nature* 252, 602 (1974), and H.E. Puthoff and R. Targ, *IEEE* 64, p. 329, Appendices I and II.

Targ, R. and K. Haray (1984) *The Mind Race, Understanding and Using Psychic Abilities*. Villard Books, New York.

Chapter 3:
The Reality of Remote Perception, Local, Long Distance, and Precognitive Experiments
by
Elizabeth Rauscher, Ph.D.

"There are no unnatural or supernatural phenomena, only very large gaps in our knowledge of what is natural...We should strive to fill those gaps of ignorance."

— Edgar D. Mitchell , 1974
Apollo 14 Astronaut

Table of Contents

Introduction 115

1. Example Experiments in Remote Perception 117

2. Brief Description of the Protocol of Real Time Remote Perception with Geophysical Targets 119

3. A Summary of Physical Models Applicable To Remote Perception and Our Remote Perception Experiments 121

4. Examples of Local, Long Distance and Precognitive Formal and Individual Remote Viewing Experiments 123

5. An Analysis and Evaluation of Formal Remote Viewing Experiment Results 202

   A. Judging Analysis Techniques We Initiated to Analyze All Our SRI and Berkeley Experiments in which I Participated 202

   B. Judging Results for Complete Remote Viewing Experiments 204

Conclusions 210

   A. Probability in Everyday Life 210

   B. Moral Implications of Spacetime Independent Psi Models 211

References 212

List of Tables

Table 1: 7-Point Evaluation for Target-Transcript Correspondence 203

Table 2: Concluding Remarks 209

List of Figures

Fig. 1a Wooden Snake Drawing 124
Fig. 1b Wooden Snake Drawing 124
Fig. 2a Pedestrian Walkway Photograph,
Oregon Expressway Overpass Palo Alto, CA 126
Fig. 2b Pedestrian Walkway Photograph,
Oregon Expressway Overpass Palo Alto, CA 126
Fig. 2c Pedestrian Walkway Drawing,
Oregon Expressway Overpass Palo Alto, CA 126
Fig. 2d Pedestrian Walkway Drawing,
Oregon Expressway Overpass Palo Alto, CA 126
Fig. 2e Remote Viewing Drawing
Entering Walkway 127
Fig. 2f Remote Viewing Drawing of where we parked 127
Fig. 3a Remote Viewing Drawing Steeple 129
Fig. 3b Vallombrosa Church Steeple Photograph......................... 129
Fig. 3c Remote Viewing Drawing of us at Sprinklers 129
Fig. 3d Rauscher Hugging Concrete Pillar 130
Fig. 4a Chabot Highway interchange Photograph 133
Fig. 4b Pedestrian walkway Photograph 133
Fig. 4c Pedestrian walkway ramp Photograph 133
Fig. 4d Remote Viewing Drawing of road 134
Fig. 4e Remote Viewing Drawing showing hillside 134
Fig. 5a Photograph of area taken by A.J. Mullins 136
Fig. 5b Remote Viewing Drawing Codornices Park...................... 136
Fig. 5c Photograph looking out of arched entrance
of the tunnel at Codornices Park 138
Fig. 5d Remote Viewing Drawing of arches 139
Fig. 6a Photograph long walkway at Bay Lands Nature
Reserve 141

Fig. 6b Photograph building Nature Reserve 142
Fig. 6c Photograph fountain Nature Reserve 142
Fig. 6d Remote Viewing Drawing
of Nature Reserve by subject Dale 143
Fig. 7a Photograph Highway underpass 146
Fig. 7b Remote Viewing Drawing of
underpass tunnel 146
Fig. 7c Photograph Highway railing 147
Fig. 7d Remote Viewing Drawing of railing area 147
Fig. 8a Photograph of street view
Of the Superdome, New Orleans 149
Fig. 8b Remote Viewing Drawing street level............................... 149
Fig. 8c Photograph Superdome aerial view.................................. 151
Fig. 8d Remote Viewing Drawing with dome 151
Fig. 8e Photograph Superdome aerial view
and surrounding area 152
Fig. 8f Remote Viewing Drawing of
surrounding area including parking lot 152
Fig. 8g Remote Viewing Drawing of
inside the Superdome 153
Fig. 8h Picture of the seating arrangement at
the Superdome stadium 153
Fig. 8i Photograph of building on Royal Street............................ 154
Fig. 8j Photograph of New Orleans street car 155
Fig. 8k Photograph of Lake Pontchartrain
Causeway.. 155
Fig. 8l Photograph of Jackson Square and
St. Louis Cathedral 156
Fig. 8m Photograph of Levee area called
the Moon Walk.. 156
Fig. 9a Photograph of United California
Bank Building.. 158
Fig. 9b Photograph of United California
Bank Building with 7-like structure... 159
Fig. 9c Remote Viewing Drawing of
7-like structure 159

Fig. 9d Remote Viewing Drawing of
window structure 160
Fig. 9e Photograph of Water Fountain 161
Fig. 9f Enlarged part of Fig. 9j 162
Fig. 9g Susan's Drawing of three outbound
experimenters passing overhang 162
Fig. 9h Photograph tossing paper airplane 164
Fig. 9i Susan's Drawing of projectile
coming towards Dave 164
Fig. 9j Susan's Drawing of entire scene 165
Fig. 10a Photograph of large concrete planter box 167
Fig. 10b Drawing of concrete planter box 167
Fig. 10c Drawing of concrete planter box 167
Fig. 10d Photograph of concrete stairwell 168
Fig. 10e Photograph of concrete stairwell 168
Fig. 10f Gary's Remote Viewing Drawing 168
Fig. 11a Photograph of Grant's Tomb 173
Fig. 11b Remote Viewing Drawing 173
Fig. 12a Photograph Washington Square Park
in 1964 175
Fig. 12b Photograph Washington Square Park
In 1970s 175
Fig. 12c Remote Viewing Drawing of
cement depression 175
Fig. 13a House in France 177
Fig. 13b Remote Viewing Drawing of house in France 178
Fig. 14a Photograph curved brick planter box 180
Fig. 14b Photograph curved brick planter box 180
Fig. 14c Remote Viewing Drawing 181
Fig. 14d Photograph Shattuck Avenue Street Sign
at Bart Station 182
Fig. 14e Photograph circular brick pattern
at Bart Station 182
Fig. 15a Photograph of Kazakhstan's Semipalatinsk
Test Site 185

Fig. 15b Photograph of trench Kazakhstan's Semipalatinsk
Test Site 185
Fig. 15c Remote Viewing Drawing of
Vortex Plasma Generator 186
Fig. 16a Photograph Macy's Department Store 188
Fig. 16b Remote Viewing Drawing brick building 188
Fig. 16c Photograph Macy's Department Store 189
Fig. 16d Remote Viewing Drawing 189
Fig. 17a Photograph of the San Francisco
Transamerica Pyramid Building 192
Fig. 17b Picture from American Physical
Society Bulletin of Pyramid Building 193
Fig. 18a Photograph overhang Indian Rock 195
Fig. 18b Photograph water fountain Indian Rock 195
Fig. 18c Remote Viewing Drawing Indian Rock 196
Fig. 18d Photograph Indian Rock 197
Fig. 18e Remote Viewing Drawing Indian Rock 197
Fig. 19a Photograph Cyclotron Magnet 200
Fig. 19b Remote Viewing Drawing Cyclotron Magnet 200
Fig. 19c Photograph Lawrence Hall of Science 201
Fig. 19d Remote Viewing Drawing
Lawrence Hall of Science 201
Fig. 20 Remote Perception Experiments Chart 205

1983-84
Lecture/Workshop Program

NATIONAL SPIRITUAL SCIENCE CENTER
5605 16th Street N.W.
Washington, D.C. 20011
[202] 723-4510

This series brings together outstanding national leaders in the New Age movement. The serious student of metaphysics, physics and parapsychology is offered a rare opportunity for gaining new insights and advanced knowledge in these fields of specialization. The remarkable fact is that these workers, while continuing specific studies and activities, display profound acceptance of the principles of synthesis and convergence.

A NOTE ON COSTS
All weekends, except where noted otherwise, carry the following rates.
Full weekend (lecture/workshop) — $35/28
Lecture only — $7 50/5.00
Workshop only — $27.50/22

OCTOBER 7, 8:00 PM, LECTURE
OCTOBER 8, 10 to 12 AM and 2 to 5 PM, SEMINAR

The Physics of Psi Phenomena In Space and Time
—E. A. Rauscher, Ph.D.

The exploration of theoretical and experimental properties of consciousness which act independently of space and time.

Remote perception and remote matter manipulation have been extensively investigated experimentally. However, little theoretical work has been conducted in the area of this weekend's subject.

The scientific method proceeds as the interaction of theoretical hypothesis and experimental test.

Dr. Elizabeth Rauscher has achieved an international reputation in astrophysics, plasma physics and the foundations of quantum mechanics. She has also conducted extensive theoretical and experimental exploration of properties of consciousness; consulting research internationally in quantum electronics, energy systems, electromagnetic theory and other fields.

Dr. Rauscher has served as a delegate to the U.N. and is listed in four *Who's Whos*. She has held staff positions at the University of California, Berkeley; Lawrence Berkeley Laboratory; Lawrence Livermore Laboratory; Stanford Linear Accelerator Center and John F. Kennedy University.

She holds memberships in the American Physical Society; Institute of Electronic and Electrical Engineers; American Chemical Society; Research Association for Regeneration; Human Dimensions Institute/West; Fundamental Research in Wholistic Health, New York; Parapsychology Research Group; Iceland Research Group, and is a member of the Board of the United States Psychotronics Association.

EAR by EAR
1996

Introduction

I started out on my path to examine the possibility of psi with rather strong skepticism, but that soon began to change as I became an outbound experimenter, next an inbound experimenter and later a subject. Details of the site were so accurate as in the experiment with Jeffrey Mishlove of University of California, Berkeley. His inbound tape recording details of my thoughts, feelings and the sequence of activities at the site amazed me. This was also my first formal experiment with Harold Puthoff and Russell Targ of the SRI program (Puthoff and Targ, 1976a). I had already conducted a formal set of trials with some of the participants of my Fundamental "Fysiks" Group at Berkeley, LBNL in 1975. This experiment was published in several publications (Kaiser, 2011; Rauscher, *et. al.*, 1975; Kane, Millay and Brown, 1993; and Milley, 2010).

My early experiments in Berkeley demonstrated the need to conduct the experiment with care and precision and also with a humble attitude among the experimenters. I also found this to be true of any experiment such as my four year experimental research program at the LBNL Bevatron from 1973 to 1977 (Rauscher with Tosabe group, 1975, 1976a, 1976b, 1977, 1978; Ioannow-Yannou, Rauscher and Rasmussen, 1975; Rauscher, Soinski and Rasmussen, 1977).

When I first called Russell Targ to arrange to meet him and the SRI team, he asked me to remote view something on his desk while I was talking to him on the phone. He was at SRI in Menlo Park, California and I was at my home in the Berkeley Hills. I closed my eyes and a vague image came up and I said, "I see a ball and socket joint." He said you are right! It was a crystal ball in a wooden cup that went half way up the sides as a ball in a socket.

Left:
Elizabeth Rauscher with Jeffrey Mishlove, planning a remote viewing experiment, 1978.

Below: Rauscher at a remote viewing site, 1974.

1. Example Experiments in Remote Perception

Examples of remote perception experiments are given throughout this chapter. It is important to note that these experiments are typical and are not particularly chosen for the pronounced superiority of the responses. Each subject generated taped narratives and drawings of their perception of the remote target locations and it was generally found that the drawings are better representatives of the target locations than the subject's narrative transcripts (Puthoff and Targ, 1976a, 1976b; Mullins and Rauscher, 1977 and 1979; Targ, 2012, Tart, Puthoff and Targ, 2002; Katra and Targ, 1999).

In our experiments of remote viewing there are three principal findings. First, it is possible to obtain a significant amount of descriptive information about remote locations. The descriptions contain accurate and relevant information that is frequently accompanied also by incorrect and irrelevant statements (or noise). Second, the physical distance separating the subject from the scene to be perceived, even if over hundreds or thousands of kilometers, does not seem to affect the accuracy of perception. Third, the theory of relativity of events in spacetime has led to the general acceptance of the concept of a symmetry between spatial and temporal events. In the experiments, we have found instances in which a subject has been able to describe a remote location before the demarcation target team arrived at the site; in a few cases, the subject has given such a description even before the target location was randomly selected. One such experiment was conducted by us in a precognitive mode such that the site was selected after the end of the subject's 15 minute narrative. This experiment is labeled Experiment 16 in this Chapter (Rauscher, 1980, Dunne, John and Nelson, 1987).

In Chapters 5, 6, 7 and 8 we will further present a brief description of my theoretical models.

Rauscher with Hal Puthoff (to her left), Russell Targ (end of row) and Ed May (behind), 1974.

Elizabeth Rauscher in Cordoba, Spain with Brian Josephson, Montague Ullman and other researchers of the nature of quantum theory and consciousness, 1981.

2. Brief Description of the Protocol of Real Time Remote Perception With Geophysical Targets

In summary, from chapter 2, we set the general protocol which involves at least three persons. They are: a remote perceiver subject, a monitor (*inbound experimenter*) for the subject and an outbound person who denotes a remote target location. The subject is put into a laboratory room with the monitor experimenter and at an agreed upon time, the monitor is to obtain from the subject, a description of an undisclosed (to preferably both subject and monitor) remote target site being visited by an outbound experimenter(s). In most experiments, an outbound experimenter serves as a target demarcation team at the remote location which is chosen in a double-blind manner. (References to these tools are from Rauscher, 1976a, 1976b, 1978, 1983a, 1983b, 1983c, 1990; Rauscher and Van Bise, 1990; Rauscher and Hasted, 1982; Houck, Nelson and Rauscher, 1981; Gough, Rauscher, Houck and Gruye, 1981; Bem and Honorton, 1994; Schmidt 1993; Schlitz and Gruber, 1980; Rauscher and Hasted, 1982.)

The outbound experimenter chooses a target location from a list of targets within a 30 minute driving time from the laboratory for real time local experiments, which is synchronized with the start of the experiment. The target location selected is kept secret or blind to both the subject and monitor experimenter sometimes by adding an experimental coordinator. The total target pool can consist of more than 50 or so target locations chosen near the laboratory area and usually for each specific experimental series a 6 or 8 target pool is used. These targets should be chosen with particular care to be distinct in form, function, "mood" and gestalt as sites distinguishable from each other. Experiments may be run on sequential days and in each case, a target replacement is made with the attention to above details in mind. Thus, for an experimental series of six targets, a total of twelve potential targets will be needed such that each individual experiment will involve a pool of six targets. Targets may be used more than once but in separate experimental runs.

To begin the experiment, the subject is seated in the laboratory with a monitor (inbound experimenter) to wait 30 minutes before beginning a description of the remote location. The outbound experimenter or team obtains a set of sealed traveling information enclosed in envelopes which have been previously prepared and randomized, sealed in opaque envelops with no markings on them. The outbound team leaves the laboratory, gets into a car, and uses a random number generator to select one of the target locations. Then the outbound team proceeds directly to the target without any communication with the subject or monitor experimenter who remains in the laboratory in order to be ready for the upcoming 15 minute time period when the viewer will conduct their remote perception. The inbound experimenter remaining with the subject at the laboratory is also not allowed to know the particular target and the target pool to eliminate the possibility of cuing (overt or subliminal) and to allow him or her freedom in questioning the subject to clarify the subject's descriptions.

The outbound team remains at the target site for an agreed upon 15-minute period following the 30 minutes allotted for travel time. When the outbound team is at the target site, the remote viewing subject is asked to describe his impressions of the target site into a recorder and to make any drawings of his or her perception. The outbound team makes a real time recording of their experiences and takes three photographs at the site to be later compared to the subject's description.

With the Princeton protocol as used in Chapter 4, a questionnaire is filled out by both the inbound and outbound experimenters. Also, following the experiment, the subject is taken to the site to provide "feedback" since it appears that remote perception is a learned experiential process and the subject can gain information as to how well they did.

We have conducted experiments with both experienced and inexperienced subjects. This researcher has conducted a number of remote perception experiments with other researchers and subject participants. Most of the subjects in the experiments reported were not known for any specific psychic abilities and some were quite skeptical about the existence of psi phenomena and yet some of these subjects performed quite well to extremely well as judged by the objective methods of the SRI protocol.

3. A Summary of Physical Models Applicable to Remote Perception and Our Remote Perception Experiments

A major consideration in our work is making use of the remote perception experimental database to deduce the relevant physical principles and laws governing paranormal functioning. We have built a stable and robust database in order to deduce the physical principles of psi. A common objection to the existence of psychic functioning is that it appears to be in conflict with the laws of physics. We have attempted to demonstrate the possible compatibility of psychic phenomena with the laws and content of physics and to develop a comprehensive model with predictability. (See Chapter 5). We have also examined limits of specific physical theories in modeling psychic phenomena (Rauscher and Amoroso, 2011; Ramon and Rauscher, 1980; Rauscher, 1978; Rauscher, 1983b, 1983c) (See Chapter 5).

In the rest of this Chapter we present experiments comparing subject response to outbound experimenter(s) reported experience. We utilize the protocol given in the previous chapter and present a judging procedure and results for these experiments. This work comprises a representative portion of my remote perception work. I also conducted group experiments with up to 200 participant subjects not reported here. Some of the experimental results presented are from formal studies and some were informal but controlled studies. We number the experiments we describe.

Rauscher at SRI, 1975.

4. Examples of Local, Long Distance and Precognitive Formal and Individual Remote Viewing Experiments

Experiment 1
An Early Remote Viewing
Request For E.A. Rauscher to be a Subject
Wooden Snake
May 5, 1976

Before a remote viewing experiment with Dale Groff, he was nervous and asked whether he should meditate or what state of mind he should be in. He asked Russell how does it work and Russell told Dale of my remote viewing of the crystal ball in his desk which I saw as a ball and socket joint. I asked Dale (a DOD engineer) whether he would like to think of something on his desk and I would see whether I could view it. Dale had an office in Dayton, Ohio which I did not know at the time, I just thought he lived east of the Rockies. We were at SRI, in Menlo Park, California. He said he had one unusual thing. I closed my eyes and right away saw a sort of shape (in a blue looking color). It was sort of "S" shape fastened at the bottom. Dale asked me what it is. I said it's an "S" shape fastened to a bottom or base. I drew Figure 1a on the blackboard which he copied. He said, "That's it. It's a wooden snake on a base, i.e., an "S" shape fastened at the bottom" and he drew Figure 1b. On my brief notes on this experiment I put "R.V." (Remote Viewing) works (It really works).

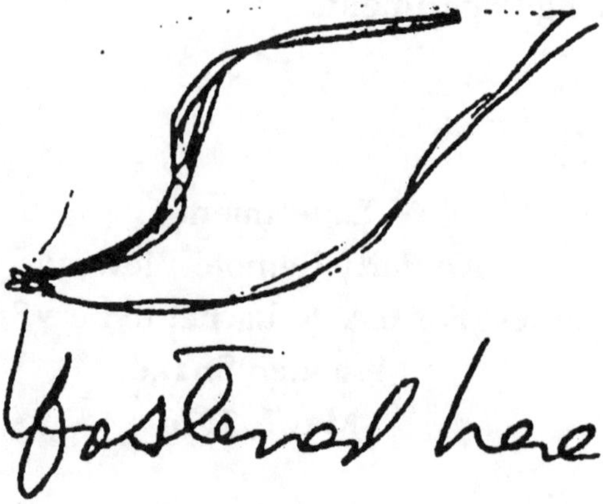

Fig. 1a

Fig. 1b

Experiment 2
Local Remote Perception:
Oregon Expressway Overpass
Palo Alto, CA
April 19, 1976

This was the first of a two-year, official remote viewing experiment I worked on with SRI, Menlo Park. The subject perceiver was a University of California, Berkeley graduate student, Jeffrey Mishlove. The monitor interviewer was Russell Targ and the outbound experimenters were E.A. Rauscher (myself) and J. Hickman. The target location came in a randomly chosen sealed envelope and after we opened the envelop we saw it was the Oregon Expressway Overpass (Figures 2a and 2b).

As we entered the overpass, Jeffrey at SRI drew the figure (Fig. 2c) and then he said, in his transcript, it "looks like clothes hangers but I do not see the clothes." Note that his drawing looks similar to 2b. The drawing is accurate but the analytic overlay was not. Then he commented on the crisscross of wires against the sky (Fig. 2d). His next drawing was where we parked at the cross street, with north to the top of the paper (which is correct) (Fig. 2f). In Figure 2e, Jeff draws us entering the overpass; compare this to the photo we took at the site (Fig. 2b).

The time sequence when Jim Hickman and I were at the site was tape recorded by us and was very accurate when compared with the time sequence mentioned by Jeff on the fifteen minute tape recording. I looked up at the cyclone fence against the sky which looks like cross wires about the time Jeff drew Figure 2d. Yes, I was very impressed.

In summary, the subject's comments were recorded in the laboratory: "Feeling of chilliness or coldness. They are outdoors and it's gotten windy" (true, very cold and windy). And Elizabeth thought — she forgot her sweater (true) "I'm getting like crisscrosses of black, like telephone wires against a blue sky" and at the target it was a cyclone fence (Elizabeth looked up at

Fig. 2a and 2b Pedestrian Overpass Target. These photographs were taken at the time by the outbound experimenters.

cross pattern of wire mesh of overpass against a clear blue sky) (Figure 2d). "I'm getting green forms, like landscaped, tall green, looks like two tall bushes or trees ahead and to the right" (correct)... . flowers yellow and violet" (also correct).

Fig. 2c

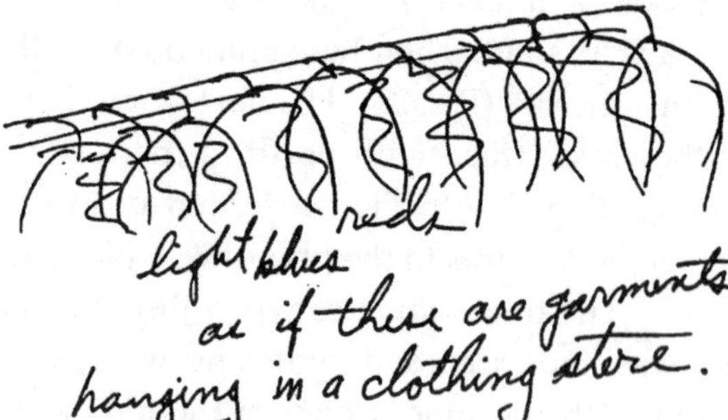

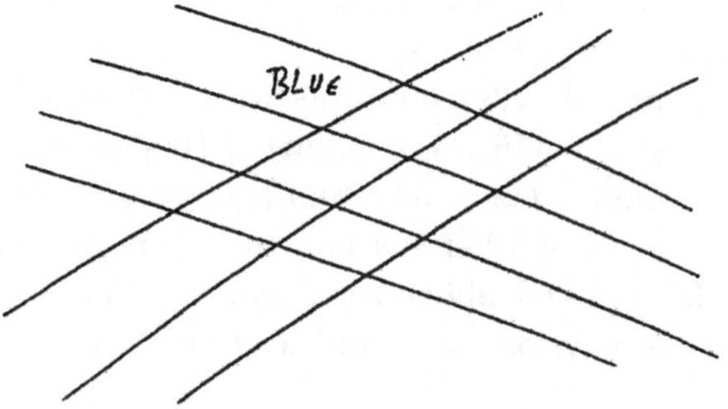

Fig. 2d
Jeff's drawing
at SRI.

Fig. 2e
Remote viewing drawing of us entering the over pass.

Fig. 2f
Remote viewing drawing of where we parked.

Experiment 3
The Vallombrosa Church
July 14, 1976

The Church target came up as a target location for the remote preceptor experiment conducted at SRI. The remote viewer was an SRI engineer, Gary Langford not noted for any psychic abilities but was agreeable to conducting the experiments. Hal Puthoff was the monitor. The outbound team consisted also of E.A. Rauscher and A.J. "Hope" Mullins, a newspaper columnist who wrote "Here's Hope" for the Oregonian Newspaper.

Gary Langford, the subject, was with Hal at the SRI Laboratory room and said on the tape recording, "Looking up to the blue sky. Looks like Elizabeth was looking up at something—a pole or steeple associated with this place (Fig. 3a; compare with photo of site, Fig. 3b), Elizabeth kneeling and Hope is also kneeling, it's something swirling with straight tentacles extending from it . . . objects whirling around hazy-like, swirling, partly man-made and partly natural."

"They are placed; that's the man-made aspect." The outbound experimenters (Hope and I) first looked up at the Church steeple and then knelt and I put my hands into the swirling sprinklers and then Hope did too (Fig. 3c). From the tape the outbound experimenters stated, "The last two minutes we walked back to the church area. . . I [E.A. Rauscher] put my arms around one of the cement pillars and hugged it (Fig. 3d). I noticed that it looked like "the kind that had been wrapped with some kind of thing which the concrete was poured into."

Gary's comments near the end of the session reported, "Not your average pole. . . It looks like that pole was metal, like an extruded pipe. It has lines that are marked."

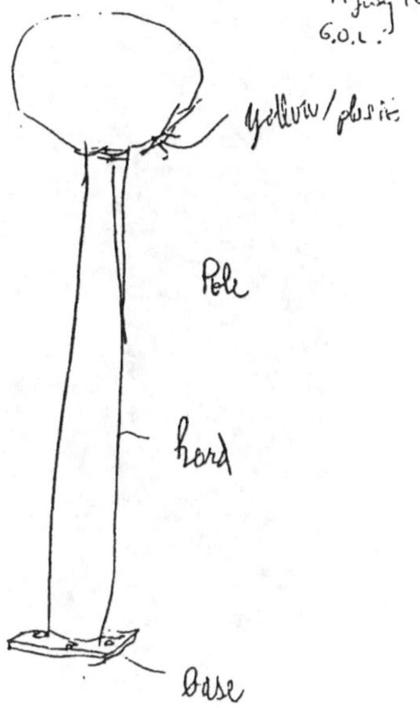

Fig. 3a
Subject Gary Drawing

Fig. 3b
The Vallombrosa Church Steeple

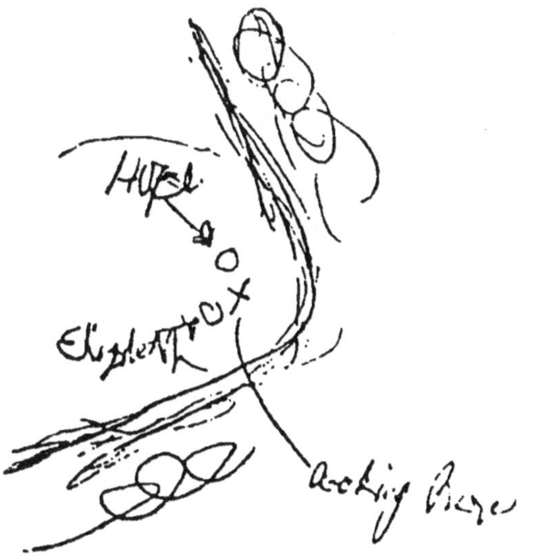

Fig. 3c
Gary's drawing of us at sprinklers

Fig. 3d
Rauscher hugging concrete pillar during the last few minutes at the target site.

Experiment 4
Chabot Highway Overpass Intersection, Berkeley, CA
October 16, 1977

Another experiment was conducted with the Berkeley Research Group which included Rauscher, Mullins, Miller, Mishlove, Rubik and others (1977 to 1983) (Rauscher and Houck, 1985). In the Berkeley Laboratory room used by the group, the subject was Ray Muller (a geophysical engineer) and Elizabeth Rauscher was the monitor. The outbound team consisted of A.J. Mullins and Jaki Kensen (a colleague of Ray Muller). The target that came up by random choice was the Berkeley Chabot Highway Overpass. A.J. Mullins conducted a detailed analysis of the outbound teams experiences at the target site and the subject's mentation. Her analysis as recorded on photos and audio tape proved useful. This work was conducted with a grant from the Parapsychological Foundation of New York (1977-1979).

The Chabot Highway Overpass Intersection consisted of a pedestrian walkway over one of the freeways at this intersection (Fig. 4a, 4b and 4c). There is a hill to the right with natural vegetation on it. Median strip with crushed gravel curves off around the bend of the hill to the right.

The following tape recording was made by the outbound team, A.J. Mullins and Jaki Kensen,

Jaki stated: There's a hill to the right with green large—leaf ground cover.

A.J. stated: "Think of long, long stretches of highway. Highway and cars, highway and cars."

Jaki then stated: "I hear the sound of the wheels."

A.J., now with her eyes closed, continued: "Think of traffic and intersections, traffic and cars, cars and wheels, cars in motion." Then opening her eyes. She said, "There's a car just going by . . . make arrows like motion, make arrows like motion." Remotely talking to Ray.

Again Jaki stated: "There's an arrow pointing one way on a sign, and another sign with two arrows on it . . . There's a sign and another arrow. Now I can see the glistening water of the bay."

Then A.J. stated: "There are arrows on the road . . . We are next to a very natural hillside; it does not look man-planted. We can see the highway way down towards the bay. Just on and on, lane after lane. The cars are coming massively. Cars, cars, cars, cars, cars. The site is an intersection, highway, roadway, overpass, traffic, cars, gasoline, movement."

Jaki then commented on the tape: "The sound of the wheels traveling fast, traveling over the surface, various malfunctions in the motors. "

A.J. added: "No wonder there's an energy shortage. There it is right there. "

On the inbound team's tape recording, the subject Ray Miller with monitor (Rauscher) said the following: "The hill moves up to the right. . . a road goes off around the bend. (See Gary drawings, Fig. 4d and 4e). It's got wheels on it. . . I just get like a distorted reflection of part of a bridge in glass, in glass like a windshield. . . ."It had wheels . . . might be wheels . . . road, rocks, ocean, bay, actually bay, broken road, parking lot, cars, hillside, vegetation there and cars." (He stated while drawing two cars, Fig. 4e). He then said, "It's an Impala . . . well, maybe a Chrysler. It's hard to say [he laughed]. You know, one of those big jobs, a gas guzzler." After Ray drew two cars, then, I indicated he need not draw any more cars. Ray responded, "I'll just put some etc." "That's one thing, if they were not using up gas anymore, and you were looking for oil wells . . ." (Compare Fig. 4c to Gary's drawing Fig. 4e).

The photographs below were taken at the site during the experimental time period.

Fig. 4a Chabot Highway interchange

Fig. 4b Pedestrian walkway

Fig. 4c Pedestrian walkway ramp view

Subject, Ray Miller's response to Chabot Highway.

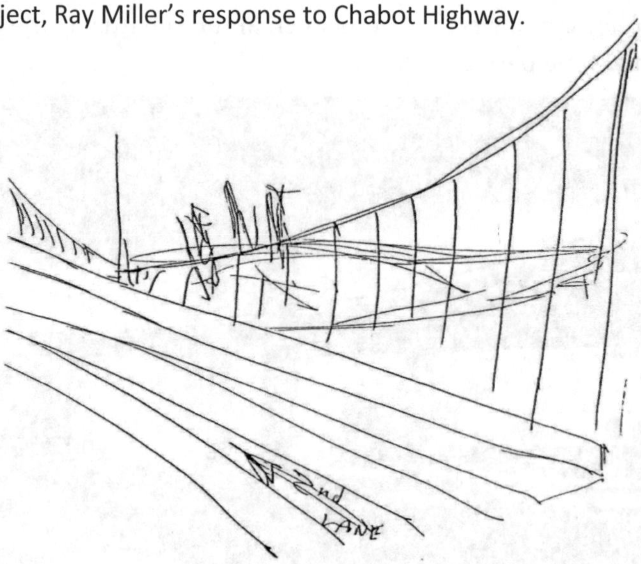

Fig. 4d Ray's drawing of a road with several lanes drawn on it. The second lane is marked with an arrow.

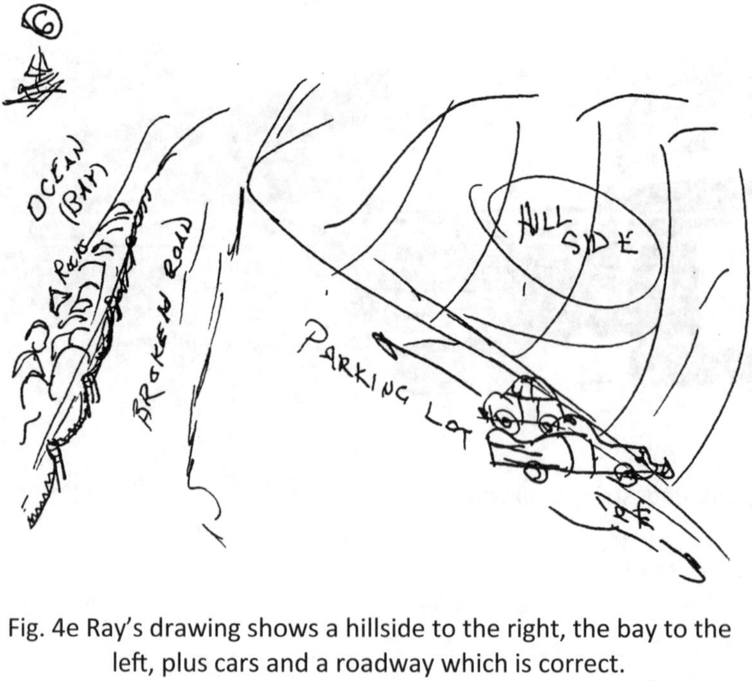

Fig. 4e Ray's drawing shows a hillside to the right, the bay to the left, plus cars and a roadway which is correct.

Experiment 5
Codornices Park and Tunnel
August 1977

The randomly chosen target was the Cordornices Park and Tunnel in Berkeley. The subject who was sequestered in the Berkeley Laboratory room was I and the outbound experimenter was A.J. Mullins working as part of the Berkeley Research Group (Mullins and Rauscher, 1977 and 1979). A.J. Mullins paid particular attention to her detailed observation and her mental imagery at the target which she recorded on her tape at the site.

The randomly selected site for this day was a densely forested hillside of tall redwoods, plus other types of trees and shrubs. The outbound experimenter, A.J. Mullins, concentrated particularly on the massive redwood trees and reported, "I shut my eyes and I can see the redwoods before my (closed) eyes with their bark on them and the light shining on them, beautiful, beautiful woods. . . I shut my eyes and I see the bay leaves before my eyes and the redwood's bark." "Redwood trees, I see their bark and bay trees." In A.J.'s tape recording "redwood," appears eight times, "trees" are reported eleven times, plus the words, "tall evergreen," "deciduous" (twice), "other bushes" and "plants." She took a picture of the trees (Fig. 5a) and made comments including the following statement on the tape recording, "See those natural, beautiful trees. Certainly has the feeling of outdoors, quiet, large old growth trees."

I was without a monitor when I drew Fig. 5b according to what I remotely saw. I was secured in a laboratory room where my comments were recorded on tape. Reporting on internal imagery I stated: "I see Hope [A.J. Mullins] looking up, looking up. . . Seems very tall . . . I get a feeling of a tall redwood tree, at the bottom of a tall redwood. I even analytically get the tall redwood trees. I get that impression of looking up, and then I follow it up and it looks like the top of a tree. . . I

Fig. 5a Photograph taken by A.J. Mullins while outbound. She reported, "I'm outside. Lot's of natural growth beautiful trees." Note the lawn at the bottom.

Fig. 5b My response to the remote viewing target.

seem to be stuck in that one spot. . . I get stuck with that outside scene. There are some trees around." Then I sketched A.J. "Hope" Mullins looking up at a redwood tree (5b). Other bushes and trees are also noted. At the site there was a curved cement walk and a lawn area at the base of the natural hillside. I drew a curved sidewalk (5b), and at the bottom wrote "lawn" which I reported twice on my tape which was correct.

In comparison to the outbound experimenter, I stated the words "redwoods" five times and "trees" nine times. On paper, I had written "redwood" three times on my sketch pad and "trees" twice. This was the only time that redwood trees have come up as a major feature at a target site. This is the only time in my experiments that I or any subject in our remote viewing experiment reported redwood trees.

Later in the experiment, the outbound experimenter, A.J. Mullins, looked into a tunnel at the site. She closed her eyes three times to give the subject afterimage impressions of arch shapes to emphasize this form (Fig. 5c). The outbound experimenter said, "I'm going through the tunnel . . . in the dark. I can look out to that light beyond. It's really something. It's an arch, definitely a perfect arch, the tunnel itself. . . There's a perfect archway of the tunnel, with the flat bottom."

I stated on my tape just prior to the end of the experiment, "I know it's a definite form. . . I see something like arches. . . I'm going to try to make a few drawings." Above my sketch of arches, I wrote, "Last impression." I also noted that, "I have a problem with the perspective. I seem to be at the wrong angle with a perspective different than normal." I also recorded that I see a metal triangle (which was a swing set, Fig. 5c) through the arches. When I flashed on the three arch shapes at Cordornices, I noted that my perspective was off by 90 degrees from gravitational perspective. I reported, "it's like arches laying on their side." Then I stated, "This last image was on the side." I then drew horizontal arches as I had seen them, but verbally noted on tape that this viewpoint was a quarter turn off normal perspective.

Fig. 5c Photograph at left taken looking out through the arched entrance of the tunnel. The photograph was taken by the outbound experimenter during the remote viewing period. A swing set which appears as a triangle is visible through the archway.

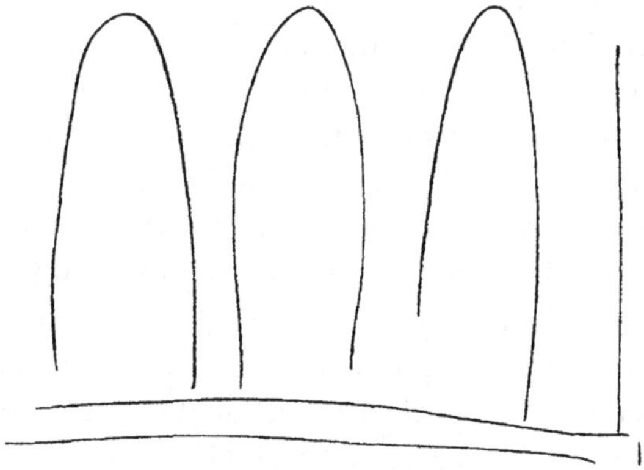

Fig. 5d To the left is my drawing of the imagery I reported, “I see something like arches” at the target site, A.J. Mullins said “arches” three times.

Experiment 6
Bay Lands Nature Reserve
May 5th, 1976

A local remote viewing experiment was conducted from SRI International. The subject was Dale Grof, a DOD engineer and with him at SRI was monitor, Russell Targ in the Laboratory room. The outbound team consisted of Hal Puthoff, Ingo Swann and Elizabeth Rauscher. The randomly chosen target that came up was the Bay Lands Nature Reserve (Fig. 6a). Dale described and drew a long wooden walkway and extensive gardens. He added a roof over the long walkway as analytical overlay. There are extensive bushes and flowers in the area with bare ground which Dale described. Dale also noted a metal shining round thing and to our right going into the long walkway (in Fig. 6b), the outbound team noted a silver drinking fountain (Fig. 6c) in his drawing. Both these elements are strongly present at the target. However, he described a tall building he had visited the previous day, which was not at the place the outbound team went to. However, the building was visible in the distance from the target site. Technically, it represents erroneous imaging on an otherwise accurate description. Sources of noise, such as imagination, memory, guessing, etc. can confuse information which may be removed with practice and learning. Dale also noted cars (in Fig. 6b) and there was a fairly large parking lot with cars near the site. Dale's complete drawing is given in Figure 6d.

Fig. 6a Long walkway at Bay Lands Nature Reserve.

Fig. 6b

Fig. 6c The Fountain.

Fig. 6d The drawing made by the subject participant, Dale. Note long wooden walkway, metal shiny thing, cars and in the distance a tall building to the right.

Experiment 7
Highway Underpass
El Camino Real and University Avenue,
Palo Alto, California
as remote viewed in Huntsville, Alabama
July 22, 1976

More experiments were conducted by the Berkeley Research Group and the SRI Group. I worked with both groups to set up, start and run various experiments. Both teams conducted local experiments and then I suggested we examine the long distance effect by doing "coast to coast" remote viewing from the Bay Area to at least 2,000 miles away (Rauscher, 2010; Kane, *et. al.* 1993; Rauscher and Houck 1985; Houck and Rauscher, 1982) to see if there were any distance effects. The SRI group also went on to examine time dependents of remote perception with various precognitive experiments.

For this experiment, we conducted a long distant experiment from SRI in Menlo Park, California, in which the outbound team was on the west coast and the subject perceiver was Gary O. Langford who had traveled to Huntsville, Alabama. The experiment was without a monitor. On the outbound team was Hal Puthoff, E.A. Rauscher and A.J. Mullins.

The randomly chosen target that came up was the Highway Underpass at El Camino Real and University Avenue. The outbound team arrived and walked into the underpass. Then they walked down the University Avenue pedestrian ramp into the main long tunnel. The tunnel was dark with bright sunlight at the end of it (Fig. 7a) and a bright rectangular opening was noticed at the sides of the tunnels where pedestrians could look over at the traffic from the tunnel. (See Gary's drawing Fig. 7b). The last five minutes of the experiment, the three outbound experimenters leaned through open concrete archways and looked at the traffic passing beneath them in the lower level and I spoke aloud and yelled Gary's name (See photograph, Fig. 7c). The outbound team listened to the loud traffic sounds which echoed through the tunnel.

Gary reported in his distant location from Huntsville: "I feel like you are inside a tunnel." He drew a figure standing inside a tubular shape (Fig. 7b). He correctly noted that an outbound experimenter, Hal Puthoff, was, "leaning against a wall of some sort (Fig. 7d). "It is both light and dark, perhaps a dim-to-light effect. You can still see everything though . . . I'm resisting describing the passageway under El Camino on University Ave." Next to his drawing of an archway, Gary wrote, "Hal may be leaning over an edge with an archway opening" (Fig. 7d).

In general, subjects are instructed to describe general forms and shapes and not to attempt to name the site as this usually invokes guessing. Sometimes, however, a subject will gain enough psychic information to recognized a location that they have visited before.

Gary made both a RHD, a "right hand drawing and a LHD a "left hand drawing." He is right handed and he thought he might be able to access Remote Viewing perception better by drawing with his left hand in order to access his right brain.

Fig. 7a Highway underpass.

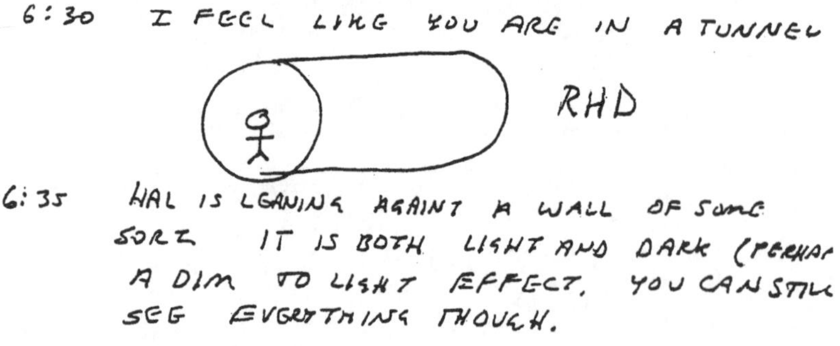

Fig. 7b
Gary's right hand drawing of tunnel which he labeled RHD.

Fig. 7c The outbound team leaned over the railing and watched the traffic below during the last five minutes of the experiment.

As Gary drew Figure 7d, he said that Hal may be leaning over an edge with an archway opening.

Fig. 7d
Gary's drawing during the last 5 minutes of his remote viewing. The label LHD refers to left hand drawing.

Experiment 8
Superdome, New Orleans, Louisiana
31 October 1976

As part of our long distance remote viewing experiment series, we conducted an experiment between SRI and the target location in New Orleans, Louisiana. Russell Targ was on travel and was the outbound experimenter and the subject at SRI was Gary O. Langford. Gary did not know Russell's travel plans. At SRI's Radio Physics Laboratory Room, Gary was the subject and I, E.A. Rauscher and A.J. Mullins were the monitors for this experiment. Post experimental detail time sequences and perceived detailed analysis of Gary's mentation and the exterior and interior of the remote viewing site was conducted by A.J. (Hope) Mullins for my Parapsychology Research Center, New York grant and for Russell Targ at SRI.

Russell's target pool location consisted of six locations: the Lace Front French Quarter Building, a street car, the Louisiana Superdome, the levee area called the Moon Walk, the Lake Pontchartrain's Causeway bridge and the Saint Louis Cathedral in Jackson Square. Photographs are given at the end of this section. The randomly chosen target that came up was the Louisiana Superdome (8a and 8c). At the site, Russell walked towards the Superdome and at noon commented on his tape recording that he was shocked by the size of it. Russell tape recorded the following on his recorder, "This is a remote viewing experiment with Russ Targ and Gary Langford. I am at the 80,000 seat New Orleans Superdome. It is a metal sided building that looks like nothing so much as a great flying saucer shining in the noon day sun."

In the SRI Laboratory, Gary was just beginning his description for Elizabeth who was recording his report. Gary said, "I have a problem . . . all I see is a damn UFO in the middle of the city!" Figure 8b is Gary's first drawing. I stated, "That's okay, Gary. Why don't you just take a break, and then make a drawing of what you are looking at." Russell called this "debriefing the initial images." Gary said he saw "a large circular building with a

Fig. 8a Street View of the Superdome, New Orleans.

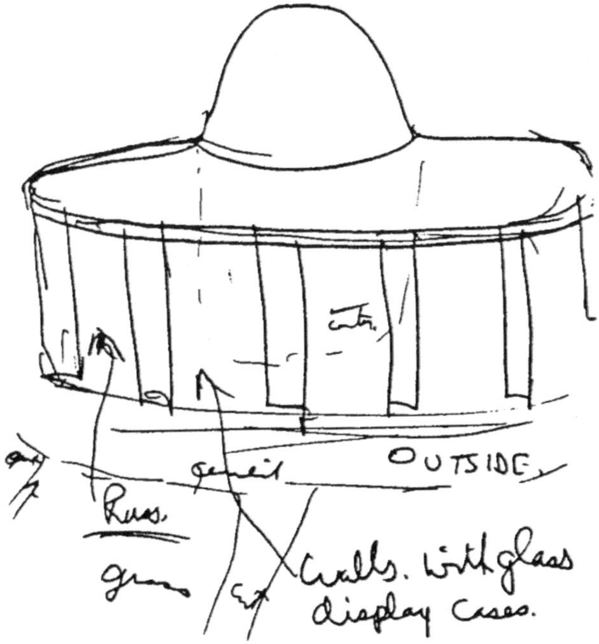

Fig. 8b Gary's Remote Viewing image, appears from the street level, although he was located in SRI, Menlo Park, California.

white dome." He went on to describe "glass cases around the inside," which we later verified as true, even though Russell did not have access to the inside of the building at the time. Gary was able to describe details beyond what was available to us in feedback photos! It is clear to all of us that he had contact with the target, and was not reading Russell's mind, and as Russell said, "Gary was psychically looking over my shoulder."

Gary reported on the inbound tape "it looks like a flying saucer that landed in the city." And "He [Russell] is inside a domed area...there's an openness about it, it's so large. There is still this arched thing like a dome, it's a building circular in shape . . . a wide road or freeway goes by here and a downtown section." Gary drew four pictures of a circular or domed structure which was definitely not associated with the other possible targets. Before the experiment, neither Gary, A.J. Mullins nor I had ever been to the Superdome (See Figures 8a and 8c).

Fig. 8c Aerial view of the Louisiana Superdome

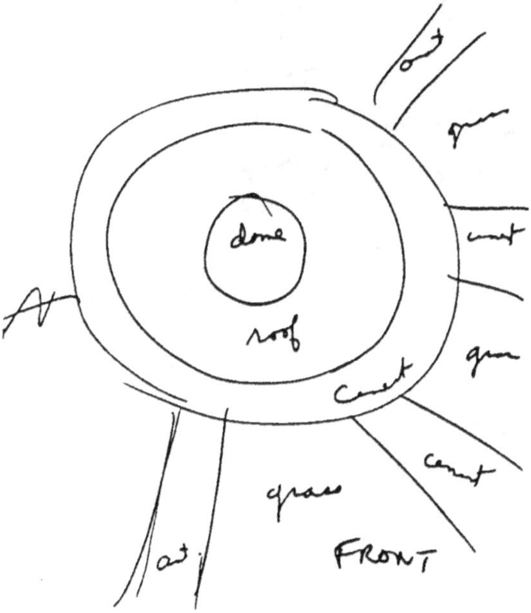

Fig. 8d Gary's Remote Viewing drawing.
Note he wrote "dome" in the Center.

Gary also drew a view of the region around the Superdome including the downtown area which was also accurate. See Figure 8d which also shows highways and tall buildings. (See Figure 8f for Gary's drawing. Note Figure 8e and 8f are almost 40 degrees off from each other). Additionally, Gary mentioned other accurate features of the Superdome target, including it was made with blown insulation, was grey in color, and had a structure on top which was also found to be true in the post hock analysis.

Fig. 8e An aerial view of the Dome and surrounding area.

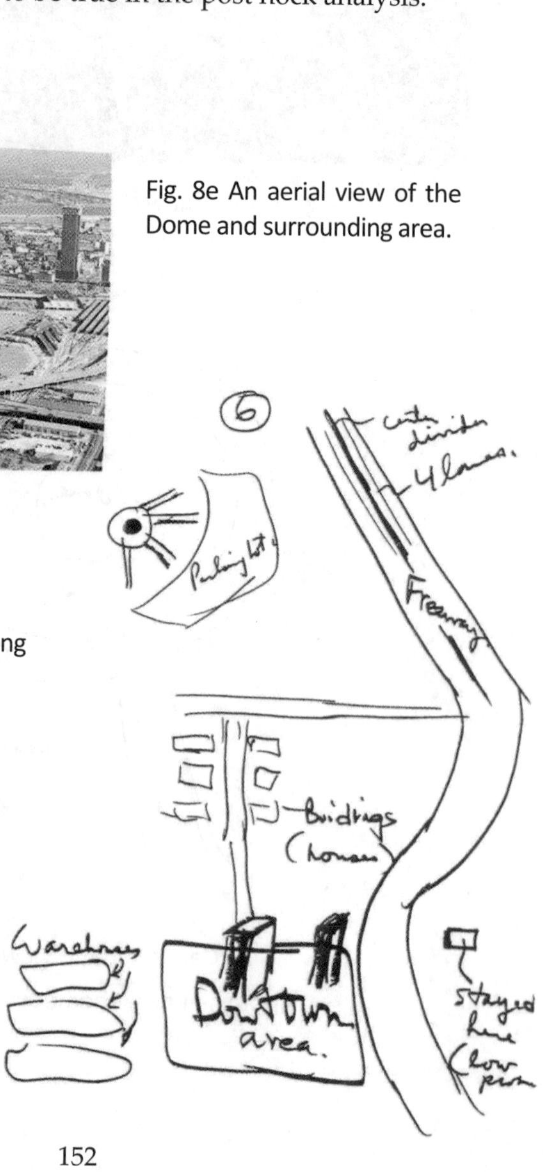

Fig. 8f Gary's Remote Viewing of the area surrounding the Superdome including the parking lot.

Gary also drew Figure 8g and stated the purpose of the inside area on his tape: "I am getting the feeling of circles. . . like there are seats . . . It is like a theatre . . . A concert hall, a stage, something like that." The Superdome is primarily used as a sports arena but is also used for concerts and theatre (See Fig. 8h). Figure 8h was obtained in A.J. Mullins detailed post hock analysis conducted for Russell Targ and I for my grant. We all agreed that this remote viewing was a remarkable one.

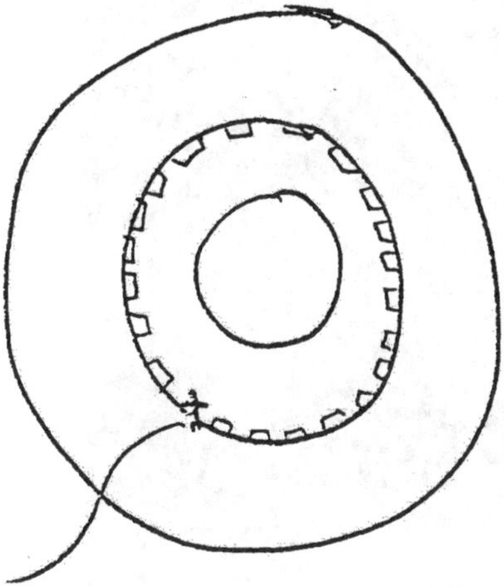

Fig. 8g Subjects drawing of inside the Superdome.

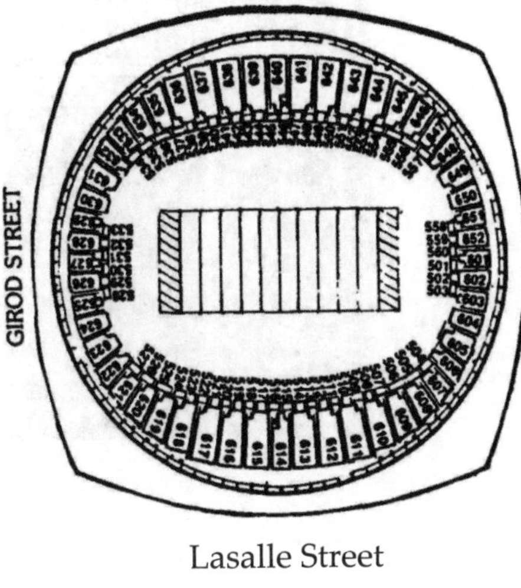

Fig. 8h Picture of the seating arrangement at the Superdome stadium.

Unselected Target Pool Sites

The other five targets in the six target pools are definitely orthogonal to each other and from Gary's description to 8i, 8j, 8k, 8l and 8m).

Fig. 8i Building on Royal Street with iron lace balconies.

Fig. 8j The target was a New Orleans street car.

Fig. 8k Lake Pontchartrain Causeway bridge which is 23.83 miles long.

Fig. 8l Photograph of St. Louis Cathedral adjacent to Jackson Square in the French Quarter.

Fig. 8m
The levee area called the Moon Walk is a tourist attraction.

Experiment 9
United California Bank (UCB) and Plaza
October 30, 1976

We conducted another long distance experiment between Palo Alto, California and New Orleans, Louisiana as part of our long distance series. The subject, in New Orleans, was a medical student by the name Susan Harris. In California, from SRI the outbound team consisted of Dave Hunt, myself and A.J. Mullins, who took real time photographs at the site and also conducted the post hock analysis. (Mullins and Rauscher, 1977, 1978).

The target site that was chosen from the random number generator was the United California Bank and Plaza (Fig. 9a and 9b). At the beginning of the experiment time period, the outbound experimenter team commented on the tape, "We have just walked under an overhang of a building. A glassed in walkway from the second story of one building to the second story in another building." All three outbound experimenters commented on tape about this overhead walkway.

Outbound member, Elizabeth commented that the columns were "7-like structures . . . that are supports for the lower part of the building." Susan made a drawing and reported, "Maybe it was what Elizabeth was seeing. She was looking up (Figure 9c). There was an overhang, a building over their heads. I'm not sure at all that it's L shaped." She drew an upside down L shape. Her drawing is given in Fig. 9c. A.J. Mullins, an Outbound Experimenter also reported, "The shape of the columns is very much like a '7'."

Fig. 9a United California Bank Building.

Fig. 9b
7-like structure of the
United California Bank.

Fig. 9c
The 7 that was
seen by the remote
viewer.

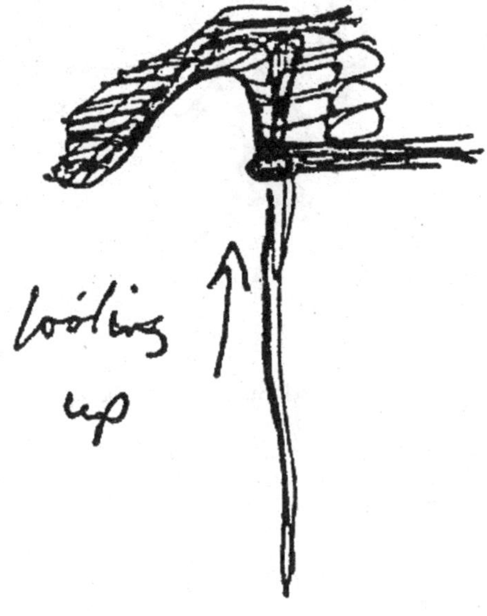

Susan commented on her tape, "It seems to be a window here. I think there is a window behind him (Dave), a large, clear glassed thing. He was up against the window" (Fig. 9a). Susan mentioned windows a number of times on her tape and drew windows (Fig. 9d) which were dominate at the site.

Fig. 9d Subjects drawing of the window structure.

Outbound experimenter Elizabeth further noted, "I looked at a fountain that is almost empty although. There's enough water in it to make water reflections. There's a ring in it, from which water spouts when the fountain is in operation." The fountain is rectangular, with a circular metal pipe in it. A.J. Mullins who took the photographs, also reported on "a fountain area that is not spraying any water, but has water in its pond that is moving in the wind." (See Fig. 9e)

Fig. 9e
Photographs were taken of the Water Fountain
at the UCB Building where we were
by A.J. (Hope) Mullins.

Susan then described a "sunken depression" with a gold rim in it. She commented that there was "something mushrooming out of that depression." Later in her transcript she again described this area. "There was this gold rim and in the depression . . . something coming out of the depression." She drew lines emerging from the circle she had drawn and made a number of intertwoven lines in the depression coming out of the contained area (Fig. 9f), which is true. Her size scale of 16 ft. was of the correct order of magnitude. The three outbound experimenters passed under an overhang (see Susan's response, Fig. 9g).

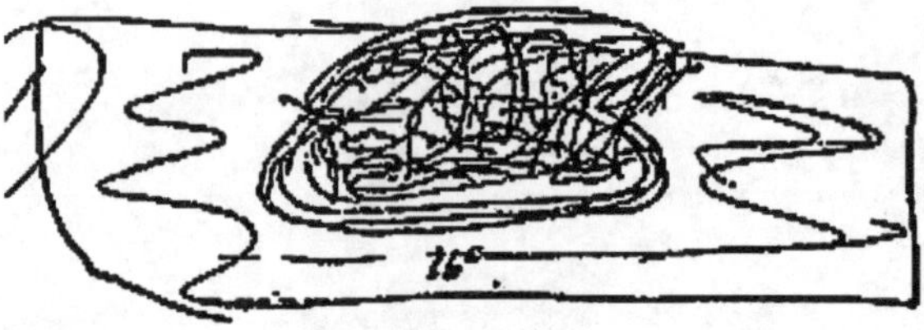

Fig. 9f Enlarged part of Fig. 9j.

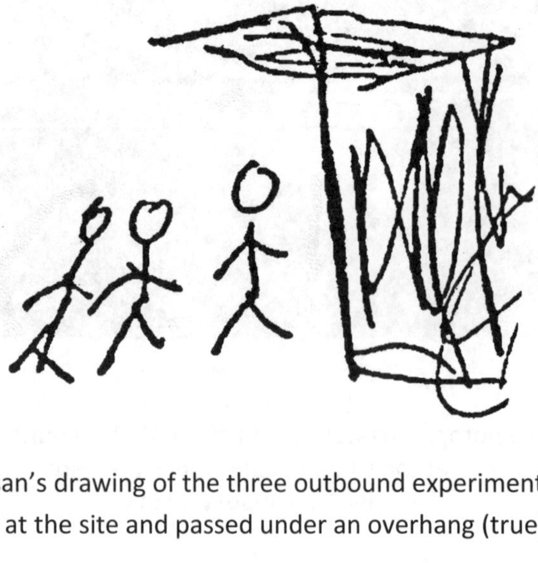

Fig. 9g Susan's drawing of the three outbound experiments who were at the site and passed under an overhang (true).

I picked up a paper airplane at the Bank site Plaza and tossed it toward Dave (Fig. 9h and Susan drew Fig. 9i). We tossed it back and forth several times but it was hard to catch. Normally transitory events are not picked up in remote viewing experiments, but Susan made a very good drawing, the action was photographed and recorded on tape by A.J. Mullins.

Susan then said, "I wonder if they're playing some type of game. I try to zoom in on Dave to see what he is doing. It seemed to me that something was moving toward him. Some projectile like a ball or a Frisbee. Something was being moved towards him and kind of going past him. As if Elizabeth has tossed him a ball. With Dave I can't really be sure about this because motions are so odd. It seemed there was a projectile coming towards Dave (Fig 9i)." Susan Harris reported the activity, the participants, and the object moving past Dave!

Fig. 9h This photograph was taken during the experiment of Rauscher (on right) on the Plaza tossing a paper airplane to Dave Hurt (on the left).

Fig. 9i Susan Harris described this drawing as a "projectile coming towards Dave."

In Figure 9j, Susan's completed drawings are given. She also mentions an amusement center, which is incorrect, but marked it off as separate and apparently unconsciously may have realized it is analytic overlay but over 95% of her transcripts are of accurate elements that appeared at the target site.

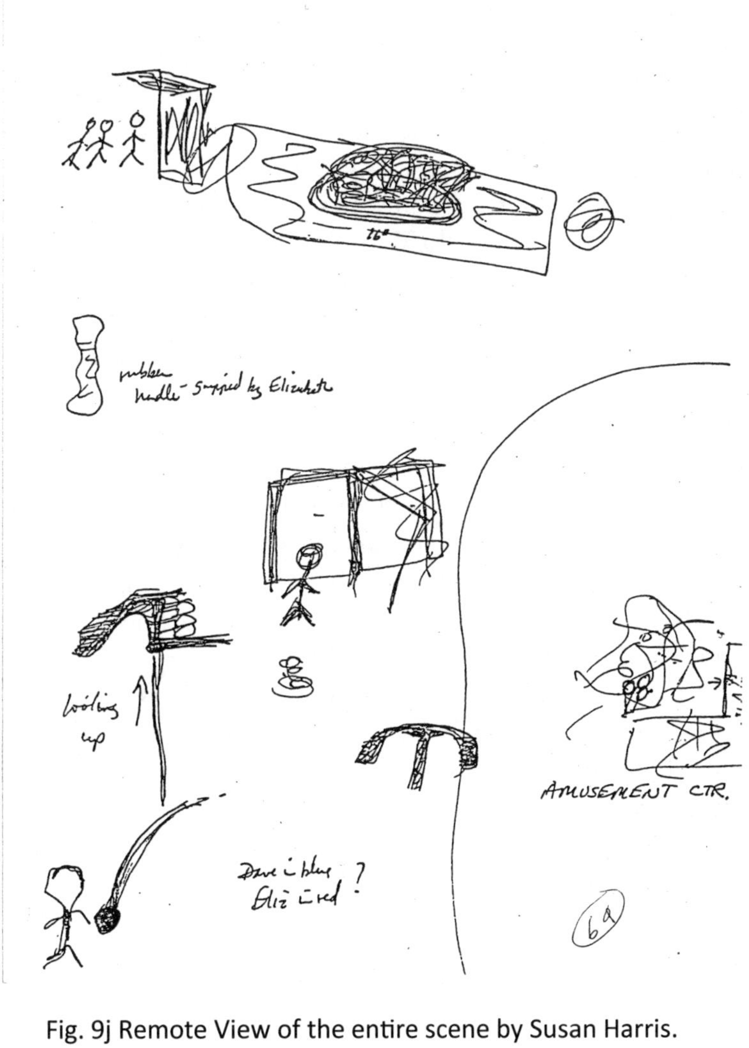

Fig. 9j Remote View of the entire scene by Susan Harris.

Experiment 10
United California Bank (UCB) and Plaza
October 30, 1976

During his travel to Huntsville, Alabama, Gary O. Langford, a systems analyst, was to remote view to the Palo Alto area "by going back in time" to view the outbound team who was at the target site the previous day. His intent was to go back in time by one day since he was unable to view at the time when our team would be at the site. He conducted "retrocognition" perception, 24 hours later on the target selection and through long distance remote viewing. The outbound experimenters in Palo Alto, California were Elizabeth Rauscher and A.J. Mullins and Hal Puthoff. The randomly chosen target was again the United California Bank building (Fig 10a), as the same target site can be put into the target pool to be randomly chosen again. One of the features we spent time near were large planter boxes with yellow flowers with green leaves (See Fig. 10a).

We had no contact with the subject, per the usual protocol, but he drew rectangular planter boxes on a brick patio (Fig 10b and 10c). He labeled the box "cement," and reported words, sunlight, outside sunny, warm and "yellow and green colors." Gary made the drawings (Fig. 10b and Fig. 10c).

All of us did not learn about the accuracy of his responses until we returned with the subject for feedback to the United California Bank (UCB). The boxes are landscaped with shrubbery plus a few yellow flowers and they are situated on a large brick patio area. The weather was sunny and warm at the time of the experiment.

Fig. 10a One example of the large concrete planter boxes
on the UCB Plaza which is brick.

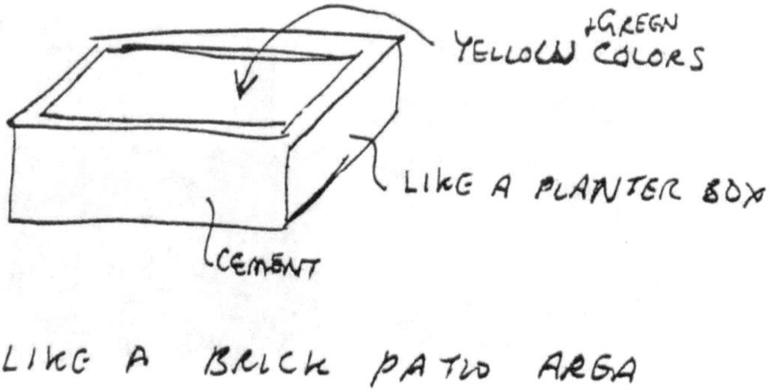

Fig. 10b Drawing the subject Gary made of cement planter box.

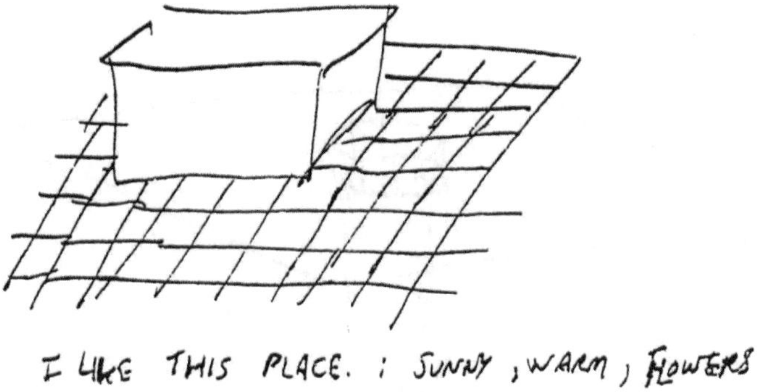

Fig. 10c Gary's drawing of one of the large concrete planter boxes
on the UCB Plaza.

Also at the site is a stairwell to a lower level garage (Fig 10d and 10e). Gary also made sketches of a circular structure on more than one level which he labeled with the following words, "Something that is roundish in shape. . . depression . . . With an iron fence around it (Fig. 10e) . . . Near a step change in surface level (Fig. 10f) . . . Like a fountain; water association . . . water fountain." The multilevel depression, iron fence and stairs which he drew are in Fig. 10f and are near the fountain (see experiment 9).

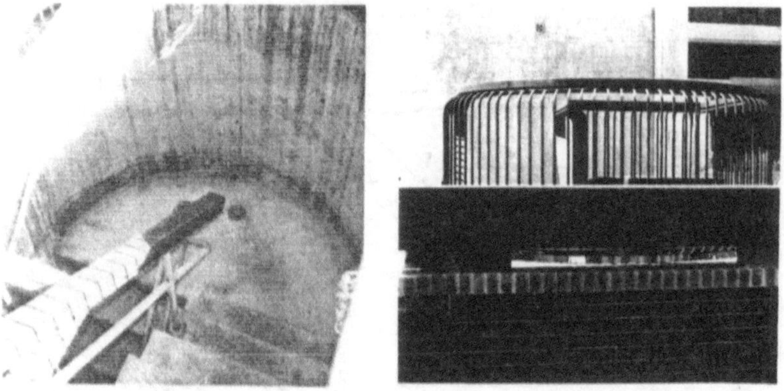

Fig. 10d and Fig. 10e Two views of a large concrete stairwell to the lower level parking garage at the UCB Plaza.

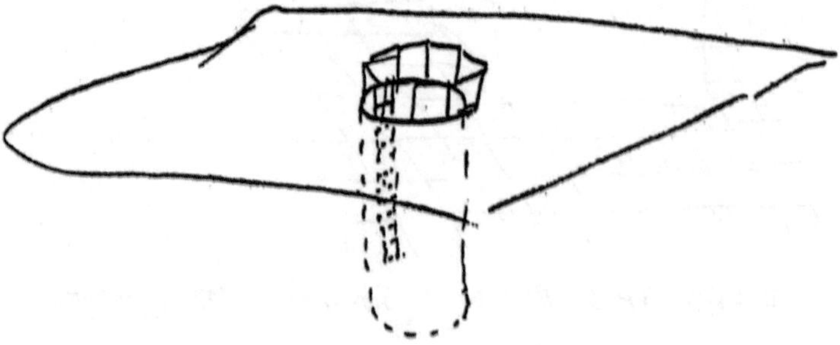

Fig. 10f Gary's remote viewing.

Although the target was the bank building and plaza, we walked around the plaza but spent time near the planter boxes, and a stairwell was nearby (Fig. 10d and 10e). Even though the tall bank building is prominent at the site, judging did relate the subject's mentation to the target.

The outbound remote viewing experimenters did not notice an underground stairwell at the site (Fig. 10d and 10e). A cylindrical like structure with a fence around it, with steps down into it, on the day that the outbounders had been to the United California Bank site. The subterranean stairwell was pointed out by Gary when he was taken to the site for feedback after he returned to California. He had even drawn the fence-like structure with vertical bars that are around the top of the stairwell (Fig. 10f).

Gary wrote the words "grey," "area is greyish" and "grey in color." The underground stairwell is constructed of grey concrete (Fig. 10d) that went to an underground parking garage. He wrote "standing in a very confining space, like walls are close." The stairwell is a tight confining space. He noted that an outbounder experimenter "can look up and see out."

Experiment 11
Grant's Tomb
Coast to Coast Remote Viewing Experiment with Grant's Tomb in New York City as Target Site
July 2, 1976

We conducted another long distance experiment between SRI and a target that was in the New York area. The subject was Gary Langford and I, E.A. Rauscher, was the monitor at the Laboratory room at SRI's Radio Physics Laboratory. On the outbound team that randomly choose the target was Russell Targ, who was visiting family in New York with his younger son, Nicky (Nicholas). Gary and I knew them both well. The random target that came up was Grant's Tomb (Fig. 11a).

Russell and Nicky walked towards the tomb next to shade trees. Russell gave Nicky some coins to purchase the postcard used as the target picture at the ticket booth. Gary reported on the West Coast about the East Coast target: "I see a path with big shade trees and coins. Someone is exchanging coins. I see a white kiosk-like structure and drew five lines in front of it (Fig. 11b).

Note the similarity of his drawing to Grant's Tomb with its five white columns. Gary's drawing matches well with the target with no extraneous elements, but his identification, scale and function were inaccurate. In Remote Viewing, the general impression can be extremely accurate, but function and site purpose, may not be.

The five possible targets in addition to Grant's Tomb were (1) a railroad bridge; (2) the New York University law library, (3) the fountain in Washington Square Park, (4) Columbia University's subway station, and (5) the 79th Street boat basin. The targets were chosen to be dissimilar and, thus, to be able to be differentiated in the judging process. The subject, Gary, said in his opening paragraph: "Outdoors, large open area, standing on and then off asphalt (rough material), dark for a path. A white building, like a ticket booth. Wooden structure, is white in color, and has an arched look about it. There is a large shade tree close to Russ," (Russell Targ, the outbound experimenter). Then he drew the drawing labeled Figure 11b. Note there were large shade trees and the five lines that match the five pillars on Grant's Tomb (Fig. 11a).

Fig. 11a
Grant's Tomb, Front View

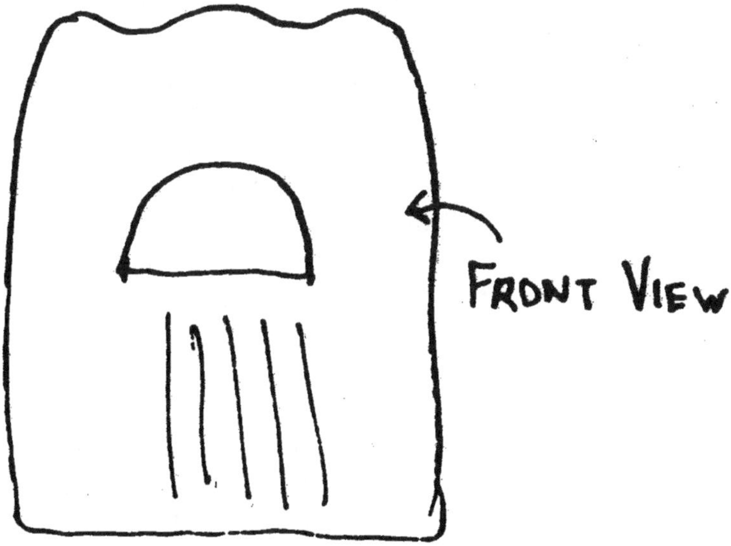

Fig. 11b
Subject, Gary described "Outdoors, Large open area... Shade Trees...White building with Arches."

Experiment 12
Washington Square Park
July 6, 1976

In another long distance experiment as part of the series between SRI and the East Coast, in this case New York, Susan Harris, a medical student from New Orleans was the subject located at SRI. She was in the laboratory room with the interviewer monitor, E.A. Rauscher. The outbound experimenter was Russell Targ. The randomly chosen target that was chosen was Washington Square Park, especially its fountain (Fig. 12a and 12b) which was dry.

Susan produced an exceptionally accurate transcript. Pictures and the subject's drawings of the fountain are shown in Fig. 12c. The subject said the following: "The first image I got at about the first minute was of a cement depression—as if a dry fountain with a cement post in the center or inside. There seemed to be pigeons off to the right, flying around the surface out of the depression. At one point I thought you were opening a cellophane bag. (Russell had in fact bought ice cream during the experimental period.) There was also a rectangular wooden frame, a window frame, but I wasn't sure if it was on a building, or a similar structure with a different purpose." There is an archway next to the fountain. (Fig, 12a and 12b). The subject's description correlates to the Washington Square Fountain and Arch to the left in Fig. 12a which was dry at the remote viewing time and there was a small pillar in the center. The outbound experimenter viewed the fountain toward the end of the experimental period. "All in all I thought you were at Riverside Park" (which was an incorrect analysis overlay). The SRI scientist who acted as the judge later was familiar with the New York City area, but blind to the target. He did, however, identify the target correctly on recording the transcript of the subject and examining her drawing (Fig. 12c).

Coast to Coast Long Distance Remote Viewing Experiment.
Target is the fountain at Washington Square Park.

Fig. 12a
Park in 1964.

Fig. 12b
Park in the 1970s.

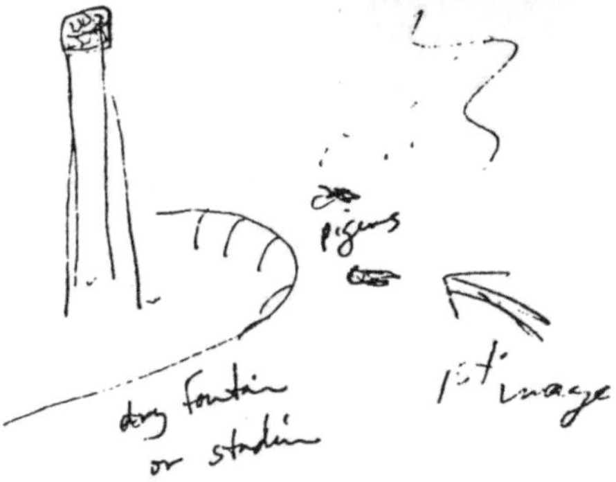

Fig. 12c Susan's drawing of her first perception was a "cement depression"—as if a dry fountain—with a cement post in the center of the inside."

Experiment 13
House in France
1977

An Interesting spontaneous remote perception experiment was conducted with Costa de Beauregard, a French physicist. He and I were flying across the Atlantic to a conference and meeting in Paris, France. We sat next to each other on the airplane. Costa asked me to view his house (Fig. 13a). My first thought was an analytical overlay and I thought of houses close together, with red tile roofs, but knew this was incorrect. I did not know if his house was in the city or not.

We were approximately 1,000 miles from the target, in a jet over the Atlantic. I commented that the house is white with a brown shingle roof. The front door has an overhang of brown shingle and the window frames were newly painted brown (which was all true). The house is two story, as are the other houses on a quiet street. The houses are widely spaced apart with little traffic.

I saw a thin green tree to the right of the house (Fig. 13a). There is a tall thin pine near the house, not shown in the photo and the house has four main window areas on the side to left of the front door. I said there was a Persian rug inside the front door which was true and wondered if it was a guess because Costa was likely to have one. Figure 13b is the drawing I made on the airplane. Several weeks later I saw de Beauregard's house and photographed it. (Fig. 13a).

Fig. 13a Two story French home that was the target site. It is located approximately 100 miles from Paris. Photograph was taken three weeks after the remote viewing. The house is built of white stone. The front door with overhang is at right side of photograph with a tall green pine tree. The roof is brown shingle and so is the front door overhang. The trim on the windows had been newly painted brown.

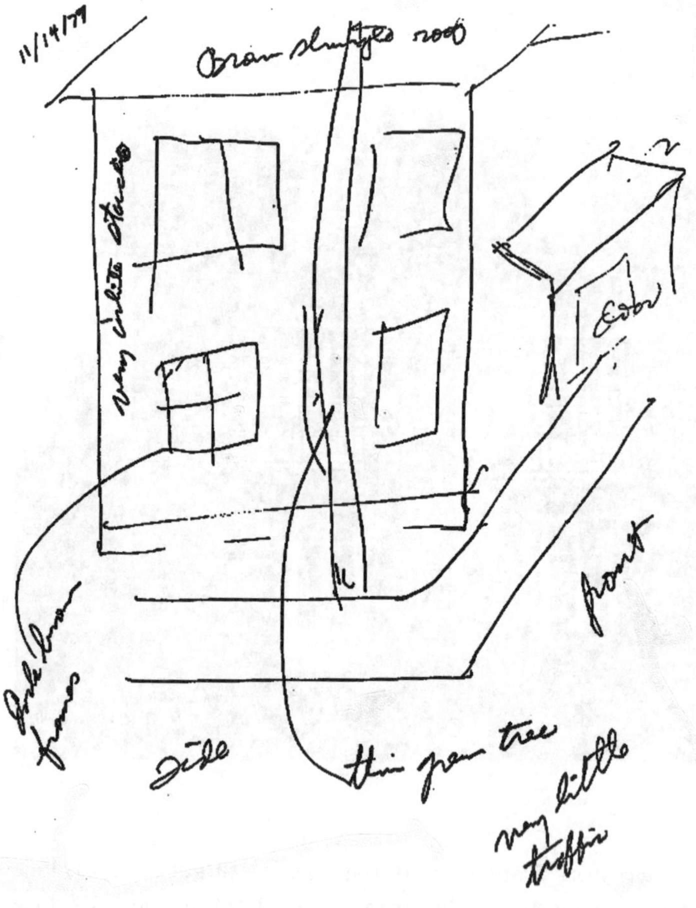

Fig. 13b Subject, I, Elizabeth Rauscher, had never been to France at the time. I drew the above sketch of the target house which is near Paris, France. After my remote viewing, the owner, Costa, explained that his is not a typical French home nor neighborhood.

Experiment 14
Search Through Time and Space: Bart Station on Shattuck Avenue Berkeley, California July 21, 1977

A local remote viewing experiment was conducted with the Berkeley Remote Viewing Group with A.J. Mullins, Jeff Mishlove and I as the subject. The target pool consisted of six targets. The protocol involved myself as the subject without a monitor. I meditated for three hours and had to pick the time and place of the randomly chosen target which I would attempt to remotely perceive. Sometime during these three hours, A.J. Mullins and Mishlove would randomly choose their target and Mullins would go there for their outbound fifteen minutes to experience the site and record photographs. The bracket of time was from 2:00PM—5:00PM West Coast Time. The target was to be within a two-hour drive from me.

I knew only that the outbound team, Jeff Mishlove and A.J. Mullins, would choose their target and go there for fifteen minutes sometime between 2:00PM and 5:00PM. I was to turn on my tape recorder and identify the time and geographical location the team had randomly chosen.

There was no monitor for this experiment, but I was to turn on my tape recorder to record my descriptions of the time and geographical location which the outbound team had randomly chosen. I turned on my tape recorder at 2:40PM and I found out later that the outbound experimenters arrived at the site at 2:45 PM. When I turned on the tape recorder I began to accurately report the site. I received feedback two and one-half months later, but I "knew" where the outbound team was on Shattuck Avenue and I could have named the cross street, but I could not remember it.

The target that came up was the Berkeley Bart Train Station. In front of the station are new brick planter boxes (at that time) with pine trees in them (Fig. 14a and 14b)

Fig. 14a and 14b: At the remote viewed Bart Station and park there were two curved, new brick planter boxes with pine trees planted in them.

The outbound experimenters commented, "We are walking by curved brick planter boxes and a red brick pattern walk way."

I made the drawing in Fig. 14c from my sequestered room in my time-space scan experiment. When I started at "20 to 3:00" I received mainly "ideas and not image". I saw and drew "sloped up raise brick, circular . . . new bricks". I saw that the target "could be on Shattuck around trees" and "sloped up bricks"...

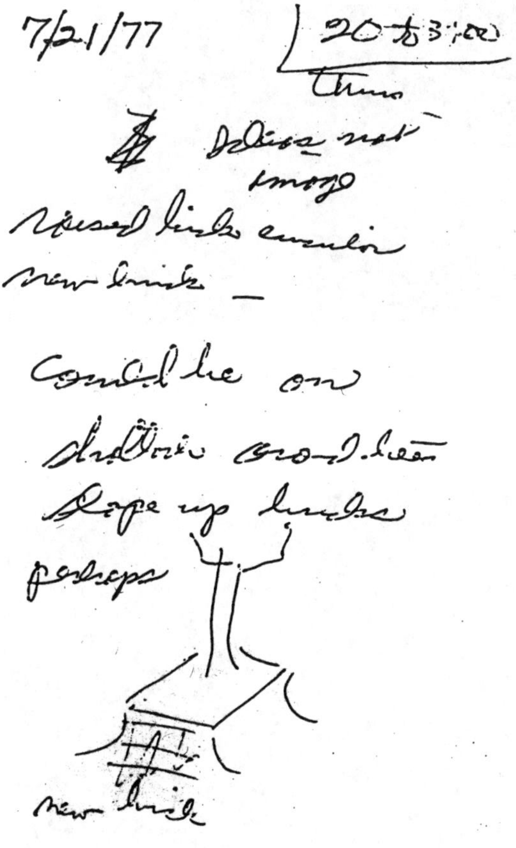

Fig. 14c My remote Viewing observation.

I knew the main street was Shattuck Avenue (14d), but I could not remember the cross street. I mentioned strong conviction about their choice even though feedback came several months later. Again, I reported during their mentation, "new brick...raised circular brick...slopes up... could be on Shattuck around trees (planter boxes)."

Fig. 14d The Shattuck Avenue Street Sign at the BART Station which is at the left of this sign.

Fig. 14e Circular brick pattern in front of the BART Station.

Experiment 15
Kazakhstan's Semipalatinsk Test Site
November 12, 1978

An example of an applied remote viewing experiment was requested of me for the ranking officers of the Air Force in Provo, Utah while I was there on an antennae theory consulting job for Eyring Institute. All I was told was to view a site in Russia (then the Soviet Union). I was told Pat Price remote viewed this site in 1972, but I had not seen or heard any details of the transcript or drawings. I believe and I wondered if I was viewing the same site, which I found out later was Semipalatinsk (Fig. 15a and 15b). I conducted my viewing with six ranking officers present. The feedback I received was positive and of amazement as to the accuracy of the remote viewing. Remote perception and psi in general requires one to tell the truth! What I described was as follows: "I see an open, flat dusty area with roads and few or no buildings but there is greater activity below ground. I see dirt, red-brown color and car ruts no roads in a very isolated area. Flat, with trees in distance. It's all underground. I don't recognize its purpose—not lasers but somewhat similar."

Pat Price remote viewed cranes in 1972 but they are gone at the time of my viewing, it is a major underground site, but at the time, I had not seen Price's response or even knew about the target and drawing which had been classified. I stated ". . . Many stories underground, sounds of machine, cranes and lifting devices for heavy machinery. Moving crane arm and below used for swinging equipment on loading crane (chains). All the remote viewing work indicates there are no more secrets and the truth will set you free. What I see is "Really large in comparison to men in white lab coats, equipment checkers. I see huge black generator spheres, with glowing plasma like in between clear plastic. (I knew it was not plastic but that was what it looked like.) There are many multiple series of these huge devices. I will call them vortex plasma generators, but I am not sure of their use" (Fig. 15c).

The target site, I found later was Semipalatinsk in Kazakhstan and I never received the details about the underground facility, only that it was a large project underground with a very large dark sphere or spheres, although later found out I had viewed the area of a test site which had a little abandoned guard station in front (Fig. 15a and 15b). There are eerie remnants of concrete diagnostic towers, which are in the vicinity of ground zero of the first Soviet nuclear tests.

Today there are kilometers of trenches dug throughout the vast site by copper cable thieves, whom the Kazaks were neither prepared nor inclined to stop. Once upon a time, the reactors at the site were amongst the most ambitious and innovative Soviet reactor facilities. I still do not know exactly what was there, underground.

Fig. 15a Kazakhstan's Semipalatinsk Test Site.

Fig. 15b Trench to remove copper from the ancient test site.

VORTEX PLASMA GENERATOR (in NE or NW Moscow)
(below ground, 3 or 4 stories)

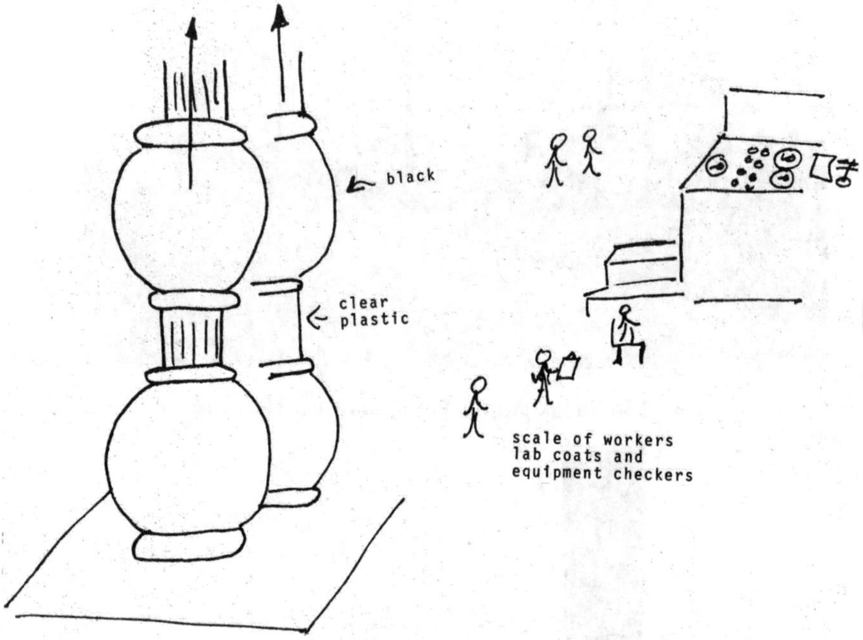

Multiple series of devices

Fig. 15c
VORTEX PLASMA GENERATOR
Location: I stated it was South East of Moscow below ground, 3 or 4 stories high
Scale of workers, lab coats, and equipment checkers
Clear plastic like with huge dark spheres.
Multiple series of devices

Experiment 16
Macy's Shopping Center
September 1976

We conducted a local remote viewing experiment in 1976 in a SRI Laboratory room with photographic artist Hella Hammid who was the subject and the monitor was Russell Targ. The outbound experimenter was Elizabeth A. Rauscher. The time sequence for the experiment was as follows:

Hella made her drawing and tape recording with Russell from 4:45PM to 5:00PM. At 5:05 PM, I randomly chose my remote viewing site from a random number generator from the target pool. I arrived at the chosen target site, Macy's Department store and spent 15 minutes outside at the site. There I noticed a very large archway on the building and several smaller arches. From the outside I noted new white mortar between the bricks that stood out (at the time) (Fig. 16a and 16c). Hella said on her tape recording "There is a very new brick building with a tower and a porte cochère that a wagon can drive through. This was the first formal precognitive experiment with which I was involved" (Her drawing is given in Fig. 16b).

Hella also stated that there was a small stream to the left of the building with bushes and trees that I did not see while being outbound (Fig. 16c). But when Russell, Hella and I later went for feedback to the target, to the left we found the small stream, trees and bushes which demonstrated she had viewed more than I did at the outbound time. She pointed this out to us as she had observed objects in the area I did not see. She also described two brown balls, which she drew when she was asked to draw the summary of her viewing (Fig.16d). It appears nothing like this was found at the site. It could have been small objects, but perhaps this was analytic overlay.

Hella's and Russell's dialog continued with major agreement. Hella further discussed the courtyard to the side of the building, which she stated as large (which is correct). They both appeared to be viewing the site.

Fig. 16a Macy's Department Store at the Stanford Shopping Center with a big archway.

Fig. 16b Hella's drawing of a brick building with archway .

Fig. 16c. Target: Macy's Shopping Center. The building is constructed of red brick with white mortar between the bricks. This is a photograph of the target where a small park-like area and stream is next to the main building.

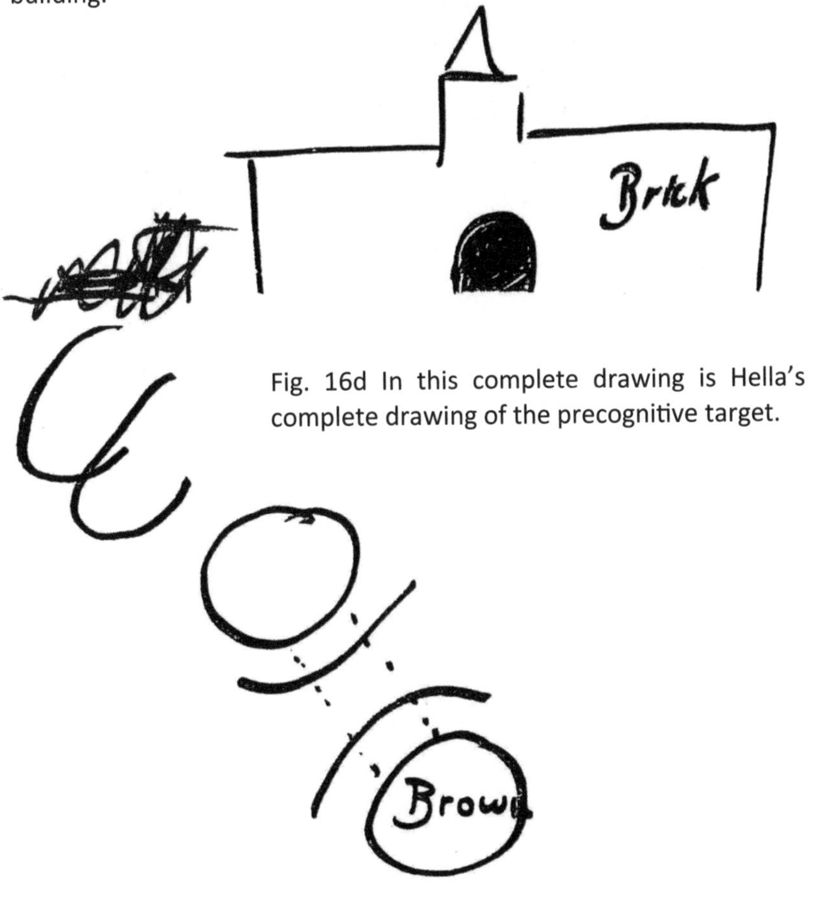

Fig. 16d In this complete drawing is Hella's complete drawing of the precognitive target.

I returned to the SRI Laboratory. I noted Hella's accuracy and joked and said: "Just tell me the rest of my life." Neither the subject nor the monitor had any knowledge of the sites in the target pool which contain these four possible sites:

The first was the "Center for Personal Growth," which has low, modern buildings that are basically dark brown and yellow. Rectangular shapes are prominent and there are extensive garden areas.

Second, a busy traffic intersection, where the building materials are concrete and asphalt, with metal fencing. The site is basically grey.

Third, an industrial site consisting of several concrete, wood and corrugated iron structures. There are semi-triangular metal bins that hold the various grades of gravel.

Finally fourth, Macy's Department Store in the Stanford Shopping Center with courtyard. The building is red brick with white arches (the target that was chosen).

Experiment 17
San Francisco Transamerica Building
Spontaneous Precognitive Remote Viewing
Dream: 1957, Experiment: 1976

A spontaneous precognition experience was noted by this author. I keep a notepad near my bed to record my unusual dreams. One of my recordings appeared to involve the precognition of a building that had not been built at the time of my dream and may not have been even considered yet. The building was the Transamerica Pyramid Building, and became the tallest building in San Francisco at the time (Fig. 17a, 17b) and was completed in 1972.

I recorded this dream in 1957 in Berkeley, "It appears I see a giant pyramid in the middle of the city (San Francisco). I look out one direction (East) and see Coit Tower and I look out another direction at a right angle to the South and see a giant pyramid. It is not quite like Cheops pyramid but it stands out on the city landscape." Also I wrote that: "I am standing on a building that stands on another building and as I look down, I can see that the two (buildings) are separated by a red roof."

I recorded this dream in 1957, feeling a great sense of strangeness about it. Through a set of unusual circumstances I found myself and Saul Paul Sirag invited to stay in Gary Zukov's apartment in San Francisco in 1976. I had just met Gary that evening after a talk I gave in San Francisco. After the talk, we found that my car was locked up in the garage where we parked it. We were wandering around San Francisco, laughing but with no place to go, and I called Gary as I had just received his card.

Gary's apartment was in a building on top of another building separated by a red roof. Looking to the East I could see Coit Tower and looking South, I could see the Transamerica Pyramid building. The dream occurred in 1956, 13 years before the famous San Francisco Pyramid building was built and so the "feedback" occurred years after the dream.

Fig. 17a The San Francisco Transamerica Pyramid Building.

As I spoke to the American Physical Society (APS) on numerous occasions, so I add their APS Bulletin cover containing of one of my talk abstracts, as an interesting addendum showing a good picture of the Pyramid building in San Francisco.

Bulletin of the American Physical Society

Program of the 1989 Annual Joint APS/AAPT Meeting, also with the AAAS, 15–19 January 1989 in San Francisco, CA begins on page 22

Volume 34, Number 1

January 1989

Fig. 17b The skyline of San Francisco showing the Pyramid Building in the American Physical Society Bulletin in which I had published a paper.

Experiment 18
Indian Rock
October 27, 1980

An experiment was conducted with a video film crew, who were part of the outbound experimenter team. This team was headed by Kit Pedler of Thomas Productions. Also outbound with Kit was Beverly Rubik. The experiment was a local experiment by the Berkeley Research Group and was not part of the formal series. The subject was Hella Hammid and I was with her, as a monitor, in the Berkeley Laboratory as the monitor. The target pool consisted of six sites: a Codornices park, Indian rock, Lawrence Hall of Science, Strawberry Canyon Tennis Courts, the Ashley Lumber Yard all located in Berkeley and the Firestone Tire Dealer on St. Pablo Avenue in Albany, California. The target that came up was Indian Rock which was randomly chosen by Kit. The video/photographer, with the outbound team was Richard Mervin. Beverly also took the photographs at the target site.

Large Eucalyptus trees were prominent at the target site as noted by the outbound team (Fig. 18a and 18d). There was also an overhang on tall poles from which a broadcast speaker and lights were mounted on a sort of odd structure (Fig. 18a). Another manmade feature was a water fountain which the outbound team also noted (Fig. 18b). Below the site were houses and a fence. The path they walked on was rocky and noisy gravelly and made a crumbling sound and some had leaves that had dropped from the trees.

Hella described and drew an arch she labeled as "Number 1," then a pool or fountain with a noisy ground walkway and she wrote gravel on her response drawing (Fig. 18c). She drew and talked about trees and shrubs at the site. Both the overhead arch and fountain Hella perceived and drew in the left side of her drawing. She also gave two cardinal directions of E and S correctly (Fig. 18c).

Fig. 18a The overhang with speaker and Eucalyptus trees prominent at the site.

Fig. 18b The water fountain across from the overhang area where the outbound experimenters spent time at the site.

There was a fence along one side of the site which she drew (Fig. 18c). There were also fairly tall buildings in the distance. Another view of the arch taken at the site is given. (Fig. 18d). She also drew what she called a "remote viewing tree of eyes" (Fig. 18e) as a whimsy.

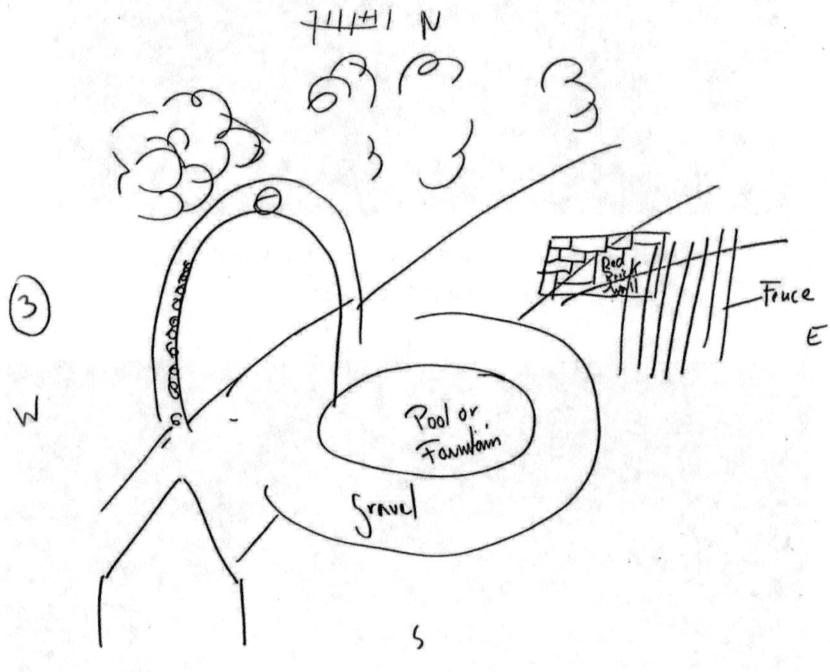

Fig. 18c After Hella's description of the remote target, she drew the above drawing. The indicated directions are correct for East and South.

Fig. 18d

Fig. 18e She drew what she called the remote viewing trees the eyes for Kit. We include this as an interesting bit of Hella's musings.

Experiment 19
Lawrence Hall of Science
June 1977

The only site in our Berkeley Target Pool that had a view of San Francisco and the University of California, Sather Tower, known to most as the *Campanile* (bell and clock tower) was the Lawrence Hall of Science. Our experiment demonstrates analytic overlays, errors from a first-time skeptical remote viewer, Jean Jernigan, a reporter from the Berkeley Gazette who turned her tape recorder on at the predicted time and tape recoded her response. This experiment was conducted by the Berkeley Research Group and was not part of a formal series of experiments. Jeffrey Mishlove was the monitor who used the tape recorder to record Jean's responses. The target pool contained four targets in sealed envelops. These were the targets: the main BART Station on Shattuck, the Hearst Mining building, the Codornices Park and the Lawrence Hall of Science at UC, Berkeley.

I, Rauscher was the outbound experimenter. I went to my car with the randomly chosen target which was the Lawrence Hall of Science. A thirty minute drive time was allowed and the remote viewing session lasted for fifteen minutes. At the target location I first looked at the old cyclotron magnet in front of the Lawrence Hall of Science. I rubbed the surface of the black magnet of the cyclotron which was rough (See Fig. 19a). I also looked out over the Bay and noted the *Campanile,* grass, trees and cars in the parking lot and an outside fountain and metal fence (Fig. 19c). I also stood in front of the cyclotron magnet and took photographs (Fig. 19b).

Jean in her office with Jeff reported on her tape that I (the outbound experimenter) saw the site had grass, trees and cars (Fig. 19c). With apparent diagnosis overlay, Jean drew the picture (Fig. 19b) and described a black object with a very similar shape and lines to the old cyclotron magnet, but identified it as my purse (which I was not carrying).

Specifically, when the subject was listening to her tape for feedback after the completion of the experiment at the site, she mentioned the cyclotron magnet structure and said what she identified as the purse. Size and scale are not always apparent. In her remote viewing, she drew the car, San Francisco Bay and a picture that she isolated which appears to be the Campanile and marked it off separately perhaps unconsciously knowing it was not the primary target. Often when a subject isolates a part of a drawing, it usually is not at the site (See Fig. 19d). It is important to note, this experiment was not part of the series and involved a novice subject.

Fig. 19a The Cyclotron Magnet from an old Cyclotron no longer in use.

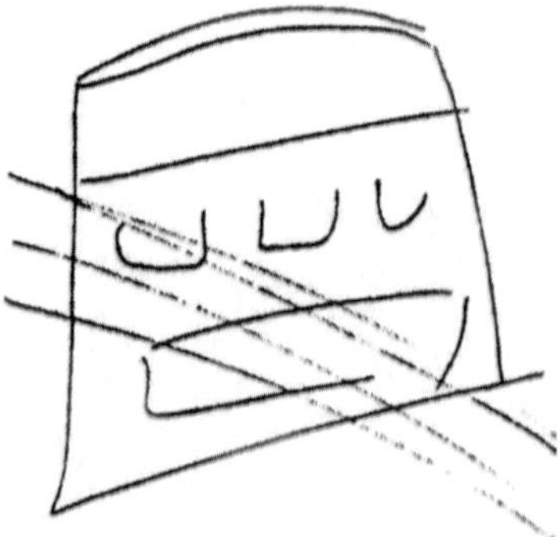

Fig. 19b The Remote Viewing that looked like a purse.

Fig. 19c The Lawrence Hall of Science and the parking lot and the view to the bay.

Fig. 19d The Remote Viewing showing the hillside, the parking lot, the *Campanile* and the bay at a distance.

5. An Analysis and Evaluation of Formal Remote Viewing Experiment Results

The SRI judging method was to conduct a series of experiments, for example, six remote viewing and geographic targets. Judges, blind to the correct matching, attempt to match subjects' description and the target location. A rank order was used from best to worse match for each set of transcripts and targets with only one making first place for each transcript and drawing of the target location.

A. Judging Analysis Techniques We Initiated to Analyze All Our SRI and Berkeley Experiments in Which I Participated

To assist in objectifying the evaluation of remote-perception, a 7-point scale has been developed (Targ, 2012) and used by the Research Group and with my other researchers (See Table 1). The scale gives results similar to those of other judging procedures. Although a few of our experiments had results at chance expectation, most of our results were statistically significant. With a chance probability, or *p* value, $p < 0.05$ of our experiments had highly significant results with *p* values of $< 10^{-6}$, or a million-to-one odds against having such a result by chance or more from all experiments, local, long distance and precognition.

Table 1

7-Point Evaluation for Target-Transcript Correspondence

7 Excellent correspondence, including good analytical detail (e.g., identifying the site by name) with essentially no incorrect information.

6 Good correspondence with good analytical information (e.g., naming the function) and relatively little incorrect information.

5 Good correspondence with unambiguous, unique, matchable elements but some incorrect information.

4 Good correspondence with several matchable elements intermixed with incorrect information.

3 Mixture of correct and incorrect elements but enough of the former to indicate viewer had made contact with the site.

2 Some correct elements but not sufficient to suggest results beyond chance expectation.

1 Little correspondence.

0 No correspondence.

B. Judging Results for Complete Remote Viewing Experiments

We also applied the transcript-to-target comparison-rating scale for both geographical targets in third dimensions and abstract targets in two dimensions for our first series of remote viewing by the F"F"G Group. I was the coordinator. In 1975, we conducted a series of eight real-time local (RTL) remote perception experiments that were judged to be non-significant by five judges matching transcripts to targets without using the point-evaluation scale. Using the scale, some positive correspondence between transcript and target was found, but the overall results were non-significant. The problem was that the experimenters took the subject participant to feedback on the day of the next experiment and shifting by one day gave quite good results but the error was made (Rauscher *et. al.*, 1975).

In 1980, we conducted a series of 12 experiments in which subject and target locations were long distance in the north-south direction. In this series, we used the Princeton 20 point feature-matching protocol and achieved significance with a single-tailed p value of .012. Using the point-evaluation scale yielded a slightly higher significance, but very similar (see Chapter 4). All other RTL, local and real-time long distant (RTD), and other RTD experiments, with the subject and target orientation in the east-west direction, were highly significant.

Fig. 20 shows data plotted for the 28 RTL and 25 RTD remote-perception experiments over a 18-year period. In addition, on LP (local precognition perception) an experimental data point is given. Each point on the plot in Fig. 20 represents a group or series of experiments in a single trial. The axes represent a plot of R_s versus t_D where R_s is the rating scale for target-to-transcript comparison and t_D is the time or date the experiment was conducted, plotted in month intervals. Subject transcripts and drawings were matched to the target for corre-

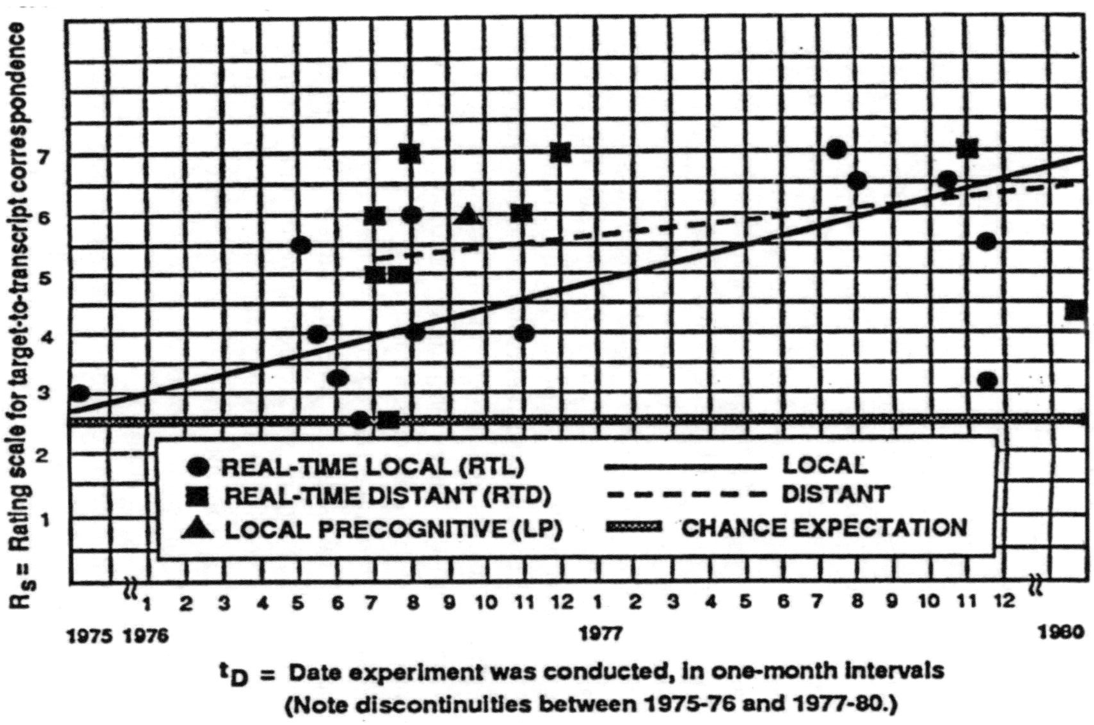

Fig. 20 Remote perception experiments conducted using geographical targets. Comparison of relative slopes of least-squares shows accuracy and learning in local and distant remote perception.

spondence to evaluate remote-perception success. All targets were geographical locations. In most cases, the outbound experimenter recorded an audiotape and took photographs during the experiments.

From Figure 20, we can generate a trend analysis in terms of the relative slope or change in R_s versus time, t_D, and we see that the slope for the RTL experiments yields a value of 4 and the slope for the RTD experiments yields a slope value slightly less of a value 3 (slope from 5.25 to 6.5). For the RTD data, both north-south and east-west orientations are grouped together. The overall average value of the 28 RTL experiments yields $\langle R_s \rangle = 5$, where $< >$ is a symbol for average, and the overall average value of the 25 RTD experiments yields $\langle R_s \rangle = 5.8$ (slope from 3 to 7). For all the RTL, we have *p* approximately equal to .0001, and for the RTD, we have a *p* value equal to approximately .00001. Note that the horizontal line $\langle R_s \rangle = 2.5$ represents chance expectation. In this Chapter, all the results from all our experiments lie on or above the chance line. In Chapter 4, three of the 12 experiments lie below or rest on the line above the chance line on the seven point scale and the rest lie above chance on the Princeton judging method. All group experiments were statistically significant.

We interpreted the positive slope as a learning curve for both the principal investigators and the subject-participants. Some experimenters were new to remote perception and some were experienced. Nearly all subjects were novices in remote perception before experiments. As can be observed from our data, no fall off for distance over kilometers was observed compared to local experiments.

We have not conducted enough precognition experiments including those of the SRI work, independently by my two groups, to deduce that there is any temporal drop off or effects. Short time periods of within a day in comparison to longer temporal distances need to be examined, but it all takes time.

It is apparent from my research in psychic phenomena,

as well as from research I conducted in accelerator physics that there is an "experimenter effect." In some standard physics experiments, some researchers are not able to achieve the results obtained by other experimental groups even when the apparatus and methods used are identical.

We concluded that there is no attenuation of remote perception over the distance we measured. In fact, we see that the opposite appears to occur; that is, the long-distance experiments are more significant than the local experiments. A possible confounding factor is that some of the local experiments were conducted first, and hence the learning effect appears to dominate over any effect of distance and subject participants may "try harder" for long distance experiments.

C. Group Experiments and Experiments Using Geometric Targets

In addition to the experiments analyzed in Fig. 20, which used geographical location targets, we conducted another series of 20 experimental targets that involve two- and three-dimensional geometric targets, conducted in 1976. These experiments had an overall significance with $\langle R_s \rangle = 6$ and were significant at a *p* value .000001, or 10^{-6}.

To gain more data and examine intersubject interaction, we conducted six group experiments in which we had a group of subjects view the same target at the same time. Four group experiments used abstract targets (AT_s); two used geographical locations (GL_s) as targets.

In 1971, with 56 student volunteers through UC Berkeley, we obtained a *p* value of .0001 using AT_s. In 1972, through the UC Stanford Linear Accelerator, 201 students using AT_s obtained a *p* value of approximately .001. In 1973, with 16 students at the UC Berkeley Extension who used AT_s, chance results of non-significance were obtained in 1977, though a UC Extension workshop of 35 students with AT_s produced just a .02 by chance significant results.

In 1978, with 44 subjects, and in 1979, with 32 subjects, using GL, we performed experiments with the CA Psychical Study Group with averaged results, significant at .01. However, this study did include a few very accurate responses. All experiments except the 1973 UC Berkeley experiment (which was a precognition experiment) were RTL (real-time local) experiments. The group experimental analysis was not included in our statistical analysis in Figure 20 because they utilized a different protocol.

Note that I reported the results of all the formal experiments I conducted and in which I participated. The overall significance of the results of these experiments from independent probabilities is many millions-to-one experiments against chance or random expectations. It is important to have obtained significance for both RTL and RTD experiments to test our theoretical hypothesis comparing spatial and temporal properties of the remote-perception phenomenon. At least terrestrially and for precognitive temporal intervals of several hours, there appears to be no attenuation in the significance of the effect, which is consistent with my theory.

D. Summary of Results and Analysis of Remote Perception Data

Different approaches to the statistical analysis and the concept of proof of existence of a phenomena have been conducted by a number of psi researchers which usually give similar results of the odds against chance that the correct matching is made between the subject description and the target location. Computer judging techniques have been developed such as those of the PEAR Princeton Group (Jahn, Dunne and Jahn, 1989). We will discuss the Remote Viewing Judging Technique further in Chapter 4 as used at other laboratories.

We utilized several different approaches as we conducted out experiments over the years which yield very similar statistical analysis results. To assist in objectifying the evaluation of the remote perception phenomena, we utilized a 7-point scale that has been used by other researchers and yields results similar to other judging techniques. See Table 2 about some conclusions about remote perception.

Table 2

Concluding Remarks from over Thirty Years of Remote Perception Research

1. Remote perception is a very strong phenomena.

2. The main constraints on the phenomena are psychological rather than restricted by a physical process.

3. It is difficult to design experiments to separate different types of psychic modalities.

4. Space and time are not restrictions on the access of remote information.

5. Transitory motion at the site can be remotely perceived by the subject in the Laboratory Room.

6. The Judging Processes carry some inherent problems related to its apparent lack of objectivity, i.e. the judges can also utilize the psychic modality but usually do not.

7. Computer judging is more objective but may not catch some of the more subtle aspects of remote perception.

8. We feel that learning to access one's psychic impressions has potential for improving the quality of one's life.

Conclusions

It has been an interesting, wonderful experience to research remote perception and psi phenomena in general from a rigorous experiment and theoretical method. Having a physical science background gave me a new unique perspective in the pursuit of this research. Once one conducts research, one needs to repeat the results.

A. Probability in Everyday Life

The current byword in science is the use of statistical analysis which is utilized in a number of fields from psychology to physics, chemistry to economics and in everyday life as we assess what results could be accomplished from what actions we take. We estimate that a particular car would service our needs, our marriage will work, having kids will be satisfying, happy and fun, we will enjoy a vacation in the south of France, Puerto Rico or the Bahamas.

Interestingly, not always the most probable will turn out to be the case. Sometimes the "long shots" come through! Events, millions and multimillions of events against chance occur. By the basic statistical analysis, the concept is that the most probable event is the most likely to occur and, of course, this can be obtained but is not always true (Targ and Harary, 1984).

In high energy physics, an announcement of the discovery of a new particle such as the Higgs particle at the CERN LHC (Large Hadron Collider) may be believed to exist based on a relatively few events, out of millions and maybe trillions of non-Higgs events, in the ATLAS or other detectors. Actually, the odds that remote viewing is valid, based on millions of postings on the internet, is far more probable than the reported identifications of some high energy particles.

B. Moral Implications of Spacetime Independent Psi Models

Our experiments as well as others of their type demonstrate the interconnectedness of people with one another and with all aspects of the environment over great distances. How easily we seem to influence one another and to share thoughts, perceptions, and feelings. There are thus potentially, an infinite number of ways to tune into and perhaps affect events and people across space and time.

In considering the practical applications of the various abilities we find emerging among people connected with psi research, we must consider the matter of the morality of the uses to which these human capabilities might be put. How can this capacity be used for good? How can we avoid a future in which it could, or would, be used for harm? Knowledge and ethics must go hand in hand. In an ultimate sense, we must tell the truth. To quote Albert Einstein, "We shall need to substantially change our manner of thinking in order to survive."

We consider a multidimensional geometrical model that appears to reconcile precognition and causality in a self-consistent theoretical framework. This complex physical variable model tested for its consistency with the main body of physics may also demonstrate a fundamental relation between relativity and electromagnetic phenomena. Remote connectedness of events appears contiguous in the hyper-dimensional complex space. With this model, a precognitive advantage can be calculated. The limits of a simple Lorentz invariant model of precognition are also examined. It is possible to demonstrate that psychic phenomena is not denied by the structure of physical law but is compatible with Poincare invariance and causality and the main body of physics. (See chapter 5 and 8).

References

Ben, D. and C. Honorton (1994) "Does psi exist? Reliable evidence for an anomalous Process of information transfer," *Psychological Bulletin* 115, 1, Jan 1994, pp. 4-18.

Dunne, B.J. John, R.G. and R.D. Nelson (1987) "Precognitive Remote Perception, Princeton Engineering Anomalies Research (PEAR) Laboratory Report.

Gough, W. C., E.A. Rauscher, G.B. Houck, and V. Gruye (1981) *"The Status of Research on the Physics of Consciousness: Working Models and Experiments,"* Assessment Meeting held September 15, 1980, at SRI International, Menlo Park, Calif. entered into the Congressional Records, Survey of Science and Technology issues present and future. Staff report of the Committee on Science and Technology, U.S. House of Representatives, Ninety Seventh Congress, First Session, Serial G, June 1981.

Houck, J., R.D. Nelson and E.A. Rauscher (1981) "Addendum to 'Los Angeles area to San Francisco Bay Area remote perception experiment': A Reevaluation," *Psi Research* 5, 108.

Houck, J. and E.A. Rauscher (1982) *"Surface change during warm-forming of metals by Mind Interaction"* (his term for psychokinesis or macroscopically remote manipulation). Metallurgical analysis with an SCM by Victor Kerlines, February 5, 1982.

Ioannow-Yannou, J., E.A. Rauscher and J.O. Rasmussen (1975) "X-ray Production by Relativistic Heavy Ions,"(accelerator physics, LBNL Bevatron), *Bull. Amer. Phys. Soc.* 20, p. 1500.

Jahn, R.G., B.J. Dunne and E.G. Jahn (1989) *"Spaces,"* Foundations in Physics, Vol. 10, 661-669.Analytical Judging procedures for Remote Perception Experiments." *Journal of Parapsychology* 2, p. 231.

Kaiser, D. (2011) *How the Hippies Saved Physics: Science, Countercultures and the Quantum Revival.* W.W. Norton and Co., New York: W.W. Norton and Co.

Kane, B., J. Millay and D. Brown, eds. (1993), *Silver Threads: 25 Years of Parapsychology Research*, Praeger, Connecticut, London and references therein.

Katra, J and R. Targ, (1999) *The Heart of the Mind.* Novato: New World Library.

Millay, J. Editor (2010) *Radiant Minds: Scientists Explore the Dimensions of Consciousness* and references therein. J. Millay Publisher.

Mishlove, J., Ph.D. thesis (1979) *"Interdisciplinary Sciences,"* University of California Berkeley, CA. on the psychology of remote viewing.

Mullins, H.J. and Rauscher, E.A. (1977 and 1979) *"The Scientific Investigation of Direct Perception Across Space and Time,"* Mind Space, Eileen Coly, President of PF, Report to the Parapsychology Foundation, November, New York.

Puthoff, H. and R. Targ (1976a) "Direct Perception of Remote Geographical Locations", SRI, International, Menlo Park, 1979. Originally presented at the American Physical Society Conference, 13, 2005. *Bull. AM. Phys.* 21.

Puthoff, H. and R. Targ (1976b) "A perceptual channel for information transfer over kilometer distances," *Proc. IEEE* 64, 3, March 1976, pp. 329-352.

Ramon, C. and E.A. Rauscher (1980)"Superluminal Transformations in Complex Minkowski Spaces," *Found. Of Physics* 10, pp. 661-669.

Ramon, C. and E.A. Rauscher (1982) "Remote Connectedness in Complex Geometries and its application to the nature and use of the Human Mind," *Proceedings of the Eleventh International Conference on the Unity of the Science,* Vol. 2, University of Pennsylvania, Philadelphia. PA, 1982, pp. 1423.

Rauscher, E.A. (1976a) "Some Physical Models Potentially Applicable to Observed Perception Data," *Bulletin of the American Physical Society,* Series II, 21, No. 11, December 1, 1976, pp. 1305-1306

Rauscher, E.A. (1976b) *"Remote perception as an objective science,"* HDI 6, 9, 1976.

Rauscher, E.A. (1978) *"Exploratory experiments in psychokinesis with subject Uri Geller,"* PSRL—367, June 1976, and in *Psi Realité* (France), 7, 34.

Rauscher, E.A. (1979) *"Some Physical Models Potentially Applicable to Remote Perception,"* The Iceland Papers: Frontiers of Physics Conference. Select Papers on Experimental and Theoretical Research on the Physics of Consciousness; foreword by Brian D. Josephson, edited by Andrija Ruborick, Acsentia Research Associates, Amherst, Wisconsin 54406, August 1979, PACE, Ottawa, Canada 1993.

Rauscher, E.A. (1980) *"Proposal to test the temporal modality in Remote Perception Experiments with Variable Precognitive Intervals,"* joint TRL and BRG and Washington Research Center (San Francisco). Project Report, September 1980.

Rauscher, E.A. (1982a) *"Conceptual Changes in Reality Models from New Discoveries in Physics,"* PSRL-1976, Preprint, September 1981. Published in Proceedings of the First International Symposium on Non-Conventional Energy and Technology; pg. 114, October 1981, University of Toronto, Ontario, Canada and Bulletin Amer. Phys., Soc., 35, 1982.

Rauscher, E.A. (1982b) *"Theoretical and Experimental Exploration of the Remote Perception Phenomena,"* Proceedings of the Eleventh International Conference on the Unity of the Sciences, ICS, University of Pennsylvania, Philadelphia, PA, 1982, Vol. 2, page 1443, 1982.

Rauscher, E.A. (1983a) "Multidimensional properties of consciousness and some laws of reality," in *Journal of Psi Research,* 2, pp.53-66.

Rauscher, E.A. (1983b) *"The Physics of Psi in Space and Time, Part I: Major Principles of Physics, Psychic Phenomena, and Some Physical Models,"* Psi Research, 65.

Rauscher, E.A. (1983c) *"The Physics of Psi Phenomena in Space and Time, Part II: Multidimensional Geometric Models,"* Psi Research a 93.

Rauscher, E.A. (1990) "Theoretical Models and Experimental Data concerning the Space-Time Properties of Consciousness and Remote Mental Influence," *TRL,* 16725.

Rauscher, E.A. (2010) "Longitudinal Comparison of Local and Long-distance Remote Perception Phenomena," in *Radiant Minds, Scientists Explore the Dimensions of Consciousness,* ed. J. Milley, forward by J. Mishlove, pp. 289-304.

Rauscher, E.A. and R.J. Amoroso (2011) *"Orbiting the Moons of Pluto: Solving Einstein's, Maxwell's, Schrödinger's and the Dirac Equations on Complex Space."* World Scientific: New Jersey.

Rauscher, E.A. and J. Hasted (1982) *"Preliminary Report on Strange Gauge Analysis of Remote Mental Influence on Laboratory by Grown Crystals with Subject."* Steven North (Unpublished manuscript), London.

Rauscher, E.A. and J. Houck (1985) "Los Angeles area to San Francisco Bay Area remote perception experiment," *Psi Research* 4, 48.

Rauscher, E.A., A.J. Soinski, and J.O. Rasmussen (1977) "Coupled Channel Alpha Decay Theory for Odd-Mass Nuclei. Es 253 and Fm 251," *Nucl. Phys.* A291, 386.

Rauscher, E.A. with TOSABE Group (1975) LBNL, "In-Beam Gamma Rays from Relativistic Proton and Carbon Ions on Various Targets," *Bull. Amer. Phys. Soc.* 20, 1497.

Rauscher, E.A. with TOSABE Group (1976a) LBNL, "K-Vacancy Production by 4.88 GeV Protons," *Phys. Rev.* A14, 2103.

Rauscher, E.A. with TOSABE Group (1976b) LBNL, "In-Beam Gamma Ray Spectroscopy with Relativistic Carbon Ion Beams," *Bull. Amer. Phys.* 21, 681.

Rauscher, E.A. with TOSABE Group (1977) LBNL, "Atomic K-Vacancy Production with 3GeV Carbon Ions," *Physics Lett.* 59A, 429.

Rauscher, E.A. with TOSABE Group (1978) LBNL "In-Beam Nuclear Gamma-Ray Studies of Relativistic Heavy Ion Reactions," *Nuc. Phys.* A308, 513.

Rauscher, E.A. and W. van Bise (1990) "Theoretical Models and Experimental Data Concerning the Space-Time Properties of Consciousness and Remote Mental Influences," TRL, *PSEL-60788*. Final report in fulfillment of the Buck Fine Arts and Science Grant, pp. 1988-1990.

Rauscher, E.A., G. Weissmann, S.P. Sirag and J. Sarfatti (1975) "Remote Perception of Natural Scenes Shields against Ordinary Perception," *Advances in Parapsychology, Parapsych.* Association, Metuchen, NJ : Scarecrow Press:.

Schlitz, M and E. Cruber (1980) "Transcontinental Remote Viewing," *Journal of Parapsychology* 44, pp. 305-317.

Schmidt, H. (1993) Observation of a Psychokinetic Effect under Highly Controlled Conditions. *Journal of Parapsychology* 57, Dec. 1993.

Targ, R. (2012) *The Reality of ESP: A Physicist's Proof of Psychic Abilities.* Wheaton, IL: Quest Books.

Targ, R. and K. Harary (1984) *The Mind Race: Understanding and Using Psychic Abilities.* New York: Villard Books.

Tart, C.T., H.E. Puthoff and R. Targ, eds. (1979) *Mind at Large.* Institute of Electrical and Electronic Engineers Symposium on the nature of Extrasensory Perception. New York: Praeger.

Chapter 4

Los Angeles Area
To
San Francisco Bay Area
Remote Perception Experiment
by
Elizabeth Rauscher, Ph.D.

"All ideas we form of the outer world are ultimately only reflections of our own perceptions."

— Max Planck, 1935

Table of Contents

Introduction 221
1. Experimental Design 223
2. Selected Free Response and Target Site Data 227
Target #1 — San Leandro Marina 227
Target #2 — Eucalyptus Grove 230
Target #3 — Lawrence Hall of Science 232
Target #4 — Berkeley Bart Train Station 234
Target #5 — White Mice Laboratory 237
Target #6 — Hyatt Regency Hotel 241
Target #7 — Mormon Temple 244
Target #8 — Bullock's Department Store 246
Target #9 — Freeway Walkway 249
Target #10 — San Leandro Garbage Disposal 252
Target #11 — Codornices Park 255
Target #12 — The Lawrence Berkeley National Laboratory, Bevatron 258
3. Quantitative Data Analysis and Concluding Remarks 260
Conclusion: Comparison and Evolution of Two Judging Techniques 274
References 275

List of Tables:

Table 1: Rauscher/Houck Remote Viewing Experiment 226
Table 2: Princeton Laboratory Remote Perception Questionnaire 261

Table 3: Experimental Results with the Princeton Questionnaire 263
Table 4: Viewer's Accuracy 266
Table 5: Experimental Results 266
Table 6: Empirical Chance Distribution of Scores 268
Table 7: Z-Scales and *p*-Values 269
Table 8: The Seven-Point Evaluation 273

List of Figures:

Fig. 1a Diagram of San Leandro Marina — Target #1 228
Fig. 1b Remote Viewing Drawing of San Leandro Marina — Target #1 229
Fig. 2a Photograph of Eucalyptus Grove — Target #2 231
Fig. 2b Remote Viewing Drawing of Eucalyptus Grove — Target #2 231
Fig. 3a Photograph Outside Lawrence Hall of Science — Target #3 233
Fig. 3b Photograph Outside Lawrence Hall of Science — Target #3 233
Fig. 4a Photograph of circular structure with trees — Target #4 235
Fig. 4b Photograph inside Berkeley Bart Train Station — Target #4 235
Fig. 4c Remote Viewing Drawing — Target #4 236
Fig. 5a Two Photographs of White Mouse Laboratory in UCB Life Science Building — Target #5 238
Fig. 5b Remote Viewing Drawing of White Mouse Laboratory — Target #5 239
Fig. 6a Two Photographs of Hyatt Regency Hotel Exterior and Interior — Target #6 242

Fig. 6b Remote Viewing Drawing — Target #6 243
Fig. 7 Photograph of Mormon Temple — Target #7 245
Fig. 8a Photograph of Bullock's
Department Store — Target #8 247
Fig. 8b Remote Viewing Drawing of
Bullock's Department Store — Target #8 248
Fig. 9a Photographs of Chabot
Freeway Walkway — Target #9 250
Fig. 9b Remote Viewing Drawing of
Chabot Freeway Walkway — Target #9 251
Fig. 10a Photograph of San Leandro
Waste Management location — Target #10 253
Fig.10b Photograph of San Leandro
Waste Management location — Target #10 253
Fig. 10c Remote Viewing Drawing of
San Leandro Waste Management location — Target #10 254
Fig. 11a Photograph Codornices Park — Target #11 256
Fig. 11b Photograph Codornices Park
With slide — Target #11 256
Fig. 11c Remote Viewing drawing of
Codornices Park ariel perception — Target #11 257
Fig. 11d Remote Viewing drawing of
Codornices Park elevation perception — Target #11 257
Fig. 12 Photograph of the Lawrence Berkeley National
Laboratory Control Room, Bevatron — Target #12 259
Fig. 13 Experimental results plotted p-values 267
Fig. 14 Score Distribution — Method A 272
Fig. 15 Score Distribution — Method B 272

Introduction

Between September 1982 and December 1983, Jack Houck and I conducted 12 real-time, long-distance remote viewing trials between Los Angeles and Berkeley, California area. Jack Houck was an engineer for both Douglas and Boeing aerospace companies. He had an MS degree in Aeronautical and Astronautical Engineering from the University of Michigan. This chapter presents both qualitative (free response data) and quantitative (single-tailed *p*-vales) results of the experiment. Also in all tests we utilized the Princeton University PEAR Computer Judging techniques used by both the subject and the outbound experimenter.

Although the overall results are statistically significant at the .012 level of significance, the data are of considerable interest for a better understanding of the mechanisms of remote viewing and designing further experiments. The main body of this research was published in *PSI Research,* E.A. Rauscher and J. Houck (1985) and J. Houck, R.D. Nelson and E.A. Rauscher (1986) and Vilenskaya (1985) and Haray and Targ (1985).

In the summer of 1982, the authors agreed to conduct a long-distance remote-perception experiment between the Los Angeles and Berkeley areas. The remote viewer or remote perceiver had been successful in a few preliminary local remote viewing trials. The purpose of these experiments are to determine if using an analytical judging technique developed by Dean Robert Jahn of Princeton University (Jahn, *et. al.,* 1982), provided clearer statistical results. There was also a desire to test the ELF model of psi phenomena (Houck, 1983) which suggests that there should be a decrease in the psi signal-to-noise ratio around 465 miles (750 kilometers), the approximate distance between Los Angeles and Berkeley, Oakland or San Leandro or San Francisco, California.

The protocol for the twelve trials (explained in this section) was carefully followed, so that both the remote viewer and monitor interviewer had no knowledge of the target pool or of the selected target for a given experimental trial. Rauscher was the outbound experimenter in the San Francisco Bay Area, Houck the inbound experimenter (monitor/interviewer) in the Los Angeles area and Shumway Poole as the subject (Rauscher, 1979, Houck, 1983).

Jack Houck with Elizabeth Rauscher in Los Angeles at ABC Awards Conference, 1992 where I received an award.

1. Experimental Design

A series of twelve remote perception trials were conducted over a distance of approximately 465 miles (750 kilometers). This was the first formal experimental series in which the remote viewer, Shumway Poole, participated, and the first time Rauscher and Houck worked together on a remote perception experiment. The outbound and inbound experimenters were situated in approximately a north-south orientation from each other. This was of interest to compare any statistical difference between East-West and North-South experiments. Jack Houck, the monitor interviewer, was with the remote viewer, Shumway Poole, in the Los Angeles area and also at Big Bear Lake. Thus, the inbound team consisted of the monitor interviewer and the remote viewer. Elizabeth A. Rauscher, the outbound experimenter, was in the San Francisco Bay area.

The target pool consisted of a total of thirty targets which were selected by Rauscher for uniqueness, dissimilarity, and coherence of the gestalt of the location. The target for a particular experimental trial was chosen within a one-hour drive time from the outbound person's point of departure. The target of the first experiment was selected from twelve envelopes, and a new envelope replaced the one chosen. The envelope number was chosen with an EC-499 Radio Shack calculator with a random number generator. The envelopes were unmarked and opaque, and the envelope containing the target information was counted down from the top of the pile. Each envelope contained a target site name, a two- or three-word description, location, and approximate drive time. The target pool included both indoor and outdoor targets. Whenever a new target was added to the target pool, a new envelope was used. The envelopes were shuffled every few days to avoid "psychometric leakage" and to make sure the targets in the pool remained in random order.

The duties of the outbound experimenter consisted of

(1) arriving at the target location at the specified time; (2) "experiencing" the target location for fifteen minutes, while the remote viewer attempted to describe it; (3) taking three to five real time photographs and (4) answering the 30 questions of the Princeton questionnaire (see Table 2) (Jahn, Curtis and Cook, 1982). Additional material, such as postcards and maps of the site, were also collected, if available, after the questionnaire was completed. The outbound experimenter (Rauscher) concentrated on the target so that irrelevant thoughts were not introduced, and attempted to undergo a "peak emotional experience" at the target to serve as a psychic beacon for the remote viewer. The contents of the target pool were not known to either the remote viewer or monitor interviewer. Upon the return of the outbound person to the laboratory, she stored the recorded target information made at the target site, and sealed the material in an envelope, and added a new target envelope to the target pool, and then shuffled the target pool. (Puthoff and Targ, 1978).

Feedback was achieved via a telephone call from the outbound experimenter. Both the general target description and the answers to the 30 questions were exchanged for comparison. Photographs, the target questionnaire, and a general target description were later sent to the inbound experimenter (Houck and Poole) in the Los Angeles region for initial documentation. The data from each experimental trial was also sent in a separate envelope from the Los Angeles team and maintained in a separate file folder.

Most of the experimental trials were conducted at a location in Big Bear, California, east of Los Angeles. Table I lists each of the trials by date, location of the inbound team, and the target where the outbound experimenter went on that date. On one occasion the inbound team was in the remote viewer's home, and on another date they were in a neurologist's office, both attached to EEG recorders.

All participants in the experiment were acquainted with each other before the experimental series began. As the time for each experimental trial approached, the interviewer would activate a tape recorder and announce the time and date of the trial.

Impressions and feelings were intentionally monitored in such a manner as to not disrupt the viewer's perception process. (Targ, 1979, Targ, 2012).

At the time that the outbound person was supposed to reach the target, the monitor interviewer would request the remote viewer to "go" to the target, in the present time, and to be his normal size in relation to the target. Pen and paper were available for sketches by the remote viewer. Free-response statements were solicited from the remote viewer during the fifteen-minute experiment by the monitor and also by the outbound person at the target site recorded their experience. Immediately after the free-response period, the interviewer read the questions on the Descriptor List (see Table 2) and recorded the viewer's yes and no answers.

Table 1

Rauscher/Houck Remote Viewing Experimental Trials

Trial No.	Date	Location	Outbound Target
1	09/25/82	Big Bear	San Leandro Marina
2	11/06/82	Big Bear	Eucalyptus Grove, UCB
3	11/07/82	Big Bear	Lawrence Hall of Science
4	11/14/82	Huntington Beach	Berkeley BART Station
5	11/17/82	Tustin	White Mice Laboratory, UCB
6	12/18/82	Big Bear	Hyatt Regency Hotel, San Francisco
7	07/02/83	Big Bear	Mormon Temple, Oakland
8	07/03/83	Big Bear	Bullock's Department Store
9	07/04/83	Big Bear	Freeway Walkway, Oakland
10	12/27/83	Big Bear	Garbage Dump, Berkeley
11	12/28/83	Big Bear	Codornices Park, Berkeley
12	12/29/83	Big Bear	Bevatron Laboratory, Berkeley

2. Selected Free Response and Target Site Data

This section includes a trial-by-trial comparison of the free-response drawings and statements by the remote viewer, with the pictures and descriptions of the actual targets recorded by the outbound experimenter while at the target. As one can see from the quantitative analysis of the data (See Tables 3, 4 and 5 in the Quantitative Data and Conclusions section), the twelve trials selected showed significant remote viewing results. (Rauscher and Houck, 1985 and Houck, Nelson and Rauscher, 1986).

Target #1 — San Leandro Marina

The first target was the San Leandro Marina (Fig. 1a), which is an outdoor scene. There is a marina with a small shed nearby us and a boat rental building farther away. The outbound experimenter (Rauscher) took her son along to the target site at the edge of a small inlet of water next to a large parking lot, bordered with planted trees, shrubs and bird sounds were present. The outbound experimenter's team was feeding ducks during the fifteen-minute remote perception period, starting at 4 p.m.

The remote viewer described a feeling of a foggy and damp place, a small kiosk type building, and plants and trees around. He said: "What I hear is natural...like birds." He mentioned traffic sounds and open space. Some additional quotes are: "What I'm getting is a most unlikely thing for her to go to. It looks like an empty parking lot with bushy trees around the edge, with some flowers. As I look down (he was asked to "look" from above), it just looks like a little shed." He continues, "Well, I think I see her right next to a shed, sort of looking around this side of the shed is like a road going by...that goes down. We seem to be quite high. It goes down to a major artery. I can't see for the trees." These excerpts constitute the main body of the transcript. The drawing produced by the remote viewer is shown in Fig. 1b. This remote perception seems to be quite accurate for the target area, even though the act of feeding the ducks was not perceived. It appears that the viewer and the outbound team were facing opposite directions in respect to the target, with the possibility of some time shift. It is often quite foggy in this area along San Francisco Bay and was partly foggy on this day. Even though there seems to be some good correlation between the viewer's information and the target area, only 16 of his answers to the 30 questions corresponded to the perception of the outbound experimenter (53% accuracy).

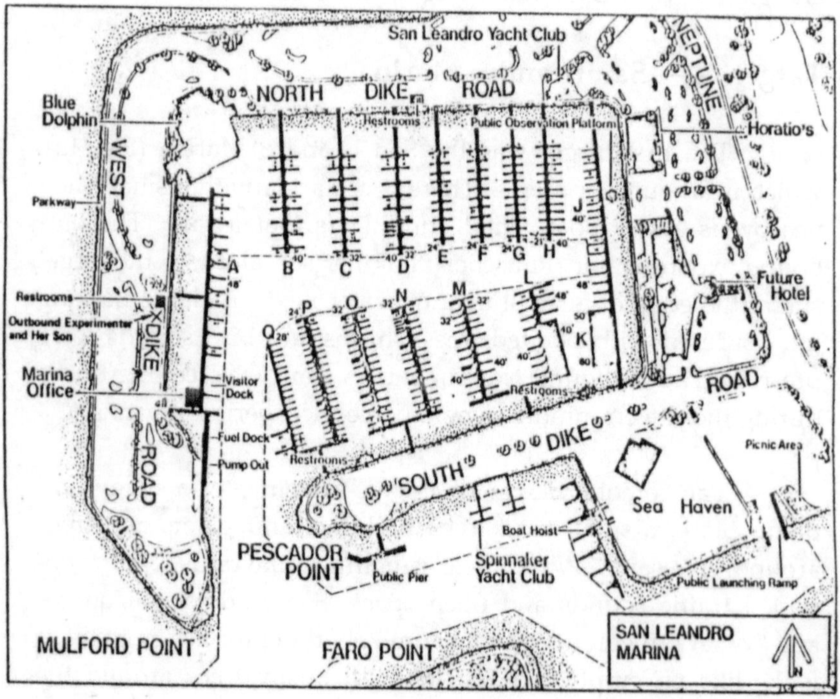

Fig. 1a

San Leandro Marina—Target #1 is a diagram of the San Leandro Marina showing where the outbound team was located, along West Dike Road near Marina office at the left on the map.

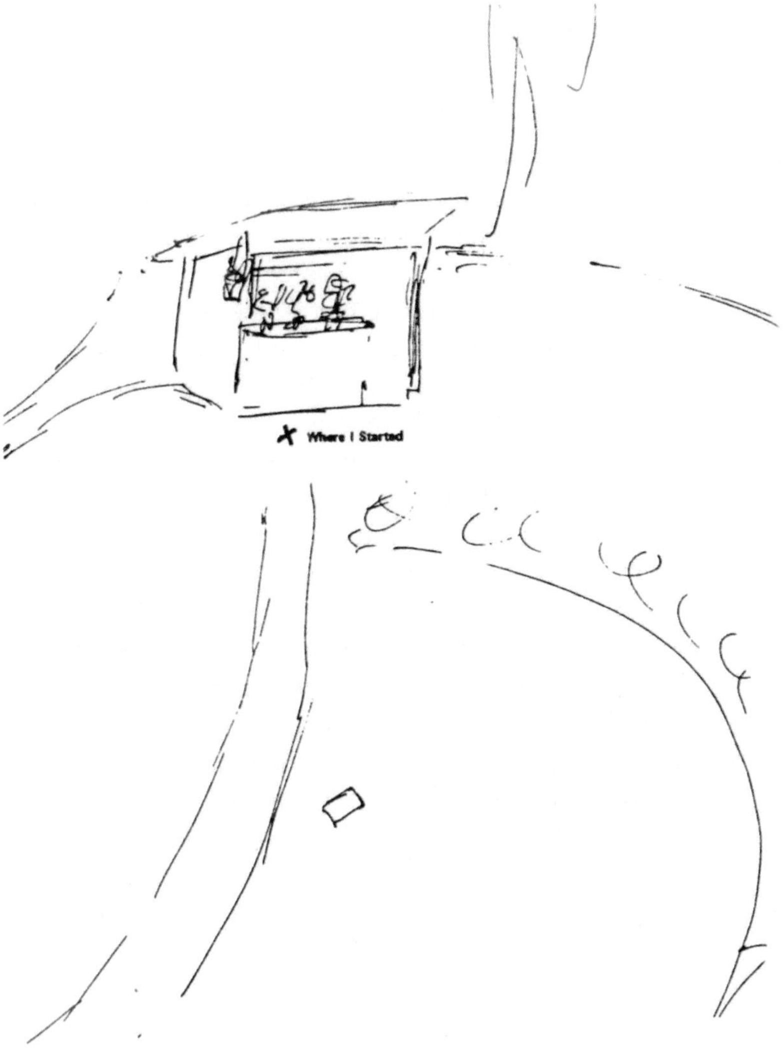

Fig. 1b Remote Viewing drawing of
San Leandro Marina—Target #1.

Target #2— Eucalyptus Grove

The second target for the second experiment was the University of California's Eucalyptus Grove, in the middle of the Berkeley campus. The intended target was a quiet outdoor area with large Blue Gum eucalyptus trees. It was noted the trees overhang the area in feathery arches. There are benches in a circle, and at 3 p.m. Saturday afternoon there were only a few other people around. It was very quiet. The closest University building is approximately 100 yards from the center of the grove. Fig. 2a contains a photograph taken in this eucalyptus grove.

The remote viewer's impression of the target was that is was outdoors, sunny and breezy, cool, large free-standing archways, a series of arches, and the outbound person yelling excitedly with a few people around. The outbound experimenter did in fact yell the viewer's name while at the target, in order to create an emotional link with the remote viewer at the time of the trial. Fig. 2b contains the sketch made by the remote viewer.

This trial appears to contain some imagery which captures the gestalt of the target location, but does not seem specifically connected to the actual target. However, on the PEAR Questionnaire, 21 of the answers to the 30 questions corresponded, resulting in a 70% accuracy. Thus, for the computer judging, this was a much better remote perception than the first target.

Fig. 2a Eucalyptus Grove—Target #2.

Fig. 2b Subject RV of Eucalyptus Grove—Target #2.

Target #3— Lawrence Hall of Science

The third target was the Lawrence Hall of Science in Berkeley (see Figs. 3a and 3b). This was again an outdoor target. The target area has a courtyard near a building-like structure with an iron gate. There is a fountain in the center of the courtyard. The building is next to a dry hill. A parking area and road cross between the hill and the building. As the outbound experimenter, I parked my car near the hill and walked across the road to the courtyard area. It was a sunny day with very thin high clouds during the perception period, at 12 o'clock noon.

Although we have retained no drawing of the session, the remote perceiver reported on tape: "It smells sort of dry. I don't know whether that means dusty dry. [True] It's as though I was up in the hills or something. It seems partly outdoors, seems partly sunny, or partly cloudy. There are a few clouds and it is not too windy. [True] Well I think I see her. It looks like she's wearing a sweater. [True] I get the impression of a natural setting of some sort. It seems like it's up in the hills, like it's carved out of a corner of a hill. . . ." [True] "O.K. from up above, I get paths. It looks like a very formal courtyard with a fountain or a stature or something like that, right in the middle of the paths, which form sort of a Greek cross [which is true]. A hedge is outside the fence and then a street."

In the experiment there was a high degree of correspondence between the target and the perceiver's description and drawing. It is interesting that his "flash" of information encompassed the parking area, general location, and first three minutes of the 15 minute period of the outbound experimenter's time. In spite of the apparently good remote perception, only 19 of the 30 questions were answered the same by the perceiver and outbound experimenter for an accuracy of 63 percent. This is a good example where 1) practice is needed in filling out the questionnaire, and 2) the outbound person should remain stationary during the perception period in order to specify one particular scene for the PEAR questionnaire method of judging.

Figs. 3a and 3b
Outside the Lawrence Hall of Science on the side of a hill overlooking a formal courtyard and fountain in the center.

Target #4— Berkeley Bart Train Station

The fourth target was the Berkeley Bart Train Station, at Shattuck and Center streets in Berkeley, California. There is a park-like atmosphere around a circular domed building. There is an eight-sided structure against a light colored roof inside the central domed building. An escalator goes down to a roped off area where the people stand in line to purchase tickets for the Bay Area Rapid Transit (BART) System. During the perception period at 4 p.m., the outbound person noted a man and woman in uniform with hats at the information area dispensing information and tickets. The outbound person rode up and down the escalator during the 15 minutes period, noting the circular dome-like structure in the main building (Figs. 4a and 4b).

The following are quotes on tape from the remote perceiver during this experimental trial:

"I see her walking along a path, maybe a park. – The path seems to lead to some sort of building. It almost looks like an observatory. It looks like it has a dome roof", then, "I think we are right in front of the building . . . Elizabeth seems to be sort of beckoning me to go inside. [True] I don't know why I keep coming back to a planetarium," He continues: "Seems like there are a lot of pictures and it seems like a souvenir kind of store thing and somebody . . . ushers, things like that. There are ropes and stands with ropes connecting. It's not well lit inside. Just a door where we came in. There is enough light, but there are no windows." [True]

Interviewer [Jack Houck]: "Are those ushers male or female?"

The remote viewer stated, "Both—Only two that I see. One seems to be a male. The guy has a hat on and it doesn't make sense why the guy has a hat on . . . She's walked in, sort of looking around. It's funny how it looks a little different than

Fig. 4a Circular structure with trees outside
at the Berkeley Bart Station.

Fig. 4b Inside Berkeley Bart Train Station—the curved ceiling.

Fig. 4c Remote Perception of Target 4.

what I think of as a planetarium. It almost looks like the seats go to one end. It seems to have it all go to one way, and then the next time I look, it looks like it goes to the center" [which the escalator did]. (Fig. 4c Subject's response.)

The remote viewer selected the original perception he obtained of the outside of the building. Twenty of the 30 answers to the questionnaire corresponded for an accuracy of 67%. In general it does seem as if the perceiver was accessing information at this target.

Target #5 — White Mice Laboratory

For the 5th trial target, from the target list randomly selected was the White Mice Laboratory in the old masonry Life Science Building at the University of California, Berkeley. The outbound experimenter (I) went into one of the laboratory rooms which had two large black laboratory benches. I then entered a very small closet-like area containing a vertical arrangement of four layers of laboratory cages in long rows. There were about 50 mice in each cage. To give the impression of a closed-in area, I closed the door to this closet-like area. I then held a small cage containing three mice and picked one of the mice up and held it by its tail. The sound of the air-conditioning unit was very loud and particularly noisy when it turned on and off. There were also arrays of water feeding bottles for the mice in the cages, and I adjusted them to attract the mice to come and drink from them. I also walked around the cages. Figure 5a includes two photographs taken at the time of this experimental trial, at 5 p.m. There were some men in lab coats when I walked in past them.

Both the inbound experimenter and the remote viewer were attached to an EEC recorder during this trial. This required that they hold very still. The remote viewer was lying down and the monitor interviewer was sitting in a chair beside him. The following are quotes from the 15-minute viewing period from the subject view:

"I just feel a cold-light breeze. Feels like we are indoors. She seems to want me to come around. . . It seems like I'm in a room. It seems like a very long room. It's fairly well lit. It looks like along the side of this thing on the wall are a lot of instruments or something, cabinets, like a bench, lots of stuff which I can't make out. Elizabeth is walking around on the other side of whatever the thing is. It's not like we are going anyplace. She's just trying to show me the whole thing, it would appear. She's putting her hands on this thing, but I don't know what it

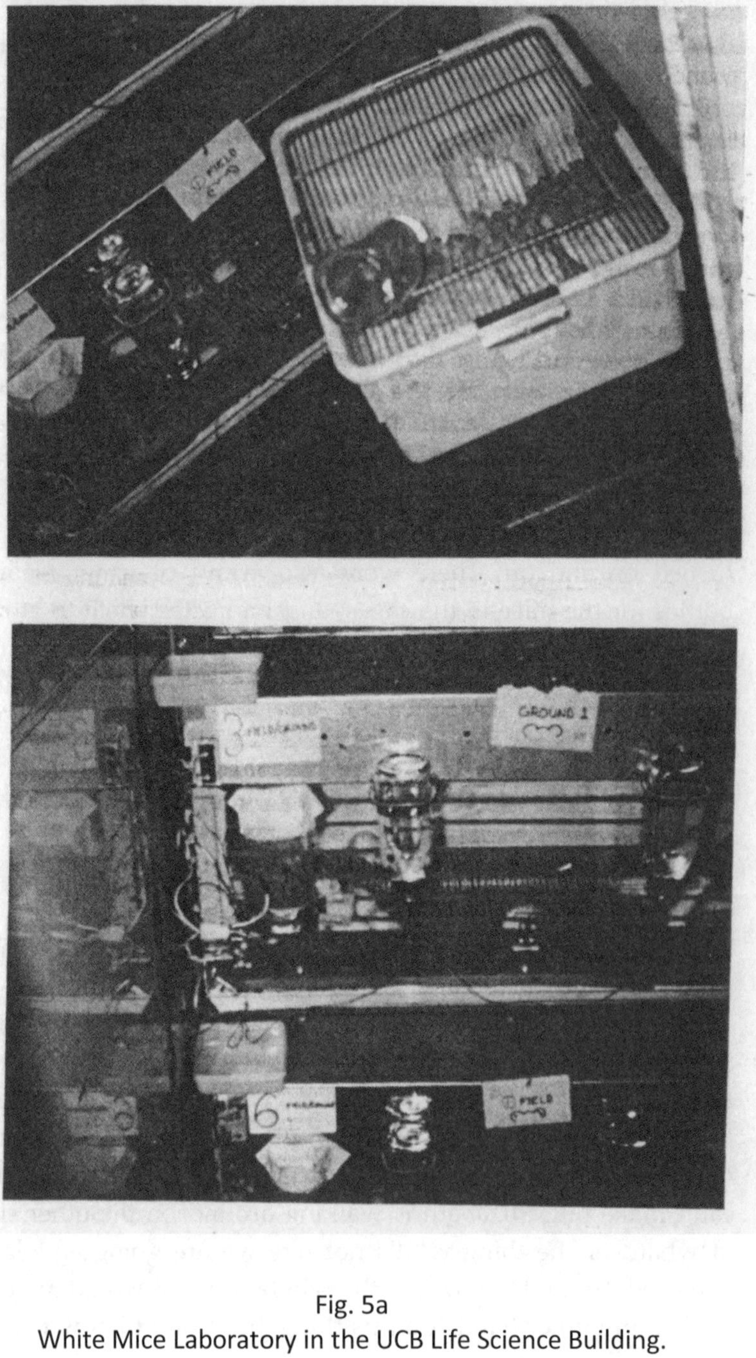

Fig. 5a
White Mice Laboratory in the UCB Life Science Building.

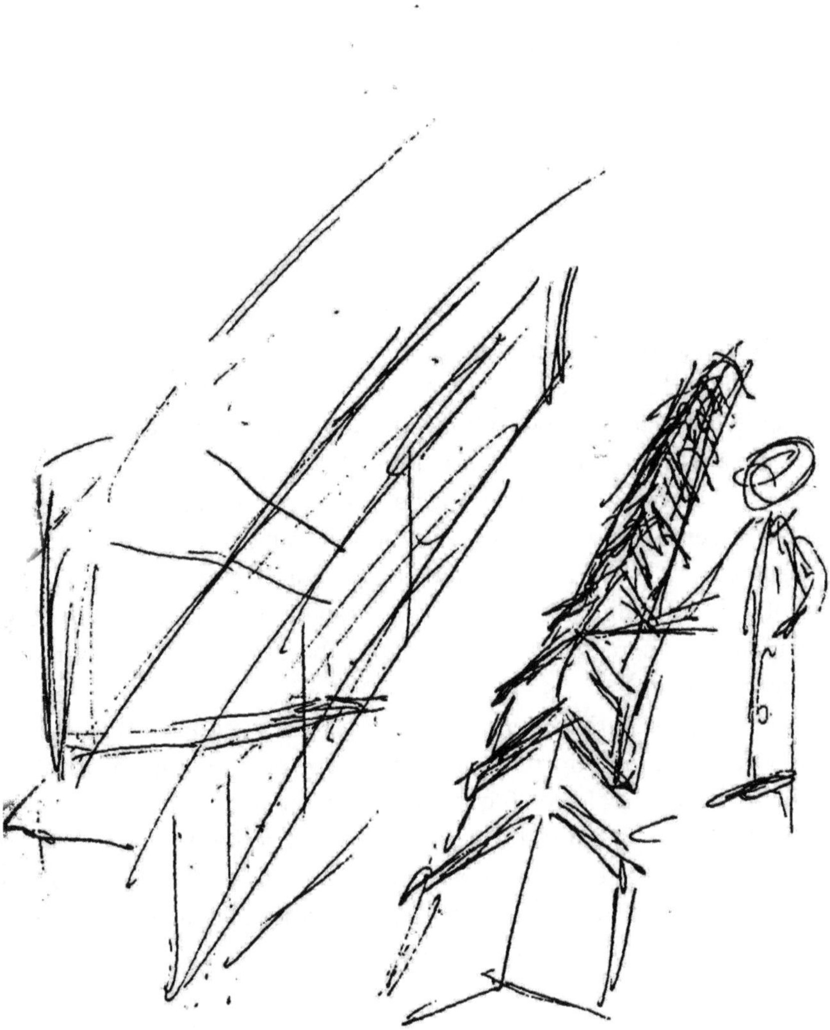

Fig. 5b Subject's response to the White Mice Laboratory.

is. It would look to be about 3-1/2 feet high, like a very thick kind of a fence or something—but it's not really a fence. I have no idea what it is. Seems shiny." [Note: the mice cages were 3 1/2 feet high and shining like a fence.]

"Quite a few steps going up from a driveway. It looks like an older building. I'm getting lab. Well, she sees me on the other side of whatever this thing is and she has her hand on what looks like a bench top or counter top. I just feel like I'm inside. Feels like a concrete building or a heavy masonry kind of building. There doesn't seem to be anybody in there. Wait a minute. People down at one end in this long room doing something, paying no attention to what we are doing." [True]

During the answers to the questions, the remote viewer said, "Seems quite loud. It is sort of a droning sound. Like a big machine. . . There is electronic equipment. There is water present, but not a significant part of the scene. The water seems to be contained in something." (Figure 4b is the drawing made by the remote viewer.)

The experimenters believe that the remote viewer was definitely getting information from the correct target in this trial. Furthermore, 24 of the 30 questions were answered the same by the remote viewer and the outbound experimenter for an accuracy of 80%. This experience was conducted in Dr. Lydia Long's office who is a neurologist and these experimental conditions may inspire the subject to try harder.

Target #6— Hyatt Regency Hotel

The target for the sixth trial was the lobby of the Hyatt Regency Hotel in San Francisco at the Embarcadero Center. The outbound experimenter was accompanied by her son, Brent Rauscher, and they arrived at 4 p.m.. This is an unusual structure with several unique features; one is an array of balconies which are vertical but start out in an over-hang fashion overhead coming together at the top. There are long, green vines which hang down from these balconies. An extremely large, nearly spherical, structure sits in the middle of this area. It is a sculpture that is primarily circular, but uneven in surface structure. The outbound team stood at the corner of the platform upon which this structure sits, glancing at it and upwards to the balconies which gave the sense of a curved roof closed in space and a curvatious atmosphere. The reverberation of general noise and distant music was prominent in this area (See Fig. 6a).

The remote perceiver described the scene that he saw as follows: "An analogy is like she climbed down sort of a ravine, sort of difficult to get down into and she thought she had an easy way of continuing getting down, but now she can't find a way to get down further. [Brent and I went down in an open view elevator at the site.] She's looking for a way to get back out of it. It is as if Brent is just standing there watching. I get the feeling that right behind her and slightly up is a huge tree or something very large; monolithic going up behind her—from up above, I get the feeling of a large rock. [The center sculpture is almost five stories high.] Huge rocks. Rocks and trees going up behind and then small rocks to the front and side. She is down . . . this doesn't make any sense at all. It seems like it is sort of up a little bit. There is foliage and stuff in front of the rocks, down below and around." A little later: "Now she is standing in a building" (Fig. 6b).

Even though most of the remote perceiver's description

does not seem applicable, looking down into this hotel lobby does seem like looking down into a ravine. Of the 30 questions, 19 were answered the same by the remote perceiver and the outbound experimenter for a 63% accuracy.

Fig. 6a The Hyatt Regency in San Francisco
(Exterior above and Interior below). Outbounder person, E. Rauscher was at the bottom center of the lower picture near the nearly circular sculpture.

Fig. 6b Remote Viewing drawing of Target 6
like E.R. in a ravine.

Target #7— Mormon Temple

For the seventh trial the target was the Mormon Temple in Oakland, California. It must be noted that trials #7, #8 and #9 were all done on the July 4th weekend, approximately six and one half months after the last experimental trial. The target is a large, white stone building with five highly pointed roof structures, some of which have gold-colored metal on them (Fig. 7). There is a fountain in front of this building, and the outbound experimenter remained outside of the building for the entire 15 minute period starting at 5 p.m.. The location of this building was on a knoll or hill-top-like area, with trees and brown grass, and a view of the San Francisco Bay.

The percipient's response to this target did not seem to fit some of the details of this target. Some of his comments were that the target was a building,"...perhaps a wooden structure, with a sort of fingernail kiosk-like thing. It looks like a half of one of those corrugated cookie-cutter-type roofs when I went up and looked down on it. It looked like sort of a park, a little knoll in a park. Hilly, grassy, trees heading for this structure." The percipient then said that he felt "mired down" when he attempted to go inside the building.

Of the 30 questions, 18 were answered similarly by the remote perceiver and the outbound experimenter for a 60% accuracy.

Fig. 7 The Mormon Temple, Oakland, California.

Target #8— Bullock's Department Store

The eighth target that came up was Bullock's Department Store, which is a large, white building with a large canvas "sail-like" roof and red bricks in the front (Fig 8a). The outbound experimenter spent the first three or four minutes outside the structure in a parking lot area which had trees and planter boxes around, and then proceeded to go inside. The most striking feature of the first observation of the outbound experimenter was that the lower half of the visual field was occupied by racks and racks of brightly colored clothing, and the upper half of the visual field was light in color as the sunlight showed through the almost white canvas roof. People walked around quietly talking and moving some of the clothes on the racks. The outbound experimenter returned to the outside for the last two minutes of the experimental time. Figure 8a contains two photographs taken at the time the outbound experimenter was at the site, 4 p.m. on July 3, 1983. [Note that the PEAR questionnaire does not fit with my and SRI style of outbound experimenter activities.]

The remote viewer's response to this target was as follows: "I do not smell anything especially strong. It seems like a lot of people running around. It seems to be relatively busy . . . it is like there are a few trees on the street, some grass and stuff . . . it is a fairly busy street in front of some building . . . looks like two stories high." [Correct]

"I am getting the color red in the building with a dark . . . it is like this is a very special building of some sort. It is like a big archway entrance. I think I see her there sort of maybe nosing around looking at stuff inside." [Correct]

The monitor interviewer suggested the word "read" for reading a sign, the percipient responded with the word "library." See Figure 8b for the drawing made by the remote viewer. This may represent an example of the monitor interviewer effecting the remote viewer percipient.

In post-hoc analysis, although the correspondence between the remote viewer's description and the target location are not as striking as in other trials in this experiment, it does appear that the remote viewer was psychically present at the target location. Of the 30 questions, 15 were similarly answered by the remote viewer and the outbound experimenter, for 50% accuracy.

Fig. 8a Bullock's Department Store, San Mateo, California, with Red brick in Front.

Fig. 8b
Remote Viewing drawing of Bullock's Department Store.

Target #9— Freeway Walkway

In trial number nine, the target for this trial was a pedestrian overpass over a freeway, in Berkeley on the border of Oakland. The sides of the overpass over a freeway were constructed out of cyclone fence material that curls up and over the top of the walkway. The overpass takes a very long circuitous route which involves some very sharp turns which loop back over 90 degrees. The surrounding area is a brown grassy hill with eucalyptus trees, vines on fences, and houses off in the distance. This site was chosen to be relatively isolated from other surrounding features. Figure 9a contains three photographs that were taken earlier at the target site. The experiment started at 4 p.m. on Sunday, July 4, 1983.

The following quotes are from the remote viewer while attempting to access this target: "Well, I get a feeling of a kind of dryness; I'm getting eucalyptus trees. . . Seems light, seems outdoors, seems like there are a lot of people nearby, but not a whole lot right where we are. . . I don't know why this popped into my head, but I suddenly see a tremendous, long structure. I suppose my 'analyzer' threw in the linear accelerator. It seems totally foolish to me. What I think I see is Elizabeth next to a great big long (structure). [True] It looks like a great big long wall. Seems warm and dry there and smells like it is kind of fresh, doesn't smell like it's in the city. [True] It feels like I can hear traffic and things not far away. . . Well, first it's a wall and then it seems like it's a moss covered thing. When the moss (covered thing) . . . it just goes into the earth. It's part of the earth. It's a pretty good size wall, but then it's just the side of a hill kind of thing. [True] It's a low structure [the freeway goes into the earth under the pedestrian overpass]. . . But there are trees all around and then when it goes into a long structure, it's like a big concrete tube. Of course, it could be all those things tied together somehow. Seems like there's a fence behind me too. What do you call them?" The monitor interviewer then

Fig. 9a
Chabot
Freeway
Walkway -
Target #9.

asks: "A chain-link fence?" [True] The remote viewer answers: "Yes, a chain-link fence . . . I need to go up higher, because all I am seeing is like hills, a few buildings here and there." [Correct]

Figure 9b contains the drawing prepared by the viewer. The viewer does seem to be getting information from the actual target of this trial. Of the 30 questions, 22 were similarly answered, for a 73% accuracy.

Fig. 9b Remote Viewing drawing of
Chabot Freeway Walkway — Target #9.

Target #10— San Leandro Garbage Disposal

A six month delay occurred before a weekend could be found to complete this experiment. This time the target location was the San Leandro garbage/Waste Management Location which was the tenth target. This site had intense odoriferous emanations and was also dominated by the noise produced by several bulldozers and was damp and cold. It had a large pit with a random supply of refuse. A number of trucks and cars were parked around this area with people dispensing refuse from their vehicles (Figs. 10a and 10b). At the end of the pit was a very large, light brown corrugated building with a peaked roof.

Three other persons accompanied the outbound experimenter to this site; this fact was unknown to the remote viewer. The outbound team participants were involved in unloading refuse with a great deal of energy and excitement. Figs. 10a and 10b are photographs taken at the scene.

The remote viewer's response to this target was that "it felt quite cold and very damp . . . Seems like there was quite a wind. . . They are attempting to create an easy target by whipping it up . . . It feels like I am in a vaulted building . . . a big parking lot . . . I am inside, wet outside. . . I see Elizabeth, she's jumping around and shouting." [True] The remote viewer continues: "The area has vivid colors." But, he adds an analytical overlay involving a church-like structure, and a cathedral with a pointed roof near a big parking lot. He adds that there are a few houses around, which is true, and also that the large barn-like building at the dump had a high-pitched, pointed roof. The remote viewer also recognized that other people were with the outbound experimenters and described a person in jeans with a leather-type jacket in his twenties. This description fits one of the outbound experimenters, Rauscher's son was wearing jeans and a leather jacket and was in his early twenties. Figure 10c contains the drawing made by the remote viewer.

Figs. 10a and 10b Photographs taken at the
San Leandro Waste Management location. Note, peaked roof on large building top (Fig. 10a).

Some of the remote viewer's transcript does appear to correspond with the target location and activities at the target, but the main area perceived by the outbound team did not appear to be perceived by the remote viewer. So, although the remote viewer appeared to be at the location, the judging correspondence was not good (14 out of 30 questions matched for 47% accuracy), perhaps because of the difference in the central focus of attention of the outbound team and the viewer and maybe because the target site is unattractive or confusing to the remote viewer.

Fig. 10c Remote Perception Drawing of Target #10, The San Leandro Waste Management, location has a Large Building with a peaked roof.

Target #11– Codornices Park

For the eleventh trial, the target came up was Codornices Park. The central features of this target are an open, park-like area with trees, bushes, walkways, and with swing sets, teeter-totters, a metal shiny slide, and a small merry-go-round. At the time the outbound team was at the target location, it was dark, cool, and partly cloudy and had rained earlier. The outbound experimenter was accompanied by two other people. This was unknown to the remote percipient (Figs. 11a and 11b).

The following are quotes from the remote percipient's description of this target which appears to be quite accurate: "A very cool, partially cloudy, damp underfoot, must have rained earlier . . . looks like stone, gray and dark . . . what I get is a courtyard of some sort . . . [True] I see a round thing, a low thing with greenery in it and a tree coming out...when I turned with the courtyard behind me looking out across a large area, there is a large, sweeping silvery thing in front of me now" [true]. Compare Subjects response Fig. 11c to Fig. 11a and Fig. 11d to Fig. 11b.

There is some analytical overlay involving questions about and responses to a building of some sort. Small buildings were present for children to play in, but no large building structure was at the site but some buildings were in sight up the hill. A little traffic noise was also noted by the subject, which was correct. In the subjects drawings, he drew a park like place with a drawing that closely resembled a slide. The accuracy for this trial was 67% (20 out of 30 questions were answered the same).

Fig. 11a Codornices Park and Merry-Go-Round.

Fig. 11b Codornices Park and slide.

Fig. 11c Codornices Park Remote Viewing drawing of Target #11 from an aerial perspective.

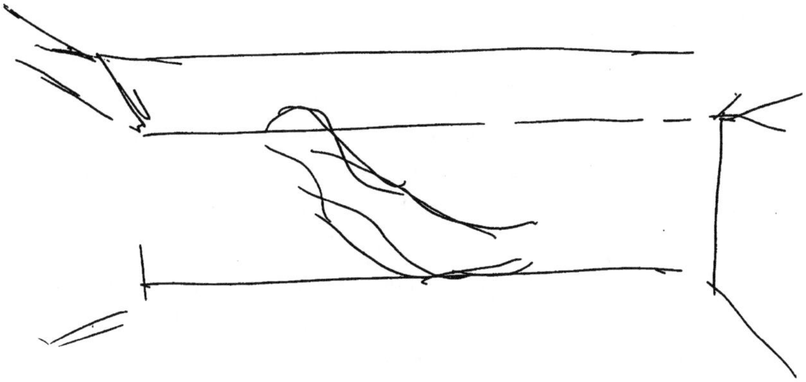

Fig. 11d Codornices Park Remote Viewing drawing of Target #11 from an elevation perspective.

Target #12 — Lawrence Berkeley National Laboratory Bevatron

The Lawrence Berkeley National Laboratory Bevatron came up as the twelve target. This target was the large Bevatron Accelerator at the Lawrence Berkeley Laboratory. The main feature of this target was a large, circular accelerator housed in a large circular building. The outbound experimenter spent the 15 minute experimental time in the control room (Fig. 12). Since the experiment was conducted over the Christmas holiday weekend, few other people were around. The control room consisted of panels of light, switches, indicators and oscilloscopes and TV monitors. The lights would often flash. The area was dominated by hardware; many wires and cables were observable. The remote perceiver's response appears to be significantly different from this target location. His response could be summarized as being outdoors in a busy-like area, downtown on a street corner. He said there were "many people around, hanging plants or something, it is like it's a hullabaloo." He talked of people showing their paintings, street vendors, etc. It appeared that he was not psychically present at the target. At the end of his transcript, the remote percipient suggested that he might be conjuring it all up. I found out later, after the completed experiment that the remote viewer was not feeling well that day and was quite sick. If one of the participants does not feel well, the experiment should be postponed. Viewer accuracy was 50%.

There is also another factor that may relate to the lack of agreement between remote perceiver's description and target location: that is, as the outbound experimenter arrived at the target location, there was some question whether or not this area would be closed for the holidays. Special permission had to be obtained to enter the target area. As this was occurring, the outbound experimenter was trying to think of an alternative location that might be used during the perception period, in a short drive time in the target pool, which was to be an outdoor target along a street in Berkeley with street venders. Note the possible displacement.

Fig. 12 The Lawrence Berkeley National Laboratory
Bevatron Control Room — Target #12.

3. Quantitative Data Analysis and Concluding Remarks

Initial Analysis

After all 12 trials in the experiment were completed, the data were submitted to the Princeton computer for judging (Nelson, 1985, 1986). With this system of analysis, one matches the target answers, as perceived by the outbound experimenter at the target, with the answers by the remote viewer, and then determines the probability that the result could have been obtained by chance or randomly. [See Table 2 for the Princeton Laboratory Remote Perception Questionnaire.]

Table 3 contains the answers to the 30 questions used in the analytical judging for each of the experimental trials by both the remote viewer participant, P and the outbound experimenter, O. Table 3 lists the percentage of yes/no answers that correspond between the viewer's and the outbound experimenter's assessment of the target for each experimental trial. It can be seen from this table that three of the trials had a correspondence of 70 or greater (Trials #2, #5, and #9). Only one trial had a correspondence to 50 (in trials 8 and 12) and one at 47% (trial 10). In Fig. 13 the success of our experimental results is plotted.

We utilized the curve labeled "weighted" which was obtained using the question weighting probability program developed for 200 typical target scenes by the Princeton PEAR group. The weighted probabilities takes into account how likely or how unique an object, sound, color, shape, outdoor, indoor, trees, water, buildings, etc. are in the average remote viewing target is most likely to be. This may be a more realistic measure and we denote it as method B and the unweighted by this method termed A.

Objects, etc. at target scenes locations are inherently of non-equal probability. The raw data shows that all but one experiment, number 10, showed positive correlation of subject

Table 2

Princeton Laboratory Remote Perception Questionnaire

1. Is any significant part of the perceived scene indoors?
2. Is the scene predominantly dark; e.g., poorly lighted indoors, nighttime outside, etc. (not simply dark colors, etc.)?
3. Does any significant part of the scene involve perception of height, or depth; e.g., looking up at a tower, tall building, mountain, vaulted ceiling, unusually tall trees, etc., or down from any elevated position?
4. From the feedback group's perspective, is the scene well-bounded; e.g., interior of a room, a stadium, a courtyard, etc?
5. Is any significant part of the scene oppressively confined?
6. Is any significant part of the scene hectic, chaotic, congested, or cluttered?
7. Is the scene predominantly colorful, characterized by a profusion of color, or are there outstanding brightly colored objects prominent; e.g., flowers, stained-glass windows, etc. (not normally blue sky, green grass, usual building colors, etc.)?
8. Are any signs, billboards, posters, or pictorial representations prominent on the scene?
9. Is there any significant movement or motion integral, to the scene; e.g., a stream of moving vehicles, walking or running people, blowing objects, etc.?
10. Is there any explicit and significant sound; e.g. auto horn, voices, bird calls, surf noises, etc?
11. Are any people or figures of people significant in the scene, other than the feedback group or those implicit in buildings, vehicles, etc.?
12. Are any animals, birds, fish, major insects, or figures of these significant in the scene?
13. Does a single major object or structure dominate the scene?
14. Is the central focus of the scene predominantly natural, i.e., not man-made?

15. Is the immediately surrounding environment of the scene predominantly natural, i.e., not man-made?
16. Are any monuments, sculptures, or major ornaments prominent?
17. Are explicit geometric shapes; e.g., triangles, circles, or portions of circles (such as arches), spheres or portions of spheres, etc. (but excluding normal rectangular buildings, doors, windows, etc.) significant in the scene?
18. Are there any posts, poles, or similar thin objects; e.g., columns, lamp posts, smokestacks, etc. (excluding trees)?
19. Are doors, gates, or entrances significant in the scene (excluding vehicles)?
20. Are windows or glass significant in the scene (excluding vehicles)?
21. Are any fences, gates, railings, dividers or scaffolding equipment prominent in the scene?
22. Are steps or stairs prominent (excluding curbs)?
23. Is there regular repetition of some object or shape; e.g., parking lot full of cars, marina with boats, a row of arches, etc.?
24. Are there any planes, boats, or trains, or figures thereof apparent in the scene?
25. Is there any other major equipment in the scene; e.g., tractors, carts, gasoline pumps, etc.?
26. Are there any autos, buses, trucks, bikes, or motorcycles, or figures thereof prominent in the scene (excluding the feedback group's)?
27. Does grass, moss, or similar ground cover compose a significant portion of the surface?
28. Does any central part of the scene contain a road, street, path, bridge, tunnel, railroad tracks, or hallway?
29. Is water a significant part of the scene?
30. Are trees, bushes, or major potted plants apparent in the scene?

Table 3
Experimental results with the Princeton Questionnaire where P stands for remote viewing perceiver and O for outbound experimenter.

Question No.	Target Number 1		2		3		4		5		6		7		8		9		10		11		12	
	P	O	P	O	P	O	P	O	P	O	P	O	P	O	P	O	P	O	P	O	P	O	P	O
1	N	N	Y	N	N	N	N	Y	Y	Y	N	Y	Y	N	Y	Y	N	N	Y	N	N	N	N	Y
2	N	N	N	Y	N	N	N	N	N	N	N	N	N	N	Y	N	N	N	N	N	N	N	N	Y
3	N	N	Y	Y	N	N	N	N	N	N	Y	Y	N	Y	Y	N	N	N	Y	N	N	N	N	N
4	Y	N	N	Y	Y	Y	N	Y	Y	Y	Y	Y	Y	Y	Y	Y	Y	Y	Y	N	Y	N	N	Y
5	N	N	N	N	N	N	N	N	N	Y	Y	N	N	N	N	Y	N	N	N	N	N	N	N	N
6	N	N	N	N	N	N	N	N	N	Y	N	Y	N	N	N	N	N	Y	N	Y	N	N	Y	N
7	Y	N	N	N	N	N	N	N	N	N	N	N	N	N	N	Y	N	N	N	Y	N	N	N	Y
8	N	N	N	N	N	N	N	N	N	N	N	N	N	N	Y	N	N	N	Y	N	N	N	N	N
9	N	N	N	N	N	N	N	Y	N	Y	N	Y	N	N	Y	N	N	Y	N	Y	N	Y	Y	N
10	N	Y	Y	Y	N	Y	N	N	Y	Y	N	Y	N	Y	Y	N	N	N	N	Y	N	Y	Y	Y
11	N	N	N	N	Y	N	N	Y	N	N	Y	Y	N	Y	Y	Y	N	N	Y	Y	N	N	Y	N
12	N	Y	N	N	Y	N	N	N	N	Y	N	N	N	N	N	N	N	N	N	Y	N	N	N	N
13	Y	N	Y	N	Y	N	Y	Y	Y	Y	N	Y	Y	Y	Y	Y	Y	Y	Y	N	Y	N	N	Y
14	Y	N	N	Y	Y	N	N	N	N	N	Y	N	N	N	N	N	N	N	N	N	N	N	N	N
15	Y	Y	Y	Y	Y	Y	Y	N	N	N	Y	N	N	N	N	N	Y	N	N	N	N	N	N	N
16	N	N	N	N	Y	Y	N	N	N	N	N	Y	N	Y	N	N	N	N	Y	N	Y	N	N	N
17	N	N	Y	N	Y	Y	Y	Y	Y	N	N	Y	Y	Y	Y	Y	N	Y	N	N	N	Y	N	Y
18	Y	Y	N	N	N	N	N	N	N	N	N	N	Y	N	N	N	N	N	N	N	N	Y	Y	N
19	N	Y	Y	N	N	N	N	N	N	N	N	N	N	N	Y	N	N	N	N	N	N	N	N	N
20	N	N	N	N	N	N	N	Y	N	N	N	N	N	N	Y	N	N	N	Y	N	N	N	N	N
21	N	Y	N	N	Y	N	Y	N	N	N	N	N	N	Y	N	N	Y	Y	N	Y	N	N	N	N
22	N	N	N	N	N	N	N	Y	N	N	N	N	N	N	Y	N	N	N	N	N	N	N	N	N
23	N	Y	Y	Y	Y	N	N	N	Y	Y	N	Y	N	Y	Y	Y	N	Y	Y	Y	N	N	N	Y
24	N	Y	N	N	N	N	N	Y	N	N	N	N	Y	N	N	N	N	N	N	N	N	N	N	N
25	N	N	N	N	N	Y	N	N	N	Y	N	N	N	N	N	Y	N	N	N	Y	N	N	N	Y
26	N	Y	N	N	N	N	N	N	N	N	N	N	N	N	Y	N	N	Y	N	Y	N	N	Y	N
27	Y	N	N	N	Y	N	N	N	N	N	N	N	N	N	Y	N	Y	N	N	N	N	Y	N	N
28	N	Y	N	N	Y	N	Y	Y	N	N	N	N	Y	N	Y	N	N	Y	N	Y	N	Y	Y	N
29	N	Y	N	Y	N	Y	N	N	N	N	N	N	N	Y	N	N	N	N	N	N	N	Y	N	N
30	Y	Y	N	Y	Y	Y	Y	N	N	N	Y	Y	N	Y	Y	N	Y	Y	N	N	Y	Y	Y	N

viewer mentation and the randomly chosen target.

A single-tailed p-value of 0.05 would have to be obtained in order for the experiment to be considered "significant." By this criterion, the experiment was judged not to be significant by unweighted procedure A. (See Figure 4). The final weighted result $p = .012$, using both the direct and weighted Princeton statistical method, is shown in Table 5. The experiment was essentially random, for the unweighted measure as judged by the computer. The data in Table 3 indicate that after the first five trials, the experiment had reached the significant level. (See Table 4 for the percentage "hits" on the Princeton judging program.) However, as the experiment proceeded with its 30 questions after the first half of the trails, there was less significance. The free-response data in the previous section demonstrate that the viewer appears to have performed some impressive remote perception on some of the trials. The long interval between the sixth and seventh trials may have been a factor in reducing the significance of subsequent trials, as practice appears to occupy a major role in obtaining good remote-perception results as seen in the single-tailed p-values for the trials (See Table 5). In Table 6, mean scores and standard deviations are given for the two methods.

Part of the problem with this experiment may have arisen from the need for the outbound person to remain fairly stationary at the target site, focusing on a single scene, in order to be compatible with the Princeton approach which analytically judges 30 questions. In many of the experimental trials, the outbound person moved around as I did in some of my past remote perception experiments, in order to enhance the phenomena, which works well with human judging procedures and the seven point scale judging. However, this made it difficult to answer the questions precisely for a single scene. The viewer answered his questions with respect to the scene he perceived, which in some cases corresponded to information at the intended target area, but the scene specified by the outbound experimenter may have occupied more area at the target. This is a general difficulty with the Princeton Judging Method.

The last three trials were conducted during two weekends, many months apart from the previous runs. The viewer was ill during the final weekend when the last three trials were conducted, unknown to me or I would have postponed the last experiments. This was a basic mistake by the experimenters, but the experiment had dragged out due to the difficulty of arranging for the trials in the schedules of three very busy people. The experiment should have been conducted at fairly regular intervals, and not at widely spaced intervals, because viewers get out of practice. In previous experiments it has been found that feeling well is important for all experiments, as is the case in my other experiments. It is also clear to the experimenters that, to use the Princeton approach, the experiment needs to be tailored to accommodate a single target scene, and that the viewers need to have practice in answering the questions.

The EEG of the viewer was taken during one trial of both participants in the inbound team. Unfortunately, the inbound experimenter's EEG was not recorded because he was improperly connected to the equipment. It had been hoped to determine if there were any frequency or phase relationships between the two EEGs, had both been obtained. Interestingly, this was the best remote-perception trial in the whole experiment. While this probably does not suggest that remote viewers and monitor interviewers need to be hooked up to an EEG recorder while conducting such experiments, it may be psi enhancing to do something unusual in an unusual environment especially if the procedure is conducted to find out more about how psi operates. Taking care to obtain more details, using specific procedures and incorporating a greater perceived challenge such as long distance *vs.* local remote viewing can yield significant statistical results.

There did not appear to be a 465 miles (750 km) drop off, so the ELF model (see Chapter 5 for details) does not appear to indicate a fall off effect or less resolution accuracy in the remote viewing results with distance. The North-South direc-

Table 4 Viewer's Accuracy
Viewer's Accuracy in each trial for unweighted probabilities.

Trial #	Viewer's Accuracy (%)
1	53
2	70
3	63
4	67
5	80
6	63
7	60
8	50
9	73
10	47
11	67
12	50

Table 5
Experimental Results
Single-Tailed *p*-Values for experimental trials

Trial	Unweighted	Weighted
1	.45	.39
2	.5	.5
3	.24	.5
4	.18	.18
5	.04	.028
6	.075	.075
7	.25	.28
8	.35	.44
9	.26	.35
10	.25	.33
11	.32	.28
12	.55	.5

Fig. 13
Experimental Results Plotted independent P-Values per trial times –1
For the Weighted and Unweighted analysis vs. Trial number

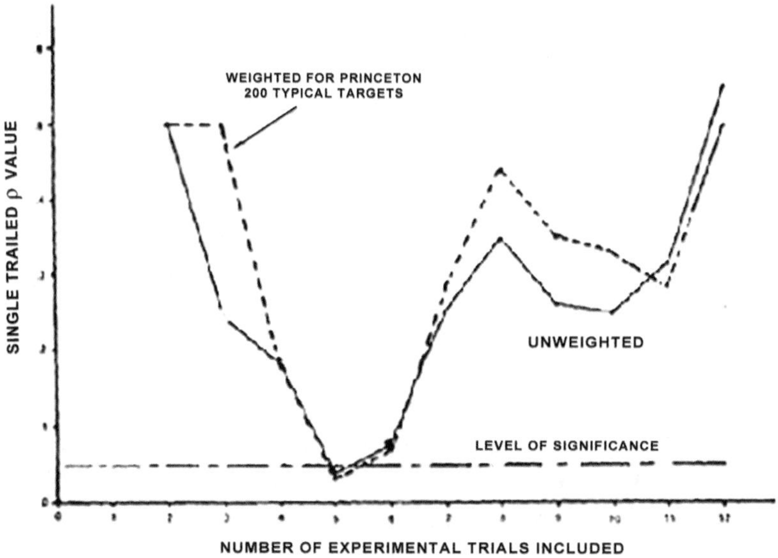

tion compared to East-West remote viewing appears to show some different results, however, both were significant (for the weighted NS Remote Viewing). However, we are comparing the work of one set of experiments including a specific remote viewer to other experiments that had a variety of remote viewers and experiments for real time local and long distance and precognitive remote perception and three different judging techniques were used; human judges, the seven point scale and the 30 question Princeton system. The only common researcher was this author. We also wished to test the Princeton (PEAR) computer judging program weighted and unweighted to object probability (Jahn, 1982).

It is shown that by comparing the results of each experimental trial to the empirically derived chance distribution, the z-score and single-tailed *p*-value of each trial can be calculated. (See

Fig. 13 where we plot the results from Table 7). Similarly the overall results of a small series of remote viewing trials can be determined by comparing the combined z-score to the chance distribution. Table 7 contains the mean and the standard deviation (one sigma) of the empirical chance distribution for the two methods (A and B) used in the original paper (Rauscher and Houck, 1985, Rauscher, 1983).

Table 6
Empirical Chance Distribution of Scores

Method	Mean	Standard deviation
A	0.551	0.1053
B	0.5042	0.1207

The values shown in Table 6 have been updated from those presented and are based on 210 sets of remote viewing trials (42,000 chance scores) (Jahn, *et al,* 1982). To make this very clear, take an example from our experiment. In Trial #1, the remote viewer answered 16 of the 30 questions the same as the outbound experimenter, resulting in 53.33% correct, Equation 1. This is also expressed as a normalized score of 0.5333, using Method A and 0.5 for method B equation. (See Table 7). If all of the question answers had matched, the normalized score would have been 1.0. Equation (1) is then used to calculate the z-score (Z_i) for an individual experimental trial:

$$Z_2 = \frac{S_T - M}{\sigma} \qquad (1)$$

where S_T is the normalized score for each trial, M is the mean of the chance distribution, and σ is the one-sigma value of the chance distribution.

The significance of this type of experiment is usually measured in terms of the single-tailed *p*-value, the probability of being able to have this or a larger normalized score by

Table 7 — Z-Scores and *P*-Values

	Method A–Unweighted			Method B—Weighted		
Trial #	**Score**	**Z-Score**	***P*-value**	**Score**	**Z-Score**	***P*-value**
1	.5333	-.1683	(.433)*	.5000	-.0351	(.486)
2	.7000	1.4153	.079	.5996	.7903	.215
3	.6333	.7817	.217	.5957	.7580	.224
4	.6667	1.0990	.136	.6115	.8889	.187
5	.8000	2.3653	.009	.6646	1.3290	.092
6	.6333	.7817	.217	.6113	.8872	.188
7	.6000	.4654	.321	.5530	.4041	.3433
8	.5000	-.4846	(.314)	.3889	-.9558	(.170)
9	.7333	1.7316	.042	.7264	1.8411	.033
10	.4667	-.8009	(.212)	.4088	-.7909	(.215)
11	.6667	1.0990	.136	.6536	1.2378	.108
12	.5000	-.4846	(.314)	.4035	-.8348	(.202)
Mean	.6194					
Composite Z		2.2518			1.5934	
Composite *P*			.012			.056

*** ( ) means the trial is worse than chance (i.e., $p > .5$)**

chance. A *p*-value less than 0.05 is generally regarded as a "significant" result in the parapsychology community. The *p*-value can be determined by table look-up in any statistical textbook or can be approximated by the following method (Abramowitz and Stogun, 1968); where *p* is the *p*-value,

$$p = f(Z_i)(b_1t + b_2t^2 + b_3t^3 + b_4t^4 + b_5t^5) + \varepsilon\,(Z_i) \qquad (2)$$

$$f(Z_i) = \frac{e^{(-Z_i^2/2)}}{(2\pi)^{1/2}}, \quad \text{and} \quad t = \frac{1}{1 + rZ_i}, \quad \text{and} \quad r = 0.2316419,$$

$$b_1 = .31938153,\ b_2 = -.356563782,\ b_3 = 1.781477937$$

$$b_4 = -1.821255978,\ b_5 = 1.330274429,\ \text{and}\ |\varepsilon\,(Z_i)| < 7.5 \times 10^{-8}$$

where a value b_x exists for every number ε of the z-score (Z_i). Once the individual z-score is determined for each remote viewing trial, they can be combined using the standard Stouffer procedure shown in Equation 3 to obtain the Z_c -score for an experiment containing n trials,

$$Z_c = \frac{\overset{n}{\underset{I=1}{Z_i}}}{n^{1/2}} \qquad (3)$$

The single-tailed *p*-value for the combined trials can be obtained using Equation 2 and substituting Z_c for Z_i.

In order to see the results of an experiment as the experiment trials are accomplished, one could use the preceding method to obtain the Z_c-score and the *p*-value of the experiment to date. After the next trial, the new trial Z_i-score can be calculated and added into combined result using Equation 3. Another manner to examine the results of the overall experiment is to determine the distribution for the experiment using the calculated scores for both methods. In using the Princeton Empirical Chance Distribution, the largest Gaussian distribution, centered on the Princeton chance mean, can be determined to fit under the experiment distribution.

Then by subtracting this chance distribution from the experiment distribution, the resulting residue distribution can be treated as that portion of the experimental results attributed to psi functioning. These calculations and plots are shown in Table 7 and Fig. 13. Table 7 contains the results of our Los Angeles Area to San Francisco Bay Area remote viewing experiment. For both Princeton Method A (unweighted) and Method B (weighted by the a prior descriptor probabilities), the score, Z_i -score, and single-tailed *p*-value are listed for each trial. At the bottom of Table 7 are the results for the overall experiment. The mean is the average of the individual trial scores. The composite Z is the Z_c-score as calculated using Equation 3. The composite *p* is the *p*-value for the overall experiment using the composite Z and Equation 2. The chance distribution against which these values were compared is the Princeton Empirical Chance Distribution described in Table 6. The values shown in Table 7 are calculated using the Princeton analysis on their computer system and program which maintained the accuracy to eight significant figures. We used the trial scores in Table 8 and, using Equations 2 and 3, the resulting numbers would have minor differences from the table in the fourth significant figure.

It can be observed from Table 7 that the composite *p*-value for the experiment was significant (< 0.05) at 0.012 when using Method A (unweighted) and almost significant at 0.056 when using Method B (weighted). The history of the composite *p*-values as the experiment proceeded is shown in Fig. 13. This type of presentation is the of interest to the experimenter as the experiment is in progress.

The Princeton method of displaying the residual distribution (that component of the experimental results due to psi) was applied to this experiment and the results are shown in Figs. 14 and 15 for Methods A and B respectively. The distribution shown for this experiment in these figures used a bin size of 0.1. This was an arbitrary choice which fortuitously resulted in a "normal" looking distribution. Of course it is desirable to have many experimental trials in order to obtain a smooth dis-

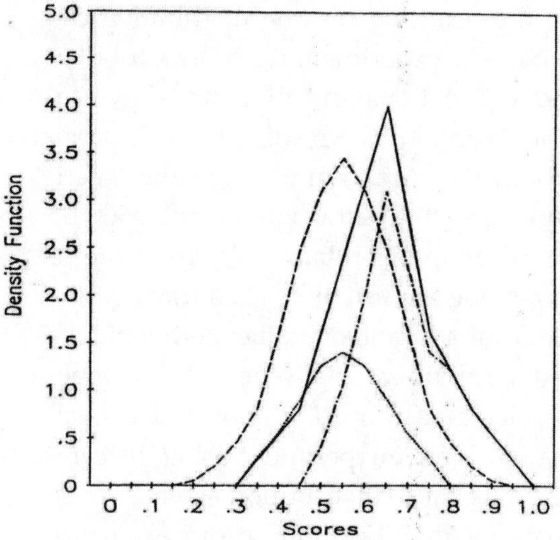

Fig. 14
Score Distribution
Method A
(Unweighted).

Legend

__________ Experiment

- - - - - - - Chance

.... Exp. Chance

__________ Residue (lowest peak)

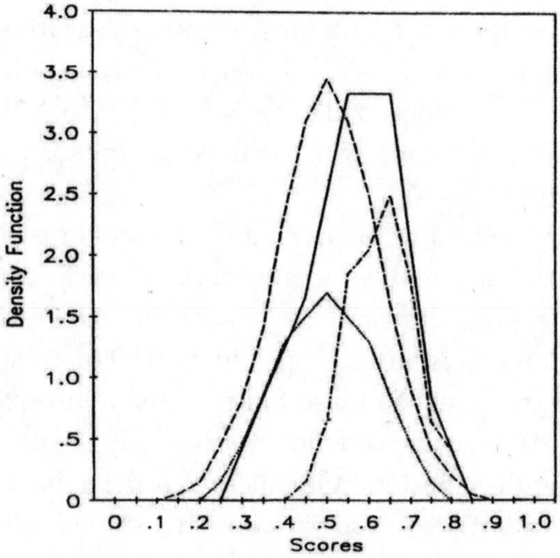

Fig. 15
Score Distribution
Method B
(Weighted).

tribution and a good curve fit of the data, if that method is employed. The resulting residual distribution for Methods A and B are both clearly shifted to the right of the Princeton Empirical Chance Distribution, consistent with this being a significant experiment.

Table 8
The seven Point Evaluation
for the Twelve Los Angeles to Bay Area Trials

Experimental Trail	Seven Point Evaluation
1	5.5
2	4.5
3	5.0
4	4.0
5	6.0
6	3.0
7	2.0
8	3.0
9	6.0
10	2.5
11	3.5
12	0

Conclusion: Comparison and Evolution of Two Judging Techniques

It appears to me that each new team of remote viewers and inbound experimenters, etc. requires a learning curve. Shumway Pool and Jack Houck were new to the remote viewing experience and each of us needed to learn to work together. I was unaware that Shumway Pool did not feel well during the last target sites. I have found that feeling good greatly enhances the psi process and on days when a member of the team is not up to par, the experiment should be postponed.

I have found that some movement and interaction at the target of the outbound experimenter appears to enhance the remote viewing phenomena, at least for some subject participants. This procedure did not appear to work well for remote perceiver Pool when the Princeton Judging Procedure was applied. In Table #8 we list the experimental run number and the corresponding number on the Seven Point evolution scale are utilized in Chapter 3.

To compare the Princeton judging technique with the Seven Point scale for remote viewing—for transcript to target using the analysis of our remote viewing experiments (see Chapter 3), in some cases, the Princeton Evaluation scoring shows stronger correspondence between target and transcript and in some cases the Seven Point evaluation scale did (Targ, 2012). We used a preliminary form of this method in the 1970's and 1980's. Also, the Seven Point scale yielded a harsher judgment. For example, on the Seven Point scale, target-transcript number 12, received a zero or psi missing, but 50% on the Princeton scale.

In general, the two judging procedures yielded a very similar evaluation for this twelve experiment trial. There were some good correspondences between subject mentation and target and some non-correspondences with this inexperienced remote viewer. The comparison of East-West and North-South long distance remote viewing cannot be comprehensively made in any detail, but both are statistically significant.

References

Abramowitz and Stegun (1968) *Handbook of Mathematical Functions,* National Bureau of Standards.

Haray, K. and R. Targ (1985) "A Few Notes About the Los Angeles Area—San Francisco Bay Area Remote Viewing Experiment," *PSI Research* 4, pp. 90-91, September/December.

Hertz, H.R. "Ueber sehr schnelle electrische Schwingungen", Annalen der Physik, vol. 267, no. 7, p. 421–448, May 1887 doi:10.1002/andp.18872670707

Houck, J. (1983) "Conceptual Model of Paranormal Phenomena," Archaeus, 1, No. 1, pp. 7-24.

Houck, J., R.D. Nelson and E.A. Rauscher (1986) "Addendum to "Los Angeles area to San Francisco Bay Area remote perception experiment:" A Reevaluation," *PSI Research Journal* 5, pp. 108-115.

Jahn, R.G., T.A. Curtis, and I.A. Cook (1982) *Analytical Judging Procedure for Remote Perception Experiments* - II. *Ternary Coding and Generalized Descriptors,* Princeton University, School of Engineering/Applied Science, Princeton, NJ: Princeton University, PEAR Group.

May, E.C., S.J.P. Spottiswoode, Utts, J.M. and James, C.L. (1995) "Applications of Decision Augmentation Theory" *Journal of Parapsychology* 59, 231.

May, E.C., J.M. Utts and S.J.P. Spottiswoode (1995) "Decision Augmentation Theory: Towards A Model of Anomalous Mental Phenomena," *Journal of Parapsychology* 59, 196.

Maxwell, James Clerk (1873), A treatise on electricity and magnetism Vol I and II, Oxford : Clarendon Press.

Mishlove, J., Ph.D. (1979) thesis, "Interdisciplinary Sciences," University of California Berkeley, CA on the psychology of remote viewing.

Nelson, R. (1985, 1986) conducted the judging analysis using the Princeton Remote Viewing computer program.

Puthoff, H., and R. Targ (1978) Standard Remote-Viewing Protocol (Local Targets) (SRI International, November) and private communication and joint work.

Ramon, C. and E.A. Rauscher (1980) "Superluminal Transformations in Complex Minkowski Spaces," *Foundations in Physics* 10, Nos. 7 and 8, pp. 661-669.

Rauscher, E.A. (1976) "Some Physical Models Potentially Applicable to Observed Perception Data," *Bulletin of the American Physical Society*, Series II., 21, No. 11, pp. 1305-1306.

Rauscher, E.A. (1978) "Complex Coordinate Geometries in General Relativity and Electromagnetism," *Bulletin of the American Physical Society*, Series 11, 23, No. 1 (January), pp. 84-85.

Rauscher, E.A. (1979) "Some Physical Models Potentially Applicable to Remote Perception," In A. Puharich, ed., Forward, B. Josephson, *The Iceland Papers: Selected Papers on the Experimental and Theoretical Research on the Physics of Consciousness* Amherst, WI; Essential Research Associates, pp. 50-93.

Rauscher, E.A. (1983) "The Physics of PSI Phenomena in Space and Time, Part II: Multidimensional Geometric Models," *PSI Research* 2, 93.

Rauscher, E.A. and J. Houck (1985) "Los Angeles Area to San Francisco Bay Area Remote Perception Experiment," *PSI Research* Journal of PRG 4, pps 48-78.

Rauscher, E.A., G. Weissmann, S.P. Sirag and J. Sarfatti (1975) "Remote Perception of Natural Scenes Shields against Ordinary Perception," Advance in Parapsychology, Parapsych. Assoc., Scarecrow Press.

Targ, R. (1979) "Direct Perception of Remote Geographical Locations," In A. Puharich, ed. *The Iceland Papers: Selected Papers on Experimental and Theoretical Research on the Physics of Consciousness.* Amherst, WI: Essentia Research Associate, pp. 18-47.

Targ, R. (2012) *The Reality of ESP: A Physicist's Proof of Psychic Abilities.* Wheaton, IL: Quest Books.

Targ, E. and R. Targ (1986) "Accuracy of Paranormal Perception as a Function of Varying Target Probabilities," *Journal of Parapsychology* 50, 17.

Vilenskaya, L. (1985) "Remote Viewing—Questions and Answers," Ed. L. Vilenskaya, *PSI Research* 4, pp. 89-97.

Chapter 5
The Physics of PSI Phenomena in Space and Time
by
Elizabeth A. Rauscher, Ph.D.

"It is not too far-fetched to say that if psychic phenomena had not been found experimentally, they might have been predicted by an imaginative theoretician."

— Brian Josephson, 1979

Table of Contents

Introduction 281

1. Major Principles of Physics and Psychic Phenomena: Poincaré Invariance, Analyticity and Unitarity 285
2. Examination of Some ELF Models of PSI 289
3. Multidimensional Geometric Models and Remote Perception 297
4. The Scientific Method and Multidimensional Models 303
5. Multidimensional Geometric Models and their Implications for Remote (PSI) Perception Phenomena 307
6. Multidimensional Geometric Models of Remote Perception in Space and Time 317
7. Other Models Related to The Mind/Body Issue 336
   - A. The Holographic Model of Pribram-Bohm 336
   - B. The Houck Emotional "Multidimensional" Space Model and Stapp's Quantum Mind/Matter Model 337
   - C. Kaluza-Klein Geometries 339
   - D. Multidimensional Model: Descartes Geometry 340
   - E. Hyperspace Physics of Sirag 340
   - F. Some Comments on Quantum Models of PSI 344
8. Remote Mental Influence, a Brief Summary 346
   - A. Healing and Psychokinesis as a Negentropic Process 346
   - B. Remote Mental Influences on Materials 347
   - C. Information Theory, Entropy and Thermodynamics 350

Conclusion 357

Appendix I: Complex Eight Space Predicts Faster Than Light Tachyonic Signal Propagation 360
Appendix II: Flow Diagrams 361
Appendix III: Faraday Cage Experiments.................................... 363
References.. 364

List of Tables

Table 1: Areas of Physics Potentially Relevant to Modeling PSI Phenomena 284
Table 2: Principles of Physics and Their Suggested Relationship to Psychic Phenomena 286
Table 3: Frequency, Wavelength and Energy list.................... 294
Table 4: Possible Difficulties with ELF Hypothesis... 295
Table 5: Further Tests of the ELF Should Involve 296
Table 6: Properties of Consciousness and Thoughts... 302
Table 7: Predictions of Complex Geometries........................... 305
Table 8: Regions of Space or Spacetime on the Minkowski Light Cone... 308
Table 9: Properties of Spacetime and Possible Velocities of Propagation... 330
Table 10: Some Categories of Theoretical Models of PSI 355

List of Figures

Figure 5a The Map of Physics and Psychic Phenomena 288
Figure 5b Causality and Precognition 298
Figure 5c Spacetime and PSI 299
Figure 5d The Light Cone 306
Figure 5e Space-Like Region on the Light Cone 309
Figure 5f Three classes of Minkowski Diagrams 312
Figure 5g Minkowski Light Cone and World Line and Events 314
Figure 5h Complex Time Model 323
Figure 5i Future, Past, Present, Remote, Normal Graph 324
Figure 5j Complex Space Multidimensional Model 326
Figure 5k Relationship of Multidimensional Geometrical Theories 328
Figure 5l Models of Possible Velocity Propagation in Complex Eight Space 329
Figure 5m Relationship of some Multidimensional Geometries 334
Figure 5n Relative Force Strengths 342
Figure 5o Appendix II Flow Diagram 361
Figure 5p Appendix II Flow Diagram 362

Introduction

An extremely strong database of the spacetime properties of consciousness has been developed by various research teams. In examining the space and time properties of consciousness, we can determine certain physical conditions and properties of the conscious perceptions termed psi phenomena. We can consider a domain of action of the mind which overlaps the domain of action of the physical aspects of reality, including our body. This picture is consistent with a mind/body dualistic view. What we term psi (or psychic) comprises that unique set of properties of consciousness which can transcend space and time, and is locally independent. This includes remote perception, psychokinesis, and psychic healing (remote mental and matter interaction).

We define psychokinesis from the words 'psychic' which means mind, and 'kinesis' which means motion. The psychic database has specific enough conditions to allow us a set of unique clues about the physical conditions on spacetime ($s^2 = X^2 - c^2t^2$) and matter (or matter-energy, $E = mc^2$). In this book, we consider primarily the phenomena of consciousness which is termed Remote Perception or the ability to access remote information, blocked from any ordinary channels of informational access.

Certain human psychological, physiological, philosophical and epistemological considerations are relevant to a discussion of psi phenomena, but here we turn our attention to the relationship between physical law and physical effects of the mind, such as recording information about a distant location and remote mental influence. A thorough and comprehensive understanding of psi phenomena involves many disciplines and their interrelationships. Presently, our consideration of other fields of knowledge involves our definition and discussion of what we will consider as the physical phenomena of psi as, say, opposed to the psychophysiological nature of psi. Detailed studies of mind/brain issues in terms of neurophysiology and neuro-anatomy and their correlation with the epistemological process is addressed elsewhere. We are on the threshold of a new fundamental and very significant understanding of ourselves in the universe.

The purpose of this chapter is to use the "real time" and precognitive psychic Remote Perception experiment database to deduce the relevant physics principles and laws of paranormal functioning (Ben and Honorton, 1994; Puthoff, 1976,a, 1976b, 1977; Jahn and Dunne, 1982, 1987). Not only can we determine a relationship between a physical law description of events in spacetime from a careful consideration of these experiments, but we believe we can use description of the physical models to generate designs for new psi experiments and also to generate theoretical models that lead to new physics. (Rauscher, 1970, 1971, 1972a, 1972b, 1972c, 1973, 2005, 2011; Rauscher and Busier, 2016).

One of the common objections to the existence of psychic functioning is that it is denied by the laws of physics. We believe that we can not only demonstrate that the phenomena and the laws and content of physics are compatible with psi functioning, but that we can use physics principles to help us understand psi phenomena and that the psychic database may well shed light on some of the current problems in physics.

We also examined the predictions and limits of specific physical theories in modeling psi phenomena (Rauscher, 1976, 1978a, 1983a, 1983b, 1983c, 2010; Rauscher and Amoroso, 2006, 2011; Amoroso and Rauscher, 2009, 2010, 2011; Ramon and Rauscher, 1980; Rauscher and Targ, 2001, 2006; 2008). The areas of physics we have considered as potentially relevant to modeling psi phenomena are listed in Table 1.

We demonstrate that multidimensional models appear to hold the best possible position in developing a comprehensive picture of psi and its action in an extended structure of the spacetime metric. We have also examined the implications of the multidimensional model for the observer/participator issue. We have solved the Schrödinger equation and Dirac equation in multidimensional geometries which shed light on the observer/participator quantum mechanical issue (Rauscher, 1981, 2006a, 2006b, 2010; Rauscher and Amoroso, 2008, 2011; Rauscher, Rowland, Amoroso, 2015). The models involving special relativity and quantum theory, which we have considered, are not necessarily mutually exclusive (Ramon and Rauscher, 1980; Rauscher, 1979, 1983b, 1983c, 1983d, 1983e, 2002; Rauscher and Targ, 2001, 2006, 2008; Rauscher and Amoroso, 2011).

In the first section of this chapter, we describe the major categories of psi and their interrelationship with the major principles of physics and their possible relationship to psi phenommena. In Section 2, we discuss some models of psi and their shortcomings and why the complex multi-geometric model is a superior model, in that it better describes psi. We will also discuss briefly the ELF hypothesis of psi since it is one of the older models proposed by a number of authors and is also readily testable. In Sections 3, 4, 5 and 6 in this chapter, we present a specific multidimensional model and its implication for the psi database and the main body of physics.

The scientific method operates by the interaction of theoretical hypothesis and its descriptions, predictions and the experimental test of these hypotheses. The new extended body of data now allows for fuller and more comprehensive discussion models of psi. Each step defines a new and better worldview. We feel that the development of a more accurate model of psi will significantly advance the field of research on the nature of our consciousness.

Table 1
Areas of Physics
Potentially Relevant to Modeling PSI Phenomena

1) Multidimensional macroscopic geometric models involving greater than four dimensions (three of space and one of time) which accommodate and predict the nonlocal nature of psi and physics.
2) Quantum mechanical models involving non-locality or Bell's theorem (Bell, 1964; Rauscher and Amoroso, 2011; Eberhand, 1978; Costa de Beauregard, 1970, 2002; Herbert, 1978, 1982, 1988; Josephson, 1991; Radin, 1997,2006; Stapp, 1975, 1981, 1998) and the EPR paradox (Einstein, Podolsky and Rosen, 1935) which appear to apply to any theory compatible with the statistical predictions of quantum theory which appears to demand that events remain correlated over remote distance, that is, remote interconnectedness. This theorem is strongly confirmed by experiment (Clauser, 1974; Aspect, 1992; Gisin, et. al, 1998a, 1998b).
3) The quantum observer/participant issue of measurement, which may relate to psychokinesis (Schmidt, 1978a, 1982; Crussand and Bouvaist, 1978; Rauscher, 1978a,1984) and psychic healing (Rauscher and Rubik, 1979, 1980, 1983; Rubik and Rauscher, 1981, 1993).
4) We have also examined energy, information and entropy considerations for models of psychokinesis, psychic healing and psychometry (Rauscher and Rubik, 1979, 1983; Rubik and Rauscher, 1993; Rauscher, 1975, 1982a, 1982c,1990).
5) The possibility that psi is mediated by extremely low frequency (ELF) electromagnetic waves (Rauscher and van Bise, 1990).
6) Also advanced-potential models may occupy a role in modeling precognition as well as relating to Bell's theorem (Rauscher, 1982, 1983a, 1983b, 1984; Rauscher and van Bise, 1990; Rauscher and Amoroso, 2010) and the ELF model.

1. Major Principles of Physics and Psychic Phenomena: Poincaré Invariance, Analyticity and Unitarity

Three major universal principles are used to determine the structure and nature of physical laws. These are Poincaré invariance and its corollary Lorentz invariance (which expresses the spacetime independence of scientific laws), analyticity (which is a general statement of causality), and unitarity (which can be related to the conservation of physical quantities, such as the conservation of energy and charge). These principles can apply to macroscopic, as well as microscopic phenomena. For example, these principles act as a condition on the wave function description in quantum mechanics, as well as the macroscopic phenomena of relativity. The quantum description of elementary particle physics has led to the detailed formulation of the analyticity principle in the complex momentum plane (Chew, 1964; Rauscher, 1979). Such phenomena as Bell's theorem involve microphysical phenomena, but may have macro-physical implications (Rauscher, 1979; Rauscher and Amoroso, 2011).

In Table 2 we list the three principles of physics with a brief explanation and their application to psychic phenomena, by our complex coordinate model; for example, Poincaré invariance relates to remote perception, analyticity relates to precognition, and unitarity relates to psychokinesis. Unitarity may also involve the physics of vacuum state polarization.

We have studied the relationships of these models to psychic phenomena in detail. In particular, we are considering a multidimensional geometric model which appears to reconcile precognition and causality in a self-consistent theoretical framework. We have examined complex physical variables which can be tested for their consistency with the main body of physics and may also demonstrate a fundamental relationship between relativity and electromagnetic phenomena. With this model we can calculate a precognitive advantage (Rauscher, 1971, 1979).

Table 2
The Principles of Physics And Their Suggested Relationship to Psychic Phenomena

We list the major principles of physics (top row), a brief statement of their interpretation (second row), and the aspect of the theoretical model (third row) that applies to a particular category of psychic phenomena (fourth row).

Principle	**Poincaré Invariance**	**Analyticity**	**Unitarity**
Brief statement of principle	Homogeneity of Spacetime	Causality	Conservation of Probability
Physical theory related to the principle of physics and Psychic Phenomena	Complex Geometry and Remote Connectedness	Complex Geometry	Entropy Models and Vacuum State Polarization
Psychic Phenomena	Remote Perception	Precognition	Psychokinesis

Fig. 5a (following page) called the 'Map' of Physics and Psychic Phenomena represents a possible relationship between physical theory and psychic data. The term PK stands for psychokinesis and RV stands for remote viewing or remote perception. We demonstrate that psychic phenomena is not denied by, but is compatible with, Poincaré invariance, and analyticity or causality and unitarity or conservation (Rauscher, 1979, 1996; Rauscher and Amoroso, 2011). The term CPT stands for charge, parity and time reversal invariance or the violation of it. In applying physical models or theories to the psychic phenomena database, it is possible to make predictions and design experiments for further research; that is, apply the methodology that defines a science. This is one of the major goals of our research.

There are many fruitful areas in physics to explore in relation to paranormal phenomena. One area we have explored in detail is the description of causality in relativity and the application of this condition to our higher dimensional space. We believe these models to be information accessing channels. It is most vital in constructing any model of psychic phenomena to use a "correspondence" principle such that we do not hypothesize a physical theory which is inconsistent with the prediction of and compatibility to normal physical data. Any model of psychic phenomena should be pragmatic, in that it is consistent with the phenomena, predicts the outcome of experiments, and is also consistent with the main body of physics.

There are very few restrictions on the ability of human consciousness to access remote information. These appear not to be limited by physics, but rather by psychology. Therefore, we proceeded with the development of a model of Remote Perception and then constructed it to be consistent with the psychokinetic (PK) phenomena, which is more difficult (Rauscher and van Bise, 1990).

We proceed from concepts developed in physics which describe the manner in which events occur in space and time. Einstein's relativity theory is designed to deal with the relationships between causes and effects in spacetime in a very careful

Figure 5a

'Map' of Physics and Psychic Phenomena

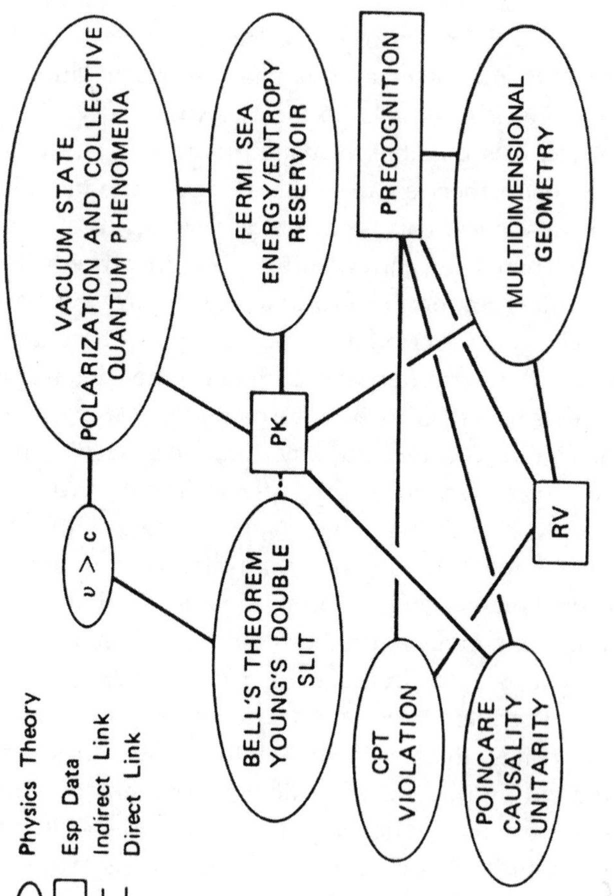

and precise manner. Remote Perception is the correlation of causal events in spacetime such as between the activities of an outbound experimenter and a subject's description which is generated and recorded in a locked laboratory.

It may be that upon detailed examination, most of the constraints of psi phenomena are primarily psychological rather than physical in origin. Inhibition and attention may not be physical constructs or limiting conditions on psi, but, rather, psychological restrictions which exist and may have physical consequences. It is therefore crucial to examine the belief structure of the research participants in order to understand their psychological and perhaps psychic conditioned responses and constraints that limit psi abilities (Harary, 1982a, 1982b).

The ELF (extremely low frequency) and other electromagnetic models have implications for the unitarity or conservation of the energy principle. There may also be local Lorentz invariance conditions (gauge or measure invariance) to redefine modifications for the ELF model. These conditions and those related to analytic continuation or causality are discussed in Chew (1964). In general, any electromagnetic model may involve a fall off rate of $1/r^3$ in the near field or $1/r^2$ in the far field. In our current experiments no fall off occurs for r compared to the size of the Earth (Rauscher and van Bise, 1988).

2. Examination of Some ELF Models of PSI

One of the early models of psi to be examined is that psi is electromagnetically transmitted. There are a number of reasons this model is not viable, particularly because of the success of remote viewing abstract coordinate targets. One model of psi claims that it is mediated by extremely low frequency (ELF) electromagnetic waves. This hypothesis is not ruled out by any obvious physical or biological consideration, although it may be difficult to find a manner in which to model a biological transmitter-receiver antennae with a high enough bit rate of information transmission.

The ELF model involves the sender and receiver concept in psi, i.e., psi afferent and psi efferent signaling in Roll's terminology (Roll, 1974). We examine, in this chapter, the multidimensional model which does not require a sender or receiver in the conventional sense of signal transmission, which the ELF model involves. A fall off effect cannot explain precognition or psychokinesis and abstract target RV acquisition.

The electromagnetic hypothesis has been put forward by a number of researchers, including I.M. Kogan (Kogan, 1966), U. Sinclair, 1971), J. Millay (2010; Millay and Johnston, 1983), W. van Bise (Rauscher and van Bise, 1990) and F. Blau (1981). This model suggests the concept that information transfer from a transmitter to a receiver, under the conditions of normal sensory shielding, is mediated by wavelengths of 200 to 2,000 km. Persinger (1975), Beck and others (Beck, 1978; van Bise, 1978, Rauscher and van Bise, 1980) have suggested that the observed data may fit with a model in which the earth's ionosphere at approximately 30 km in elevation, may act as a trapping mode wave guide. The argument against such a model is that there may not be a daytime/nighttime difference in psi functioning that is physical, but perhaps psychological. Ionospheric propagation changes in the daylight from that of the night sky (Rauscher and van Bise, 1999). Also for such long wavelengths, the source-transmitter and participator-subject-receiver would lie in the near induction field rather than the radiation field and hence fall off as one over the distance cubed. Such a model leads to a low bit rate of information carrying capacity of around 0.005 to 1 bits/second (Puthoff and Targ, 1976). In addition, an ordinary Faraday shield would not attenuate long waves as it shields against RF (radio frequency) waves. Blau discusses the issue of antennae theory and biological transductions as does Callahan and both suggest that appropriate signal-to-noise ratios may be accommodated (Callahan, 1980). (See Table 3 for the electromagnetic spectrum. The term eV stands for electron volts.)

Puharich examined the possible effects of ELF on brain

waves in an extensive set of experiments conducted from 1950-1956 (Puharich, 1950-1956; Rauscher and van Bise, 1990). Detailed studies were conducted of remote perception, not dependent on the usual modalities, with some tests conducted under shielded Faraday cage conditions. Attenuation of psi was not found under these conditions and some psi was enhanced by the use of a Faraday cage. (See detailed studies of ELF and RF effects in Puharich, 1950-1956 and Chapter 11 here; J.J Hurtak and D. Hurtak and also Rauscher and van Bise, 1990; van Bise, 1978). (See Tables 3, 4 and 5.)

Current data suggests difficulties with the ELF model of psi also because of the bit rate issue, precognition and long distance high quality data acquisition as stated before. Analysis of Remote Viewing has shown that the subject perceives information and what appears to be faster than the speed of light and hence lies outside the formulation of the usual ELF models. (Rauscher and Targ, 2001). In the next sections we discuss the need for a more applicable model. Arguments for the multidimensional model are presented in detail. It may be possible to develop a model which combines the ELF model with the complex multidimensional model. Since psi is a goal oriented task which appears to utilize the most efficient available system, acting as a "least action principle," only under certain conditions, the ELF model requires a modulated ELF carrier wave.

Perceivers in the laboratory room speak of receiving an image as a "flash" often in "three dimensions and color." They often start reporting a flood of information, usually very accurate (as validated by their description of the randomly chosen target and determined in later analysis). It is difficult to form an accurate measure of "bit rate" as the perception and analysis of sensorial input involves a person's memory, concepts and imagination and, particularly, psi which involves both our usual perceptual modality, as well as our remote perceptual modality. From the great accuracy of some remote perception experiments, the bit rate must be high. (See Chapters 3 and 4.) The information content measured gives a large degree of information from the remote perception process. This information content can be greater than direct perception, as people can remotely "see through walls" and also "see" forward and backward in time. Hence, we think that the data rate of remote perception appears to be far larger than is able to be modeled by an ELF model. One suggestion has been that telepathy involves ELF, but perhaps other modalities of psi involve other mechanisms. (Hynik, 1983; Persinger, 1975). Telepathy seems the most likely candidate to be an ELF mediated phenomena, but other modalities, such as precognition or abstract coordinate remote perception, work equally well, although unable to be described by a standard ELF model. (Targ, 2004; Targ and Harary, 1984).

It is difficult to measure the relative percent of telepathy vs other psi modalities from our data, but our data indicates that direct telepathy is less than 15% of our data content and may not be a good description of terms, that is why we term our experiments "Remote Perception." It is clear that remote perception is much more than telepathy, since perceivers can look inside of areas and containers that are targets that outbound experimenters are not able to view directly (Ullman and Kripper, 1978). We can only deduce that aspect of telepathy where there is a "frame-by-frame" matching of the outbound team and subject participant's recorded perception which we have done. Specific experimental design can be made to attempt to define conditions where telepathy operates or does not operate. For example, "abstract targets," where the target is designated by coordinates, eliminates direct subject/outbound person connection. The SRI Program researchers have conducted research with this experimental design (Puthoff and Targ, 1976, 1977; Targ, May and Puthoff, 2002; Jahn and Dunne, 1987, Targ, 2004; Rauscher and Targ 2001, Targ and Hurtak, 2006).

There are other possible mediators of psi phenomena than the ELF hypothesis. As before mentioned, we have solved the Schrödinger wave equation in the complex multi-dimensional geometry (Rauscher and Amoroso, 2008, 2009, 2011) and have found coherent soliton or solitary wave solutions.

Unlike the usual quantum wave solutions, these waves can propagate long distances over spacetime without distortions or loss of form and information. Soliton wave forms "re-cohere" and overcome the usual dispersive losses, and may comprise a mechanism for mediating nonlocal connections in the manifold. The soliton waves are also describable within the context of tachyonic signals which are superluminal but finite in velocity, as well as having subluminal components (See Appendix I) (Ramon and Rauscher, 1980; Rauscher and Targ, 2001; Rauscher and Amoroso, 2008).

The possible relationship between an ELF model and a quantum model may be made by use of a formalism involving the solution of Maxwell's equations in complex space. Solitons involve electromagnetic (longitudinal) soliton signals which may have a counterpart in ELF waves (Rauscher and Amoroso, 2011; Rauscher 1983e). As we stated, since psi is a goal-oriented task, information transmission may be made by the most available mechanism in nature through a generalized least action principle and such a mechanism could sometimes utilize an ELF modulated carrier wave. However, in a general hyperdimensional geometry, energy transmission is not an issue. There is much to be considered and on which to speculate and formulate mechanisms of psi (Targ and Puthoff, 1976). See Tables 3, 4, and 5 for considerations related to the electromagnetic model of psi.

Table 3
Frequency, wave length and energy are listed for each primary electromagnetic frequency bands

	Frequencies	Wavelength	Energy
Gamma (g) rays	$v = 10^{21}$Hz	$l = 10^{-11}$ cm	$E = 10^{7}$ eV
X rays	$v = 10^{18}$Hz	$l = 10^{-8}$ cm	$E = 10^{4}$ eV
Visible light	$v = 10^{15}$Hz	$l = 10^{-4}$ cm	$E = 10$ eV
TV, FM, shortwave	$v = 10^{8}$Hz	$l = 10^{2}$ cm, (1 m)	$E = 10^{-6}$ eV
Standard broadcasts	$v = 10^{6}$Hz, 1 mHz	$l = 10^{4}$ cm, (10^{2} m)	$E = 1^{-8}$ eV
LF, ULF	$v = 10^{3}$Hz, 1 kHz	$l = 10^{7}$ cm, 10^{5} m	$E = 10^{-11}$ eV
ELF	$v = 30$ Hz	$l = 10^{9}$ cm	$E = 10^{-13}$ eV

Table 4
Possible Difficulties
with ELF Hypothesis

Possible difficulties with such a general ELF hypothesis include:

1) Needing to invoke additional hypotheses, such as advanced potentials, to attempt to model precognition but in a very limited scope.

2) Successful data acquisition from abstract coordinate targets or a print of photographs where there is not an easily identifiable transmitter (coding mechanism) and receiver (decoding mechanism).

3) A manner in which to biologically define a somatic (body field) source and receiver and its connection with a psi ELF field.

4) Apparent lack of distance and temporal attenuations of psi data, both terrestrially and in outer space (Mitchell, 1974).

5) The apparent high resolution, real-time and precognitive descriptions of remote perception target activities, which are of sufficient detail to require a channel capacity that may be greater than that allowed by a conventionally modulated ELF signal.

6) Consideration of energy and information conservation and transmission at source (target) and sink (receiver).

Table 5

Further Tests of ELF

Should Involve the Following

Further tests of the ELF hypothesis should involve:

1) Longer interval precognition times and a better estimate of the bit rate.
2) Use of ELF sources as targets.
3) Possible diurnal variation of real-time, long distance remote perception to examine the validity of the resonance counting hypothesis, since there should be a day-night effect (Rauscher and van Bise, 1988, 1999; Rauscher and Van Bise, 1999).
4) Interference by high intensity ambient electromagnetic fields of the psi phenomena.
5) Possible shielding effect of the Earth or by water or electromagnetic media.
6) Extraterrestrial long distance attenuation or nonattenuation of the channel examined by computers in deep space flights. Some multidimensional geometric models also predict attenuation.

3. Multidimensional Geometric Models and Remote Perception

The phenomena of precognition and remote spatial perception can be reconciled with the main body of physics, principally causality, by multidimensional geometries. Although there are some quantum models of psi, they appear inadequate to deal with macroscopic event connections in space and time (Rauscher, 2006a, 2006b, 1981; Rauscher and Amoroso, 2008; Walker, 1979, 2000; Radin, 1997, 2006, Herbert, 1982, 1988; Costa de Beauregard, 1976, Mattuck, 1977, Mattuck and Walker, 1979). In four space, the phenomena of precognition would exhibit closed time-like loops which would give rise to paradoxes and multi-connected realities. In a higher dimensional space, the issue of closed time-like loops is resolved.

We live in a world of events or occurrences in space and time! If we are going to meet someone, we specify where (space) and when (time) to meet for a movie. We appear, as individuals, to occupy one place-space at one time. Minkowski formulated time as the fourth dimension of space and Einstein used formalism in his special and later general theory of relativity (Lorentz, Einstein, Minkowski and Weyl, 1923).

On the Einstein-Minkowski light cone, which we discuss in detail in Section 6, we represent x, y, z as space, and time as t. In this two-dimensional Minkowski representation of four space, we have a world line of connected events which is single valued. If information of a future event is perceived in the present, this is represented as a loop in the world line and many such events might be represented as a spiral. In four space this is represented in Fig. 5b (following page). In this analogy, the world line can be seen as a spiral or a "spring" in two dimensions, making the sides of the spring look like they are in contact (Fig. 5b(a)), but if we look down upon the spiral from a higher dimensional space, the spiral looks non-connected and the paradox is resolved in the higher dimensional geometry (Fig. 5b(b and c)). In the world line

Figure 5b

CAUSALITY AND PRECOGNITION

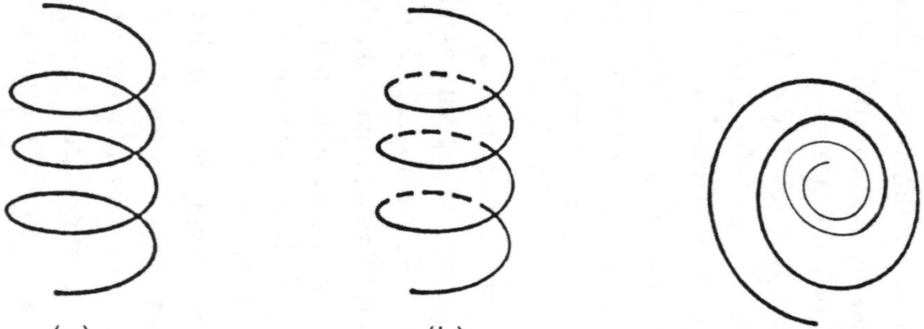

(a) We represent the world line of past to future and future to past with closed time like world lines looks like having multiple value nows or being at two places at once.

(b) Only a greater than four dimensions of space and time allows the disconnect so there are only single valued "nows." We cannot represent fully three space, since paper is two dimensional.

(c) We show the perspective looking down at a world line from a higher dimensional view, then one has no closed time like loops.

SPACE-TIME AND PSI

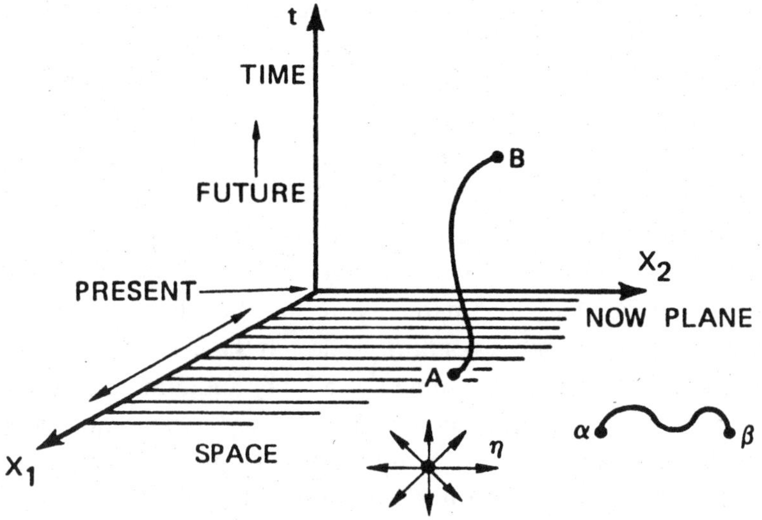

A can cause B by passage of time, known by precognition, A connects B instantaneously. α can connect β, "action at a distance" — PK (Kinetic), α connects β (Static) — telepathy (over space and time), η represents clairvoyance.

Figure 5c

A can cause B by the passage of time and can be linked to precognition, A connects B instantaneously and α can connect β, as remote viewing over space and time (sometimes "telepathy"), "action at a distance" PK Psychokinetic, η represents "clairvoyance" or universal knowledge. This division of psychic attributes may be artificial and historical. This figure represents a modified Minkowski space concept by Rauscher.

representation, time is taken as the vertical axis and space as the horizontal axis. (See Figs. 5b, 5c.)

A simple analogy is the case of the "psychic flatlander" (Abbott, 1984). If people existed as flatlanders in the x, y plane of a two-dimensional surface as two-dimensional beings, and were presented with a secret in a three-dimensional box, physically the secret would remain unknown. The "psychic flatlander," with access to the third dimension, could raise his consciousness (so to speak), look into the box and report his experience to his flatlander friends. To verify his result they could slice into the bottom of the box and check his perception (his record of his experience on a tape recorder and reporting to his $N = 2$ dimensional friends). This analogy gives us some clues as to the idea of consciousness having access to the availability of $N > 4$ dimensional space and a resulting action in the usual four space. There are two properties common to all the multidimensional geometries we examined and presented here. They are 1) remote connectedness properties and 2) superluminal signaling which are possible in ordinary spacetime. (See Appendix 1).

The properties of four-space of X, t (where X stands for x, y and z) geometries cannot account for precognition. In the case of the Einstein "time machine" twin paradox (which is a general relativistic phenomena because acceleration is involved and Lorentz time dilation occurs, which can be calculated by special relativity), information can only be carried into the future but, as we have explained, it would violate causality in ordinary spacetime if one could consciously access future information and return it to the present time. This paradox is resolvable when we consider a higher dimensional $N > 4$ space available for conscious perception.

As stated before, one of the main issues in addition to causality, is that of unitarity, or conservation of energy. This issue involves whether information can be transferred without energy transfer. Energy processes can be accessed if information transfer does not require informational energy, which may be local (Mattuck, 1977; Mattuck and Walker, 1979; Walker, 1970,

1979, 2000). We consider information and energy related to Shannon's law which defines the relation between a change in entropy with a change in information. We will discuss Shannon's law (Rauscher, 1983e, 1983f), but our multidimensional interpretation does not directly associate information with entropy or energy.

In some sense the issue of "levels of consciousness," referred to in the Vedic literature and elsewhere, may be related to information accessing in different dimensional spaces. In relationship to the concept of levels of consciousness is the concept of "morphogenetic field theory" by Sheldrake (1981). According to Sheldrake's work, non-genetically related rats in separate laboratories sequentially learn more rapidly how to run mazes when one group is trained to do so. This may be an issue related to psi research.

Perhaps with each psi experiment, the "barrier" against the "new paradigm" is reduced or overcome and the phenomena become stronger and stronger as it is replicated. In this model of "formative causation" the barrier is weakened as is a metal wire which is repeatedly bent and then broken. Scientific breakthroughs are perhaps like "quantum tunneling through a barrier" and may involve a new discrete state of consciousness with which to conceive and perceive a new reality.

We can speak of information and levels of consciousness which may not be represented as a spatial hierarchical scale. If we treat an aspect of conscious awareness in terms of information, we can define the level of consciousness in terms of an abstract concept of information. The level of information is proportional to the state of awareness and the state of alertness or awareness relates to the level of consciousness. These levels are not simple levels of emotional or cognitive response, etc. For example, states such as lucid dreaming may represent a clear state of high information as a complex cognitive state, as well as precognitive dreams. Higher states or levels of consciousness may be definable in terms of life enhancing choices relative to that organism and other organizable support systems of survival. (See Table 6.)

Table 6
The Properties of Consciousness and Thoughts

We ask where do thoughts come from and what are some of the properties of consciousness? We list some issues for consideration,

1) Location—Where and when is it?
2) What are the Mechanisms and processes of thought?
3) "Density" or amount of information of Consciousnesses.
4) The relationship of consciousness to space and time and the distribution and conservation of Thought.
5) Is there a Velocity of propagation of Thought?
6) Does it have "Shape" and "Form"?
7) How does Thought relate to energy and force?
8) What is the interaction of mind with matter?
9) How are Information and Communication related?
10) The relationship of goal orientation and Thought processes.

4. The Scientific Method and Multidimensional Models

A number of multidimensional or hypergeometric models have been proposed. We define such a hypergeometric or higher dimensional geometry as one with greater than three spatial and one temporal dimensions or $N > 4$. As we have said before, each model has been proposed to describe a particular physical process or relationship of different phenomena. For example, the Kaluza-Klein five-dimensional geometry with four space and time dimensions in which one spinor dimension or temporal dimension was introduced to demonstrate a possible relationship between gravitational and electromagnetic phenomena. In fact, many multidimensional geometries such as the Descartes geometry are introduced as an attempt to develop a unified field theory with a primary set of eleven dimensions (Rauscher, 1971). Sirag's 24 and higher dimensional element space is an attempt at a unified theory (Sirag, 1979, 1982, 1983, 2016). In Fig. 5c, we represent various forms of psi related to space (represented by x_1 and y_2) and time.

In each case, for any multidimensional model or any theory, it should describe a particular set of physical processes, make testable predictions about these processes, and be consistent with the main body of generally accepted physics. A new theory or model should present a useful formalism that clarifies our understanding of natural phenomena and expresses new relationships. We might even hope that a new viable model will "explain" more observed natural phenomena. In fact, scientists cannot, in a strict sense, use science to explain natural phenomena, but a theoretical model helps order and summarize many experiences or experimental results. The power of this ordering ability not only increases clarity, but also predictability for similar untested cases or future experiments. Predictability takes us beyond strict summary and categorization and more towards "explanation," which has to do with the cause or origin of a phenomena. Newton's gravitational laws "summarize" how objects behave in a gravitational field, but they do not explain what gravity is nor what causes it. However, they still have great predictive capabilities. It is perhaps the question of what gravity is that led to the formulation of the laws originally. Einstein's theory of general relativity takes us closer to the origin of the description of gravity in terms of the curvature of space and time.

Let us pose the question of what is the physical reality and nature of extra-dimensional space? This issue may be similar to the question of what is gravity or what is space? We speak about the properties of space, say four "space" of (x, y, z, t), or actually the relationship of events in four-space. It may be better to pose the question of "what are extra or additional dimensions?" rather than "what do we accomplish by the introduction of extra dimensions or $N > 4$ in terms of understanding the relationship of physical processes"? Does the introduction of an $N > 4$ dimensions assist us in "explaining," or relating and summarizing physical, as well as psychic experience?

We list some of the predictions of introducing greater than four dimensions in Table 7. We have developed and examined three main classes of multidimensional geometries, and have discussed motivation for their introduction, examination and interpretation.

Table 7
Predictions of Complex Geometries

We list and briefly discuss some properties and predictions of complex geometries.

1) Remote connectedness properties exist between physical events and processes.
2) "Superluminal" signals appear to exist in greater than four space.
3) Coherent non-dispersive phenomena exist, such as plasma oscillations or so-called instabilities. One-such example may be "ball" lightening, another may be "sun spots."
4) A mechanism for physical effects in a plasma or other medium by a change in conductivity and dielectric properties in four space based on vacuum polarization properties in complex space.
5) A model of unification of electromagnetic and gravitational phenomena through the one-to-one mapping of the spinor calculus of the Kaluza-Klein geometry and twister algebra of complex eight space.
6) A mechanism of formulating the so called "collapse of the wave function" in terms of the geometric structure of space and time, and interpretation of the "observer effect."
7) Interpretation of nonlinear effects in multidimensional geometries as an interpretation of the mechanism of the collapse of the wave function to a specific particular state. One possible interpretation of such a model is that "consciousness" generates "geometric" models or constraints of reality which relates to a particular potential or "*potentia*," (Heisenberg's term) being actualized as a specific event, which is a possible mechanism of the physical effects or a manifestation of thought. Such an interpretation is key to a model which includes psi phenomena, since it demonstrates a mechanism in which intention to a goal is physically actualized.

THE LIGHT CONE

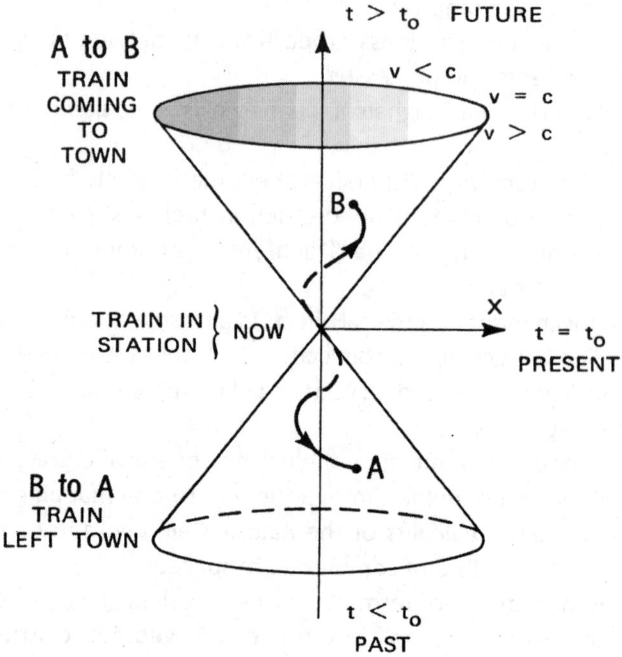

Figure 5d
The Light Cone

Albert Einstein gave an analogy of the manner in which past, present and future occur on the Minkowski light cone. A train is coming to a small town at $t > t_0$. This event lies in the forward light cone at (B), it arrives in the town's train station at the now or present $t = t_0$ time and then leaves the train station which lies in the past (A) at $t < t_0$, then (A) and (B) are the world lines. These events are said by Einstein to be only connected in his four spacetime by signaling at $v \leq c$, at less than the velocity of light or at the upper limit of the velocity of light.

5. Multidimensional Geometric Models and Their Implications For Remote (PSI) Perception Phenomena

For event connection on the Light Cone, one of the major features of the mass energy relation $E = mc^2$ is the "connecting quantity"— the velocity of light squared, or c^2. Einstein, Lorentz, and Minkowski described the relationship of space and time; this relation is given by special relativity as $s^2 = X^2 - c^2t^2$, where X = (x ,y, z) representing the three components of space, and the component of time, t, is related again by the velocity of light squared, c^2. (See Figs. 5d and 5e.) The quantity s^2 is denoted as the spacetime "distance" in four space or the spacetime metric. This distance is an invariant or constant. The metric invariant gives the causal or cause-effect relationship of events in space and time. Essentially, s^2 represents the distance between events in four space.

We can make an analogy between the Pythagorean theorem for a right triangle and the four dimensions of Minkowski space which are fundamentally related to each other by the very structure of space and spacetime. The Pythagorean theorem is a two special dimensional representation that states that the square of the hypotenuse of a right triangle with one 90 degree angle is equal to the square of the other two sides a and b, where the hypotenuse is h. Then $h^2 = a^2 + b^2$ which is a fundamental geometric statement about the structure of space. Geometry is the fundamental form of the universe and the structure of events in spacetime.

In the case of the Minkowski spacetime metric or measure of the spacetime we have the invariant spacetime metrical length, s, the three coordinates of space X = x,y,z and the temporal coordinate minus *ict* where $i = \sqrt{-1}$ and *c* is the velocity of light. It is the metric length or measure of spacetime squared, s^2, that represents the invariance of the world line or the event on our path in spacetime. This four dimensional invariant is expressed as $s^2 = X^2 - c^2t^2 = x^2 + y^2 + z^2 - c^2t^2$. Points to consider are that: (1) Minkowski space is four space invariant, $s^2 = x^2 + y^2 + z^2 - c^2t^2$; (2) analogy can

Table 8
Regions of Space or Spacetime on the Minkowski Light Cone

Region I	$X_1^2 + X_2^2 + X_3^2 - X_4^2 < 0$ *Time-like vectors* relate past and future
Region II	$X_1^2 + X_2^2 + X_3^2 - X_4^2 = 0$ *Null vector on* light cone hyperboloid surface
Region III	$X_1^2 + X_2^2 + X_3^2 - X_4^2 > 0$ Space-like vectors relate absolute "elsewhere"

Region I defines all events connected by $v < c$; Region II defines the light cone null vector surface where all events are connected by $v = c$; and Region III defines all parts of the space-time diagram connecting events superluminally by $v > c$. Note that $X_1 = x$, $= X_2 = y$, $X_3 = z$, and $X_4 = t$. In this notation $c^2 = c = l$ units are used, which is standard nomenclature.

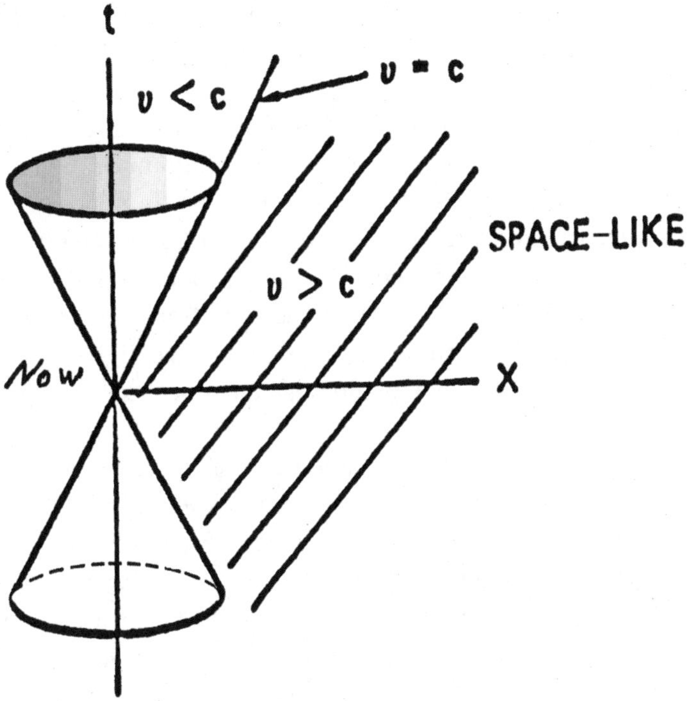

Figure 5e
Space-Like Region on the Light Cone

The usual Minkowski diagram 4-space of space-time is derived on a light cone. The now of this space is defined as a single value $(X, t) = x_0, t_0$ at the origin. Event correlations in 4 space are restricted to the forward and backward light cone for $v < c$, the surface of the cone defines $v = c$; elsewhere is defined outside the light cone for $v > c$. For $N > 4$ dimensions, causality relation can occur in the elsewhere and are also accessible as psychic events.

be made of the geometric metric and the Pythagorean theorem, $a^2 + b^2 = h^2$, which is a measure of the geometry of space, and (3) in Minkowski's words, "You cannot have a place without a time or time without a place." Events occur at a specified place, at a specified time.

We use this metric to clearly define causal events in spacetime, and we use the Minkowski diagram or "light cone" diagram to define the occurrence of events in space and time and their relationship. The limitations on the cause-effect relationship are defined by one of Einstein's axioms, that is, that no material object can exceed transmission at greater than the velocity of light, according to his belief. The light cone then demonstrates which events can have a connection to what causes. (See Fig. 5d.)

This constraint is depicted as the surface or wall of the light cone, called the null vector for all cases where the velocity $v = c$. Three regions are depicted in Figs. 5d and 5e and Table 8. They are the connection of events for $v < c$ (for velocity less than the velocity of light, or subliminal signals) called time-like signals; the forward (future) and backward (past) light cones, or Region I; the surface of the light cone where all events are connected by the velocity of light $v = c$ (Region II); and all points for events connected by signals for $v > c$ (for velocities greater than the velocity of light, or superluminal signals) are in Region III, which are called space-like signals, often termed "elsewhere." (See Fig. 5e and Table 8.) Event connections in this region are usually called nonphysical or space-like, described as the lined area in Fig. 5e.

The form of the metric allows one to connect events of the past, present and future. The connection of such a set of events in space and time is consistent with causality relationships and is called a world line. If one walks around in a circle, coming back to one's original point of departure in space, one has also traced a path in time because the Earth has rotated and moved around the sun and the galaxy has rotated, and so forth. One traces a path in space and time, and as Minkowski pointed out, one cannot have a space without a time or a time without a place. (See Figs. 5e and 5f.)

Although Einstein presented one of his axioms of special relativity that denies that physical matter has access to the space-like region in four space, the structure of his theory does not preclude such a connection, as pointed out by Gary Feinberg at Columbia University (Feinberg, 1967; Rauscher, 1971). [See Appendix I]. A particle with finite mass or signal, termed a "tachyon" (which means swift in Greek), is allowed for $v > c$ or superluminal signals, but it has an imaginary mass, that is a mass multiplied by $\sqrt{-1}$. The number in a square root should be equal to a number when squared which gives a real number. If $A = \sqrt{-1}$, or squaring both sides of the previous equation, $A^2 = -1$. But we know no solution exists for A to satisfy this equation, since all pairs of negative numbers multiplied by themselves yield a positive number. Hence the square root of a -l or any negative number is termed "imaginary." Although no physical tachyon has been discovered, the use of imaginary numbers and quantities is very useful and is prevalent in physics and engineering so long as the final *physical* or *observable* result is a real mathematical quantity. We will make use of imaginary dimensions in our model, used in a manner to yield a real final result. Through this approach we can understand the analyticity or causality conditions in elementary particle physics.

The issue of precognition is related to a description of causal connections on the light cone. Is it possible that we can define a condition for precognition consistent with the causal connections on the light cone? One has to have a mechanism of mentally accessing future information and "bringing it back" into the present as we stated.

Relativity theory describes a method of traveling into the future by the "time machine" or "twin paradox" effect, but it appears impossible to access future information and bring it into the present in a useful manner. We depict three types of causal connections in Fig. 5f, that is, the past to the future event. The first case Fig. 5f(a) is where there is no possible connection

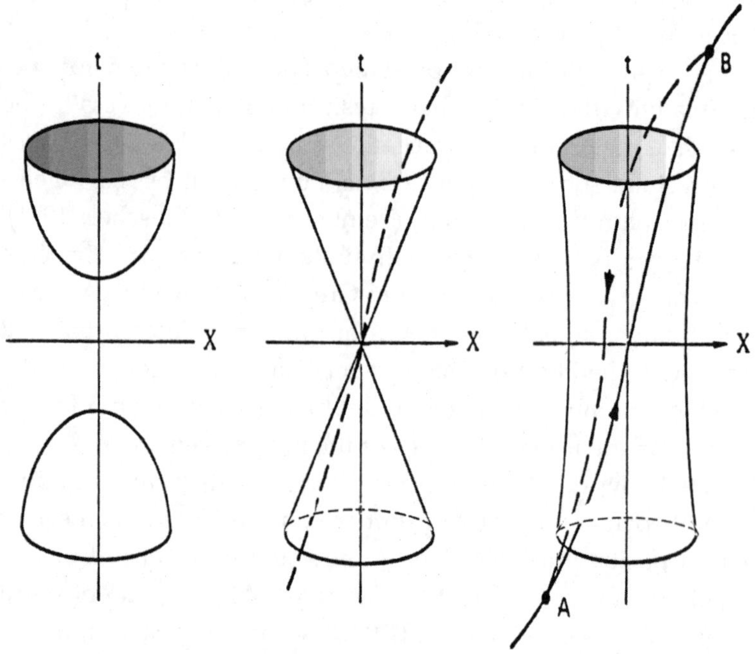

Figure 5f

One can consider three classes of Minkowski diagrams with three types of causal connections of events along world lines. In this figure we represent three light cone configurations. In Fig. 5f(a), there is no connection between the past in the lower light cone region and the upper future light cone region, which represents the impossibility because there is no now. In Fig. 5f.(b) we represent the usual future or upper light cone constrained by event connections at $v \leq c$ and the events in the lower, backward (past) light cone. The dashed line represents the world line we can travel from the past, now and future. In Fig. 5f(c) this light cone can accommodate our physical world line path from the past (A) to future (B), but also allows not only $v \leq c$ informational signaling which allows for a precognitive path to the future brought into the present, but contains the paradox of closed time-like loops (CTL).

of past and future events; Fig. 5f(b) the usual light cone; and in case 5f(c) we can create multiple world lines. Note this Fig. 5(b) represents the light cone case that permits only one single value for "now" which is the usual spacetime case; and case Fig. 5f(c) is where there is the possibility for a multiple connected present reality. In four space or spacetime though, it appears that the only way to access future information in the present is by a system similar to that described in this Figure. Not only is this case experientially unique, but such a system involves physical effects of the precognitive experience, such as acting upon precognitive information to avoid a potential disaster, or making tapes in a remote precognitive perception experiment before the target is chosen and visited, the effects of which would drastically violate the usual four space physical formulation of causality.

Let us turn to Fig. 5f for an example of such a violation from a higher dimensional perspective (see Fig. 5f(c)). A graphic description of the problem of "closed time-like loops," or CTL which can be depicted by an example. The issue of CTL is depicted by the two paths from A, the lower temporal location, to B, the later temporal, and back to A, the earlier temporal, now. The path (forward in time) is depicted as a solid line from A to B and then a dashed line from B to A (backwards in time) which macroscopically violates relativity in ordinary four space, but is resolved in a higher dimensional geometry.

In Fig. 5g, we denote two ways of examining world line events. The first is the usual world line (the same as Fig. 5f as also Fig. 5g(a)). This is the single valued world line involving one history. In Fig. 5g(b), we see that there appears to be more than one apparent history as we stated (as in Fig. 5f(c)).

There does not seem to be any manner to describe precognitive temporal advance, even if we introduce tachyonic or $v > c$ signaling (Feinberg, 1967). Tachyons or a superluminal signal alone will not explain precognition. Feinberg states that tachyonic signals even at near the velocity of light will net one only a few nanoseconds/foot into the future. Let us

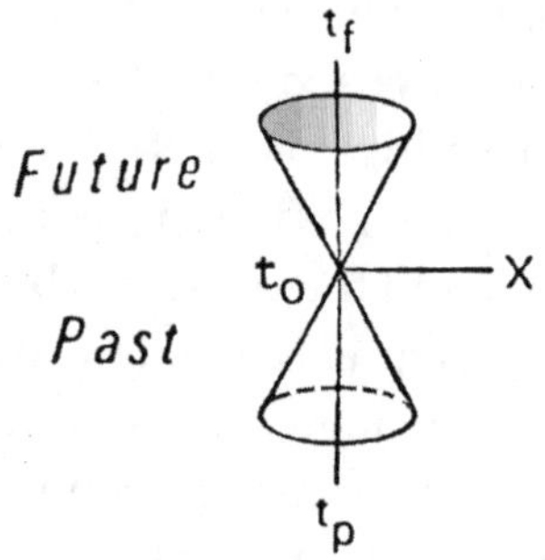

(a) Light Cone
Minkowski Four Space

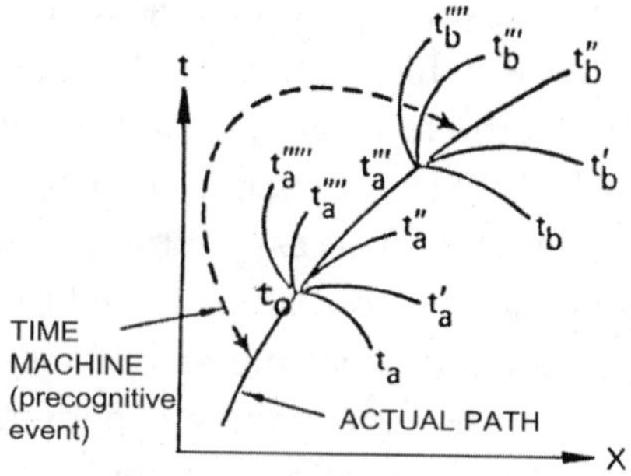

(b) World Line and Events

Figure 5g

Possible world lines and actual world lines: we depict the usual single-valued world line possibilities in Fig. 5g(a) This figure is equivalent to Fig. 5f(b). Only single valued "nows" as t_0 are admissible and we have one-point events in space time within the uncertainty of the Heisenberg uncertainty principle. Fig. 5g (b) depicts the solid world line as the actual world line, where at each point $t_0 > 0$, a number of *possible* realizable world lines exist that can be collapsed into a single *actuality*. Also depicted is the path of an "anti-time machine" and twin paradox into the past which appears as a dashed line. This is a paradox if we consider precognition and retrocognition only in four spacetime. The point on the light cone at the apex of the two cones is on single valued now. In Fig. 5g(b) multivalued nows are represented. In Fig. 5g(b) is represented as a quantum like history multivalue possibilities exist at each instant. The classical analogy is as we drive down a freeway we have multiple choices as to which freeway exit to take Fig. 5.g (b) as time passes. The dashed line represents moving information back in time from a precognized event into our present. The vertical axis is time and the horizontal axis is space, as is usually denoted.

look at the light cone. If we choose a space like signal of v ~ c and for ~ 3×10^{10} cm/sec, then 1/c ~ $1/3 \times 10^{-10}$ sec/cm and a nanosec = 10^{-9} sec so that 1/c nanosec x 1/30cm. If 2.54 cm=1 inch then 2.54 cm x 12″/ft = 30.48 cm/ft or ~30 cm/ft therefore 1/c ≈ 1 yields a nanosec/foot.

We consider Fig. 5g(b) in more detail. The issue involves the manner in which the possible becomes actualized as "time progresses." We denote the "now" time as t_0. In Figs. 5g(a) and 5g(b), we then denote the possible future events connected by world lines to the now event at t_0. As we move along a world line, in space and time, Fig. 5g(b) displays possible or potential futures, denoted by t_a, t'_a, t''_a, etc., becoming actualized as a single valued reality, t'''_a, etc. as the world line moves into the future. Then at a later instant these potential realities are actualized and "collapsed" to a single reality t''_b and so on. Suppose instead of only being able to move into the future (as in relativity), we could move into the past also. We could, for example, trace the dashed line in Fig. 5g(b) from the future to the past. Again in the CTL paradox, if one was born before all the possible t'''_a's and lived to t''_b, then built a "time-machine" which allowed one to travel to another spacetime world path outside one's normal life along t'''_a and t''_b, back before one was born but after one's mother was born. Then suppose one killed one's mother! The paradox becomes: how can one be born in order to go into the future, invent a time machine, go back to before one was born, and kill one's mother?! This is called the closed time-like loops (CTL) problem, known as the grandfather paradox. (See Fig. 5g(b).) I heard a science fiction program on this issue at 9 years of age and it sure got my attention!

As we said before regarding space, we do not need the frame of reference of the solar system or the whole of the cosmos, but only this earth frame of reference. There is an implied assumption about the relevant frame of reference. For example, as the subject waits 30 minutes to observe the future event, the earth has rotated approximately 300 miles at the San Francisco

Bay area's latitude. Also the Earth is going around the sun and the sun is moving on its own spiral arm of our rotating Milky Way galaxy. What frame of reference do we need to consider? It appears that the Earth frame of reference will be valid at least for short precognitive times just as one assumes it is valid for one's ordinary operational mode. For example, we can plan to meet someone in London next week without considering the rotation of the Milky Way galaxy!

6. Multidimensional Geometric Models of Remote Perception in Space and Time

In order to effect the proper causal connections to accommodate psi phenomena, we need the spacetime metric to be expanded by four more carefully constructed dimensions. To fulfill this criterion, we introduce an additional set of four imaginary complex dimensions in terms of a Lorentz invariant complex eight space. Specifically, we introduce the four real dimensions of spacetime and four imaginary dimensions in such a way that locations or events, which are distant in four-"space" or spacetime allow for nonlocal events to appear to be juxtaposed in our multidimensional complex eight space.

In remote perception experiments, we have a subject in the laboratory psychically viewing an outbound experimenter a distance away who is "observing" a target location, such as a bank building. We describe a method to make these two appear simultaneous and juxtaposed, that is, contiguous to each other. Most remote viewers describe their experiences as looking at their "mental screen" (they do not all close their eyes, but most of them either stare with their eyes out of focus or close their eyes). They say "I see as though the distant event, is in 'here and now'."

The possible ways of "mixing" space and time dimensions are present in such a way as to create a complex dimensional "eight space" invariant. We present this formalism briefly in this book. Some equations are utilized in order to make clear our procedure. One can follow the general procedure without a detailed comprehension of the mathematics. Essentially we 'complexify' the usual four-space metric. We mathematically construct an eight-dimensional space, which is the most simple or fundamental of the expanded space beyond four dimensions that is consistent with Lorentz invariance (Rauscher, 1979; Ramon and Rauscher, 1980; Rauscher and Amoroso, 2011, Rauscher, Rowlands and Amoroso, 2015).

As we stated, the relativity theory formally describes the

relationship of macroscopic events in spacetime and, in particular, their causal connection is well specified. In our model, the higher dimensional geometries appear to reconcile precognition and causality and define a formalism in which the spatial and temporal separation of events (in four-space) appear to be in juxtaposition to the higher eight-dimensional geometry.

In relativity, causal connection of events is described by the invariance of the Minkowski line element, which is the expression of the square between two points, which in special relativity is given as

$$s^2 = |X|^2 - c^2t^2$$

where c is the velocity of light, and where the exchange of information between an event cause and an event effect are limited by the velocity of light in Einstein-Minkowski four space. Again X stands for the coordinates x, y, z.

It is proposed that the ordinary Minkowski four space (three spatial and one temporal coordinates) is simply the real part of an eight-dimensional complex spacetime, or that real (Re) space is a projection of, or a slice through, a complex eight space (Hanson and Newman, 1975). For this generalized coordinate model we let the spatial coordinates be $X \rightarrow X_{Re} + X_{Im}$ and similarly for time, $t \rightarrow t_{Re} + t_{Im}$ where $i = \sqrt{-1}$ and then X and t are complex numbers.

We have introduced complex spacetime-like coordinates as a space-like part X_{Im} and a time-like part t_{Im} the imaginary parts of X_{Re} and t_{Re}. Now we have the invariant line elements represented as

$$s^2 = |X|^2 - c^2|t|^2$$

for

$$X = X_{Re} + iX_{Im}$$

and

$$t = t_{Re} + it_{Im}$$

as our complex dimensional components. Then we write the

square of the complex number, recalling that the square modulus of a complex number is real (this is the key to this formulism) and is given as

$$X^2 = |X|^2 = X^2_{Re} + X^2_{Im}$$

$$t^2 = |t|^2 = t^2_{Re} + t^2_{Im}$$

$$|X|^2 = XX^* = (X_{Re} + iX_{Im})(X_{Re} - iX_{Im}) = X_{Re}^2 + X_{im}^2$$

for X_{Re} and X_{Im} are themselves real and X^* is the complex conjugate of X. Therefore, we have for the "eight space" line element

$$s^2 = X_{Re}^2 - c_1^2{}_{Re}^2 + X_{Im}^2 - c_2^2{}_{Im}^2$$

Where c_1 may not equal c_2, where c_1 and c_2 are velocities of propagation

$$X_{Re}^2 = x_{Re}^2 + y_{Re}^2 + z_{Re}^2$$

and

$$X_{Im}^2 = x_{Im}^2 + y_{Im}^2 + z_{Im}^2$$

Causality is defined by remaining on the light cone, in real spacetime, as

$$s^2 = X^2_{Re} - c^2t^2_{Re} = X^2_{Re} - t^2_{Re}$$

We can use what are termed "natural" units so that we have the condition c = 1 for simplicity. (I discuss the role of velocity in remote perception in Rauscher, 1979; Rauscher and Targ, 2001; Rauscher and Amoroso, 2011.)

Then generalized causality in complex spacetime is defined by

$$s^2 = X_{Re}^2 + X_{Im}^2 - t_{Re}^2 - t_{Im}^2$$

in the X_{Re} t_{Re}, X_{Im}, t_{Im} generalized light-cone eight-dimensional "space."

We calculate the interval spatial separation between two event occurrences $(X_{Re,1}, X_{Im,1})$ and $(X_{Re,2}, X_{Im,2})$ with real separation $\Delta X_{Re} = X_{Re,2} - X_{Re,1}$ and imaginary separation $\Delta X_{Im} = X_{Im,2} - X_{Im,1}$ and temporal separation for $(t_{Re,1}, t_{Im,1})$ and $(t_{Re,2}, t_{Im,2})$ where Δ stands for difference. Then the distance along the line element is

$$\Delta s^2 = X^2_{Re} + X^2_{Im} - t^2_{Re} - t^2_{Im}$$

and it must be true that the line interval of separation Δs^2 is a real value! Then (for the choice of units for $c = 1$),

$$\Delta s^2 = (X_{Re,2} + X_{Re,1})^2 + (X_{Im,2} - X_{Im,1})^2 - (t_{Re,2} - t_{Re,1})^2 - (t_{Im,2} - t_{Im,1})^2$$

or

$$\Delta s^2 = (X_{Re,2} - X_{re,1})^2 + (X_{Im,2} - X_{Im,1})^2$$

for the space part

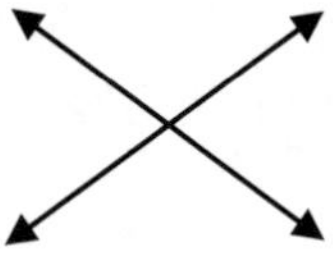

for the time part $\quad - (t_{Re,2} - t_{Re,1})^2 - (t_{Im,2} - t_{Im,1})^2$

Because of the relative signs of the real (Re) and imaginary (Im) space and time components, and in order to achieve the causality connectedness condition between the two events (or $\Delta s^2 = 0$), we must "mix" space and time. That is, we use the imaginary time component to effect a zero spatial separation as in real time remote perception and use the imaginary space component to effect a zero time separation as in precognition. We identify $(X_{Re1}, t_{Re,1})$ with a subject receiver remotely perceiving information from an event target $(X_{Re,2}, t_{Re,2})$.

The remote perception experiments consist of a subject

receiver in a laboratory room with an experimenter monitor who elicits a response about an outbound experimenter's location some kilometers or thousand kilometers distant from the laboratory. Correlation of the subject's response is made to the outbound experimenter's activities at the remote site (See Chapter 3 and 4). The experiment involves a real physical separation

$$\Delta X_{Re} = X_{Re,2} - X_{Re,1} \neq 0$$

and can either involve a current time observation, such that

$$\Delta t_{Re} = t_{Re,2} - t_{Re,1} = 0$$

or a precognitive time interval

$$\Delta t_{Re} = t_{Re,2} - t_{Re,1} \neq 0.$$

By introducing the complex time component $\Delta t_{Im} \neq 0$, one can achieve a condition in which the apparent separation in the real physical plane defined by X_{Re}, t_{Re} is zero, given access to the imaginary space and time in the X_{Im}, t_{Im} plane. Note that the X_{Re}, t_{Re} plane defines the usual light cone relations.

Figs. 5h and 5i(b) represents the case where there is no precognitive time element, or $\Delta t_{Re} = 0$ and $\Delta X_{Re} \neq 0$ denoted between P_1 to P_2 and $\Delta t_{Im} \neq 0$ denoted between P_1 to P_4 with the origin at P_1 (Fig. 5i (b)). In the simplest causal connection then, $\Delta X_{Im} = 0$ and

$$\Delta s^2 = 0 = (X_{Re,2} - X_{Re,1})^2 - (t_{Im,2} - t_{Im,1})^2$$

That is, if we have real-time remote perception, then

$$(t_{Re,2} - t_{Re,1}) = 0 \text{ and } (X_{Im,2} - X_{Im,1}) = 0$$

The metric is presented where the spatial separation between, say, California and New York, is made contiguous in a higher dimensional space by the imaginary temporal component $t_{Im,2} - t_{Im,1}$ which "subtracts off" the spatial separation by moving into the imaginary temporal plane. (See Fig. 5i(b)).

In order to make the apparent separation of events $t_{Re,1}$ and $t_{Re,2}$ appear to be zero for example for local precognition between P_1 and P_3, then we move into the *Im* spatial plane (See Figure 5i(c)).

We have

$$\Delta s^2 = 0 = (X_{Im,2} - X_{Im,1})^2 - (t_{Re,2} - t_{Re,1})^2$$

$$\text{or } (X_{Im,2} - X_{Im,1})^2 = (t_{Re,2} - t_{Re,1})^2$$

$$\text{or } t_{Re,2} - t_{Re,1} = \pm (X_{Im,2} - X_{Im,1})$$

As we stated, this is the simplest case for precognition, one in which there is no spatial separation between the subject receiver at P_1, on ($X_{Re,1}$) and the precognitized event and P_3 on ($X_{Re,2}$). In this case, the subject gains information about a future event occurring in the laboratory separated by a time interval $t_{Re,2} - t_{Re,1} > 0$ and $X_{Re,2} - X_{Re,1} = 0$. We construct the diagram in Fig. 5i(c) such that we define an X_{Re}, t_{Re} plane and a X_{Re}, t_{Im} plane.

The picture is like the omnipresent view of a helicopter pilot who sees the potential meeting of two cars traveling towards each other around the curve of a two-lane road on a mountain. The pilot's consciousness precedes the drivers' future awareness.

There can be an associated velocity in the t_{Re}, t_{Im} plane which we can denote as $V_{t_{Re},t_{Im}}$ and which is a complex quantity (Fig. 5j). In the case where the precognitive event occurs outside the laboratory, then $\Delta X_{Re} = X_{Re,2} - X_{Re,1}$ is no longer zero. We cannot represent this by a simple three coordinate diagram since we will have both the $\Delta X_{Im} \neq 0$ for $\Delta t_{Re} \neq 0$ and imaginary time component $\Delta t_{Im} \neq 0$ for $\Delta X_{Re} \neq 0$. See Fig. 5j for a schematic

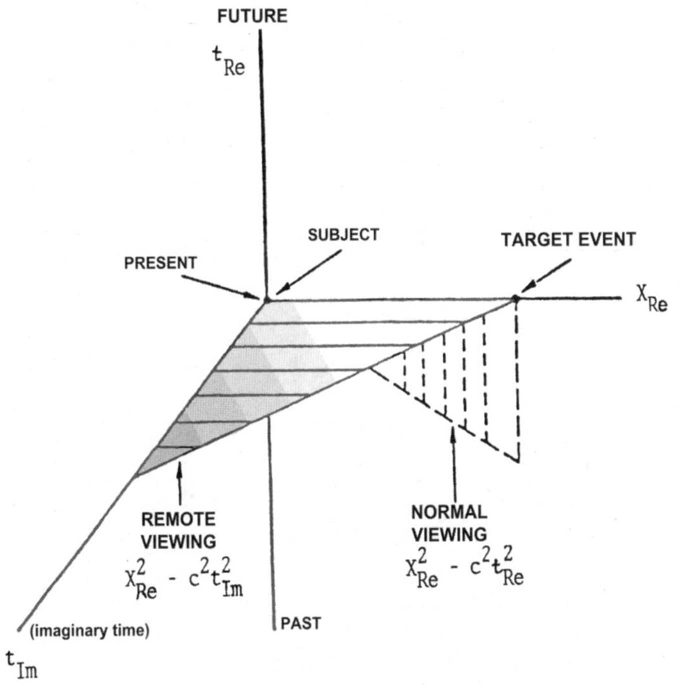

Figure 5h
Complex Time Model

Complex time model of remote viewing. We have the usual physical spatial separation of events on the X_{Re} axis in the $X_{Re}t_{Re}$ plane which appears separated by a zero separation by "moving" in the $X_{Re}t_{im}$ plane. Thus we have a mechanism for remote perception if consciousness can access higher dimensional information.

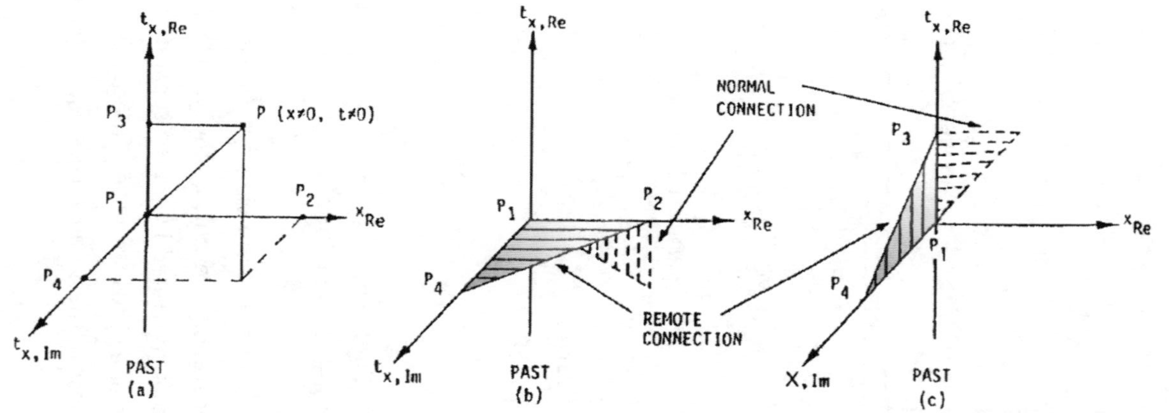

Figure 5i showing the location of four points in the complex manifold. In Fig. 5i(a), point P_1 is the origin, and P is a generalized point which is spatially and temporally separated from P_1. In Fig. 5i(b), the Points P_1 and P_2 are separated in space but synchronous in time. This represents real-time remote viewing with access to P_4. In Fig. 5i(c), points P_1 and P_3 are separated temporally and spatially contiguous. This represents a precognitive perception of P_1 and P_3 by access to P_4.The author thanks R. Targ and E. May for discussions at SRI international on the presentation of this figure.

of a complex eight dimensional space represented in two dimensions as two intersecting light cones one for real dimensions X_{Re}, t_{Re} and one for X_{Im}, t_{Im}, having a phase angle θ between real and imaginary components. The causality condition in eight space is then the full eight space metric

$$\Delta s^2 = 0 = (X_{Re,2} - X_{Re,1})^2 + (X_{Im,2} - X_{Im,1})^2 - (t_{Re,2} - t_{Re,1})^2 - (t_{Im,2} - t_{Im,1})^2$$

We can no longer represent this as a three-dimensional diagram (on two-dimensional paper) (See Fig. 5j for a schematic). We rewrite the above expression as

$$(X_{Re,2} - X_{Re,1})^2 - (t_{Im,2} - t_{Im,1})^2 = (t_{Re,2} - t_{Re,1})^2 - (X_{Im,2} - X_{Im,1})^2$$

where the left side relates to that aspect of Remote Perception in space and the right side refers to the precognitive aspects. The complex time and space in the eight space representation make it appear in that modality that one can access distant information as though it is not distant and access information about future events as though it were being accessed in current time. In Fig. 5k, we present some related theoretical models to my complex geometry.

In fact, we cannot define the velocity of light or any velocity as one can adjust one's time perspective through precognition and retrocognition (Rauscher and Targ, 2001). We have worked out the details of the connection velocities for both the real time and precognitive remote perception cases (Rauscher, 1979; Rauscher and Amoroso, 2011) (See Fig. 5l for the real time velocities).

In Fig. 5l, we examine the relationship of the possible velocity of signal connections in real time and precognitive remote perception. For real time remote perception, we represent the relationship of velocities where a subject S observes an event E utilizing the ability of his consciousness to access information about E in the complex eight space representation. For

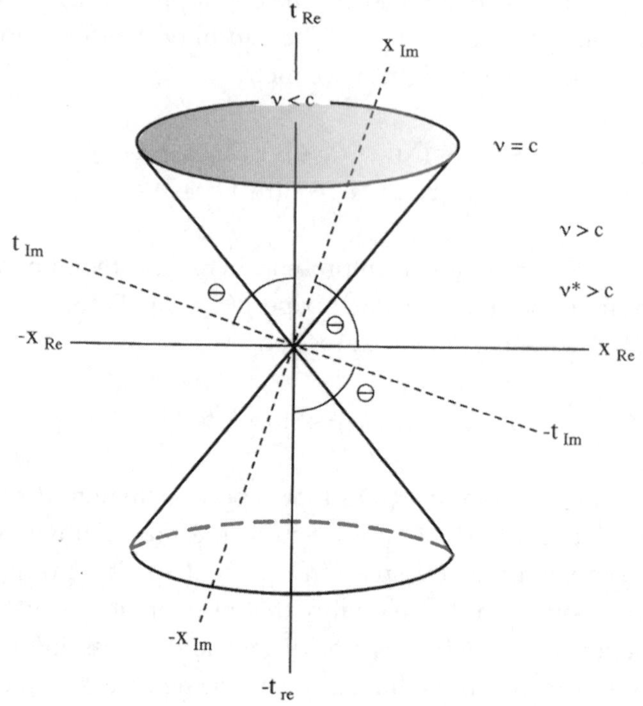

Figure 5j

In the complex space multidimensional model, we introduce, in addition to the usual orthogonal four-space, four imaginary components, three spatial and one temporal. This is necessary in order to model remote connectedness and to retain the causality land symmetry condtions in physics. We can consider the right orthogonal dimensions to be constituents of two intersecting light cones, one of real (X_{Re}, t_{Re}) and the other (X_{Im}, t_{Im}) coordinates. Credit: Rauscher, 1971 and Rauscher and Amoroso, 2011.

real-time remote perception, a five-dimensional space representation is adequate (See Fig. 5l(a)). In compact notation where each set of three spatial dimensions is taken as a single spatial dimension, this representation becomes a three space.

We represent a subject's precognitive experience in the $X_{Re}X_{Im}t_{Re}$ space. The subject S at time t_{Re} describes an event E which occurs at t_{Re}. The subject's consciousness S' can access this information from the "vantage point" of the X_{Im} axis. It may be possible to associate this case with a complex velocity Vt_{Re},t_{Im} (See Fig. 5l(b)).

The quantity t_{ES}, or time separation between subject's response at $t_{Re,1}$ and event occurrence at $t_{Re,2}$, is not associated with a spatial distance and hence a normal velocity cannot be associated with this elapsed time. (See Figure 5l.) Since velocity is a derivative quantity of space with respect to time (such as miles per hour), we must calculate in general complex derivative forms for Vt_{Re} and VX_{Re} which vectorially add to the real velocity VX_{Re},t_{Re} which can be the velocity of light. (A detailed calculation of possible proportions of velocities is given in Rauscher, 1979; Rauscher and Amoroso, 2011; Rauscher and Targ, 2001, 2006; where we examine in detail the manner in which one can shift one's temporal frame of reference to make the apparent velocity appear to be instantaneous.)

We can experimentally examine the time delay in spatially separated events between target location and subject response, but even in the Solar system, Earth and Jupiter can "look" instantaneous in complex eight space or recognition. See Table 9 for possible considerations of the velocity of propagation (Rauscher and Puthoff, 1976).

ELLIS
- De Sitter space
- Fifth Dimension
- EM field equi-potential surfaces
- Electromagnetics

Kaluza-Klein
- Fifth dimension And $Y\mu$ or $Y_{55} = 1$ Rotation
- Correspondence: EM and Gravity
- (Φu and $g_{\mu\nu}$)

Standard Model
- Complex 8 dimensions
- Kaluza-Klein

Stratton
- Complex EM Maxwell's equations
- Spacetime invariants

Hanson and Newman
- Complex space-time
- QM and Relativity
- (twistor spin)

Weyl
- Weak field approximation
- $K\mu$ or Φu and $g_{\mu\nu}$
- Real space-time consistent with complex dimensions

Evans and Sen
- Five dimensions Kaluza-Klein in Weyl space
- Maxwell's equations
- Gravitation

Rauscher
- Multidimensions (8 thru 12)
- Complex Spacetime
- Generalized wave equations
- $g_{\mu\nu}$ and $Y\mu$
- ($t< 1973$)

Figure 5k Relationship of Multidimensional Geometrical Theories: Listed are some major topics of some work on multidimensional geometrical models. The study of the comparison and differences of the concepts in these models is of interest. These models may yield a unification of electromagnetic and gravitational phenomena and model remote consciousness and nonlinear phenomena. See References as follows: Ellis. 1974; Evan and Sen, 1973; Klein, 1926, Rauscher, 1979, Stratton, 1941; and Weyl, 1920, 1957.

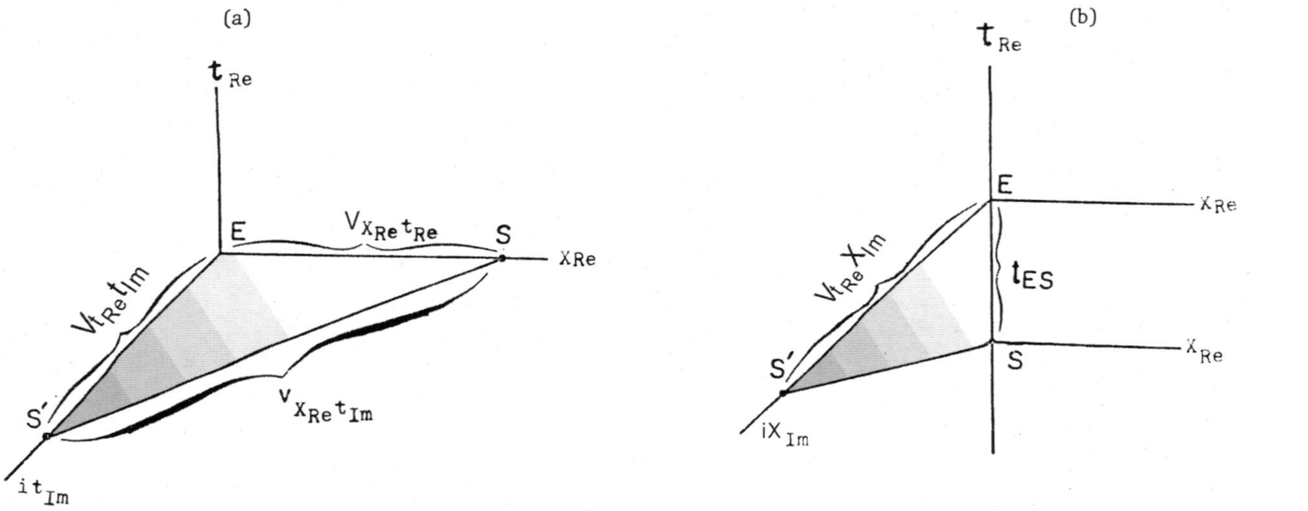

Figure 5I Models of possible velocity propagation in eight space. In (a) velocities are defined between a remote viewing subject, S of an event E from “position” S’ Figure (b) defines a subject, S precognizing an event E by access to “position” S’.

Table 9
Properties of Spacetime
and
Possible Velocities of Propagation

Region I of time like signals in the light cone connects all events for $v < c$. Region II, on the light cone defines all even connectors on the null vector surface of the light cone for $v = c$. Region III defines all space-like events connections for $v > c$. (Rauscher and Puthoff, 1976) (See Table 8)

PREDICTIONS:

A. Spacetime dependent

a) $v<c$	b) $v=c$	c) $v>c$	d) $v = \infty$
no	yes	yes	no

B. Space independent and temporal dependence

a) $v<c$	b) $v=c$	c) $v>c$	d) $v = \infty$
no	no	yes	no

C. Time independent and spatially dependent

a) $v<c$	b) $v=c$	c) $v>c$	d) $v = \infty$
no	yes	yes	no

D. Space and time independent

a) $v<c$	b) $v=c$	c) $v>c$	d) $v = \infty$
no	no	no	yes

We may be able to test the issue of a possible distance effect on psi by looking to space travel. We would have to look to deep space travel to get outside the near field (in the ELF model). There may be a $1/r^2$ fall off of psi bit rate and psi quality in the far field or $1/r^3$ in the near field, such as the electromagnetic field. To reformulate this issue and make new physics predictions, we complexify Maxwell's equation (Rauscher 1983, 2002; Rauscher and Amoroso, 2011) which is consistent with the complex eight spaces. We formulate longitudinal or non-Hertzian waves, as well as the transverse which do not fall off as $1/r^2$ and may fall off at a slow rate. (This work has also led to new antennae designs.)

The reaction to a psi signal requires a finite time to process mentally, as does any sensorial input. In order to examine a possible signal velocity of psi (if this velocity is rapid but finite), we need to be outside the domain of the finite reaction time process. The apparent reaction time would require that we test the possible finiteness of the signal velocity of psi by requiring a deep space probe target source and no precognition or retrocognition allowed!

So as we stated psi uses a least action principle or the Tao, so we can't preclude any aspect of consciousness. The least action principle is also fundamental to physical process. Space and time are connected, as we see, by the terrestrial distance experiment test in which subject and target are spatially separated. Long-distance spatial separation transcends time zones and can demonstrate precognition. Since we have demonstrated terrestrial long distance remote perception, we need to examine the comparison between the psychological and physical condition of psi to determine if there is a finite time process connected to psi phenomena or not.

Again, the psychological condition relates to the fact that psi is a goal oriented task. One must understand the manner in which the subject interprets "real time" across time zones or "real time" from the frame of reference of Earth to the frame of reference of remote space. For example, if targets were randomly chosen on a deep space probe, such as one going to Mars or Jupiter, does the viewing of that target occur in the frame of reference of Earth or that of the space probe? From our current research it appears one can adjust one's psychic vantage point so that the apparent velocity of thought is instantaneous (Rauscher and Targ, 2001, 2006)!

Let us return to the case of a terrestrial precognition experiment. If we conduct a remote precognitive perception experiment in which the subject mentation and target choice are separated by six months, the apparent frame of reference is the Earth (not the Sun), despite the fact that the Earth has moved half way around the Sun, but the subject participant does not consider this an issue in his or her data acquisition. This is similar to the traveler going to London in six months; the frame of reference is the Earth frame. This is part of the least action principle.

A person can psychologically perform a task that is precognitive and produce a psi result which appears to be instantaneous in information transmission (Targ, 2004). This possibility relates to the action of the domain of consciousness and the mental frame of reference of the psi observer. Let us consider an experiment in which a target or series of targets are specified on Jupiter or on a Jupiter probe (the frame of reference is Jupiter). The subject participant is requested to respond to these targets in real time. We then synchronize the time and content of the subject's perception and the time of selection and content of the target. We may utilize relatively simple target content to eliminate ambiguity of correlation between target and its perception. The question then becomes: what is the time of correlation? Is it (1) synchronized at the same time in the Earth frame, or (2) does it differ by the time of flight of light from Jupiter to Earth (about 8 minutes), so that the scatter of responses we observe would appear 8 minutes before the target was known on Earth, that is, the subject's mental frame is Jupiter? We are comparing the psi modality to that of the electronic receiver modality of the signal from the spacecraft detected electronically, which is restricted by the velocity of light. Ingo Swann said there were too many moons on Jupiter to do an experiment in which an RV subject would predict the occultation of the next of Jupiter's moons. He predicted that there were many moons orbiting Jupiter in 1976, which were later observed by astronomers. For Earth bound experiments and targets, this appears not to be the case as when the outbound experimenters are late, for example five minutes, in an experiment. Sometimes the remote viewer in the laboratory will view objects on the way to the target and at the target creating noise in the signal. In other cases, the subject views the target only, appearing to wait until the outbound experimenters reach the target.

We may be able to test some issues about the velocity of psi, but since psi is a goal oriented task and we are able to specify "real time" on Earth we need to also consider the possibility that even if one is mentally accessing remote information in the Earth frame of reference, one can be 8 minutes precognitive in one's response and make it appear that the mental perception frame is the Jupiter frame of reference.

We have interviewed our subject participants and they describe remote perception as seeing a distant place as though it is not distant. Ingo Swann spoke of traveling in a type of perceptual view of an out of body-like experience (OBE), but other subjects spoke of the experience of the frame of reference being in the vicinity of their bodies. The key to the velocity issue does depend on the psychological frame of reference, but a psychic one! The velocity of psi issue is related to an ELF type model which would be carried by the velocity of light restrictions in determining a possible finite velocity of psi.

It is of interest to examine both the apparent psychological and physical constraints. These may not be totally independent of each other, as such, independence assumes the Cartesian view of the mind-body duality that is prevalent is western science. The quantum measurement issue implies that the process of measurement affects the observed measured outcome by the effect of the Heisenberg uncertainty principle. Other systems of thought, such as the Vedic and Upanishads litera-

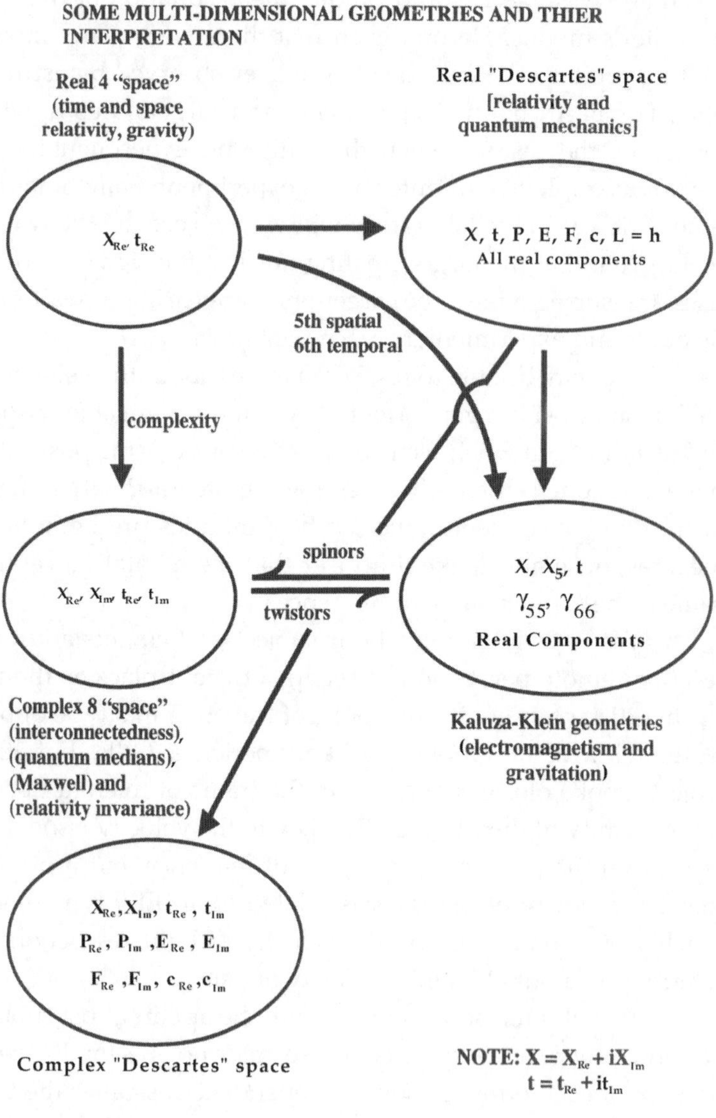

Figure 5m The relationship of some of my multidimensional geometries and other geometries

ture, suggest that the mental process of thought itself not only determines what we observe but creates what we observe! These issues ultimately are vital to our understanding of consciousness.

The possible effect of our state of mind and its influence on our view of reality is paramount. (Batten, 1995). The fit to the properties of psychic phenomena, in particular remote perception, is best served by our complex eight space model which also holds ramifications for technology such as antenna designs and understanding biologic processes (Tegmark, 2000; Rauscher and Busier, 2016).

In the next section we will continue to present some other researchers' models such as the previously described ELF model and examine some of their short comings and their incompleteness. Other contemporary physicists have presented popular literature on these issues (Capra, 1975; Zukov, 1979). In Fig. 5m, we present a schematic of four different aspects of multidimensional geometries I have examined and their interrelationships. All are an extension of Minkowski space (X,t). (The multidimensional Descartes space is explored and developed in Rauscher, 1968a, 1970, 1971, 1972a, 1972b, 1972c, 1973, 2015).

Saul Paul Sirag's model (Sirag, 1979, 1982, 1983, 2016) appears to be the only one to include our model in the main body of physics. Note our main purpose is to construct a model involving the least number of additional parameters and dimensions to formulate Remote Perception and be consistent with the main body of physics. (See Chapter 6, 7 and 8.)

7. Other Models Related to the Mind/Body Issue: Some are Models of Brain/Mind and Some Attempt to Incorporate PSI, Some Are Conceptual in Nature

In Rauscher and Targ (2001), we first discussed our model of psi in addition to other models including electromagnetic effects discussed in Section 3 of this chapter (Sinclair, 1971). In this section, we discuss some other models that may relate to psi phenomena and also to complex eight space and Descartes geometry and will discuss the shortcomings in explaining the remote perception phenomena.

A. The Holographic Model of Pribram-Bohm

K. Pribram (1976) and D. Bohm (1980) have presented a holographic model in terms of group theoretical considerations of the perception process. Let us comment here upon the compatibility of the holographic concept with the remote connectedness property of multidimensional geometries (Rauscher, 1983b). Group theoretical considerations detail the process of information mapping from one four-"space" location to another and this mapping demands a higher dimensional, $N > 4$, geometry. Just as writing (or using a computer) occurs as a mapping on paper in an $N = 2$ space, from a third dimension $N = 3$ for the pencil or key touch pad to operate, so four-"space" (X,t) requires $N > 4$ dimensions for remote events to be correlated (such as in spatial remote perception to produce the mapping process that correlates these events). The holographic models are not necessarily consistent with the main body of physics and are more metaphorical. Bohm associates the holographic picture with the greater collective mind. (See Chapter 13.)

B. The Houck Emotional "Multidimensional" Space Model and Henry Stapp's Quantum Mind/Matter Model

Houck (1982) presented a metaphorical spacetime model in which perceptual slices are made (such as of remote perception phenomena) that accounts for "the high emotional content of past or future or distant events." He may be able to assign this model with an energy and information content This may give us an additional parameter to define which allows for some mapping processes of the holographic picture to standard physics. Obviously being physically contiguous has an enhancing parameter to visual detection of a site, if light is present, but for distant psi events (without the normal channels of perception), emotional factors as well as others may give us a larger mapping parameter and hence more psi.

How are remote senses "mapped" from the mind to the brain? Stapp (1975, 1981, 1998) presents a detailed quantum mechanical model that addresses itself to this vital question on the issue of the "power of thought." Stapp's model is a "process" model in which "creative act" thoughts are represented by a collapse of a wave-function in the physical world. According to his model, a mechanism can be found for thoughts in four-space, or $N > 4$ space, through quantum events on a physical level. Partially collapsed future events are also possible. The concept of process or dynamics or event relationship is key to this issue and also in the interpretation of the Descartes geometry (Rauscher 1971, 1972a, 1972b, 1972c, 1973; Rauscher, Hurtak and Hurtak, 2013a).

We have also suggested that the quantum geometry itself determines, at least in part, the state of the wave function (Rauscher, Hurtak, Hurtak, 2013b). Stapp, Chew (1964), Wheeler (1978), Radin's (1997, 2006) and my own work all suggest that space and time should be "removed" from the position of immutable standards, as in the classical world view, to a "role of the relative" and in some cases a role in which they are mutable creations of a deeper level of reality.

Harary presents an innovative theory of psi in which he presents a perspective in which all natural laws are not known and that psi is an aspect of nature. This view is counter to the view that most of the laws of nature are known and that psi refers to a certain set of interactions that occurs rarely. Harary's approach assumes that a set of interactions occurs that is not completely observed. Psi involves certain of these relationships that we do not always notice or observe. Some of the limits of perception involve the borderline to psi, so therefore psi is observer defined (Harary, 1982a, 1982b). This author believes we should start with the simple theory that accommodates psi and is consistent with the main body of physics (Rauscher, 1979; Ramon and Rauscher, 1980, Rauscher and Amoroso, 2011). Additional elements may be required to explain mind-matter interactions

The view that psi is a fundamental aspect of physical reality is perfectly consistent with my multidimensional geometry. This model is also consistent with other models that do not involve just ELF. Houck and Roll present a detailed discussion of the need to utilize a multidimensional model to formulate a meaningful description of psi. Such a model should encompass clairvoyance, telepathy and precognition, as well as the possibility of human consciousness imprinting on objects termed psychometry, which is a fundamental tenet of Roll's considerations (Houck, 1982; Roll, 1974). An object which has been contiguous to a person remains "contiguous" in a higher dimensional geometry ($N > 4$). He terms this "psi space"; we term it the domain of action of consciousness. If psychometry occupies a role in enhancing psi, this issue should be incorporated into our experimental design to enhance psi and understand it.

Psychometric or mind-measure processes may involve an imprinting of energy on the spacetime manifold. If this is the case, then there may be an analogy to psychokinesis or mind-motion. The relationship between psychometry and psychokinesis can be found in energy and entropy relationships to space and time (Rauscher, 1983a, 1983b).

An example of an experimental design based on this model involving the importance of the psychometric phenomena may imply that long time duration targets are easier to remote view. Transitory targets such as slides projected on a screen or on a computer screen near where a painting had been removed or previous targets displayed, may be likely to involve psychometric noise. Sometimes, we can use the psychometric modality to enhance psi. Psychometry may lead to what we describe as the "essence" of a place. In Remote Perception, the use of geographical locations as targets occupying a place over time, instead of having a temporal duration, appear to increase its psychometric existence. Having a more stable duration may increase the interaction with the psychic perceiver within the spacetime contiguity of the observers. Slides or computer targets have short spacetime duration and may be less desirable.

C. Kaluza-Klein Geometries

Kaluza (1921) and Klein (1926) introduced a five-dimensional covariant geometry which appears to have properties suggesting a method of unifying the electromagnetic gauge invariant field (Maxwell's equations) and the gravitational field. This particular multidimensional model appears to be useful to examine further because it not only demonstrates the relationship between electromagnetic and gravitational relativistic phenomena, but is also consistent with the main body of physics for the standard model (See Chapter 8). The spinor calculus is an excellent framework for coupling the electromagnetic and gravitational phenomena, as well as quantum phenomena (Rauscher and Amoroso, 2008). The spinor calculus can be related one-to-one with the twistor algebra of the complex eight space. (This work is detailed in Rauscher, 1979; Rauscher and Amoroso, 2011 and is also detailed in Sirag's hyperdimensional geometry, Sirag, 2016).

D. Multidimensional Model: Descartes Geometry

In the late 1960s and 1970s, I worked on a ten-dimensional geometry which places such quantities as force, velocity, acceleration, momentum, and energy, etc., on an "equal footing" with space and time thus taking spacetime out of being the arena of action of matter and energy to being part of the action itself (Rauscher, 1971; Wheeler, 1978)! Predictions of this geometry are: 1) superluminal signals and remote connectedness properties; 2) new Heisenberg-like relationships (Rauscher, 1972a, 1972b); 3) closed cosmological solutions (validated by x-ray data) (Rauscher, 1972c, 1978b); 4) properties of cosmogenesis validated by D-abundance data; and 5) a four-force unified theory (with predictions about certain elementary particle properties) (Rauscher, 1968b). The initial motivation in 1964 to examine multidimensional geometries was to develop a formalism for the unification of the four force fields of nature. (See Fig. 5n.) These are the strong nuclear force, the weak nuclear decay force, the electromagnetic and the gravitational interactive forces. The initial geometric model I developed was the Descartes geometry. This geometric model does point to a possible unification of the four force fields. L. Motz has developed a formalism which contains aspects of my Descartes geometry (Motz, 1972; Motz and Epstein, 1979).

E. Hyperspace Physics of Sirag

Sirag (2016) has developed an extensive formalism for a group theoretical model of a unified field theory and we detail more here. This theory describes a manner in which to unify the four force fields in Nature, that is the strong and weak nuclear forces and the electromagnetic and gravitational forces.

The spectra of elementary particles are also predicted by this supersymmetry theory.

Sirag (1979, 1982, 1993b, 2016) states as I do, that the quantum theory alone will not explain consciousness. Walker (1972, 1979), Radin (1997, 2006) and Wolf (1981) believe that quantum mechanics might account for psi, but Herbert (1988), an expert in quantum theory, believes that it will not explain psi. Sirag explains in a most definitive manner, how a theory of everything is necessary to explain consciousness and, yes, everything! (See Chapter 8). As I do, Sirag (1993a, 1993b, 2016) takes a geometric approach that is hyperdimensional at many dimensions. What Sirag formulates is a comprehensive theory involving group theory, that includes particle physics and is specific in formulating the domain of the quantum theory of strong and weak nuclear forces (See Chapter 8). This includes the electromagnetic theory through the electroweak force involving electromagnetism and nuclear weak decay. (See Fig. 5a for the fundamental four force fields.)

The complex group algebra $\mathbb{C}(S_4)$ embeds the subgroups U(l) x SU(2) x SU(3) and S_4 appears to act as a supersymmetry model. The relation of my complex spacetime theory and Sirag's formalism is that my complex spacetime is implicit in the (McKay) group algebra $\mathbb{C}[\mathcal{OD}]$. Embedded in this algebra is the unitary group U_1 x U_1. This is the exact spacetime form required for the twistor theory (Penrose, 1978; Penrose and Rindler, 1985). We discuss the relationship of the twistor spaces and my complex eight space in Rauscher and Amoroso (2011). My complex space in terms of $\mathbb{C}^4$ space in this nomenclature.

Sirag argues that at least ten dimensions are required to construct a theory that encompasses the quantum theory and general relativity called a theory of everything, in terms of physics (See Chapter 8). His geometry is a different, but related, approach to my ten dimensional Descartes space, which involves extended dimensions (Rauscher, 1971). Some of the current concepts in physics involve superstring theory of the E_8 x E_8 group space of 496 dimensions! (Peat, 1988; Witten, 1995).

RELATIVE FORCE STRENGTHS

FORCE	COUPLING CONSTANT OR RELATIVE STRENGTH	RANGE (fm)	INTERACTION TIME (sec)
STRONG (nuclear)	1 to 10	1 fm	10^{-23}
ELECTROMAGNETIC	10^{-2} (or 1/137)	∞	10^{-21}
WEAK (decay)	10^{-11} to 10^{-14}	SHORT RANGE	10^{-6} to 10^{-9}
GRAVITATIONAL	10^{-39}	∞	∞

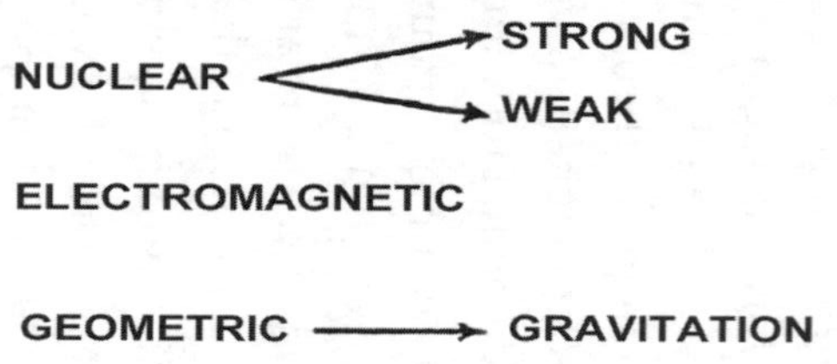

Figure 5n We list the four major force fields in nature. They are listed in order of the strength of the force coupling constant. Also the range of these forces is given with their time of interaction. They are the nuclear strong force, the weak nuclear decay force which are short range and the electromagnetic and gravitational forces which are long range.

The group E_8 is what is termed a reflection space which is an eight dimensional space of 248 dimensions (Millay, 2010; Sirag, 2016). A reflection space is developed as a mirror symmetry type space (Hurtak, 1973).

Note the purpose of my theory is to seek the least number of dimensions to accommodate the properties of remote perception in the main body of physical principles. Additional dimensions than the complex eight space are likely to be needed to accomplish a model of psychokinesis. It may also require additional dimensions to incorporate the quantum domain. To quote Sirag, "Paranormal phenomena seems universal because the spacetime projection (twistor algebra) provides only a partial view of hyperspace events" (Milley, 2010).

Sirag relates the S_4 permutation group to $\mathbb{C}[\mathcal{O}]$, the octahedral group which forms a 24-element complex algebra. He formulates the subgroups of $\mathbb{C}[\mathcal{O}]$ is as unity U(l)'s and Lie group, SU(3)'s, the elements of which can be identified with electromagnetic, weak interactions and strong interactions (color, anti-color, quantum numbers, etc.). He forms a double group of $\mathbb{C}[\mathcal{O}]$ and $\mathbb{C}[\bar{O}]$. These 24 element groups correspond to Boson (integral spin) and Fermion (half integral field) fields. This 48-element system also includes gravity. The Kaluza-Klein geometry comprises a subset of the Boson field. This geometry maps to my complex eight-dimensional geometry $\mathbb{C}_4$ and comprises the Yang-Mills field, defining the structure of space and time (Sirag, 2016). Sirag derives the spectrum of elementary particles comprising the Fermion fields and matter fields, involving $\mathbb{C}[\bar{O}]$, the minor symmetry to the Boson field $\mathbb{C}[\mathcal{O}]$.

Sirag addresses the quantum measurement issue by considering the role of the Klein group as a subgroup of S_4 where the Klein group appears to define a set of operations which relate to Piaget's model of perception. It is an exciting prospect to relate the complex Minkowski space and our quantum formalism as an applied form of Sirag's theory (Peat,1988, Rauscher, 1983f).

F. Some Comments on Quantum Models of Psi

Other quantum models of psi have been developed by Schmidt (1978a, 1982) Phillips (1978) and Costa de Beauregard, (2002). These models may be well suited to formulate the microscopic effects of psi and perhaps some macroscopic properties, as well as related to quantum nonlocality (Chapter 6 and 7). The quantum approach may shed light on the so-called observer/participator effect on the collapse of the wave function issue.

Schmidt discusses the possibility that the "psychokinetic effect" may indeed be a way to describe the collapse of the wave function. Since the quantum formalism does not define a unique reality, this fact allows a manner in which consciousness can enter. Other researchers, for example von Neumann (1966) and Wigner (1967), allow for the role of consciousness. However, can an automaton be psychic? This may distinguish silicon based digital robots from carbon based analogue and digital beings. Can one truly build a conscious robot? I think not. To be fully conscious, the robot would have to be psychic! Schmidt has examined in experiments binary RNG processes in great detail in terms of spacetime correlations (Schmidt, 1978b, 1982).

Phillips also discusses the issue of precognition as a vital element to be reconciled with the main body of physics. As we have presented at the beginning of this book, he presents a set of non-linear transformations in Hilbert space which may be consistent with the non-local properties of psi. This model is consistent, in general features, to our model developed at SRI in the early 1970's (Rauscher, 1979) which was later expanded upon (Rauscher, 2015). The complex Minkowski space leads naturally to a non-linear quantum mechanics.

We have solved the Schrödinger and Dirac equations in complex space and obtained "non-dispersive" solutions which are consistent with the remote connectedness properties of the space. The form of these equations in complex space are nonlinear and yield soliton solutions. The geometric form of the complex metric spaces allows the determination of specifically defined quantum states (Rauscher and Amoroso, 2011). The observer/participator issue in quantum mechanics may find possible resolution in terms of this formalism. The so-called "collapse" of the wave function is fundamental to psi and the interaction of consciousness with matter. Stapp's formalism also addresses this issue. I have also solved Maxwell's equations in the complex Minkowski spaces and found Higgs field soliton-like solutions appear to describe a monopole state (Rauscher, 1983).

The quantum vacuum state formalism provides a space for the local energy available to produce psychokinetic effects. Although quantum mechanics appears to provide part of the picture of the local interaction of consciousness with matter, the macroscopic description of events in spacetime requires a macroscopic geometric description. Our solution of the Schrödinger and Dirac equations in the complex geometry provides a link between the causal relation of events in macroscopic spacetime and micro-local quantum energy events (See Chapter 6).

In the following chapters, we address quantum interaction, nonlocality and the so termed collapse of the wave function. In this manner we express how the set of possibilities in the future collapses in its now (See Fig. 5g(b)).

The question has been posited by Wheeler (Wheeler, 1978; Wigner, 1967), the Fundamental "Fysiks" Group (Keiser, 2011) and others that it is the observer's collapse of the wave function. The fundamental question that arises is: Does the collapse of the wave function to a specific state involve some participation of the observer? Does this participation involve an action such as a psychokinetic one that produces a local change in the global universe (Walker, 1979; Rauscher, 1980)?

8. Remote Mental Influence, A Brief Summary

In this section, we briefly discuss other psi phenomena such as healing and psychokinesis, in general, which requires additional considerations such as possibility energy, entropy and information transfer issues.

A. Healing and Psychokinesis as a Negentropic Process

We have examined in detail the effect of a healer's remote "hands on" treatment on the growth rate and motility (movement) of sterile cultures of salmonella typhemerium using both control and treated samples (Rauscher, 1990; Rauscher and Rubik, 1979; Rubik and Rauscher, 1981, 1993). In our study, we applied antibiotics and examined the effect of the healer, Olga Worrall (Worrall and Worrall, 1970) in overcoming the deleterious effects of the antibiotic that was applied to the salmonella culture. The healer cupped her hands, during the experiment, around sterile test tubes without contact.

It was shown that when Worrall intended to heal the bacteria, the result of the study demonstrated a highly statistically significant motility and survival rate even with application of both high and low doses of antibiotics (chloraphenicol and tetracycline). We further conducted dose response studies and found that under increased concentration of antibiotics, the growth rate was less affected under the healer treatment than with lower concentrations of antibiotics. Motility and growth effects of a healer were clearly established. In over 50 base line studies of non-psi researcher studies in comparison with our controls, we found less than a 1% deviation in the growth rate over 24 hours for all the control cases.

In all healer treated cases for treated and control samples, where redundancy was achieved by the use of multiple test tubes for each condition, we conducted a full statistical analysis. Our results demonstrated a 20% to 120% effective treatment by the healer for the different doses of different antibiotics over controls (Rauscher and Rubik, 1979).

A non-healer run was conducted in which a participant who was not a healer, cupped his hands around "heated" samples, with no intention to heal and the results were the same as the control samples. Maximum effect was found with 10 μ/ml. of chloramphenicol (Rauscher, 1990, Rubik and Rauscher 1993).

B. Remote Mental Influences on Materials

We also conducted experiments to examine effects on the micro-structure of macroscopic psychokinetic treatment. Electron micrographs were made of materials treated psychokinetically and compared to those made from untreated controls. These materials were metals and laboratory grown crystals (each with control materials) and these were examined by seven crystallographers and metallurgists at four national laboratories such as, Case Western Reserve University and Lawrence Livermore Laboratory (LLNL).

Control materials were bent and broken by metallurgists in the equivalent place on the control samples as that accomplished through the paranormally affected materials at Livermore National Laboratory. All control samples displayed normal properties at low and high magnifications, between 400 to 4,000 times magnification using a scanning electron microscope (SEM). Paranormally bent or broken samples were found to be affected abnormally, as evidenced in their microstructure. All PK samples had smooth and ropy fractures and the control samples kept in the Laboratory had the usual jagged factures when mechanically broken. Of the four major laboratories, two of the laboratories' scientists were unaware of how the "heated" samples were produced, but all correctly identified the treated samples as anomalies and the controls as normal (Rauscher, 1983b).

We determined that materials which contain residual stress were easier to affect paranormally. We found changes in crystal boundaries and crystal dislocations. The effects appear to be thermodynamic, that is, metals appear to be "annealed." We exposed subjects to two samples of similar tensile strength, one of which was annealed before psychic treatment and one which contained a significant number of internally stressed crystal dislocations. Materials with internal stresses were more readily psychokinetically affected than annealed materials of similar rigidity and strength (Houck, 1982, Rauscher, 1983c; Rauscher and van Bise, 1990).

Electron microscope analysis yielded examples of significantly more movement along crystal boundary dislocations, as well as apparent annealing in psychokinetically affected materials as compared to controls. Analysis indicates that annealing may be affected by the process of psychokinesis. Stresses that are formed within the material when it is initially prepared are released by the mental interaction with the materials.

Psychokinetic interaction with the material appears to release stress (and disorder), thus increasing the ordered crystal pattern array and thus apparently decreasing entropy. We hypothesis that the domain of mental interaction by the subject participant increases information in materials utilizing the local available energy stored in the stressed crystal boundary, due to internal crystal dislocations. We relate information and entropy through Shannon's law (Rauscher, 1983a). We define this nonlocal negentropic entropy variable as ε and its associated local energy release as ε_Λ. Negentropic processes may involve systems which are nonlinear and far from equilibrium. These systems involve processes which may reconcile psychokinesis and psychic healing with thermodynamics, information theory and energy conservation (the First Law of Thermodynamics). Thermodynamic theories also involve quantum mechanics in terms of microscopic particle processes.

Linear processes are always isotropic as long as the

equilibrium state is isotropic. Isotropy is lost for nonlinear systems. In order to maintain a steady-state continuous non-equilibrium state it is necessary to pump a continuously negative flow of energy of magnitude equal to the value of the internal entropy production (Glausdorss and Prigogine, 1971; Nicolis and Prigogine, 1977). This relates to Prigogine's model of the manner in which biological systems operate. Prigogine states that in a system that is near steady state, the entropy flux cannot, in general, be arbitrarily imposed from an external source but becomes a state of the system (generated inside the system). This issue involves the definition of open vs closed systems. Equilibrium is just one case of a steady-state system, but all steady-states are not equilibrium states. The principle of minimum entropy production guarantees steadiness of the steady non-equilibrium state. The entropy does not always increase in these systems.

Both conditions on the geometric structure of the system and the specific properties of the energy flux, which act as a source of order, must comply with the criterion set by the thermodynamics of Prigogine. Prigogine uses the term "dissipative structure" to describe the manner in which certain states with applied or self-generated energy fluxes "dissipate" into a state of increasing order (or decrease in entropy). States which increase order or complexity are negentropic ($\Delta S \leq 0$) but do not violate the second and third laws of thermodynamics because they are open systems. Dissipative structures do not refute the laws of thermodynamics anymore than an airplane flying refutes the law of gravity. One familiar example Prigogine cites as an example of macroscopic effects dictated by microscopic processes is that of freeway traffic. In an uncrowded freeway each car driver is affected minimally by other vehicles. As the traffic becomes heavier, a point is reached when each driver (micro) is "driven" by the total traffic pattern. The traffic (macro) becomes a self-organizing system. A "feedback" is formed between the microscopic events and the macroscopic order. Here the density of traffic becomes a key variable in the problem.

C. Information Theory, Entropy and Thermodynamics

The issue is whether all nonlocal information acquisition and transfer also demands energy transfer. In our discussion of remote perception and of Bell's theorem (Bell, 1964) correlated information can be synchronized (which is nonlocal) if energy transmission from one point in spacetime does not occur. If Shannon's law holds, then a change of information content, ΔI, is associated with a change of "order" or entropy, $\Delta S = -k \ln \Delta I$, where k is the Boltzmann constant and we take the natural logarithm of the change in information. Entropy change is associated with energy change, δq, by the Second Law of Thermodynamics,

$$\Delta S > \int_0^{\Delta} \frac{\delta q}{T}$$

where T is the absolute temperature from the Clausius inequality for irreversible systems.

In the case of Bell's theorem, the frame of reference issue is involved in the concept of information transfer. The nonlocal connectedness of two events can be interpreted as a space-like superluminal connection or as a prior luminal connection (Rauscher, 1979; Ramon and Rauscher, 1980). If the former interpretation of Bell's theorem is valid, then we have the issue of energy transfer between the two synchronized events and this could involve energy conservation issues or tachyon signal propagation, but the synchronistic explanation does not work for macro-psychokinesis. (This issue has been explored in detail but see Herbert, 1988 and Walker, 1979.)

We may then have super energy conservation principles which conserve energy even if Shannon's law should hold. Walker and Mattuck treat the issue of psychokinesis and energy conservation by considering the phenomena of local energy ordering or the coherence of local random processes that cause macroscopic effects (Mattuck and Walker, 1979). Certainly the issues of "synchronicity" (in real time) with or without a prior cause, remote correlation of information, and local information and psychokinetic effects are manifestations of thought information and events in the physical world. One consideration in the relationship of Shannon's law and the Second Law of Thermodynamics is that the entropy functions in these two equations which may be related but not equivalent. Both entropy functions measure order or the relationship between order and disorder. Another major issue is that both Shannon's law and the Second Law of Thermodynamics apply to closed, near equilibrium systems. In reconciling and modeling properties of consciousness, the system of interest which is also reconciled with known physical processes, most likely involves open dissipative systems which are nonlinear. Information theory, as applied to self-referential, creative, space-time independent systems such as consciousness, may necessitate the consideration of Prigogine's view of open dissipative structures. This requires a consideration of more general cases, such as nonlinear systems.

For example, in Le Châtelier's principle, the criterion for stability (where there is a movement to restore a system to equilibrium) may involve discrete metastable states rather than continuous processes. This view has been described via the catastrophe theory. In a sense such processes involve macroscopically discrete processes. The concept is that non-equilibrium conditions may be a source of order. If a system is pushed far enough from equilibrium it will become unstable and evolve toward a new "steady state." Biologic processes may, hence, lie on the edge of nonlinear stability and instability. This criterion for stability of developmental processes may relate to the force towards evolution and the so-called issue of "levels of consciousness" may be described by a model which involves these considerations.

The whole area that considers information, entropy, energy, and process (dynamics) is of great interest. Recent exciting ideas such as multidimensional geometric models, group theory, holographic concepts morphogenetic field theory, dissipative and associative structures are of interest in regard to the issues of the physical process and the manner in which it is connected to the nature of consciousness (Rauscher, Hurtak, Hurtak, 2014).

Classic thermodynamic models can be compared to those of Walker and others in which local quantum processes lead to local target energy availability for psychokinetic intervention. We have also examined in detail the local available energy of the Fermi vacuum in a field theoretic model (Rauscher, 1968)

Also the relationship of information and entropy is of interest and does not represent independent variables. Detailed calculations are in progress to determine the values of ε and ε_Λ consistent with the phenomenological data derived from the residual stress release in various materials subject to psychokinetic effects. We have also estimated the energy investment in the differential increase of bacterial growth of salmonella typhemerium.

Let us estimate the energy necessary to produce the apparent psychokinetic (PK) effect we have observed. We consider the case of the low concentration of tetracycline (1 microgram per milliliter) from our 1981 run. We found that the Worrall-tested sample contains 120% more bacteria over the control sample at 23 generation times. Percent difference is defined as treated sample (number of bacteria) minus control number, both divided by the control times of 100%. Controls in this run and for over 30 experiments in our base line studies do not deviate from each other by more than 1% (Rubik and Rauscher, 1993; Rauscher, 1990).

We consider the additional energy needed to produce the excess growth of the treated vs. control sample in terms of the metabolic process needed to produce this growth. The number of additional bacteria is about 10^8 bacteria for 23 generation times. If we estimate the metabolic process over 23 generations this gives us 10^2 calories/sec. This gives the energy involved in the psychokinetic intervention as

$$\varepsilon_{\Lambda_1} \cong 4.2 \times 10^9 \text{ erg/gm sec.}$$

We can also estimate the energy content of apparent psychokinetic intervention in crystalline materials derived from experimental research. We make this estimate based on the energy required to produce psychokinetic changes in the crystals observed in electron micrographs. It is difficult to measure the depth of the psychokinetic action in the same way the electron microscope measures the perturbation of about one atomic layer. We have examined the comparison of PK action defining a layer. This bit rate is quite small (Crussard and Bouvaist, 1978).

We have examined the comparison of PK action defining a treated sample. Each sample also has a similarity prepared control. By slicing below the surface, analysis has shown that PK is not just a surface phenomena. It may be possible to estimate PK interaction by use of thermistor experiments or attached heat sensitive liquid crystal test patches (Houck, 1982a). Use of these datum lead to a crude estimate of the energy needed to produce surface perturbations on a crystal surface. Both metals and laboratory grown aqueous crystals have been examined for crystal dislocations in treated versus controls. We estimate

$$\varepsilon_{\Lambda_2} \sim 4 \times 10^9 \text{ erg/gm} \cdot \text{cm}^3$$

This energy is possibly a little high, but it is estimated from an average sample. Some RNG (random number generators) would yield a lower ε_{Λ_2} but claims for larger samples bending (2 inches diameter aluminum-titanium to a 30° PK bend) (Crussard and Bouvaist, 1978).

We have examined possible sources of such energy. Perhaps consciousness can access vacuum state polarization energy. We examine this in the context of mechanical perturbations that are affected by the available energy of the polarization of the virtual vacuum energy states. We plan further research in the area.

It may be that the remote action of the consciousness can bring order out of nonlinear non-equilibrium processes. The research of stresses in metal and the increase in salmonella growth are examples. The analysis, because PK and psychic healing both represent an increase in order, appears to be a Prigogine type process which involves negentropy.

We can estimate an associate entropy and information and $\Delta S \sim \int \delta q/T$. If we have an energy ε_{Λ} of 4×10^9 erg/gm · cm^3, this is 0.04 watts per gram. Let us consider this energy distributed over a small temperature range of $\Delta T \sim 1^\circ$ K giving $\Delta S \sim 0.04$ watt/gm° K. We can also estimate an information content, or bit rate, from Shannon's Law; this bit rate is quite small.

As before stated, Mattuck and Walker (1979) have developed a quantum mechanical information model in which they calculate possible sets of available energy for psychokinesis. In one example calculation, they estimate that the local lowering of a 10 kilogram tank of water by about 0.03°C provides about 10^{10} ergs of kinetic energy. This is a large area to PK. The energy to PK a system may depend on what that system is. (Note that an 'erg' is about the energy of a flea doing push ups.) They consider thermal and other energy sources. We have demonstrated elsewhere that vacuum polarization energy can also supply sufficient energy to make possible psychokinetic interactions (Rauscher, 1968). See Table 10 for a summary of theoretical models of psi and some additional ideas.

Table 10
Some Categories Of
Theoretical Models of PSI

I. Physical models

   a. Quantum mechanical, quantum measurement, primarily of detail microscopic. The quantum measurement issue is primarily a mathematical artifact or a clue to the manner in which conscious interacts with physical phenomena (Tegmark, 2000; Josephson, 1991, Rauscher, 2006b, 2010)?
   b. Electromagnetic mediated psi, usually associated with ELF (extremely low frequency) signal propagation modalities (Rauscher and van Bise, 1980). These models were, in general, put forward by Russian researchers particularly to model telepathy (can be micro or macro).
   c. Space-time independence of consciousness "information transfer" or event relationship, causality, or a -causality, and multidimensional geometries, N > 4.
   d. "Energy conservation," information and entropy, self -organizational models.

II. Neuronal, physiological models

   a. Synaptic cleft of neuron firings, Josephson junction quantum models (See point I.a above).
   b. Hypothalamic, pituitary axis, pineal, and physiochemical role of memory, information recording, storage and assessment (relate to cortex) (Rauscher, 2011, Rauscher and Busier, 2015).
   c. Electromagnetic waves, magnetic fields, and neurons, bone piezoelectric effects (Rauscher, 2011).
   d. Mind/matter or mind/body connection by PK interaction (model of life in terms of PK, psi).

e. Collective, circulating brain currents as measured by EEG, Fourier components, and the holographic metaphor (Pribram, 1976; Bohm, 1980; Rauscher, 1980).
f. Magnetic fields and biological systems, states of consciousness, and psi enhancement in Russia (Ostrander and Schroder, 1970).
g. Information, neuronal propagation system, magneto-acoustic soliton waves, and remote information transmission (Rauscher, 1982, 1983).

III. Psychological and psychosocial, cultural, and anthropological models

a. Jungian archetypes and the unconscious, collective knowledge, synchronicity and subconscious psi processing.
b. Role of emotions, feelings and intuitions.
c Beliefs such as in some eastern and western religions; mystical, spiritual, or social traditions.

IV. Models with meaningless labels, i.e. untestable within the scientific paradigm

a. Some of the sociological, psychological models in point III above.
b. "Bioplasmic cosmic consciousness," or vague undefined labels for unspecified phenomena used in Russia and elsewherer (Ostrander and Schroder, 1970).

V. The Development of the local/nonlocal complex eight space by the author for remote perception and precognition by this author and colleagues.

Conclusion

We have discussed multidimensional geometries, that is, models with N > 4 dimensions, and some of the predications made for these models on psychic and physical processes. One of the major issues in physics is how possible potential events and intentions become actualized as physical events. It is felt that the multidimensional view holds clues as to the interpretations and understanding of some of these significant issues. We have briefly discussed other physical theories and their possible relation to psi, such as the ELF model and quantum mechanical prediction and their limitations. We also examined thermodynamic formalism and psychokinesis. (Rauscher, 1983a).

As before stated, there are exciting prospects in the theories presented here, that not only do we have a possible unified theory, but also a manner in which to incorporate a role for the conscious process in the physical world.

In the calculations presented in this chapter, we have attempted to relate the major principles of physics to the various aspects of human capabilities to access information, shielded from normal channels of communication, over space and time. Apparent conflicts between causality and precognition may be ultimately reconcilable by considering higher dimensional complex geometries, which show great promise not only in describing psychic functioning, but also in unifying the major branches of physics. (See also Chapter 6, 7 and 8.) We plan to test further the spacetime independence of the remote perception database over extended space and time separation and also possible finite or instantaneous signal velocity dependence. Experiments which are tests of these models, as suggested and tested in Chapter 3 and 4, and which further examine spacetime functional relationships, will be most helpful for the development of our theoretical models.

The models not only describe the remote perception database, but also become a most valuable tool for understanding the fundamental problems in physics. This is one of the most desirable uses of the psychic database. Ultimately it is believed that this exploration will lead to a better comprehension of ourselves and our place in the Universe.

As I said, it is not as if psi is not as old as humankind, but then gravity is much older and it took Newton and Einstein and others to realize its existence and to be able to describe it. The study of the properties of consciousness, then also, when reasonably well mathematically described, may bring about a new era in human conception and a deeper understanding of the fundamental nature of reality. Let it be noted that this author does not believe that all aspects of conscious perception are amenable to detailed mathematical description.

It appears that the state and fundamental nature of consciousness connects intentionally with dimensionality. States of consciousness, such as remote perception, involve mental access to higher dimensional spaces for $N > 4$. "State-specific science" relates to states of consciousness and perceptual mode. These states relate to access of multidimensional modes of perception which is constrained by some physical symmetry principles (Tart, 1969).

We conclude with some more comments on the nature and implications of expanded consciousness. Below is a flow chart of the Role of Intention to Action,

ROLE OF INTENTION → SENSE → PERCEPTION → AWARENESS → THOUGHT→ CONCEPT AND MEMORY → DECISION → WILL → INTENT → ACTION

A concept must be created and formulated in order to create an action or result. For example, Leonardo da Vinci and Jules Verne suggested certain possibilities which then could be defined, specified, and created, such possibilities as heavier than air aircraft for human flight in 1903 (da Vinci) and man going to the moon and landing on it in 1969, as in Jules Verne's prophetic novel "From Earth to Moon" about 100 years before the first complete orbital flight. Each orbit was about 96 minutes and Jules Verne predicted 90 minutes.

The source and origin of moral judgement arises from many factors including psychic perception. Each decision one makes is not just with one or a few individuals but involves the fundamental laws of the universe. These laws involve the manner thought transforms and moves into action. In fact, each decision involves a multitude of aspects of the universe, each act involves the whole of what underlies our experience of reality. These decisions, to be complete, must involve psi perception. This perspective becomes more in alignment with the Universal.

CONCLUSIONS

- We have assumed a multidimensional model in which ordinary spacetime coordinates are simply the real components of a complex 8-dimensional spacetime.

- Under this assumption, we obtain terms which subtract to zero on a description of the metric. In principle, this could account for remote viewing and precognition.

Appendix I
Complex Eight Space Predicts Faster Than Light Tachyonic Signal Propagation

We demonstrate that the complex eight space predicts faster than light tachyonic signal propagation in the complex eight space manifold. In the ordinary real X_{Re} t_{Re} plane then we have the usual Einstein mass relationship as

$$m = m_0/\sqrt{1-v^2/c^2} \text{ for } v \le c$$

Where m and m_0 are real as is v and c and we can compare this to the tachyonic mass relationship in the X_{Re} t_{Re} plane

$$m = m_0^*/\sqrt{1-v^2/c^2} = im_0/\sqrt{1-v^2/c^2}$$
$$= m_0/\sqrt{v^2/c^2-1} \text{ for } v > c$$

Where m* stands for m* = im or m* = m_{Im}.

$$m = m_0/\sqrt{1+v^2/c^2}$$

For m real, we can examine two cases on v as v < c or v > c so we will let v be any value from $-\infty < v > \infty$, where the velocity, v, is taken as real.

If we choose v imaginary or v* = iv then $v^{*2}/c^2 = -v^2/c^2$ and $\sqrt{1+v^{*2}/c^2}$ becomes $\sqrt{1-v^2/c^2}$ or

$$m = m_0/\sqrt{1-v^2/c^2}$$

We get the form of this normal Lorentz transformation if v is imaginary. If both v and m are imaginary as v* = iv and m* = im then we have

$$m = m_0^*\sqrt{1+v^{*2}/c^2} = im_0/\sqrt{1-v^2/c^2} = m_0/\sqrt{v^2/c^2-1}$$

or the tachyonic condition (Feinberg, 1967; Amoroso and Rauscher, 2010; Rauscher and Amoroso, 2011).

Appendix II
Flow Diagrams

We present two more flow diagrams to our map, Fig. 5a text, these figures indicate some relationships between physics and psi as well as the interrelationship of physics concepts and the interrelationships of psi and related phenomena. In Fig. 5o displays the manner in which geometry, physics, space-time relate to psychic and related phenomena. In Fig. 5p, we display such concepts as Brain/Mind, sense awareness and altered or varied states of consciousness. Perhaps the key to Figs. 5o and 5p is that everything is connected to everything else, that is, it is all entangled anyway!

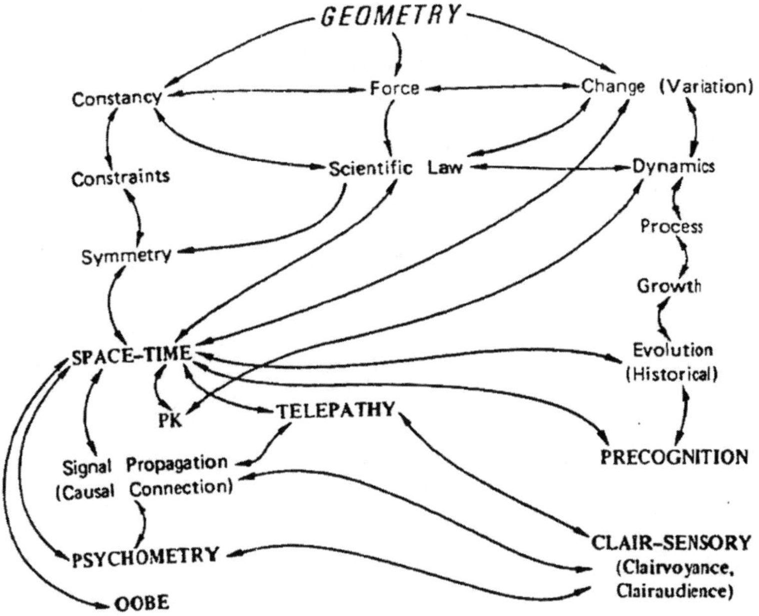

Figure 5o Flow diagram of conceptual ideas and their possible interrelations, to geometry, psi and other processes.

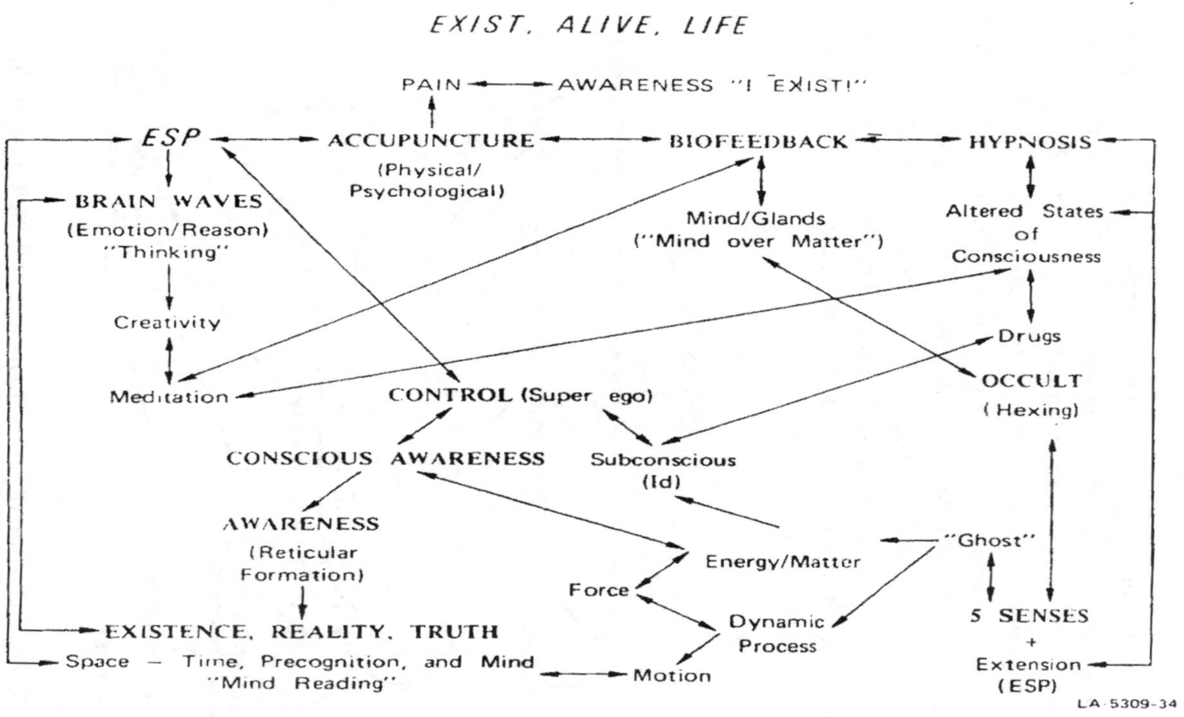

Figure 5p A more universal detailed chart of interrelations of various concepts.

Appendix III
Faraday Cage Experiments

Early SRI experiments were conducted in a μ-metal shield or a Faraday cage. The specific frequency range of electromagnetic waves which are shielded against in the ELF region are given in the reports of the SRI work and in the IEEE and Nature papers at the Stanford University shielded condition and no attenuation of the phenomena was observed. Also in the summer of 1976, an experiment was conducted in which the target area was a cave and the outbound experimenters were shielded by approximately 200 feet of earth. The subject correctly identified the target area. (See Chapter 11).

In the case of gravity, all gravitational (material) bodies appear to exhibit attractive gravitational phenomena. If gravitational repulsion was discovered, then a gravitational shield could be developed. The psychic modality of information accessing may be found to be "jammed" by some form of psychic interference, but it appears not to be possible to inhibit the phenomena by a matter (gravitational shield) or electromagnetic shield.

Further examination of long distance precognitive remote perception will be made by a Menlo Park, California, USA, and an experiment in, for example, China. Of course, ultimately, a detailed examination would have to be conducted in which it was considered whether "propagation" of information occurred through or around the earth.

Nuclear force and nuclear decay rate experiments in which subject and nuclear processes interaction can also be examined. The link of the psychic interface and the four major force fields should be studied in detail in order to illuminate the nature of psychic phenomena.

References

Abbott, E.A. (1984) *Flatland,* New American Library, New York.

Amoroso, R.L. and E.A. Rauscher (2009) *The Holographic Anthropic Multiverse; Formalizing the complex Geometry of Reality,* World Scientific.

Amoroso. R.L. and E.A. Rauscher (2010) "Empirical Protocol for Measuring Virtual Tachyon/Tardow Interactions in a Dirac Vacuum, pp. 199-216. Eds. R.L. Amoroso, P. Rowlands and S. Jeffers. Search for a Fundamental Theory. Imperial College, London, UK, American Institute of Physics, A*IP Conference Proceedings,* 1 p. 1316, Melville, New York.

Aspect, A. P. Grangier and G. Roger (1993) "Experimental Test of Bell's Inequality using Time Varying Analysis," *Phys. Rev. Lett*. 49, p. 1804.

Batten, A.H. (1995) "A most rare vision: Eddington's thinking on the relation between science and religion," *J. Sci. Exploration* 9, p. 231.

Beck, R. (1978) Private communication. He was interested in LF and ELF radiation for over 15 years and possible ELF entrainment of EEG.

Bell, J.S. (1964) "On the Einstein, Podolsky, Rosen paradox," *Physics* 1, pp. 195-200.

Ben, D. and C. Honorton (1994) "Does Psi Exist? Replicable evidence for anomalous processes of Information transfer," *Psychological Bulletin* (January).

Bisaha, J.P. and B.J. Dunne (1976) *"Replication of the Stanford Experiment: Precognition, Remote Viewing in the Chicago Area: Advances in Parapsychology*. Parapsychological Association, Scarecrow Press, Metachen, New Jersey.

Blau, F. (1981), *Telepathy,* private preprint.

Bohm, D. (1980) *Wholeness and the Implicate Order,* Routledge and Kegan Paul, London, and private communication in 1973.

Bohm, D. and B. Hiley (1993) *The Undivided Universe,* Routledge, New York.

Callahan, P.S. (1980) *Physiolog. Chem. Physics* 12, p. 31.

Capra, F. (1974) "Bootstrap and Buddhism," *Am. J. Physics* 42, pp. 15-19.

Capra, F. (1975) "*The Tao of Physics: An Exploration of the Parallels Between Modern Physics and Eastern Mysticism,*" Shambhala, Berkeley.

Chew, G. (1964) *The Analytic S-Matrix,* Frontiers of Physics, Benjamin. And private conversation.

Clauser, J.F and W.A. Horne (1974) "Experimental consequences of objective local theories", *Phys. Rev.* 10D, 5, p. 26.

Costa de Beauregard, O. (1976) "Time symmetry and the interpretation of Quantum Mechanics," *Found. of Phys.* 6, pp. 539-559, and private communication.

Costa de Beauregard, O. (2002) "Wavelike coherence and CPT invariance, sesames of the paranormals." *J. of Scientific Exploration, 16,* pp. 651-654.

Crussard, C. and J. Bouvaist (1978) Mémoires Scientifiques Revue, Mátallurgie Février (France, 1978), p. 178.

Eberhard, P.H. (1978) "Bell's Theorem and the different concepts of locality," *II. Nuovo Cimente* B46, pp. 392-419.

Einstein, A., B. Podolsky and N. Rosen (1935) *Phys. Rev.* 47, p. 777.

Einstein, A. (1955) *Relativity,* Princeton University Press.

Ellis, H.E. (1974) *Found of Phys.* 4, p. 311.

Evan, G.T. and D.K. Sen (1973) "Maxwell's Equations in complex Minkowski space." *J. Math. Phys.* 14,1668.

Feinberg, G. (1967) "Possibilities of faster than light particles." *Phys. Rev.* 159, 1089 and private communication, 1976.

Gisin, N., W.J. Tittel, J.H. Prendel and H. Zbinden (1998) "Violation of Bell's Inequality on photons more than 10km apart." *Phys. Rev. Lett.* 81, p. 3563.

Glausdorff, P. and I. Prigogine (1971) *Thermodynamic Theory of Structure, Stability, and Fluctuations,* New York: Wiley-Interscience, and private communication with Pirgogue.

Hanson, R.D. and E.T. Newman (1975) "A Complex Minkowski approach to Twisters," *General Relativity and Gravitation* 6, p. 216.

Harary, K. (1982a) Research in parapsychology, abstracts and papers from the PA (1981) Scarecrow Press, Inc., Metuchen, New Jersey and London, p. 75.

Harary, K. (1982b) "Psi as nature," *European Jour. of Parapsych.* 4, p. 278.

Herbert, N. and J. Karush (1978) "Generalization of Bell's Theorem," *Foundation of Physics* **8**, pp. 313-317.

Herbert, N. (1982) "Superluminal Communication based upon a new kind of Quantum Measurement," *Foundation of Physics* 12, pp. 1171-79.

Herbert, N. (1988) *Faster Than Light: Super Luminal loop-holes in physics*, New American Library, New York.

Houck, J. (1982a) "Surface change during worm farming," February 5, 1982, and private communication with J. Houck on the worm farming process, May 1982.

Houck, J. (1982b) "A conceptual model of paranormal phenomena," revision, Huntington Beach, CA and collaboration, September 21, 1982.

Hurtak, J.J. (1973) *The Book of Knowledge: The Keys of Enoch®*, Los Gatos, CA: Academy for Future Science.

Hynik, J.A. (1983) private communication, SRI International.

Jahn, R. and B. J. Dunne (1982) *IEEE* 70, p. 136.

Jahn, R.G. and B. Dunne (1987) *Margins of Reality. The role of Consciousness in the Physical World.* Harcourt, Brace: New York.

Josephson, B. (1991) "Biological Utilization of Quantum Non-Locality," *Foundation of Physics*, 21, p. 197.

Kaiser, D. (2011) *How the Hippies Saved Physics: Science, Counterculture, and its Quantum Revival*, W.W. Norton and Co.

Kaluza, T. (1921) Sitz. Berlin Preuss. Adad. Wiss, p. 966.

Kane, B., J. Milley and D. Brown Eds. (1993) *Silver threads: 25 years of Parapsychology Research*, Praeger.

Klein, O. (1926) *Z. Phys.* 37, p. 895.

Kogan, I.M. (1966) "Is telepathy possible?," *Radio Eng.* 21, p. 75.

Kogan, I.M. (1968) Telepathy, Hypotheses and Observatory. *Radio Eng*, 23, p. 122.

Lorentz, H.A., A. Einstein, H. Minkowski and H. Weyl (1923) *The principles of Relativity*. Dover Pub.

Mattuck, R.D. (1977) "Thermal noise theory of psychokinesis: modified Walker Model with Pulsed Information Rate," *Journal of Psychoenergetic Systems.* p. 3.

Mattuck, R.D. and E.H. Walker (1979) "The action of Consciousness on Matter: A Quantum Mechanical Theory of Psychokinesis, pp. 111-159, of *The Iceland Papers: Select Papers on Experimental and Theoretical Research on the Physics of Consciousness*. Eds. A. Puharich, Amherst, Wisconsin: Essentia Research.

Millay, J. and J. R. Johnston (1983) "Electrophysiological measurements," *Psi Research* 2, p. 98.

Millay, J. (2010) *Radiant Minds: Scientist Explore the Dimensions of Consciousness,* Ed. J. Miller, pub J. Millay.

Mitchell, E.D. (1974) Ed. John White. *Psychic Exploration, A Challenge for Science.* New York: GP. Putnam and Sons, and private communication.

Motz, L. (1972) *Il Nuovo Cimento* 12B, p. 239.

Motz, L. and J. Epstein (1979) *II Nuovo Cimento* S1A, p. 88.

Nicolis, G. and I. Prigogine (1977) *Self-Organization in Nonequilibrium Systems; from Dissipative Structures to Order through Fluctuations.* New York: John Wiley & Sons, .

Ostrander, S., and L. Schroeder (1970) *Psychic Discoveries Behind the Iron Curtain.* New York: Prentice Hall.

Peat, F.D. (1988) *Super-strings and the Search for a Theory of Everything.* Chicago: Contemporary Books.

Penrose, R. (1978) "The Geometry of the Universe." Ed. L.A. Steen, *Mathematics Today*, Berlin: Springer Verlag.

Penrose, R. and W. Rindler (1985) *Spiners and Space-Time.* Vol. 2.

New York: Cambridge U. Press.

Persinger, M.A. (1975) *Psychoenergetic Systems* 1, p. 63.

Phillips, P.R. (1978) *Found. of Phys.* 8, p. 547, and private communication.

Pribram, K. (1976) "Problems concerning the structure of Consciousness," Ed. G. Globus, *Consciousness and the Brain*. Plenum Press, New York and private communication.

Puharich, A. (1950-1956) "A laboratory study of human cognition not primarily dependent on the classical sensory system, conducted under the special environmental conditions of a Faraday cage enclosure," 1950-1956, Round Table Foundation.

Puthoff, H. E., and R. Targ (1976a) A perceptual channel for information transfer over kilometer distances: Historical perceptive and recent research. *Proceedings for the Institute of Electrical and Electronic Engineers, 64*, pp. 329-254.

Puthoff, H.E. and R. Targ (1976b), "Remote Viewing of Geographical Locations," in *Parapsychology,* Metachen, NJ: Scarecrow Press.

Puthoff, H. and R. Targ (1977) "Direct Perception of Remote Geographical Locations," Invited Paper for the IEEE Nation Convention, Electro, 77, April 17, 1977, New York.

Radin, D. (1997) *The Conscious Universe*. NY: Harper and Row.

Radin, D. (2006) *Entangled Minds. Extrasensory Experience in a Quantum Reality*. New York: Simon and Schuster.

Ramon, C. and E.A. Rauscher (1980) Superluminal transformation in complex Minkowski spaces. *Foundations of Physics* 10, pp. 661-669.

Rauscher, E.A. (1968a) Collective interactions and quantum plasma physics. *Journal of Plasma Physics, 2,* pp. 517-541.

Rauscher, E.A. (1968b) A unifying Theory of Fundamental Process, *Bull. Am. Phys. Soc.* 15, p. 1639.

Rauscher, E.A. (1970) "Bootstrap and a Uniform Formalism of the Four Force Fields" in *LBNL, UCRL-20068, October.*

Rauscher, E.A. (1971) *A Unifying Theory of Fundamental Processes,* UCRL-20808 (June) UCB, book.

Rauscher, E.A. (1972a) "A Set of Generalized Heisenberg Relations and a Possible New form of Quantization, Lett. AL *Nuovo Cimento* 4, p. 757.

Rauscher, E.A. (1972b) "A Group Theoretical Representation of the Generalized Heisenberg Relations," *Lett. AL Nuovo Cimento* 5, p. 925.

Rauscher, E.A. (1972c) "Closed Cosmological Solutions to Einstein's Field Equations," Lett. AL *Nuovo Cimento* 3, p. 661.

Rauscher, E.A. (1973) "Minkowski Metric for a multi-dimensional geometry." *Lett. Nuovo Cimento* 7, p. 361.

Rauscher, E.A. (1974) "Possible Complex Geometry as a Model of Psi, Preprint PSRL-2761A.

Rauscher, E.A. (1976) "Some physical Model's potentially applicable to Remote Perception," *Bull. Am. Physics Soc.,* 21, pp. 1305-1306.

Rauscher, E.A. (1978a) "Exploration experiments in psychokinesis with subject Uri Geller," PSRL-367 (June 1976) and in *Psi Realité* (French) 7, p. 34.

Rauscher, E.A. (1978b) "Complex Coordinate Geometries in General Relativity and Electromagnetism," *Bull. Am. Physics Soc.* 23, pp. 84-85.

Rauscher, E.A. (1979) "Some physical models applicable to remote perception," in *The Iceland Papers: Frontiers of Physics.* Select papers on experimental and theoretical research on the physics of consciousness; foreword by B.D. Josephson, edited by A. Puharich. Amherst, Wisconsin Essentia Research Associates, 54406, pp. 50-93, and republished, PACE, Ottawa, Ontario, Canada (1996).

Rauscher, E.A. (1980) "Proposal to test the temporal modality in remote perception experiments with variable precognitive intervals," funded by Parapsychology Foundation, New York, September 30, 1980.

Rauscher, E.A. (1981) Coherent Solutions of the Schrodinger Equation in Complex Eight Space, *Proceedings of the Tenth International Conference on the Science,* Vol. II, New York: ICF Press, pp. 1407-1731.

Rauscher, E.A. (1982a) "Healing and psychokinesis as a negentropic process," Tecnic Research Laboratories publication PSRL-2417 (June 1982).

Rauscher, E.A. (1982b) "Application of Soliton Physics to Plasma-MHD and Superconductivity-BCS," PSRL-3107 (November 1982), contract report to PET Corp., Los Angeles.

Rauscher, E.A. (1983a) "Psychokinetic Interaction with Laboratory Prepared Materials: A Prototype Experimental Design, *Psi Research,* 3, pp. 26-40, San Francisco, CA: Washington Research Center.

Rauscher, E.A. (1983b) "The Physics of Psi Phenomena in Space and Time. Part I. Major Principles of Physics, Psychic Phenomena and some Physical Models. *Psi Research,* Vol. 3, pp. 64-88, San Francisco, CA: Washington Research Center.

Rauscher, E.A. (1983c) "The Physics of Psi Phenomena in Space and Time": Part II. *Multidimensional Geometric Models*. Vol 3, pp. 93-120, San Francisco, CA: Washington Research Center.

Rauscher, E.A. (1983d) "Multidimensional Properties of Consciousness and some Laws of Reality." *Psi Research* 2, p. 53. Presented at the CIPRES Conference, Fez, Morocco, May 11-15.

Rauscher, E.A. (1983e) *Electromagnetic Phenomena in Complex Geometries and Non-linear phenomena, Non-Hertzian waves and Magnetic Monopoles*. Millbrae, CA: Tesla Book Co.

Rauscher, E.A. (1983f) "EM and Nonlinear Phenomena in Complex Minkowski Spaces" *Bull. Amer. Phys*. 28, p. 351.

Rauscher, E.A. (1990) "Human Volitional Effects on a Model Bacterial System," *Subtle Energies* 1, p. 21.

Rauscher, E.A. (1996) "Some Physical applications to Remote Perception," pp. 50-63, The *Iceland Papers: Frontiers of Physics Conference,* eds. A. Puharich and B. Josephson, Amherst, WI.: Essentia Research Associates, (1979), Second Editor, PACE, Ottawa, Canada.

Rauscher, E.A. (2002) "Non-Abelian Gauge Groups for Real and Complex Amended Maxwell's Equations," in *Gravitation and Cosmology,* 183-188. From the Hubble Radius to the Planck Scale. Proceedings of a Symposium in Honor of the 80th Birthday of J.-P. Vigier, Eds. R.L. Amoroso, G. Hunter, M. Kafatos and J.P. Vigier, Kluwer Academic: Dordrecht, Boston, and London, pp. 43-72.

Rauscher, E.A. (2005) Cosmogenesis and Quantum Gravity, Eds. R.L. Amoroso, B. Lehnert and J.P. Vigier, Beyond the Standard Model: Searching for Unity in Physics, the Noetic Press, Inc., Orinda, CA.

Rauscher, E.A. (2006a) "Quantum Mechanics and the Role for Consciousness in the Physical World," *Journal of the ISSSEEM, Energy Medicine* 16, 1.

Rauscher, E.A. (2006b) "Complex Dimensional Space, Penrose Twisters, Nonlocality and Consciousness," Unified Theories Scientific Conference Proceedings, Institute for Strategic Research, Hall of the Hungarian Cultural Foundation, Budapest, Hungary.

Rauscher, E.A. (2010) "Quantum Mechanics and the Effect of Intentional Will," in *Complementarily of Mind and Body Realizing the Dreams of Descartes, Einstein and Eccles.* Nova Scientific Publishers, pp. 35-63.

Rauscher, E.A. (2011) "Methods and Devices for Measurement and Treatment of Pain and the Treatment of Inflammation and Osteoporosis." US Patent 8, 062,2 29 B2, November 22.

Rauscher, E.A. (2015) Deuterium Abundance and Cosmogenesis and Current Cosmology, R. Amoroso, L Kauffman and P. Rowlands, Unified Field Mechanisms: Natural Science Beyond the Veil of Spacetime. World Scientific.

Rauscher, E.A. and R. Amoroso (2008) "*The Schrödinger Equation in Complex Minkowski Space, Nonlocality and Anticipatory Systems,*, CASYS, International Journal of Computing Anticipatory Systems: Ed. D.M. Dubois, Vol. 22, CHAOS Pub., Institute of Mathematics B37 University of Liege, Belgium.

Rauscher, E.A. and R.L. Amoroso (2009) "Relativistic Physics in Complex Minkowski Space, Non-locality, Ether Model and Quantum Physics," Eds. M.C. Duffy and J. Levy, *Ether Space-Time and Cosmology* 3, Physical Vacuum, Relativity and Quantum Physics. Aperion: Montreal, pp. 23-47.

Rauscher, E.A. and R. Amoroso (2011) *Orbiting the moons of Pluto, Solving Einstein's, Maxwell's, Schrödinger's and the Dirac Equation in Complex Space,* World Scientific.

Rauscher, E.A. and M. J. Busier, (2015) "Enhancement of Biological function by the use of Electromagnetic fields", *RRD,* Arizona, 101941.

Rauscher, E.A. and M.J. Busier (2016) *Mathematical Medicine.* (book to be published).

Rauscher, E.A., J.J. Hurtak and D.H. Hurtak (2013a) "Universal Scaling Laws in Quantum Theory and Cosmology," Ed. R.L. Amoroso, L.H,.Kufman and P. Rowlands, *The Physics of Reality, Space, Time, Matter, Cosmos,* World Scientific, pp. 376-387.

Rauscher, E.A., J.J. Hurtak and D.H. Hurtak (2013b) "The Role of Consciousness in Modern Physics" Ed. Deepak Chopra *Brain, Mind, Cosmos: The Nature of Our Existence and the Universe,* Sages and Scientists Series1, Chapter 24.

Rauscher, E.A. and H. Puthoff (1976) Discussion at SRI about a Theory of the Velocity of Psi Propagation.

Rauscher, E.A.,P. Rowlands and R. Amoroso (2015) "Dirac Equation in Nilpotent Quaternionic Space-Anti Space and Complex Eight Space." R. Amoroso, L. Kauffman and P. Rowlands, *Unified Field Mechanics, Natural Beyond the Vale of Time,* London: World Scientific.

Rauscher, E.A. and B.A. Rubik (1979) "Effects on Mobility Behavior and Growth Rate of Salmonella Typhimurium in the Presence of a Psychic Subject," *Research in Parapsychology,* Metuchen, NJ: Scarecrow Press, pp. 140-142.

Rauscher, E.A. and B.A. Rubik (1980) Research in Parapsychology 1979, Abstracts from Parapsychological Association Annual Meeting, W.G. Roll, editor. Metuchen, NJ: Scarecrow Press.

Rauscher, E.A. and B.A. Rubik (1983) "Human Volitional Effects on a Model Bacterial System," *Psi Research* 2, pp. 38-48.

Rauscher, E.A. and R. Targ (2001) The Speed of Thought: Investigation of a Complex Space-time Metric to Describe Psychic Phenomena. *Journal of Scientific Exploration,* 15, pp. 331-354.

Rauscher, E.A. and R. Targ (2006) "The Speed of Thought, Investigation of a Complex Space-Time Metric and Non-Locality," pp. 121-146,

Frontiers of Time: Retro-causation, Experiment and Theory, Ed. D.P. Sheehan, University of San Diego, CA., Presentation, AAAS Meeting, June 2006 and AIP Conference Proceedings, Vol. 863.

Rauscher, E.A. and R. Targ (2008) "Integration of a complex spacetime and nonlocality," D.P. Sheehan Ed., *AIP Proceedings* 863, pp. 121-146.

Rauscher, E.A. and W.L. van Bise (1988) "Fundamental Excitatory Models of the Earth and Earth-Ionosphere Resonant Cavity," pp. 34-69. Eds. S.R. Elswick and T. Wright, IEEE *Proceedings of the International Tesla Symposium*, ITS Inc., Colorado.

Rauscher, E.A. and W. van Bise (1980) "Multiple wave analysis measurements of low frequency (LF) and extremely low frequency (ELF) artificial and natural radiation," Pacific NW Center, Portland, Oregon (June 9).

Rauscher, E.A. and W. van Bise (1990) "Theoretical Models and Experimental Data Concerning the Space-Time Properties of Consciousness and Remote Mental Influences, PSL-60788, Tecnic Research Report. Final Report in fulfillment of its Black Fine Arts and Science Grant (1988-1990).

Rauscher, E.A. and W. van Bise (1999) "The Relation of Extremely Low Frequency Electromagnetic and Magnetic Fields Associated with Seismic and Volcanic activity and Artificial Ionospheric Disturbances and Ionospheric Electromagnetic Phenomena Associated with Earthquakes," Ed. W. Hayakawa, Terra Scientific Pub. Co. (Terra Pub.), Tokyo, Japan.

Rauscher, E.A., P. Rowlands and R. Amoroso (2015) "Dirac Equation in Nilpotent Quaternionic Space-Anti Space and Complex Eight Space." R. Amoroso, L. Kauffman and P. Rowlands, *Unified Field Mechanics, Natural Beyond the Vale of Time*, London: World Scientific.

Roll, W.G. (1974) *Earlier RSPK Cases, Research in Parapsychology*, 1974, editor J. D. Morris, W. G. Roll and R. L. Morris. Metuchen, NJ: Scarecrow Press, pg. 1134 and private communication.

Rubik, B. and E.A. Rauscher (1981) presentation to the Annual Holms Research Center, Los Angeles, CA, April 25, 1981.

Rubik, B. and E.A. Rauscher (1993) Human Voliational Effects on a Model Bacterial System," *Silver Threads*, 25 years of Parapsychology Research, Eds. B. Kane, J. Millay and D. Brown, Westport, Connecticut, London, Praeger, pp. 181-187.

Schmidt, H. (1978a) "PK Effect on Pre-recorded Targets," *J. Am. Soc. For Psychical* Research and Private Communication.

Schmidt, H. (1978b) "Can an effect precede its cause?" *Found. of Phys.* 8, p. 463.

Schmidt, H. (1982) "Collapse of the state vector and psychokinetic effect." *Found. of Phys.* 12, p. 565.

Sheldrake, R. (1981) *A New Science of Life: The Hypothesis of Formative Causation*, J. P. Tarcher and private communications.

Shimony, A. (1981), Meeting of Physics and Metaphysics, *Nature* 291, pp. 435-436.

Sinclair, V. (1971) *Mental Radio*, Collier Press: New York.

Sirag, S.P. (1979) "Gravitational magnetism," *Nature* (April 5, 1979) and private communication. ("Science does not explain, it is a summary of many experiences," February 1982).

Sirag, S.P. (1982) "Why there are three Fermion Families," *Bull. Am. Phys. Soc.* 27, p. 31.

Sirag, S.P. (1983) *International Journal of Theoretical Physics* 22, p. 1067.

Sirag, S.P. (1993a) Hyperspace reflections. In *Silver Threads: 25 Years of Parapsychology Research*, edited by B. Kane, J. Millay and D. Brown, pp. 156-165. New York: Praeger.

Sirag, S.P. (1993b) "Consciousness: A hyperspace view." Appendix to *Roots of Consciousness* (2nd Ed.), by J. Mishlove, pp. 327-365. Tulsa, OK: Council Oak Books.

Sirag, S.P. (2016) *ADEX Theory: How the ADE Coxeter Graphs Unify Mathematics and Physics.* Singapore: World Scientific.

Stapp, H. (1975) "Theory of reality," *LBL-3837* (April 1975).

Stapp, H. (1981) "Mind, matter and quantum mechanics," *Law-*

rence Berkeley Laboratory publication LBL-l2631 (April 1981) and private discussion.

Stapp, H.C. (1998) In Nadeau, R., and Kefatos, M. (Eds.), *The Nonlocal Universe: The New Physics and Matters of the Mind.* Oxford, UK: Oxford University Press.

Stratton, J.A. (1941) *Electromagnetic Theory,* New York: McGraw-Hill, p. 69.

Targ, R. (2004) *Limitless Mind: A Guide to Remote Viewing and Transformation of Consciousness.* New World Library: California.

Targ, R. and H. Puthoff (1974) "Information Transfer Under Conditions of Sensory Shielding," Nature 251, p. 602.

Targ, R., and K. Harary (1984) *The Mind Race: Understanding and Utilizing Psychic Abilities.* New York: Villard.

Targ, R., and J. Hurtak (2006) *The End of Suffering.* Charlottesville: Hampton Roads.

Targ, R., E. May and H. Puthoff (2002). Direct Perception of Remote Geographic Locations" in Mind at Large. *Proceedings of the IEEE,* Hampton Roads: Charlottesville, VA.

Targ, R. and H. Puthoff (1976) *Nature* 252, 602 (1974), and H.E. Puthoff and R. Targ, *IEEE* 64. p. 329, Appendices I and II.

Tart, C. (1969) *Altered States of Consciousness.* New York: John Wiley & Sons Inc.

Tegmark, M. (2000) "Importance of Quantum Decoherence in Brain Proceses, *Phys. Rev.* E61, pp. pp. 41094-4206.

Ullman, M. and S. Krippner (1978) "Experimental Dream Studies," (Telepathy), pp. 409-422, ed. M. Ebon, *The Signet Handbook of Parapsychology,* New American Library, New York. Private Communications with Monteque Ullman and Stanley Krippner.

van Bise, W. (1978) Physiological Chemistry Physics 10, p. 387.

von Neumann, J. (1966) "Theory of Automata: Construction, Reproduction, Homogeneity, Par II of A.W. Burts," *The Theory of Self Reproducing*, University of Illinois Press.

Walker, E.H. (1970) "The Nature of Consciousness," *Mathematical Biosciences* 7, p. 131.

Walker, E.H. (1972) Quantum Mechanical Tunneling in Synaptic and Ephaptic Transmission," *Intern. Jour. Quantum Chemistry* 11, pp. 103-127.

Walker, E.H. (1979) The Quantum Theory Psi Phenomena, Psychogenetic Systems.

Walker, E.H. (2000) *The Physics of Consciousness: the Quantum Mind and the Meaning of Life*. Cambridge, MA: Persens.

Wheeler, J.A. (1978) *Frontiers of Time*. International School of Physics, Enrico Fermi Center for Theoretical Physics. University of Texas, Austin, Texas, and private communication.

Weyl, H. (1920) *Phys*. Z 21, p. 649.

Weyl, H. (1931) *The Theory of Groups and Quantum Mechanics*, H.P. Robertson (trans), Dover Pub. Inc.

Weyl, H. (1957) *Space-Time-Matter*, Dover Pub. Inc.

Wigner, E.P. (1967) *Symmetries and Reflections*, Scientific Essays," Indiana University Press, Bloomington, Indiana, 1967 and private communication.

Witton, E. (1995) "String Theory in Various Dimensions." *Nuclear Physics*, B4, pp. 85-126.

Wolf, F.A. (1981). *Taking the Quantum Leap*. Harper and Row: San Francisco.

Worrall, A. and O. Worrall (1970) "*The Healing Touch*," New York: Harper and Row.

Zukov, G. (1979) *The Dancing Wu Li Masters*. New York: William Morrow and Co., Inc.

Chapter 6
Non-Locality as a Fundamental Principle of Reality: Bell's Theorem and Space-Like Interconnectedness
by
Elizabeth A. Rauscher, Ph.D.

"Some physicists are interested in another observation about the microscopic domain which implies that systems (such as particles) which are correlated (or related in their physical properties) remain correlated even when great distances separate them. This form of interconnectedness is termed Bell's theorem. It is as if a spider in its web feels each disturbance in the web's far reaches as it sits at the web's center."

— *The Philosophy of Science,* E.A. Rauscher, Ph.D., 1971, 1975.

"The world thus appears as a complicated tissue of events in which connections of different kinds alternate or overlap or combine and thereby determine the texture of the whole."

— *Physics and Philosophy,* Werner Heisenberg, Ph.D., 1938.

Table of Contents

Introduction 381

1. Experimental Verification of J.S. Bell's Theorem 382

2. The Velocity Paradox of Bell's Theorem and the Young's Double Slit Experiment Resolved 394

3. Other Nonlocal Micro and Macro Phenomena 395

   A. Young's Double Slit Experiment and Nonlocality 397

   B. Wheeler's Delayed-Choice Gedanken Experiment 401

   C. Aharonov-Bohm: A Venture into Nonlocality? 404

   D. Ernst Mach and Possible Macroscopic Nonlocality 406

Conclusion 409

References 411

List of Tables

Table 1: Some Topics for Consideration for Interference Experiments 404

List of Figures

Figure 6a Bell's Theorem In Time and Space 384
Figure 6b The Stern Gerlach Experiment 386
Figure 6c Common Point of Origin of Two Events Connected by a Light Signal 388
Figure 6d Quantum Reality 392
Figure 6e A Double-slit experiment with light 396
Figure 6f Wheeler's delayed experimental set up 400
Figure 6g Schematic representations of experiments which involve interconnectedness and supercoherence 402

Introduction

Two very significant principles with vast ramifications discovered in the 20th century are the Heisenberg Uncertainty Principle (Heisenberg, 1938) and the Nonlocality Principles of the Einstein, Podolsky, Rosen (EPR) paradox (Einstein, Podolsky, Rosen, 1935). These aspects of quantum theory have major physical and philosophical implications. The fundamental bases of nonlocality in quantum theory lie in the EPR paradox, as well as other experiments that demand a nonlocal explanation for the phenomenon they display. The fundamental basis of nonlocality in the universe is fundamental to the properties of consciousness.

In my junior level quantum mechanics class at the University of California, I asked, "How do you interpret the quantum principle? What does it all mean?" I was told to shut up and calculate. The term Copenhagen View, which is also called the Copenhagen Picture, arose out of a meeting and discussion of Niels Bohr, Albert Einstein and Werner Heisenberg about the nature of the quantum theory in Copenhagen, Denmark before WWII. Before World War II there had been philosophical discussions on the meaning and interpretation of physics among the major physicists of the day. Famous among these debates were the Bohr-Einstein debates about the interpretation of quantum theory. This was an era of deep exploration and spirited discussions.

As the attention turned to the war effort, and atomic bomb research was classified at Edward Teller's insistence, the major open discussions ceased. Edward Teller told me that classification of fundamental physics research might destroy physics. It certainly made it more a process of doing it and less about thinking of its meaning. It appears that in recent years a few physicists have been re-exploring the meaning, interpretation and relationship of consciousness and quantum theory.

At Lawrence Berkeley National Laboratory (LBNL),

where I was a staff member in the 1970's, I started, named and chaired the Fundamental "Fysiks" Group (F"F"G) with George Weissmann, Nick Herbert, Saul Paul Sirag, Henry Stapp, Phillip Eberhard, Jack Sarfatti, Gary Zukav, Fritjof Capra and John Clauser. (I obtained a guestship for Fritjof Capra at Lawrence Berkeley Theoretical Physics group.) (F"F"G, 1973-1979).

The purpose of the group was to discuss the fundamental meaning and interpretation of the body of physics and in particular quantum mechanics. I had met John Clauser in 1972 and had seen his experimental test set up of the Bell's theorem, nonlocality experiment on the UC Berkeley campus. I was most impressed and thought the experiment a most vital one. John Clauser joined the F"F"G group as did 40 other physicists. (Clauser, 1975; Clauser and Horne, 1971,1974). We had weekly meetings and I would choose a speaker and then we would have the most lively and spirited discussions! Some of our activities are written up by David Kaiser in "How the Hippies Saved Physics" (Kaiser, 2011) about our explanation of quantum nonlocality and quantum entanglement. In the next section I describe the tests of Bell's theorem and its verification.

1. Experimental Verification of J.S. Bell's Theorem

J.S. Bell's (1964, 1966) formulated one of the most significant theorems in relation to quantum mechanics. His theory was developed from the A. Einstein, B. Podolsky and N. Rosen (EPR) "completeness" formulation of quantum theory (Einstein, Podolsky and Rosen, 1935). Heisenberg introduced the uncertainty principle in 1927 that states that one of the principal features of quantum mechanics is that not all the classical physical observables of a system can be simultaneously precisely defined. To explain this phenomena, Bohr further suggested the Copenhagen Interpretation as an explanation for quantum physics. The quantum interpretation is defined by the uncertainty principle which stated that it is not possible to precisely determine the exact position and momentum of a particle at any specific time.

Einstein did not want to rely on probabilities even at the quantum level so Einstein, Podolsky and Rosen came up with a thought experiment, "Does a particle have a position in the moments just before it is measured?" (Einstein, Podolsky and Rosen, 1935). If not, the quantum theory is *incomplete*. The conclusion to the EPR paper stated: "While we have thus shown that the wave function does not provide a complete description of the physical reality, we left open the question of whether or not such a description exists. We believe, however, that such a theory is possible." For the quantum description to be complete, it implies fundamental nonlocality!

Einstein sought to maintain the single state vector approach and seriously questioned the uncertainty principle, and the statistical nature of the quantum theory stating "God does not play dice with the universe." His fundamental vision was to determine the position and momentum of each particle in the universe and develop a unified field theory of the four force fields and explain all of reality! The hitch in this plan was that the position (or location), and momentum cannot be accurately measured nor can the energy and time be scientifically accurately measured, i.e., the Heisenberg uncertainty principle (Rauscher, 1972). The Heisenberg uncertainly relations,

$$\Delta \mathrm{x}\, \Delta p \geq \hbar \quad \text{and} \quad \Delta E\, \Delta t \geq \hbar$$

where $\Delta \mathrm{x}$ is the uncertainty in the position of a particle, Δp, or we can consider that the uncertainty in energy, ΔE, and the uncertainty in time, Δt implies restrictions on the absolute knowledge of the universe, that is, it is impossible to know the measurement of position and the momentum of a particle at the same time, or the energy and time measurement to a degree of accuracy which is restricted by the value of Planck's constant $\hbar$.

Einstein continued to seek to define a unique state vector, but was willing to agree that it may not be the state of an individual object, but the statistical group of objects or the ensemble. For example, there should be within quantum physics,

BELL'S THEOREM IN TIME AND SPACE

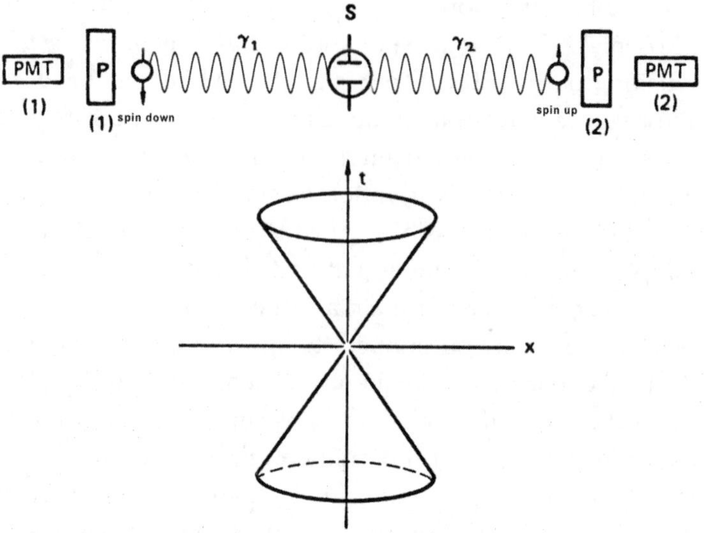

Figure 6a Schematic diagram of J. Clauser-Bell's Theorem Correlation Function Experiment

The two detectors at positions (1) and (2) are Photomultiplier tubes (PMT) and P(1) and P(2) are polarizers for photons γ_1 and γ_2 produced by the atomic cascade of a Calcium source. The detectors of photons at (1) and (2) appear to be outside each others' light cones; events $E_j(t)$ are purely time-like and events $E_j(x)$ are purely space-like. The vertical axis is time from past to future and the horizontal axis represents the three dimensions of space, x, y, z as X. The intersection of x and t is defined as now. Einstein thought that its velocity of light was the upper limit of object or event propagation connections which is represented as event connections in the forward and backward Minkowski light cone (see Chapter 5).

for every electron or particle in the universe, an assignable wave function, Ψe. If the completeness principle holds, we can understand that although the preciseness of measurement may be beyond an individual object, it may be sufficient to describe the ensemble.

In the EPR paper, the completeness of quantum theory implies nonlocal interactions. The concept of nonlocality, which Einstein called this "spooky action at a distance," is now called quantum entanglement and is basic to the development of quantum computing.

Bohm, in order to explain nonlocality (or "spooky action at a distance") in real terms, introduced additional quantum non-observable variables, or "hidden variables," in order to make the EPR quantum hypothesis and Bell's theorem appear local. Experimental demonstrations and mathematics continued to show that locality is incompatible with the statistical predictions of quantum mechanics. (Bohm, 1952, 1977; Bell, 1964, 1966, 1987; Freedman and Clauser, 1972; Amoroso, Kaufman and Rauscher, 2010). Thus, Bell's theorem states that the quantum-mechanical description of a physical system is incomplete and the state of the system cannot be exactly defined without nonlocal interactions.

The test of quantum completeness implied nonlocality, as demonstrated by the EPR formalism. J. Clauser and W.A. Horne (1971, 1974) confirmed this possibility of a stochastic system and hence nonlocality. Indeed, in Clauser's two photon system, which emitted from a singlet state, spin 1 particles or photons. Two photodetectors remote from each other are each preceded by independent, randomly-oriented polarizers (P(1) and P(2)). The measurements made at the two photomultiplier tubes (PMT1 and PMT2) bore out the statistical predictions of quantum mechanics (See Fig. 6a) (Rauscher, 1979). They imply that that nonlocal correlations exist between the two photons at the moment of emission which could be a remnant of their common causal past as further verified by the experiments in-

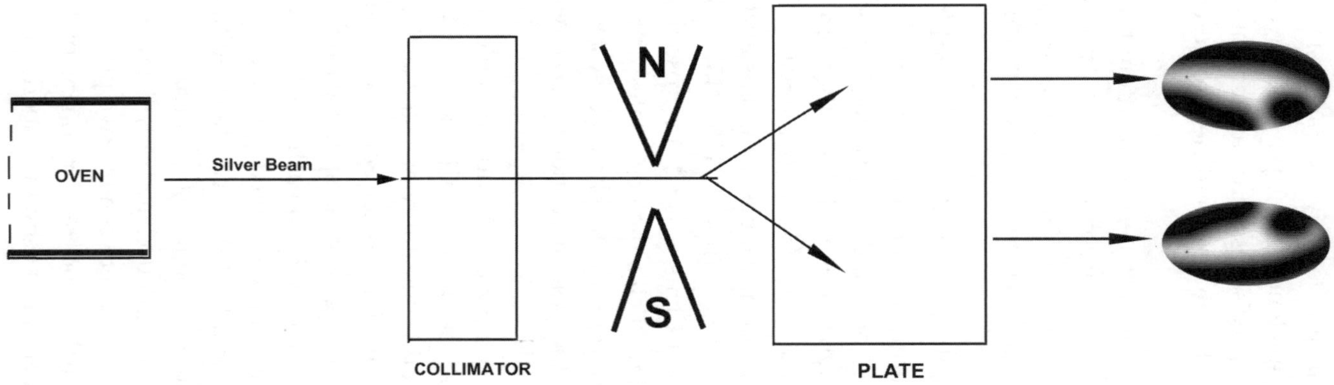

Figure 6b

The Stern Gerlach Experiment

Silver atoms are heated in an oven. The beam goes through a small hole called a collimator and then is exposed to a non-uniform magnetic field. The results show that the components were separated into two values of spin up and spin down.

vestigated by Aspect, *et.al.* (1977) and Gisin (1998b).

J.S. Bell states that "no theory of reality, compatible with quantum theory, can require spatially separate events to be independent." That is confirmed by the measurement of the J. Clauser experiment (Clauser and Horne, 1974; Freedman and Clauser, 1972; Herbert, 1975), where the polarization of one photon determines the polarization of the other photon at its respective measurement site when the two emitted spin 1 photons are initially correlated. Bell discusses a specific experiment, that is, Stern-Gerlach measurements in which two spin one-half particles in the singlet spin state move freely in opposite directions. Specifically, their experiments showed the quantization of electron spin into two orientations, spin up and spin down.

Specifically, Stern and Gerlach (1922) directed a beam of silver atoms into a magnet producing a non-uniform magnetic field (Fig. 6b). What they discovered was that the magnetic field separated the beam into two distinct parts, showing the two possible "spin" states of the electrons, called s_1 and s_2. In quantum mechanics, spin is quantized. Precisely, once the particle is measured in one of the spin states, the results of the other state will be also predetermined in a reaction that takes place nonlocally.

The key was that the spatial orientation of angular momentum states that there are discreet points on the plate which displays the quantized effect. Two spin states along the z axis are spin up $j = +\hbar/2$ and spin down $j = -\hbar/2$. We can write in the Dirac bra-ket notation:

$$|\Psi> = c_1 \mid \Psi_j = +\hbar/2 > +c_2| \ \Psi_j \ = \ -\hbar/2>$$

before measurement where c_1 and c_2 are complex numbers. Note that before measurement this looks like the Schrödinger cat paradox (See Chapter 1, Section 4). Later this approach led to magnetic resonance imaging or MRI.

According to Bell (1964): "In a theory in which parameters are added to quantum mechanics to determine the results of individual measurements, without changing the statistical

BELL'S THEOREM REVISITED

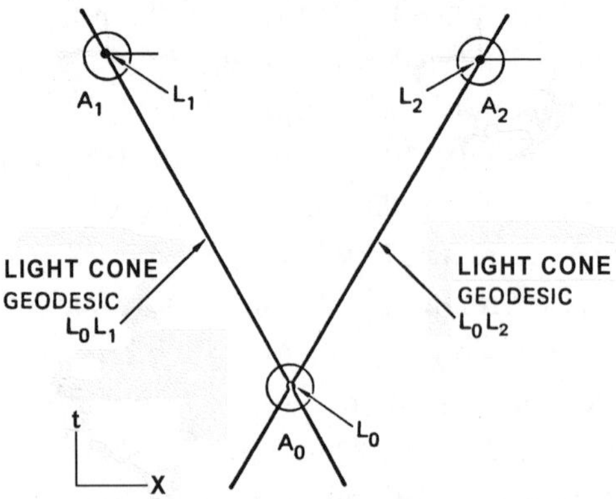

Figure 6c
Common Point of Origin of Two Events
Connected by a Light Signal

In this figure is displayed a common point of origin, A_0 connected to two nonlocal events A_1 and A_2. These events A_1 along world line L_0L_1 and A_2 along L_0L_2, the events A_1 or A_2 are superluminally connected as pointed out by H. Stapp (1975, 1999).

predictions, there must be a mechanism whereby the setting of one measuring device can influence the reading of another instrument, however remote. Moreover, the signal involved must propagate instantaneously, so that such a theory could not be Lorentz invariant." The Lorentz invariant acts as a constraint for $v \leq c$ signaling (Herbert, 1975). In his examination of the relationship between Lorentz invariance and superluminal signals, G. Feinberg (1967) found that they were not incompatible. Despite the lack of definitive evidence that superluminal signals must be invoked to derive Bell's theorem, this author does believe that Bell's theorem almost certainly involves superluminal signaling. (Ramon and Rauscher, 1980). Einstein states in his explanation of the theory of relativity that if a train goes at the velocity of light and has a headlight emitting light at the velocity of light, the velocity of light is constant and the head light beam also still goes at the velocity of light (and not two times the velocity of light).

The conclusion from Bell's Theorem's implies remote connectedness in that any hidden variable theory that reproduces all statistical predictions of quantum mechanics must be nonlocal. While, to date, all these formulations involve microscopic properties only, in terms of a microscopic spin correlation function, usually for photons (spin 1) or electrons (spin 1/2), some recent formulations seem to imply possible macroscopic non-quantum remote correlated effects. The key appears to lie in the formulation of the correlation function which represents the interconnectedness of previously correlated events.

In the Bell's Theorem experiment, remote macroscopic effects do occur over distances of kilometers. One such example of a Bell's Theorem like correlation is the Brown-Twiss effect (Brown and Twiss, 1956) which involves long distance correlations. The pragmatic view of Bell's Theorem has recently been expanded by Stapp, who discusses the role of the macroscopic detection apparatus, as well as the possible role of superluminal signals. (See A_1, L_1 and A_2, L_2 in Fig. 6b).) (Stapp, 1925, 1976; Stapp, Nadean and Kafatos, 1999). Stapp has explored both cases for superluminal propagation or subluminal connection issuing from the points in common to the backward light cones coming from the two regions (See Fig. 6c).

The research into and verification of the physics of nonlocality has been repeatedly verified even over kilometers. This research covers the period from 1971 when the author met John Clauser through the meeting with David Bohm in the late 1970's at Berkeley (LBNL) and at the University of London Birkbeck College, 1977, where I met Alan Aspect at Orsay in France, 1977 (Aspect, Grainger and Roger, 1992). The long distance research has continued with more recent long distance measurements by Gisin, *et. al.* (Gisin, *et. al.*, 1998a and 1998b) and Salart, *et. al.* in Geneva (2008). In 2015, three experiments were conducted stretching over several floors of a campus building, using multiple devices sending photons through fiber optics and random number generators to pick one of two polarization settings for each polarization analyzer. Other experiments were set up over entire campuses, with similar conclusions, all with excellent results (Hensen, 2015) revealing a nonlocal affect.

I observed the experimental set ups of both Clauser and Aspect and was extremely impressed with the experimental designs and implementations. Even though I am a theoretical physicist by training, I have conducted years of experimental work and always like to see the hands-on work. In the Clauser experiments, the position of the polarizers are set before the photons leave their source to reach the photomultipliers (PMT). Aspect added a "delayed choice" component to the experiment in which the polarizers are randomly set after the two photons leave the source. The photons' spins remain correlated in both cases. John Clauser described his impressions of these nonlocality experiments to Rauscher and Targ (2001), stating that quantum experiments have been carried out with photons, electrons, and may be carried out with atoms, and even 60-carbon-atom Bucky balls. He claimed that "it may be impossible to keep anything in a box anymore."

Bell emphasizes that "no theory of reality compatible with quantum theory can require spatially separate events to be independent of each other." A surprising coherence between distant entities, fundamental to the basis of nonlocality, is a property both of space and time whereby the measurement of the polarization of one photon determines the polarization of the other photon at their respective sites. In writing on the philosophical implications of nonlocality, physicist Stapp of the University of California at Berkeley and LBNL and the Fundamental "Fysiks" Group, stated that these quantum connections could be the "most profound discovery in all of science" (F"F"G, 1973-1979). In Figure 6c, we enumerate some of the various interpretations of Bell's Theorem.

Bohm discusses the illusion in space and time (Bohm and Hiley, 1975, 1993), as he and Hiley write about the quantum-interconnectedness of all things. In his book, *The Undivid-*

ed Universe, Bohm states that "the essential features of the implicate order are, that the whole universe is in some way enfolded in everything, and that each thing is enfolded in the whole." His holographic metaphor which was inspired by the indications of nonlocality in Bell's theorem, states that, like a hologram, each region of spacetime contains information about every other point in spacetime. Bohm continues, "For the human being, all of this implies a thoroughgoing wholeness, in which mental and physical sides participate very closely in each other. Likewise, intellect, emotion, and the whole state of the body are in a similar flux of fundamental participation. Thus, there is no real division between mind and matter, psyche and soma. The common term 'psychosomatic' is in this way seen to be misleading, as it suggests the Cartesian notion of two distinct substances in some kind of interaction." (Bohm and Hiley, 1993) Bohm states that there exists a unity of consciousness, a "greater collective mind" which has no boundaries or limitations of space or time (Bohm and Hiley, 1993).

Bohm also states that the Wheeler delayed choice experiment "can be designed to show that, according to quantum theory the choice to measure one or another of a pair of complementary variables at a given time can apparently affect the physical state of things for considerable periods of time before such a decision is made." These complementary variables are typically momentum and distance, phase space variables. In Wheeler's experiment, as observed in a two slit interference apparatus, reference is made to the dual wave and particle nature of light (Wheeler, 1978a, 1978b, 1979, 1979b). We discuss the design of Wheeler's delayed choice in Rauscher and Amoroso (2011). It is clear that this principle of nonlocality has profound implications about the nature of a nonlocal universe. The fundamental nature of nonlocality supersedes either microscopic or macroscopic phenomena, of which the quantum domain is a subset expressed in a complex Minkowski eight space. (See Chapter 5.) The Bell's theorem correlation of distant events is just one of the interesting forms of the principle of nonlocality.

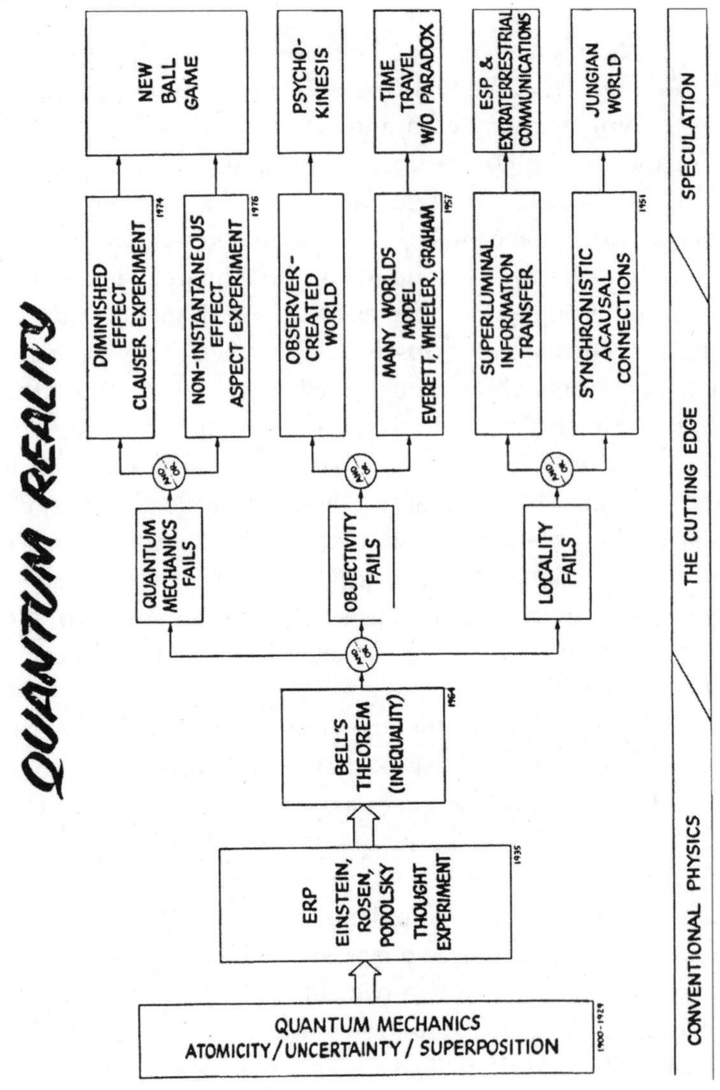

Figure 6d Historical development of the quantum theory from the turn of the last century through the second half of that century and to the current status of the quantum theory. This figure is a collective construct of the members of the Fundamental "Fysiks" Group at LBNL started, organized, conducted by E.A. Rauscher of the Department of Theoretical Physics LBNL.

Bohm and Hiley, in their assessment of the fundamental nature of reality based upon nonlocality as an acting principle of the universe, make the following statement: "Our attitude is that we can sooner or later drop the notion of the quantum potential (as we can drop the scaffolding when a building is ready) and go on to radically new concepts, which incorporate the wholeness of form which we feel to be the essential significance of quantum descriptions. This implies that we have to explore deeply all our basic notions of space, time and the nature of matter, which were in the recent past inseparably intertwined with the idea of localizability, i.e., that the basic form of existence is that of entities that are located in well-defined regions of spacetime in the mechanical view. We have, instead, to start from nonlocality as the basic concept, and to consider locality as a special and limiting case, applicable when there is relative functional independence of the various "elements" appearing in our descriptions. This means that our notions of space and time will have to change in a fundamental way" (Rauscher, 1971, Wheeler, 1979a, 1979b; Bohm, Hiley, 1975). The complex eight-dimensional space is intrinsically a nonlocal spacetime geometry. Locality, in four space, becomes an approximation to exact nonlocality. (Rauscher and Ramon, 1980). Work is in progress to formulate Bell's Theorem in complex Eight Space (Rauscher, 2016). This approach may alter the concept we have of space and time.

In Rauscher and Amoroso (2011), we explore some of the physical interpretations of Bell's theorem, together with the ontological and epistemological, philosophical and possible metaphysical implications of the theorem. Experimental verification of nonlocality and hence the completeness of the quantum theory, leads to the conclusion of the fundamental existence of nonlocal interactions, indicating that some super psi wave function (Ψ) that was the origin of quantum entanglement at the big bang, exists. Was it this Ψ function that led to everything remaining correlated throughout cosmic evolution? Stapp *et. al.* acknowledges this current physical theory and nonlocality (Rauscher, 2010; Stapp, Nadeau, and Kafatos, 1999) when he states that "...the universal on a very basic level could be a vast web of particles, which remain in contact with one another over any distance and in no time." In his participation in the F"F"G, he stated that the confirmation of the nonlocality of Bell's Theorem is one of the most fundamental discoveries of the 20th century along with the Heisenberg uncertainty principle (Stapp, 1976; Heisenberg, 1938). See Figure 6d for the summary of its concepts that the members of the Fundamental "Fysiks" Group came up with on the interpretation of quantum theory, Bell's Theorem and nonlocality (Kaiser, 2011).

2. The Velocity Paradox of Bell's Theorem and the Young's Double Slit Experiment Resolved

We formulate Bell's Theorem and the Young's double slit experiment in complex eight space. For this procedure, we compare Figure 5i in chapter 5 to Figure 6a. The velocity resolution is achieved in that the nonlocal connection of Bell's Theorem and the paradox at the Young's double slit experiment involve luminal or subluminal signaling in complex eight space.

For a real time separation from P_1 (photomultiplier 1) at the origin and P_2 (photomultiplier 2) separated by a real part on X_{Re} axis. For these photons to appear contiguous i.e., simultaneously detected for state spin up or down determined at PMP_1 and PMP_2, we require access to $t_{x,Im}$, from P_1 and P_4 along the $t_{x,Im}$ axis (Fig. 5i(b)). Hence, causality is maintained in the complex eight space and nonlocality explained. This is analogous to the nonlocality of remote viewing.

We can also compare Fig. 5i to Fig. 6d (section 4 in this chapter) for Young's double slit experiment in an analogous manner as we did for Bell's theorem in order to formulate it in complex eight space. We discuss the Young's double slit experiment in detail in section 3a of this chapter.

We understand the Young's double slit experiment only in terms of a hyperdimensional geometry. Consider the case of a photonic source, s, or we can use a source of electrons going through one slit at a time because the source emitter is of such low intensity. Consider the case of the emission of two sequential photons $\gamma_1(t_1)$ and $\gamma_2(t_2)$ respectively where $t_1 \neq t_2$ in the case of a lower intensity source. In complex eight space then by having access to dimension x_{Im} (see Fig. 5i(c)), we use the metrical line element in complex eight space as

$$s^2 = |x|^2 - c^2 |t|^2$$

for $X = X_{Re} + i\ X_{Im}$ and $t = t_{Re} + i\ t_{Im}$.

The key is that it is the square of the variable that occupies the role in Minkowski four space, as well as the complexified Minkowski eight space. The square of the modulus of an imaginary yields a real quantity. Then essentially, t_1 appears for $t_1 = t_2$ so that γ_1 (t_1) and γ_2 (t_2) appear to be emitted simultaneously. In Fig. 5i(c), we associate γ_1 (t_1) with being located at P_1 and γ_2 (t_2) located at P_3. Now these two photons appear to the contiguous by access to X_{Im} so that at P_4, we have the appearance that $t_1 = t_2$ where the origin is at P_1 (Rauscher, in progress).

In complex eight space, the frame of reference for $t_{x,Im} \neq 0$ corresponds to real time remote viewing (Fig. 5i(b)), and for $X_{Im} \neq 0$ corresponds to precognition (Fig. 5i(c)).

3. Other Nonlocal Micro and Macro Phenomena

Other theoretical constructs experiments that appear to exhibit nonlocality are presented in this section and its associated subsections. Young's double slit experiment (1804), conceived and conducted before the development of the quantum theory, and Wheeler's (1978a, 1979a, 1979b) delayed choice experiments elucidate some of the quantum properties of nonlocality as quantum entanglement, as well as some of the issues related to the wave-particle phenomena paradox, potential models and possible nonlocality. Whereas, light and even billiard balls via de Broglie $P = \hbar/l$ exhibit wave and particle like properties, where P is momentum, $\hbar$ is Planck's constant and l is the associated wavelength, the issue of nonlocality is not an

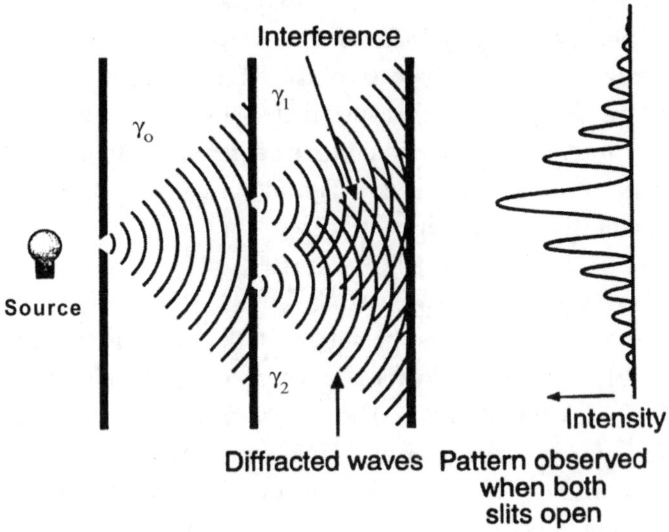

Figure 6e A Double-slit experiment with light. When a beam of pure light from a source chamber through a hole (first vertical line), passes through the experiment with the two holes open (second vertical line), the diffracted waves interfere to produce a characteristic pattern of light and shaded regions on a screen or photographic plate (third vertical line).

issue of locality and nonlocality, but that nonlocality exits and that is it!

EPR stated that there could be no action at a distance but quantum theory seems to require action at a distance. What happens in one part of the Universe can have nonlocal consequences in other parts, regardless of the distance between the points and regardless of the speed of light. Before entering the process, neither photon or electron "knows" which spin orientation to have. After leaving the source, it appears that each "knows" instantly through nonlocally what state its twin is in and so behaves accordingly. To understand the notion of nonlocality, we must also understand Gisin's experiment where two photons originating from the same source are sent to separate locations some 18km distance apart (Gisin, 2013). In modern quantum physics, entanglement is fundamental. Then it appears that space is no longer basic, at least at the quantum informational level and neither may time. The key is in the measurement which seems to trigger a collapse of the wave function of the system! Wheeler states that "no elementary phenomena is a phenomena until it is recorded and analyzed in the world of quantum theory."

Other experiments such as the Aharonov-Bohm experiment can be interpreted as displaying occurrences of nonlocality. The Aharonov-Bohm effect (1959) may even show a relation to the theory of everything (TOE), where potentials are extended to "gauge fields" and regarded as a fundamental physical quantity.

A. Young's Double Slit Experiment and Nonlocality

Young's double slit experiment of 1803 was designed and conducted to elucidate whether light was a particle or a wave. This was a hot topic of interest in his time and it continues today (Young, 1804). The question was to determine, whether particles, and especially photons (or light particles) have wave-like or particle-like properties.

Sir Isaac Newton conducted fifteen years of optical experiments involving reflection and refraction. Nevertheless, he chose to maintain the corpuscular-particle theory of light. Seeing the world as being composed of wave fields was not suitable for 17th-18th century concepts. However, Christiaan Huygens, a Dutch contemporary of Newton and a member of the French Academy of Sciences had already asserted the importance of the wave theory of light. He understood that light was wave-like in nature and showed that light, when considered as a wave, could travel in straight lines and follow the laws of reflection and refraction. Huygens interpreted light as a longitudinal wave with oscillations taking place along the line of propagation.

Young demonstrated his double slit experiment which uncovered the wave like nature of light. He hypothesized that light was wave-like in analogy to ripples or waves such as in water when two opposing water waves meet, they would reinforce or destroy each other. His equipment was primitive by modern standards. Using only sunlight diffracted through a small slit as a source of coherent illumination, he projected the light rays from the slit onto another screen containing two slits placed side by side, allowing the light to fall onto an observation screen.

Young experimented with different size slits and also different distances between the holes and the screen. Then when he reduced the size of the slits and brought them closer together, the light went through the slits and created distinct bands of light separated by dark regions in a serial order on the screen. With both slits open, there was an interference pattern, or diffraction pattern demonstrating the wave nature of light. He immediately understood that what he was looking at was light acting like a wave and it was showing what he called "interference fringes" which were the variations of white and dark bands he recorded (Young, 1804).

A schematic of Young's double slit experiment is represented in Fig. 6e. Young's double slit experiment has also been conducted with electrons (Jönsson, 1961; Feynman, 1965). Also, tests were made where one slit is closed and one is open. Today this is done by random number generators. Here the implication of the appearance of the pattern on the screen when both slits are open or when a particle passes through one slit seems to be that the particle or photon "knows" or carries information to the screen that appears to contain information about what would have happened had the particle gone through the other slit concurrently or simultaneously.

A form of nonlocality appears to be required for the so-termed "knowing" that the other slit is open or closed by the single photon or electron. Just as the hidden variable hypothesis of Bohm is an attempt to explain Bell's nonlocality, so a pilot wave or advanced potential hypothesized by Heisenberg was an attempt to find a mechanism for this nonlocality. Young's work was furthered by Augustine Jean Fresnel, leading to the construction of a mathematical basis of a wave theory of light. Young and Fresnel (Crew, *et.al.,* 2010) both adopted the transverse theory of light, which Maxwell (1873) formulated in detail.

The corpuscular-particle quantum nature of light having an energy $E = h\nu$ where ν is the frequency of light was presented by Einstein. One of the three majorly important papers of the five Einstein published in 1905, dealt with the photoelectric effect, which shows that light shining on certain metals stimulates the emission of electrons. Einstein formulated the photoelectric effect using the Planck quantum, momentum $P = \hbar/\lambda$ where h is Planck's constant and $\hbar = h/2\pi$ and λ is the wavelength of light.

In the photoelectric effect, a photon hits a metal and ejects electrons from the surface that can produce a current flow (often used in automatic door openers). What is the fundamental nature of light? What is light, a particle or a wave? This is the particle-wave paradox. There is actually no paradox in nature. Paradoxes arise from our misunderstanding or ignorance as to the manner in which nature works. Both waves and particles obey quantum nonlocality. To resolve this and other paradoxes may require going beyond our western based logic system or Aristotelian logic of the concept of "either-or". At its most basic nature, light may be neither or both (Zen four logic) a particle or a wave but display particular attributes depending on what experiment is performed to examine its nature as discussed by Targ and Hurtak in their book (2006) and also Targ, Rauscher and Brown (2003; Targ, 2004).

At first Huygens and Young assumed that light was a longitudinal wave. Then the double refraction of calcite or Island spar in which objects observed through the crystal are refracted through two different angles, was carefully observed by Erasmus Bartholin. This phenomena was explained by Fresnel as one ray, the primary ray, which could be considered as a

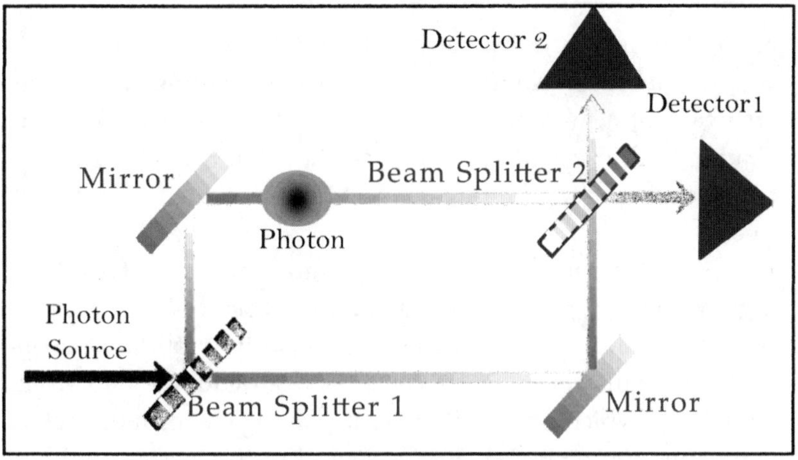

Figure 6f Wheeler's delayed choice experimental set up. Two paths are created by half silvered mirror BS1 and recombined at BS2 which go to the two detectors. Displayed is the photon source, double slitted metal screen on first lens to the second lens where the photographic plate is made into Venetian blind like configuration which can be open or closed after the photon leaves the source and detected by a photosensitive screen.

wave oscillating in one particular plane, with the secondary ray oscillating in a plane perpendicular to the first plane. The transverse mode of light propagation resulted from these observations. Young changed his mind and settled on the transverse model of light. Like the particle-wave paradox and the Hertzian -non-Hertzian wave paradox, transverse or longitudinal waves may depend on what experiment one conducts and the corresponding relevant formalism such as what antenna one uses (Rauscher, 1983; Rauscher and Amoroso, 2011).

The debate continues. Light traveling through a vacuum, before the end of the 1800's, was considered to be supported by a light-carrying aether. The aether concept was rejected because at the results of the Albert Michelson's and later the Michelson-Morley experiment that used interferometry to measure the earth's movement through the aether (Michelson and Morley, 1887). The concept was that if aether existed there would be some type of interference in terms of speed of two beams of light. Specifically, it was expected from the Michelson -Morley experiment that interference would be observed in right angle light beams measured in parallel and perpendicular to the motion of the earth through the aether. As no interference fringes were found, it has been assumed there is no aether, at least, as defined aether that Michelson and Morley. However, the aether model is not dead, as other aether models have arisen, including the suggestion that the Higgs field (Higgs, 1964) comprises an aether and some others that are primarily mathematical in nature (Amoroso and Rauscher, 2009).

B. Wheeler's Delayed-Choice Gedanken Experiment

Wave-particle duality is further exemplified in Wheeler's delayed-choice gedanken experiment. Wheeler believed we live in a participatory Universe (which is counter to Bohr's Copenhagen view). He proposed a modification of Young's double slit experiment which he termed the "delayed choice" experiment. Using a standard configuration of a two-path interferometer, the photon enters the path via beam splitter 1 and is recombined by beam splitter 2. The delayed choice is introduced by determining when the beam splitter 2 needs to become active. If splitter 2 is used, a "wave" property of interference is detected. If it is not used, the "particle" property is detected.

As can be seen in Figure 6f, the photon source is to the left, where the photon enters. It then targets the first beam splitter and travels to either mirror. In the "delayed choice" version, the observer (see Chapter 7) performs a last-minute choice, after the photon has already traversed the first beam splitter, whether to open beam splitter 2 or to close or change its position. (See Fig. 6f).

Many variations of the experiment have been per-

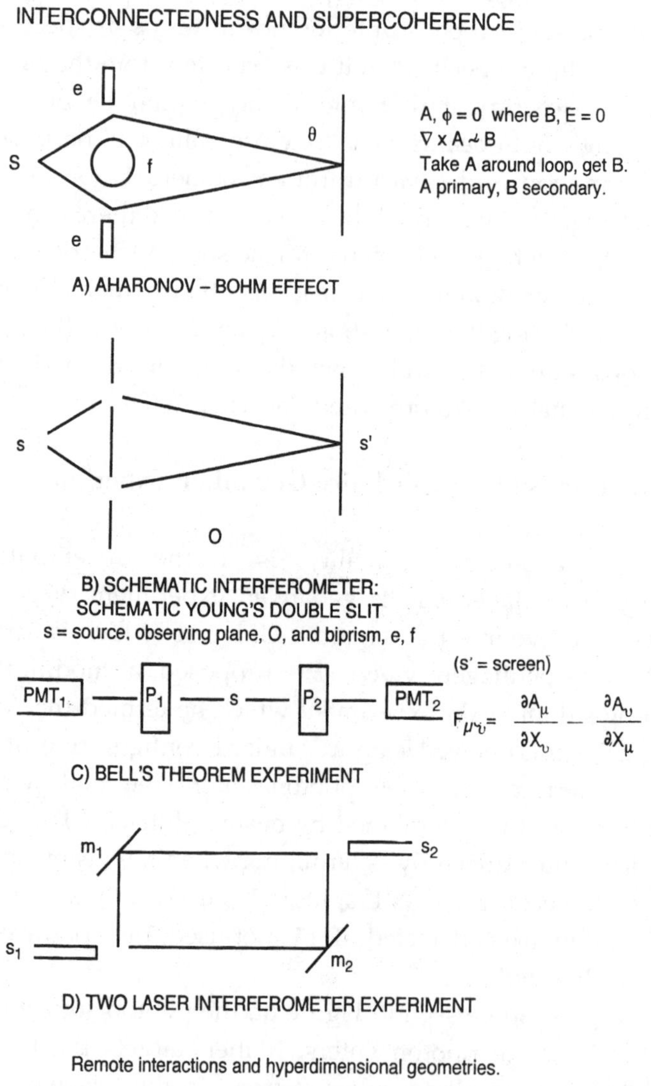

Figure 6g Schematic representations of experiments which involve nonlocal interconnectedness and supercoherence phenomena for four experimental set ups.

formed (e.g., Hensen, 2015). One can also determine "through which slit" each quantum goes. As in Wheeler's description all the features to the right of the photographic plate, including the slicing of the splitter into venetian blind-like slats are fundamental to the "delayed choice" experiment. Is this the basis for deducing that a photon has "gone through both slits," creating a divided photon? Not possible.

According to de Broglie-Bohm (1993), this may be explained by the fact that there is a pilot wave (quantum potential) and the particle is a photon that is led by the pilot wave. This means that the wave is nonlocal and the particle is local. This theory satisfies both physical laws and causality.

Einstein objected, stating that, deciding which slit the photon went through is a logical inconsistency of the quantum theory. Einstein argued that by measuring the vertical component of the kick that the photon imparts to the photographic plate, would indicate whether it had come from the upper hole, kicking the plate down, or from the lower hole, kicking the plate up.

Bohr responded that two separate experiments, not one had been conducted. Both experiments could not be performed at the same time according to Bohr's complementarity principle (Rauscher, 2010). In this author's opinion, the "delayed choice" experiment further exemplifies the property of nonlocality and is becoming more and more an established concept, with the latest experiment in combination with the National Institute of Standards and Technology (NIST) (Hensen, 2015), and more expected to follow.

An obvious experiment is the triple or multiple slit experiment. My idea, as well as others was to add a third slit. Max Born, however, in the 1920's, proposed that only pairs can interfere and that adding one or more slits would not contribute any changes to the two slit interference pattern on the screen. He was right, but there is still no clear reason why quantum interference stops at two slits.

Sinha *et. al.* of the University of Waterloo, Canada re-

Table 1
Some Topics for Consideration for Interference Experiments

1. The relation of the remote connectedness properties of Bell's theorem, Young's double slit experiment and laser interferometry from independent beams.
2. The relationship between the advanced potential models and complex multidimensional geometries formulation of remote connectedness properties of the manifold.
3. Interference effects produced by the superposition of light beams from two independent single-mode lasers for low beam intensities.

cently conducted an experiment using three parallel slits in a stainless steel plate, each 3 x 10^{-3} cm wide and 3 x 10^{-2} cm tall (Sinha, *et. al.*, 2010). The results confirmed Born's hypotheses that the three-slit interference pattern is the same as a double slit interference pattern, as there were no new fringes observed (Rauscher and Amoroso, 2009). It appears, though that the Bohr hypothesis holds. Let us now examine some aspects of nonlocality on the microscopic level which may relate to the nonlocal nature of consciousness (Amoroso and Rauscher, 2009; Rauscher and Targ, 2001).

C. Aharonov-Bohm: A Venture into Nonlocality?

The phase shift observed in the coherence of two electron beams in the Aharonov-Bohm effect (1959) is another interesting experiment and theory and in some interpretations may imply non-local interactions. The experiment designed by Aharonov and Bohm reveals the physical importance of the scalar part of the electromagnetic potential. In their experiment, a charged particle, such as an electron, that passes close to, but does not encounter, a magnetic or electric field will change its dynamics slightly, in a manner that can be measured. The Aharonov-Bohm effect, thus, describes how the potentials, and not the fields, act directly on the particle charges. It also demonstrates the manner in which the amplitude of the electron's wave function gives the probability of finding the electron at a particular location at a particular time.

The quantum wave function that describes an electron is its amplitude and phase angle. Changes in interference patterns are produced outside the direct actions of the electric field, E, and the magnetic field, B, the vector and scalar potentials A and ϕ are formulated for the electric and magnetic fields. The effect of A and ϕ outside the domain of E and B may represent macroscopic nonlocality. The potentials were introduced to obtain the canonical or period variable formalism (Rauscher, 1972). Using a solenoid Aharonov and Bohm theoretically formulated conditions where A and ϕ have physical consequences and where both E and B are measured to be zero. The Aharonov and Bohm effect has been replicated a number of times (Aharonov and Bohm, 1959). Experimental tests have demonstrated that outside radiation fields, pure potentials can exist without their associated E and B fields (Olariu and Popesca, 1985).

Figure 6f represents the relationship between the Aharonov-Bohm experiment, the Young's double slit experiment, Bell's theorem set up and a dual laser interferometry experiment which I have proposed. Dual path interferences between two correlated lasers as correlated coherent sources are examined in the latter case. In Figure 6g, s_1 and s_2 are two lasers and m_1 and m_2 are two half-silvered mirrors and detectors. d_1 and d_2 are not shown. (See also Table 1).

Experimentally testing the theoretical hypothesis developed in points 1 and 2 of Table 1 using the dual laser source system, is the central purpose. The nature of the quantum measurement problem would be strongly affected by positive results from such an experiment.

D. Ernst Mach and Possible Macroscopic Nonlocality

Ernst Mach, whose principle and philosophy influenced Einstein (Mach, 1959) (Rowlands, 2007), states in his principle (which appears to imply a nonlocal connection of a remote inertial frame of reference) that the inertia of a body (or particle) is due to the action of forces produced by all other bodies in the Universe. He concluded that the configuration of water in a spinning bucket was directly related to the entire matter in the universe.

Following Mach's conclusions for longer scale correlations, is there a counterpart of nonlocality, even possibly a classical nonlocality? Although Mach's principle relates to an absolute frame of reference in the Universe, it is not inconsistent with the mathematical formalism of relativity for both inertial and non-inertial frames of reference as has been demonstrated unequivocally by the author and others. (Rauscher, 1971).

Sir Isaac Newton conducted an experiment with a rotating and an at rest bucket of water. The bucket of water was hung at the end of a twisted rope and then the rope was let go. Newton's description is as follows, "... then the surface of the water will at first be level, just as it was before the vessel began to move. But after the vessel, by the force gradually impressed upon the water, has caused the water also to begin revolving perceptibly, the water will gradually recede from the middle and rise up the sides of the vessel, assuming a concave shape (as experience has shown me), and, with an ever faster motion, will rise further and further until, when it completes its revolutions in the same times as the vessel, it is relatively at rest in the vessel" (Newton, 1726 [1999]).

Newton concluded that it was not the rotation of the water relative to the bucket that was important, since this relative rotation was initially associated with a flat water surface and finally with a curved surface and thus was related to absolute space. Mach postulated that Newton's experiment informs us that the relative rotation of the water produces no noticeable centrifugal forces, but that such forces are produced by its relative rotation with respect to the mass of the Earth and the other celestial bodies. Is an asymmetry somehow represented by the more massive body such as the Earth, affecting a smaller bucket and water to a greater extent in what is considered an inertial frame of reference? From the point of view of Newton's law of Universal gravitation

$$F = \frac{1}{4\pi G} \frac{m_1 m_2}{r^2}$$

where the universal gravitational constant G is associated with two different masses, m_1 and m_2 separated by r, where m_1 is the mass of the water in the bucket, as m_2 is the mass of the Earth (or the whole universe). In this sense, if $m_1 >> m_2$ then does m_1 (e.g., the Earth) have more inertial frame effect on m_2 (the mass of the water in the bucket)? Newton's force on the two masses is now concluded to be the same.

Jean Bernard Foucault conducted experiments on a pendulum with a heavy bob and long cord or wire in the mid 1850's. The behavior of the pendulum appears to imply an absolute frame of reference for the rotation of the Earth, or the fixed star system, especially at a point away from the equator. Foucault noted that at a particular location, the pendulum remained in the same plane of oscillation, no matter how the point of attachment was twisted or rotated. With the pendulum at the north pole or the south pole, the earth will make a complete twist under it in twenty four hours, while at the equator, where the earth's rotation and velocity is the greatest (about one thousand miles per hour), there is no twist at all. It is the rotation of the Earth under the pendulum to create the observation of the pendulum rotation.

The logical question is suggested by Mach, "How do we measure the inertial or actual mass of a body?" From Newton's second law $m_1 = F/a$ inertial mass is measured by the ratio of the sum of applied forces F to a mass m_1 to accelerate it. The measurement of absolute acceleration requires the measurement of absolute displacement; however, what we can really measure is the displacement of that body relative to other bodies. According to Mach, only by virtue of the presence of other bodies can a given body be said to have inertial mass (Rauscher and Amoroso, 2011). Furthermore, both Newton's bucket experiment and Foucault's pendulum appear to demonstrate that in defining inertial frames of reference large masses at great (nonlocal) distances have greater importance than small masses nearby. My complex Eight Space is a formalism of a multidimensional geometry with the features of nonlocality having micro and macro implications. (Rauscher, 1979, 1981, 2005; Rauscher and Targ, 2001).

Mach's principle relates to the motion of local material bodies and their properties as relative motion to the center of all other masses in the Universe (Rauscher, 1971). Mach's explanation involves relative motion whereas Newton considered space to be absolute. The stars and the Earth all have some presence as does the observer. Mach was followed by Hubble, who around 1921, discovered the movement of stars by the analysis of stellar red shift data. The rate of expansion to distance is Hubble's constant, as

$$H = \frac{\dot{R}}{R}$$

where $\dot{R}$ is the velocity of recession of an astrophysical object and R is its distance away. This expansion comprises the redshift. The Hubble expansion yields multiple frames which may not preclude another form of so termed fixed frame as a type of aether. The relative frames, as in Newton's bucket, may represent a large scale, at least earth size, of nonlocal influence. Einstein was influenced by Mach's principle in his development of General Relativity. Newton's gravitational law is formulated in terms of an absolute frame whereas Einstein's General Relativity is formulated in terms of the principle of equivalency between inertial and gravitational mass.

Sciama (1969) developed a detailed formulation of Mach's Principle and applied it to develop an accurate model of rotation curves of galaxies without the need for dark matter (Sciama, 1953). Rowlands (2007) discusses Sciama's approach and makes a Machian analogy of the so-termed all pervasive Higgs field.

The Higgs field was formulated by Peter Higgs to describe how the elementary particles of matter gain the property of mass. In 1964, Higgs (1964) proposed a Higgs field that acts as a "sticky substance" or viscous fluid and this property gives rise to what gives mass to particles when they penetrate the field. The Higgs field also acts as a non sticky field for massless particles like the photon. The Higgs theory is part of the Standard Model of physics which does not include gravity. The Higgs particle was said to be discovered at CERN. The LHC or large hadron collider, announced the discovery of the Higgs particle July 4, 2012 for which Peter Higgs received the Nobel Prize in 2013. The mass of the Higgs is identified as 126.5 MeV, between the supersymmetry prediction of 114 MeV and the multiverse prediction of 140 MeV. One might consider the Higgs field as a kind of aether.

Conclusion

Intense debate has revolved around the particle-wave nature of light over the last five centuries, often resulting in the breaking of life long friendships. Light appears to be either and both a particle or/and a wave. The debate over the fundamental existence of locality and nonlocality has also been contested. The existence of nonlocality is now no longer in question. In the study of physics, there is a striving toward a more basic knowledge of the nature of reality. Using the precise and logical language of mathematics, physics is assumed to be the most fundamental of all sciences and perhaps the basis for all human knowledge. It is our attempt to understand the natural world that has led to the growth of our current understanding of physics. A succession of inductive and deductive inferences derived from observation and theoretical hypothesis, theory explanation and prediction has led to our accumulated knowledge.

The concept of a unified theory of physics or a theory of everything (TOE) assumes there is a point at which the origin of everything is explained and also that the origin of everything can be explained in terms of a single obvious source. This is a basic desire of all philosophical and scientific endeavors. Should a fundamental theory even exist, it has to accommodate the fundamental nature of nonlocality in both micro and macro systems. It is therefore imperative that a theoretical framework be constructed to accommodate nonlocality at a very basic level. The formulation of the complex Minkowski space which has nonlocality in space and time deeply embedded in its structure exemplifies this. Consciousness is an integral part of reality and cannot be excluded from the search for a fundamental theory (Millay, 2010; Rauscher and Targ, 2001; Rauscher, 1983; Herr, 2012)!

References

Aharonov, Y. and D. Bohm (1959) "Significance of Electromagnetic Potential in the Quantum Theory," *Phys. Rev.* 115, p. 485.

Amoroso, R.L., L.H. Kaufman, E.A. Rauscher and P. Rowlands (2010) "Hidden Parameters Describing Internal Motion Within Extended Particle Elements," pp. 1-27, Eds. R.L. Amoroso, P. Rowlands and S. Jeffers, The Search for Fundamental Theory, *American Institute of Physics*, AIP Conference Proceeding #1316, Melville, NY.

Amoroso, R.L. and E.A. Rauscher (2009) *The Holographic Anthropic Multiverse Formalizing the Complex Geometry of Reality*. London: World Scientific.

Aspect, A., P. Grainger and G. Roger (1977 and 1992) Experimental tests of Bells inequalities using time-varying analyzers. *Phys. Rev. Lett..49*, 1804 and private communication with A. Aspect, Orsay, France.

Bell, J.S. (1964) "On the Einstein Podolsky Rosen paradox," *Physics* 1, p. 195.

Bell, J.S. (1966) On the problem of hidden variables in quantum theory, *Rev. Mod. Physics*, 38, p. 447.

Bell, J.S. (1987) *Speakable and Unspeakable in Quantum Mechanics*, Cambridge University Press.

Bohm, D. (1952) Phys. Rev *85,* 166 and 180 and private communication at LBNL when he spoke to the Fundamental Physics Group also called the Fundamental "Fysiks" Group (1978) and at Birkbeck College, physics department, University of London during my (EAR) teaching summer 1977 and E.A. Rauscher, discussion on the physics of hyperdimensional geometrics. University of London presentation.

Bohm, D. (1977) "Bell's Theorem and Hidden Variables," presentation to the Fundamental Physics Group, LBNL chaired by E.A. Rauscher April 7.

Bohm, D. and B. Hiley (1975) "On the Understanding of Nonlocality as Implied by Quantum Theory," *Found. of Phys.* 5, p. 93.

Bohm, D. and B. Hiley (1993) *The Undivided Universe* London. Routledge and private communication with D. Bohm and B. Hiley.

Brown, R.H. and R. Twiss (1956) A Test of a new type of stellar interferometer on Sirius, *Nature* 178, p. 1046. This reference was brought to the author's attention by S.P. Sirag of the F"F"G.

Chew, G. (1968) Science 161, 762 and presentation "S-Matrix bootstrap and models of Physical Reality," the Fundamental Physics Group Chaired by E.A. Rauscher at the Lawrence Berkeley National Laboratory LBNL, February 13, 1976.

Clauser, J.F. (1975) "Counter Efficiencies and Bell's Theorem," presented to the Fundamental Physics Group. Chaired by E.A. Rauscher at LBNL October 31.

Clauser, J.F. and M.A. Horne, (1971) Phys. Rev. 100, 526 private communication with J. Clauser UCB with EAR and presentations to the Fundamental Physics Group, or F "F" G at LBNL (1974).

Clauser, J.F. and M.A. Horrne (1974) Experimental consequences of objective local theories *Phys. Rev.* D 10, 15 July 1974, p. 526,.

Crew, H., *et.al.* (2010) *The wave theory of light; memoirs of Huygens, Young and Fresnel.* Nabu Press.

DeWitt, B.S. and N. Graham (1973) "The Many Worlds Interpretation of Quantum Mechanics," Editors. includes papers by H. Everett, J.A. Wheeler, N. Graham and B.S. DeWitt, Princeton University Press and private communication with J.A. Wheeler and B.S. DeWitt

Eberhard, P. (1978) *Nuovo Cimento* B46, p. 392.

Einstein, A., B. Podolsky, and N. Rosen (1935) Can a quantum mechanical description of physical reality be considered complete? *Phys. Rev.*, 47, p. 777.

F"F"G (1973-1979) The Fundamental Physics Group for the Fundamental "Fysiks" Group (F"F"G) named by EAR (1973-1979) also termed the Fundamental Physics Group.

Feinberg, G. (1967) *Phys. Rev.* 159, 1089 and private communications with E. Rauscher and H. Puthoff the University of Columbia (1975).

Feynman, R. P., et.al (1964) *The Feynman Lectures on Physics* (Vol-III), Addison Wesley.

Freedman, S. and J. Clauser (1972) Experimental test of local hidden variable theories, *Phys. Rev. Lett.*, 28., pp. 934-941.

Gerlach, W. and Stern, O. (1922) Der experimentelle Nachweis der Richtungsquantelung im Magnetfeld. *Z. Phys.* 9, pp. 349–352.

Gisin, N., W. Tittel, J. Brendel and H. Zbinden (1998a) Violation of Bell inequalities by photons more than 10 km apart. *Phys. Rev. Lett.*, 81, p. 3563.

Gisin, N., J. Brendel, W. Tittel and H. Zbinden (1998b) Quantum correlation over more than 10 km, *Optics and Photonics News,* 9, p. 41.

Gisin, N. (2013) "Quantum Nonlocality: How Does Nature Do It?" *Science Magazine*, July 27, 2013, p. 1358.

Hensen, B. *et. Al.* (2015) "Loophole-free Bell inequality violation using electron spins separated by 1.3 kilometres" *Nature*, 526, pp. 682–686 (29 October 2015), doi:10.1038.

Heisenberg, W. (1938) *Der Durchgang sehr energiereicher Korpuskeln durch den Atomkern, Nuovo Cimento* Vol. 15, 31–34; *Verh. Dtsch. physik. Ges.*, 19, p. 2..

Heisenberg, W. (1938 and 1972) Physics and Philosophy and private communication with Heisenberg.

Herbert, N. (1975) "An Elementary Proof of Bell's Theorem on the Incompatibility of Local Hidden Variable theories with Quantum Mechanics," *Am. Jour. Physics* 43, 315 and "Bell's Theorem and Superluminal Signals" presentations to the Fundamental Physics Group of EAR at LBNL (1977).

Herbert, N. (1988) *Faster Then Light: Superluminal Loopholes in Physics,* American Library.

Herr, E. (2012) *Consciousness: Bridging the Gap Between Conventional Science and the New Science of Quantum Mechanics.* Faber, VA: Rainbow Ridge Books.

Higgs, P.W. (1964) Broken Symmetries and the Masses of Gauge Bosons, *Phys. Rev. Lett.* 13, p. 508.

Jammer, M. (1973) *The Philosophy of Quantum Mechanics,* Wiley. The Bohr-Einstein debates are covered in detail in this book.

Jönsson, C. (1961) *Zeitschift für Physics.*

Kaiser, D. (2011) *How the Hippies Saved Physics,* W.W. Norton.

Lamport, L., P. Eberhard, and E.A. Rauscher (1976) "Everett-Graham-Wheeler many worlds interpretation of Quantum Theory," Fundamental Physics Group. LBNL. Chaired by E.A. Rauscher, March 5).

Mach, E. (1959) *The Analysis of Sensations,* Dover Pub.

Maxwell, James Clerk (1873), *A treatise on electricity and magnetism Vol I. and Vol 2.,* Oxford : Clarendon Press.

Michelson, A.A. and F.W. Morley (1887) *Am. Jour. Science* 34, p. 333.

Millay, J (2010) *Radiant Minds: Scientists Explore the Dimensions of Consciousness,* Editor J. Millay, PRG Anthology, pub by J Millay.

Newton, Sir Issac (1726), *The Principia: Mathematical Principles of Natural Philosophy.* ed and trans. I. B. Cohen and Anne Whitman. Berkeley: University of California Press.

Olariu, S. and I.I. Popesca (1985) "The Quantum Effect of Electromagnetic Fluxes," *Rev. Mod. Phys.* 57, p. 3390.

Peat, F.D. (1990) *Einstein's Moon: Bell's Theorem and the Curious Quest for Quantum Reality.* Chicago: Contemporary Books, Inc.

Penrose, R. (1994) *Shadows of the Mind: A Search for the Missing Science of Consciousness,* Oxford University Press.

Ramon, C. and E.A. Rauscher (1980) "Superluminal Transformation in Complex Minkowski Spaces," *Found. of Phys.* 10, 661, demonstrates the compatibility of superluminal signals and multidimensional geometries.

Rauscher, E.A. (1971) *A Unifying Theory of Fundamental Processes,* LBNL/UCB, UCRL-20808, book.

Rauscher, E.A. (1972) "Generalized Heisenberg Relations," *Lett. Al. Nuovo Cimento* 4, p. 747.

Rauscher, E.A. (1981)"Conceptual Changes in Reality Models from New Discoveries in Physics," PSRL-1976, Preprint, September 1981. Published in *Proceedings of the First International Symposium on Non-Conventional Energy and Technology*; pg. 114, October 1981, University of Toronto, Ontario, Canada and Bulletin American. Physical Society, 35.

Rauscher, E.A. (2005) "The Unity of Consciousness Experience and Current Physical Theory," Journal *of ISSEEM,* 15 pps. 87-116, Boulder, CO.

Rauscher, E.A. (2007) "Quantum and the Role for Consciousness in the Physical World and the Complete Mind & Body," *Journal of IS-SSEEM,* 16, pp.1-42.

Rauscher, E.A (2010) "Quantum Mechanics and the Effect of Intentional Will," Chapter 3, pp. 35-63, *Complement only of mind and body: Realizing the Dream of Descartes, Einstein and Eccles.* ed. R.L. Amoroso, Nova Science Pub.

Rauscher, E.A. (2016) "Formulating Bell's Theorem in Complex Eight Space," in progress.

Rauscher, E.A. and R.L. Amoroso (2008) "The Schrödinger Equation in Complex Minkowski Space Nonlocality and Anticipatory Systems," CASL/S: *International Journal of Computing Anticipatory Systems,* Editor D.M. Dubois, Val 22, pp. 370-388, CHAOS, Belgium.

Rauscher, E.A. and R.L. Amoroso (2009) Relativistic Physics in Complex Minkowski Space, Nonlocality, Ether Model and Quantum Physics, in the *Ether Space-Time and Cosmology* 3, Physical Vacuum, Relativity and Quantum Physics, Ed. M.C. Duffy, Apeiron, Montreal.

Rauscher, E.A. and R.L. Amoroso, (2011) *Orbiting the Moons of Pluto: Solving Einsteins, Maxwells, Schrodingers and Dirac Equations in Complex Space*, London: World Scientific.

Rauscher, E.A. and R. Targ (2001) The Speed of Thought: Investigation of a complex Spacetime Metric to Describe Psychic Phenomena, *Jour. Sci. Explorations*, p. 331.

Renshaw, K. (2009) *Beyond Einstein's Horizon: Science, Remote Viewing*. Constellation Press, CA and references therein.

Rosen, N. (1965) *Ann. Phys.* 35, p. 426.

Rowlands, P. (2007) *Zero to Infinity: The Foundation of Physics.* London: World Scientific.

Salart, D., Baas, *et. al.* (2008): "Testing the speed of 'spooky action at a distance'", *Nature,* 454, pp. 861-864.

Scaul, D. (1968) Phys. Rev. 137, p. 166.

Sciama, D.W. (1953) "The Origin of Inertia." Monthly Notices of the Royal Astronomical Society, Vol. 113, p.34.

Sciama, D.W. (1969) *The Physical Foundation of General Relativity,* New York: Doubleday.

Schmidt, H. (1976) Psychokinetic Effect on Prerecorded Targets, *J. Am. Soc. Psy. Research* 70, p. 267 and private communication.

Sinha, U. (2010) "Ruling out Multi-order Interference in Quantum Mechanics," *Science.* Vol. 329, p.418.

Sirag, S.P. and E.A. Rauscher (1975) "Space-time Quantum Signals and Heisenberg's Potentia Theory for Bell's Theorem and the Young Double Slit Experiment, presentation to the Fundamental Fysiks Group, LBNL, chaired by E.A. Rauscher, December 12.

Stapp, H. (1975 & 1976) presentation on "The Interpretation of Bell's Theorem" presented to the FFG, chaired by E.A. Rauscher at Lawrence Berkeley National Laboratory, LBNL. October 31 and June 2.

Stapp, H., R. Nadeau and M. Kafatos (1999) *The Nonlocal Universe: The New Physics and Matters of the Mind,* Oxford, UK, Oxford University Press and extensive conversations with Stapp at LBNL (1966-1996).

Targ, R (2004) *Limitless Mind: A Guide to Remote Viewing and transformation of consciousness*. San Francisco: New World Library.

Targ, R., E.A. Rauscher, and D. Brown (2003) "The Physics of Zen in Four Logic," Draft.

van Bise, W.L. and E.A. Rauscher (1988 and 1990) Theoretical Models and Experimental Data Concerning the Space-Time Properties of Consciousness and Remote Mental Influence. Buck Fine Arts and Science Grant, PSRL-607882, pp. 1-222, also revised.

van Bise, W.L. and E.A. Rauscher (2004) "Quantum Mechanics and the Role of Action for Intentional Will," Towards a Science of Consciousness, Consciousness Res. Proc. Un of Arizona, Tucson, AZ, p. 73.

Weinberg, S. (1964) "Photons and Gravitons in s Matrix Theory: Derivation of Charge Conservation and Equality of Gravitational and Inertial Mass." *Phys. Rev*. p. 135, B1049-B1056.

Wheeler, J.A. (1978a) The "Past" and the "Delayed Choice" double slit experiment, ed. A.R. Marlow, *Mathematical Foundations of Quantum Theory*. Press.

Wheeler, J.A. (1978b) The "Past" and the "delayed choice" Double Slit Experiment, Ed. A.R.M. Marlo, Mathematical Foundation of Quantum Theory, Academic Press, NY. Also, private communication University of Texas, Austin, TX, June.

Wheeler, J.A. (1979a) *Beyond the Black Hole, Center for Theoretical Physics.* University of Texas, Austin, Texas.

Wheeler, J.A. (1979b) *Frontiers of time, Center for Theoretical Physics,* University of Texas, Austin, Texas.

Young, T. (1804) Experiments and calculations relative to physical optics. Philosophical Trans of the Roy. Soc. of London 94, p. 1-16.

Chapter 7
Quantum Mechanics
and
the Observer as a Participator
by
Elizabeth A. Rauscher, Ph.D.

" The world, once believed exists 'out there' independent of any act of observation.— in the real world of quantum physics, no elementary phenomena is a phenomenon until it is a recorded (observed) phenomena.

— John Archibald Wheeler, 1974

Table of Contents

Introduction 423

1. The Proper Premises of the Quantum Theory 428
   - A. The principles of quantum mechanics 428
   - B. The expectation values and probabilities 430
2. Derivation of the Schrödinger Equation, Other Wave Equations and the Reciprocity and Paired Variables 432
   - A. Canonically Conjugate Variables and Reciprocity 432
3. Other Wave Equations 443
4. Quantum Mechanics, Nonlocality, Canonically Conjugate Dualism and The Observer's Intention 445
5. The Schrödinger Cat Paradox and The Particle Wave Paradox and Their Implications for Nonlocality 452
6. The Schrödinger Cat Paradox Explained 460
7. Comments on the work of E.A. Rauscher 465
8. Quantum Measurements and the Collapse of the Wave Function, 'Psi' 468

References 473

List of Tables

Table 1: Philosophical Viewpoints or "Who Killed Schrödinger's Cat?" 462
Table 2: Some Quantum Mechanical Attributes and Evaluations 467
Table 3: Tenets of The Properties of Consciousness and Quantum Measurement 471

List of Figures

Figure 7a Structure of Physical Theory 433
Figure 7b 2D and 3D Figures 442
Figure 7c The quantum domain as a linear variable 448
Figure 7d Cat, Bat, Gnat 454
Figure 7e Possible versus actual 457
Figure 7f Original Cat Drawing with Curtain 459

Introduction

"I believe the observer is a participator on Mondays, Wednesdays and Fridays but not the rest of the week in which the observer is just an observer." John Archibald Wheeler, PhD. Private communication with Elizabeth A. Rauscher, Ph.D., at the University of Texas, Austin, Texas, 1978. Wheeler was a valued colleague and good friend to me.

This chapter will address important considerations for the structure of a physical theory and the need and implications for the conscious observer and creator. It is clear that one's meaningful existence directly involves one's intent and action, having both mental and physical consequences. Hence, it is vital to understand what intentional will is, how it arises, and one's ethical responsibility and life's meaning described and understood. We investigate the role of conscious intention in the physical and mental world. In this chapter we examine the theoretical constructs of the properties of intentional will as demonstrated earlier in Chapters 3 and 4 where we presented Remote Perception data.

One begins by sensing a physical or psychic input and then becoming consciously aware of it as a perception and thought, which results in concepts developed for memories, reasoning and feelings. Through this a decision, thought or intent of a Remote Perception or any perception is carried into action in the physical, mental and psychic world. This can occur in everyday life, but is particularly noticed when recording information in a remote viewing task on psychokinesis and such as for psychic healing. In this chapter, we investigate the role and action of intentional will and thought in quantum processes. In order to proceed in our investigation, we present the basic tenets of quantum mechanics, the structure of the theory and how it appears to demand a role for consciousness and its nonlocal perception and intentional choice.

The quantum theory is an important formalism to examine because, inherent in its structure, is the role for *an observer,* and some physicists believe *a participator,* in physical processes. It is the only highly accepted standard physics theory that appears to contain a role for consciousness and this role is at the seat of resolving the paradoxes in the theory. The two major theories developed in the last century, highly regarded and accepted, are relativity and quantum mechanics. These theories are accepted as being universally true for small and large scale phenomenon and for high velocities, near the velocity of light c (relativity) and where $\hbar$ is significant (quantum theory). Consideration of our theoretical model of nonlocal consciousness involves: (1) substantially accepted physics and (2) physics which is relevant to what we are studying. We have examined the relativity theory (special relativity) for macroscopic events in spacetime in chapter 5 in detail in the correlation of events in forward, backward and elsewhere Minkowski space (Rauscher and Amoroso, 2011). In this chapter we detail some of the major tenets of quantum mechanics, its implications for nonlocality and the possible reconciliations of some of the paradoxes of quantum theory with the consideration of the action of consciousness in the physical domain. (See Chapter 6.)

In Chapter 5 and elsewhere, we have addressed electromagnetic theory, its structure, limitations and application to physical aspects which are relevant to consciousness. Both electromagnetic models and quantum theory require detailed consideration in our development for a description of the action of consciousness on mentally sensitive chemical and electronic devices to psychokinetics (van Bise and Rauscher, 1990).

The standard and universally accepted form of quantum mechanics is linear and the accepted interpretation of quantum mechanics is the Copenhagen View as we stated before. This View states that the principal interpretation of quantum mechanics is that the theory will predict certain results of experimental data. In the Copenhagen View what the meaning or interpretation of the theory and its structure is, is not to be asked, questioned or addressed (van Bise and Rauscher, 2004).

This author's opinion is non-Copenhagen, as presented in Chapter 6 (Rauscher, 2005, 2010; Rauscher and Amoroso, 2006, 2008, 2011), that is, it is important and vital that one questions why and how a particular theory predicts the outcome of a particular set of experimental results; how well it works and what are its possible implications about a model of reality and its limitations. Note the EPR paradox, as well as the Schrödinger cat paradox and particle-wave paradox arose out of such questioning.

The term Copenhagen interpretation of quantum mechanics arose from the location of a conference in Copenhagen, Denmark in which Niels Bohr said, to paraphrase him, "we should only utilize quantum theory and not question how it works." Erwin Schrödinger, Werner Heisenberg, Albert Einstein, Lewis de Broglie, and other physics luminaries of the 1920's and 1930's attended one of the Solvay conferences in 1927 where this was discussed. The Copenhagen "school of thought" currently dominates physics and only a few physicists are committed to interpreting the meaning of quantum theory (F"F"G, 1975-1978; Kaiser, 2011).

Essentially, the fascination for interpreting the foundations of quantum theory is that the paradox the theory implies is that the observer (in the usual case, human observer) determines the state of the system i.e., the wave function that corresponds to the state of the system. This is called "the collapse of the wave function." Hence, in some interpretations human consciousness "enters the equation" or occupies a role in physical processes.

Since certain predictions of the quantum theory are so accurate, and if the observer does somehow participate in determining (and possibly creating) the state of the system, we have a very strong statement for the existence of and certain properties of consciousness called the "observer effect." The quantum mechanics formulism is very successful, for example, in describing the photoelectric effect, the Compton effect, the spectrum of the hydrogen atom and the implications for nonlocality in John Bell's formulation (Bell, 1964) of the EPR paradox (Einstein, Podolsky, and Rosen, 1935). There is some controversy over the concept of nonlocality and the Young double slit experiment. Perhaps Heisenberg's "potential" model is relevant here (Rauscher and Amoroso, 2011).

It is interesting to note that states of consciousness appear to be definite and discrete such as awake, excited, or bored, asleep; asleep, dreaming; meditative bliss, reverence for life, "in the now," past memories, future precognition, etc. The Hindu's formulate and describe some of these discrete states in detail in the Vedic tradition and also some shamans of various cultures. Discrete nature is quantum like. The fundamental tenet of quantum theory is discreteness or individual quantum states and possibly we can form an analogy to the perception of discrete states of consciousness, which are subjectively perceived, but also can be correlated with the monitoring of external, physiological responses.

The psi aspect of consciousness that involves nonlocal perception is also consistent with Bell's theorem, Clauser (Clauser and Horne, 1974), Alan Aspect's (Aspect, *et. at.*, 1992) experimental test of the theorem and later by N. Gisin (Gisin, *et. al.*, 1998a and 1998b). Essentially, if quantum mechanics fits the Bell's theorem test, which it does, then nonlocality must be true! (See Chapter 6, some of the material has been presented in the previous chapter, but we visit it again for completeness.)

If we can demonstrate that the form, structure and verification of the quantum theory truly imply the existence of our role for consciousness, then we have found that physical processes, manifest in ordinary four space, demand that there exists other dimensions and a higher dimensional geometry to explain reality. Amoroso and Rauscher (2009) and Renshow (2009) is a generalized discussion of nonlocality and the complex eight space. The richness and universality, as well as the success of the quantum theory leads us to examine in detail this complex theoretical structure and the nature and function of human intentionality. The basis of quantum mechanics is the concept of discreteness of the microscopic domain or the idea of "quanta" discreteness as particle-like waves.

The structure and formalism of quantum theory deals in abstract vector spaces, such as Hilbert space, group theory such as special unitary groups and Lie algebras and more advanced concepts such as Cartan spaces, Clifford algebras and fiber bundle spaces and manifold topological structures (Rauscher and Amoroso, 2011; Sirag, 2016).

Although so termed ordinary perception does not directly "see these spaces" nevertheless, vector topology might well be a good description and model for Remote Perception, involving process and intentional will, since quantum theory appears to demand a role for conscious interaction in physical processes and also physical and remote perceptual and interactive nonlocality. In the next section we discuss some of the principles of the foundations of quantum theory. For those who are not mathematically inclined this section can be skipped. The reader can skip to Sections 2 and 3 and acquire the essential meaning of this chapter. Those who enjoy math can keep reading!

1. The Proper Premises of the Quantum Theory

We shall outline some of the basic, or proper, premises of the quantum theory. The concept of quantum mechanics is those aspects of the world of the atomic or microcosmic domain which involve discreteness and nonlocality rather than intergralness and smoothness. This domain of physical theory occurs when the quantum of action or Planck's constant, $\hbar$ is significant, that is, cannot be approximated as zero or non existent as in the classical domain. Note that there are non-relativistic and relativistic quantum theories which are considered (Rauscher and Amoroso, 2011; Rauscher, *et.al.*, 2015). The general basis of quantum theory can be summarized in the following twelve axioms or postulates:

A. The principles of quantum mechanics: the basic postulates are for physical observables and the state of a quantized system.

Postulate 1. All observable physical quantities correspond to Hermitian operators. The only measurable values of a physical observable are the various eigenvalues of the corresponding operator. That is, the eigenvalues of a Hermitian operator are real. This formalism involves complex numbers.

Discussion: The final result of a mathematical quantity is real not imaginary, this includes calculations in complex eight space that yield real results.

Postulate 2. Any classical physical quantity must be considered to be constructed for pairs of canonically conjugate variables. The corresponding quantum-mechanical operator is then obtained by replacing the classical canonical variables by their corresponding quantum mechanical operators.

Discussion: This is a very significant point and is how quantum mechanics, classical mechanics and relativity can basically be related, which in turn may imply a basic dual structure of nature. This structure implies the manner in which certain aspects of nature come into being related to force and conserved quantities such as energy, mass, mass-energy, momentum charge, CPT invariance, etc. (for the product of charge, C, parity, P, and time reversal invariance, T).

Postulate 3. For all pairs of the basic canonically conjugate operators the following Heisenberg commutation rules hold:

$$[q_i, q_k] = 0,$$
$$[p_i, p_k] = 0,$$
$$[p_i, q_k] = \frac{\hbar}{i}\delta_{ik}$$

Discussion: Here $[A,B] \equiv AB - BA$ denotes the commentator of two variables A and B, and $\hbar \equiv h/2\pi = 1.0544 \times 10^{-27}$ erg sec. Note that p is a momentum function and q is a generalized coordinate or spatial function. (The first two equations obey an abelian algebra and the third a non-abelian or commutative algebra.) This formalism distinguishes the quantum theory from the classical theory.

Postulate 4. The state of a physical system is exclusively characterized by a vector of Hilbert space, upon which the operator's corresponding observables act.

Discussion: The notion of "state vector" upon which operators (which are the observables) act. This is the first point that distinguishes quantum mechanics from classical mechanics in terms of mathematical structure.

Postulate 5. Actual measurement of a physical observable carries over the state vector of the system into an eigenvector of the observed quantity, namely into the eigenvector belonging to the observed eigenvalue of the measured observable. $H\Psi = E\Psi$.

B. We now consider the expectation values and probabilities in the quantum theory.

Postulate 6. If, at the instant of the measurement, the state vector of the system is one of the eigenvectors of the measured observable, then the result of the measurement will certainly be the corresponding eigenvalue.

Postulate 7. In the general case, the measurement of a physical observable does not lead with certainty to a definite value. Any one of the possible eigenvalues may be obtained, but with different probabilities. The average expectation value of the result of the measurement of Ω is given by the expression in the Heisenberg notation

$$\langle\Omega\rangle = \frac{(\Phi,\Omega\Phi)}{(\Phi,\Phi)} \equiv \frac{\langle\Phi|\Omega|\Phi\rangle}{\langle\Phi|\Phi\rangle}$$

Discussion: Quantum theory is basically a theory of probabilities or essentially possibilities that become actualized through the act of measurable determination, which is recorded by an observer. (See Chapter 5)

Postulate 8. All Hamiltonian operators are Hermitian because all eigenfunctions of Hermitian operators are real and, hence, observable.

Postulate 9. The linear superposition of wave functions can be constructed from an orthogonal set. The orthogonal set of wave functions are linearly independent and the orthogonality requirement can be expressed as

$$\int\Psi_1(x)\Psi_2(x) = 0$$

Postulate 10. The total probability of wave functions is conserved. The probability of finding a particle with wave function Ψ in a volume $d\underline{r} = dxdydz$ is $P(\underline{r})d\underline{r}$ and is proportional to $|\Psi(\underline{r})|^2 d\underline{r}$ where $\Psi^* \Psi = |\Psi|^2$ is interpreted as a probability density for a particle in state Ψ. For the entire space $\int P(\underline{r})\, d\underline{r} = 1$. For a normalized wave function

$$\Psi_1 = \frac{1}{\sqrt{N}}\Psi$$

for $N = \int \Psi^* \Psi d\underline{r}$ for Ψ^* the complex conjugate of Ψ then $P(r) = \int \Psi_1^* \Psi_1 d\underline{r}$ and the wave function Ψ^* satisfies the equation $\int \Psi_1^* \Psi_1 d\underline{r} = 1$ when defined in the above manner and is said to be normalized. The normalization constant is determined from the theorem which states that $N = \int \Psi^* \Psi d\underline{r}$ over all space for all times, $dN/dt = 0$.

Postulate 11. Using the probability density, the expectation value of a dynamical quantity can be immediately calculated. For a particle in state $\Psi(\underline{r})$, the expectation of a function $f(\underline{r}) = f(x,y,z)$ of particle is by definition

$$\langle f \rangle = \int p(\underline{r})\, f(\underline{r})\, d\underline{r} = \frac{\int f|\Psi|^2\, dr}{\int |\Psi|^2\, dr}$$

the quantity $\langle f \rangle$ is thus the weighted average of the possible values of the function $f(\underline{r})$.

Postulate 12. Because of the symmetry principle, if $\Psi(x)$ is an eigenfunction, then $\Psi(-x)$ is also an eigenfunction which is nondegenerate i.e., they do not reduce to each other, therefore they are linearly independent and there must exist a number such that $\Psi(-x) = c\,\Psi(x)$ is an identity in x. If the transformation $x \rightarrow -x$ is performed then the result is $\Psi(x) = c\,\Psi(-x) = c^2\,\Psi(x)$ hence $c = \pm 1$ and $\Psi(-x) = \pm \Psi(x)$. Every eigenfunction for a bound state in a symmetric field $[\mu(x) = \mu(-x)]$ is therefore an even or odd function of x. This statement is that $\Psi(x)$ has a definite parity; if $\Psi(-x) = \Psi(x)$, the parity is even and if $\Psi(x) = -\Psi(-x)$ the parity is odd. The result $\langle x^{2m+1} \rangle = 0$ can be deduced immediately from parity considerations and the concept of parity is of fundamental importance for the classification of a quantum state.

2. Derivations of the Schrödinger Equation, Other Wave Equations and the Reciprocity and Paired Variables

In this section we will detail some of the form and structure of the ubiquitous quantum formulism, particularly detailing the successful Schrödinger equation. A successful theory predicts and describes natural phenomena completely and in accurate detail. Current thought holds that one of the most vital and successful theories of the 20th Century is the quantum theory. We shall examine this view in detail including quantum mechanical paradoxes. These paradoxes appear to demand a role for consciousness in physical processes to resolve some of the results of quantum experiments, such as the Young double slit experiment and Bell's theorem and paradoxes, such as the Schrödinger cat paradox and particle-wave paradox.

A. Canonically Conjugate Variables and Reciprocity

We consider the role of canonically conjugate variables and reciprocals, constants and variables and their relationship. It may be useful to examine the implications of inverse relationships in the Schrödinger equation, other quantum mechanical equations and the structure of quantum mechanics and its possible implications for intentional intervention in material, primarily microscopic systems. (See Fig. 7a for the Historical Perspective of the History of physical theory.)

Hamilton-Jacob classical mechanics was developed in terms of canonically conjugate or paired variables. These variables are next to each other by law; "married variables?" They are x and P or space and momentum and also E and t or energy and time. These are the paired variables that Heisenberg utilized to develop his principle for $\Delta x \Delta p \geq \hbar$ and $\Delta E \Delta t \geq \hbar$. (See Chapter 6.) These paired variables are the foundation of the quantum theory and are also related to the Poisson equation

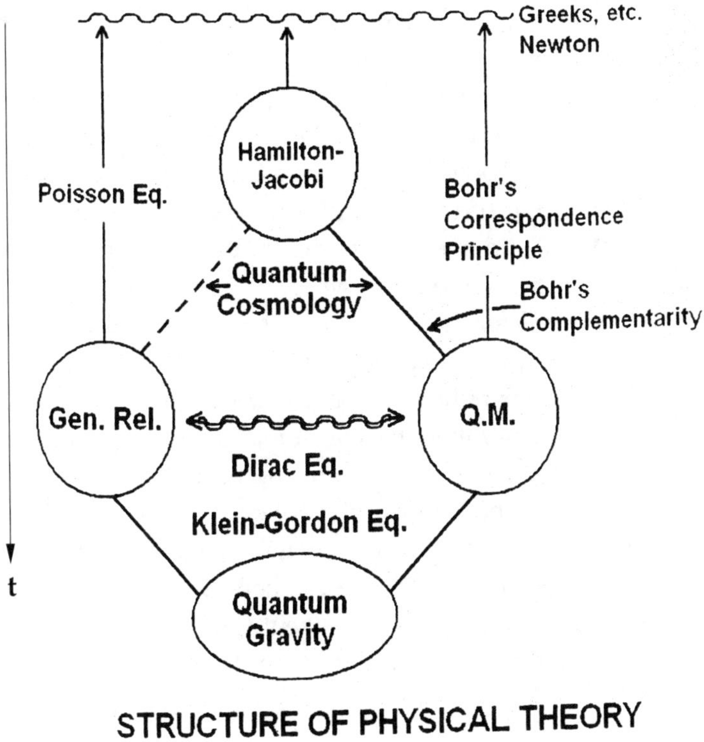

Figure 7a Structure of Physical Theory—the time evolution of physics. The top represents the past and the bottom the future where time is designated by t.

which is fundamental to the derivation of general relativity. (See derivation by this author Chapter 12, pages 213 to 215 in Rauscher and Amoroso, 2011.)

Reciprocal relations occur in the canonically conjugate variables and applications which use phase space (p, x). We will demonstrate some of these reciprocity relations, the manner in which they relate to the Schrödinger equation, and a conceptual derivation of the Schrödinger equation which can easily be made for both the time dependent and time independent forms. The following derivation of the Schrödinger equation is the author's own and is based on the de Broglie relation and the Einstein photoelectric effect equation (Rauscher, 1972a and 1972b).

We proceed for the energy Hamiltonian, H which has the dimensions of energy. Two basic equations of quantum mechanics are first, the de Broglie relation $p = \hbar/\lambda$ where we can define $k \equiv 1/\lambda$ as the wave number. This term relates the momentum of a "wavelet" particle-wave to its wavelength, λ.The second equation $E = h\nu$ relates the energy of a photon or electromagnetic quantum to its frequency and was developed and applied by Einstein to the photoelectric effect where a beam of photons impinging on a metal produces a current flow. For $E = \frac{1}{2} mv^2$ and momentum $p = mv$ and m is the energy mass of a particle then

$$E = \frac{p^2}{2m}$$

which is the form we can use on the energy Hamiltonian in the Schrödinger equation. In quantum theory we have a set of operators expressed as matrices which operate on a wave function which can be expressed as a row or column vector. The wave function has a classical analogy in a wave amplitude in a media.

Returning to the de Broglie relation of $p = \hbar/\lambda$, where λ is in dimensions of length and can be written as an operator as

$$p_{xop} \rightarrow \frac{\hbar}{i}\frac{\partial}{\partial x} \quad for \quad \frac{1}{\lambda} \rightarrow \frac{\partial}{\partial x}$$

where ∂ denotes the partial derivatives and the arrow denotes "goes to" then

$$p_x^{\,2} \rightarrow \frac{-\hbar^2\,\partial^2}{\partial x^2}$$

Now consider the photoelectric equation $E=h\nu$ for ν given in terms of l/t where ν is frequency and t is time. In operator form then (note the use of $i = \sqrt{-1}$ as fundamental to the Schrödinger equation.)

$$E_t = \frac{\hbar\partial}{i\,\partial t}$$

We note that the wave number k is reciprocal to $1/\lambda$ and that v is reciprocal to 1/t,

$$E_t \rightarrow \frac{\partial\hbar}{i\,\partial t}$$

The Hamilton operator can be written as:

$$H = \frac{P^2}{2m} = \frac{-\hbar^2}{2m}\frac{\partial^2}{\partial x^2}$$

in the one dimension of space, x. Equating the two energy operators in short hand notation we write the Schrödinger equation as $H\Psi = E\Psi$ where Ψ is the wave function of the system and Ψ is a function of x and t as Ψ (x, t). We now have

$$\frac{-\hbar^2}{2m}\frac{\partial^2\Psi\,(x,t)}{\partial x^2} + V(x)\,\Psi\,(x,t) = -\frac{\hbar}{i}\frac{\partial\Psi\,(x,t)}{2t}$$

this is the potential free space or no potential V(x,t)=0 time dependent form of the Schrödinger equation. Since the energy Hamiltonian represents the total energy of the system, then (H + V) Ψ = E Ψ which is the time independent form of the Schrödinger equation for a quantum phenomena in a potential V. The total energy $E_t = E_k + V$ for E_k the kinetic energy and V, the potential energy, where E_t is a conserved quantity.

Returning to the time dependent form in a potential free space, the solutions to this equation of the form

$$\Psi(x,t) = e\left[\frac{i(px - Et)}{\hbar}\right]$$

which is the general solution to the Schrödinger equation and satisfies this equation and $i \equiv \sqrt{-1}$. The measurement of a quantum system is made in terms of its real probability function $\Psi^*\Psi$ or $|\Psi|^2$. Here $e^{[\,]}$ represents a function [ ] taken to the natural logarithm exponent, e.

If we define $(\underline{p} \cdot \underline{x} - Et) = \eta$ then $\Psi = e^{i\eta} = \cos\eta + i\sin\eta$ by Euler's equation and $e^{-\varepsilon}$ can represent the wave's envelope. Note that x or $\lambda \propto 1/k$ from $p = \hbar/\lambda$ the wave number k and $t \propto 1/\nu$ the frequency from $E = h\nu = \hbar\omega$ and ω and t are the variables of Fourier analysis (Rauscher and van Bise, 2002).

In atomic processes where the Schrödinger equation well applies, the potential term is to be the electric Coulomb potential of the electric attraction of electrons and protons and mutual election repulsion for free elections not in Bohr orbitals. Quantum theory applies to small scale phenomena where $\hbar$ is effectively not zero.

A conceptual derivation of the Schrödinger equation can easily be made for both the time dependent and time independent forms. We proceed from the energy Hamiltonian H which is in the dimensions of energy. The two basic equations of $p = h/\lambda$ and $E = h\nu$ can then be utilized. Recalling that $E = p^2/2m$ where E is energy $E = 1/2\ mv^2$, p is momentum; $p = mv$ and m is mass, we can now use the relation p in the Hamiltonian,

$$H = \frac{p^2}{2m} = \frac{1}{2m}(h/\lambda)^2 = E = h\nu$$

Now recall that λ is length and in the derivative form $\partial/\partial x$ so that in one dimension of space ν is proportional to time $\nu = 1/t$ or in the derivative form $\partial/\partial t$ so that we have a form for a potential free space of the derivative for ∂.

$$\frac{\hbar^2}{2m}\frac{\partial^2}{\partial x^2} = \frac{\hbar}{i}\frac{\partial}{\partial t} \text{ or } \frac{\hbar^2}{2m}\frac{\partial^2}{\partial x^2} = \frac{\partial}{it}$$

These forms are operators that must operate on a wave function Ψ so that

$$\frac{\hbar^2}{2m}\frac{\partial^2\Psi}{\partial x^2} = \frac{\partial\Psi}{i\partial t}$$

Now consider the case of the Time Independent Schrödinger equation. For energy conservation the total energy, E_t or we can refer to it as H is $E_t=E_k+V$ where E_k is the kinetic energy and V is the potential energy; we can write the Schrödinger equation form as

$$-\frac{\hbar^2}{2m}\frac{\partial^2}{\partial x^2}\Psi + V\Psi = -\frac{\partial\Psi}{i\partial t}$$

in a potential field, V and combining terms on the left side we have,

$$\left(\frac{\hbar}{2m}\frac{\partial^2}{\partial x^2} - V\right)\Psi = \frac{-1}{i}\frac{\partial\Psi}{\partial t}$$

The potential term is taken to be the Coulomb electric charge attraction or repulsion of atomic particles and is effectively relevant when we are considering small scale phenomena.

We can write the time independent Schrödinger equation for E replacing the $\partial\Psi/\partial t$ term so that

$$\left(\frac{\hbar}{2m}\frac{\partial^2}{\partial x^2} - V\right)\Psi = E\Psi$$

or in shorthand $H\Psi = E\Psi$. In general Ψ, m and V are dependent variables on the independent variables (x,y,z,t) for the three dimensional (spatial) form of the Schrödinger equation. An exception is the Lippmann Schwinger equation treated in (p,x) phase space which utilizes p and x as independent variables instead of *x, t* as in the usual Schrödinger equation. (Rauscher, 1972a and 1972b). We will explore this point further.

Let us point out that in general x and t are chosen as independent variables and Ψ is a function of these as $\Psi(x,t)$. The potential V is usually dependent on dimension x or r can be expressed in spherical coordinates. Of course, also a three dimensional form of the Schrödinger equation can be written as

$$-\left[\frac{\hbar^2}{2m}\left(\frac{\partial^2}{\partial x^2}+\frac{\partial^2}{\partial y^2}+\frac{\partial^2}{\partial z^2}\right)+V(x,y,z)\right]\Psi\,(\mathrm{x,y,z,t}) = -\frac{\partial\,(\mathrm{x,y,z,t})}{i\partial t}$$

or we can write

$$-\left[\frac{\hbar^2}{2m}\nabla^2+V\right]\Psi = \frac{-\partial\Psi}{i\partial t}\text{ for del operator }\nabla^2 \equiv \frac{\partial^2}{\partial \mathrm{x}^2}+\frac{\partial^2}{\partial \mathrm{y}^2}+\frac{\partial^2}{\partial \mathrm{z}^2}$$

We can write the de Broglie relation as $p = h/\lambda$ which are equivalent forms. The form that Schrödinger derived in 1926 is of the potential free form

$$\frac{-\hbar^2}{2m}\nabla^2\Psi+\frac{\hbar^2}{i}\frac{\partial\Psi}{\partial t} = 0$$

and is equivalent to the previous form. The generalized three dimensional wave packet solution with proper normalization

$$\nabla^2\Psi = \frac{1}{(2\pi\hbar)^{3/2}}\int\frac{-p^2}{\hbar^2}\,\mathrm{a}(\underline{\mathrm{p}})\mathrm{e}\left[\frac{i}{\hbar}\,(\underline{\mathrm{p}}\cdot\underline{\mathrm{r}})-Et\right]\mathrm{d}\underline{\mathrm{p}}$$

where $\underline{\mathrm{r}}$ is the radius vector, $\underline{\mathrm{p}}$ is the momentum vector and the limits of integration are over the space where Ψ is defined (Schrödinger, 1926a, 1926b, 1926c, and 1926d). Parseval's formula gives $\int|\Psi|^2\, d\underline{r} = \int|a(p)^2|\, dp$ = constant. The derivatives which depend on momentum and energy occurring in the Schrödinger wave equation are

$$\frac{\partial\Psi}{\partial t} = \frac{1}{(2\pi\hbar)^{3/2}} \int \frac{-p^2}{\hbar^2}\, a(\underline{p}) e \left[\frac{i}{\hbar}\,(\underline{p}\cdot\underline{r}) - Et\right] d\underline{p}$$

So that the left side of the Schrödinger equation becomes:

$$\frac{1}{(2\pi\hbar)^{3/2}} \int \left(\frac{p^2}{2m} - E\right) a(\underline{p}) e \left[\frac{i}{\hbar}\,(\underline{p}\cdot\underline{r}) - Et\right] d\underline{p}$$

where $d\underline{p} = dp_x dp_y dp_z$ which vanishes because

$$E = \frac{p^2}{2m}$$

and hence the above is the solution to Schrödinger's wave equation (See Fig. 7b for representation of wave packets.) Note that $d\underline{r} = dxdydz$ and $d\underline{p} = dp_x dp_y dp_z$.

The major principles of physics can be enumerated as in Chapter 5. They are the three fundamental principles of quantum particle physics: (1) Poincaré invariance or Lorentz invariance of the energy Hamiltonian which implies the conservation of energy, E, momentum, p, and angular momentum, L in the vernacular of the S - matrix formalism. Also the equivalence of different inertial frames of reference is assumed under this principle; (2) causality which implies analyticity of scattering amplitudes of functions of particle energy and momenta, (See Chapter 5 Table 2, Rauscher, 1979, Chew, 1964) which is associated with isolated singularities in the complex plane and is determined by the cause-effect event structure of space-time; and (3) unitarity, which implies the conservation of probability, as well as the super possibility of wave function amplitude.

The first principle relates to the homogeneity principle of spacetime and the principle of nonlocality and hence to remote perception in space. The second principle relates to the analytic continuation in the complex plane and includes anticipatory systems such as precognition. The third principle of unitarity, which is the conservation principle, relates to action at a distance or psychokinesis and psychic healing in which information transmission allows local energy access.

The significance of the Schrödinger equation and more generally the quantum approach in general is the possibility, at least in part, of describing possible micro psychokinetic links between the intentional observation and the effect on a system. This in some sense links body, the physical, and the spiritual "unseen," while producing effects on the physical domain.

We can interpret the Schrödinger wave functions in physical terms. The Schrödinger equation for the wave function of a free particle arises directly from the Einstein-de Broglie relations and is, in a sense, equivalent to them. However, until suitable boundary conditions and requirements concerning the continuity of solutions are imposed, the properties of the wave function are not completely described by the Schrödinger equation. Indeed, the application of Fourier's theorem that has been applied previously is only justified for functions for which the integrals involved are convergent functions and this obviously implies that $(\underline{r},t)$ should become zero at a very large distance from the center of the wave packet. Moreover, it will usually be true that Ψ is a continuous function of x, y, and z. In a very general sense, any continuous solution of the Schrödinger equation which vanishes at infinity in such a way that the integral $\int|\Psi|^2 d\underline{r}$ exists, can be represented as superposition of plane waves, and the two descriptions of the wave function are entirely equivalent. This is a matter of great practical importance, because many of the properties of Ψ which are of physical interest are brought out more clearly by the Schrödinger equation than by the direct representation of Ψ in terms of its harmonic components. Here, the harmonic oscillator form of the potential $V(\underline{r},t)$ gives rise to harmonic oscillator wave functions.

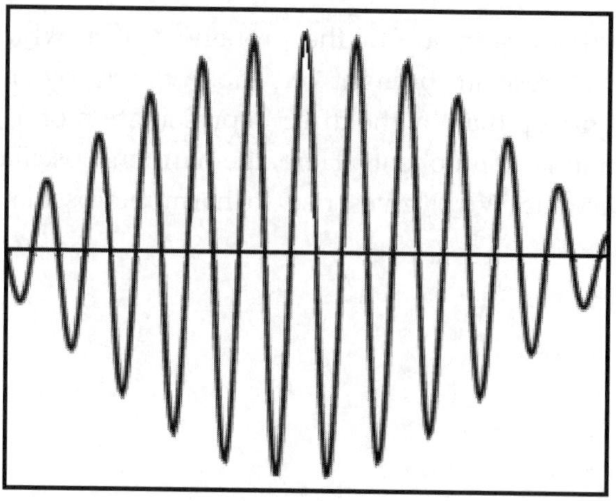

a) **2-D**

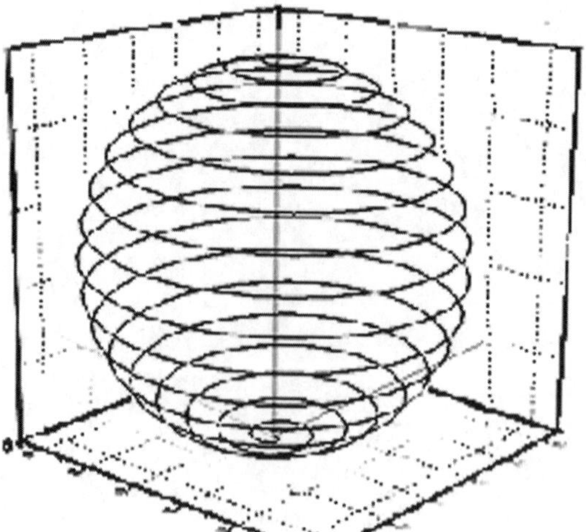

b) **3-D**

Figure 7b In Figure a, we represent a two dimensional packet in the x and y plane and in Figure b a wave packet figure in three dimensions in the x, y, and z plane.

3. Other Wave Equations

For completeness, we present the classical wave equation in one spatial dimension by way of comparison in terms of the wave amplitude *U* (*x*, *t*) as a function of space and time, as it is the basis of the quantum formalism as the wave function,

$$\frac{\partial^2 U}{\partial x^2} = \frac{1}{C^2}\frac{\partial^2 U}{\partial t^2}$$

where C is the propagation velocity of the wave and is far less than the velocity of light and the solution of the equation is in the form U=A sinΘ + i cosΘ standing wave solution.

The Schrödinger wave equation previously discussed is for applications for non-relativistic physical processes. It is an inhomogeneous hypergeometric equation, for the time dependent form. Two utilized relativistic quantum wave equations are the Dirac electron theory equation and the Klein-Gordon equation. Perhaps the clearest analogy is between the classical wave equation and the Klein-Gordon equation. The Klein-Gordon equation is a four-dimensional form where the wave function depends on (x,y,z,t) and is written as (Rauscher and Amoroso, 2011; Rauscher and Targ, 2002):

$$\Box^2\Psi + \frac{2m}{\hbar}\Psi = 0$$

where $\Box^2$ is the d'Alembertian operator as a four dimensional second derivative

$$\Box^2 = \frac{\partial^2}{2x^2} + \frac{\partial^2}{\partial y^2} + \frac{\partial^2 z}{2z^2} - \frac{1}{c^2}\frac{\partial^2}{\partial t^2}$$

and m is the mass of the particle under consideration. Note that this equation is second order both in space and time as is the classical wave equation, whereas the Schrödinger equation is second order in space and first order in time, in part the reason for the i= $\sqrt{-1}$ term in the equation. The first order in time term requires the i term in it. The imaginary number $\sqrt{-1}$ occupies a fundamental role in physical theory and practical applications such as electronics. (See Chapter 4.) The Dirac electron theory equation is also a second order in space and time equation or it can be written as two equations which are first order in space and time. The four vector form for spin 1/2 fermion particles is the spin s =1/2 relativistically covariant manner. It was emphasized by de Broglie that the theory satisfies, at least to this degree, the requirements of special relativity.

4. Quantum Mechanics, Nonlocality, Canonically Conjugate Dualism and The Observer's Intention

Quantum theory is considered complete, that is, in all microsystems and perhaps for some macrosystems. It appears that the quantum description is also ubiquitous in these systems. 'Microsystems' includes a system of small size where $\hbar \neq 0$ and quantum effects are experimentally observed. (See Chapter 6 for the implications of the completeness theorem and nonlocality.)

The correspondence principle states that there exists for each physical entity, particle, wave or "universe," etc. a mathematical description or wave function that corresponds to and describes this physical entity. This point is central to the EPR paradox and the Bell's Theorem test (Bell, 1964, 1966). Also that the quantum description, corresponds or makes a smooth transition to a classical system in the case where it no longer applies to the micro quantum system. This is the Bohr correspondence principle.

The complementarily principle is basic to the quantum description and arises out of the definition of the energy Hamiltonian and Hamilton-Jacobi mechanics, as does the duality concept of canonically conjugate variables, phase space, variables of p and x. Some of the most interesting are the Heisenberg uncertainty or indeterminacy relations as the canonically conjugate expressions $[p,x] \geq \hbar$ or $\Delta x \Delta p \geq \hbar$. As we know the interpretation of the later expression is that as the uncertainty of position x becomes larger, the determinacy of momentum p can be made more accurately with less inconsistency, where 1.0544 x 10^{-27} erg-sec. Also considered is the indeterminacy of the canonically conjugate expression $[E,t] \geq \hbar$. This is a non-commuting algebra in terms of the energy uncertainty ΔE and temporal uncertainty Δt as $\Delta E \Delta t \geq \hbar$ (I discuss other possible canonically conjugate variables in Rauscher, 1972a and 1972b.) In the classical limit of $\hbar \rightarrow 0$ then $[p,x]=0$, i.e., the commutation relations of the canonically conjugate variables are zero that is $\Delta x \Delta p=0$.

The quantum domain is not the only domain where the issue of nonlocality arises. For example, in the classical domain of physical theory the issue of nonlocality can occur. Historically Kepler's theory of planetary motions, Newton's law of universal gravitation and the aether construct in electromagnetic theory have involved addressing the existence and meaning of nonlocality. In Kepler's case, he drew a radius vector from the planets to the sun that described their orderly orbits. As we said before, the force drawing these solar system bodies together was "unseen" or nonlocal, the church doctrine at the time was that there are no nonlocal effects and that you cannot draw a radius vector from an archangel (planet analogy) to God (the Sun analogy)! In general, physicists abhor the concept of nonlocality as much as nature "abhors" a vacuum, but there is good and perhaps universal evidence for nonlocal phenomena.

Other experimental evidence for nonlocality is collective electron behavior in plasmas (Rauscher, 1968), and the Young double slit experiment, the BCS theory in superconductivity (Rauscher, 1982a) and a magnetic domain lining up in a strong external magnetic field. Regardless of this evidence, the current physicists and earlier natural scientists have held a tendency to abhor nonlocal correlations and interactions in physical systems and perhaps other systems such as psi phenomena.

Current physical theory is based on the work of Galileo on moving bodies and Newton on laws of motion and universal gravitational theory that are accepted on firm experimental grounds. It is also accepted that these descriptions apply in non-quantum domains and non-high velocity relativistic domains. They apply "exactly" and analytically to only two body interactions. The description of three or more bodies involves approximations. Electromagnetic theory and Maxwell's equation encompassing Faradays' law, etc. apply quite well, but for complex electrical engineering practices they become an approximation. In fact, Newton's laws for complex multibody systems require approximations as well. (Rauscher, 1971b).

As we said, one of quantum theory's major tenets that

relates to our discussion and description of the fundamental properties and nature of consciousness is the observer effect on the "collapse" of the wave function to a particular state, mathematically representing a physically realizable, observable and hence, recordable, state. As exemplified by the so- termed "Schrödinger cat paradox," (see the next section and Chapter 6) the linear superposition principle of two or more possible states of a system is "collapsed" by the act or process of observation (including recording) of the state of the system. The superposition principle is only possible in a linearized system. The "picture" that most quantum physicists hold of the collapse of the wave function is that the unobserved "object" or particle or quanta appears as a wave spread out over space, but the instant it is observed, or measured, the wave collapses to a point or vibrating string and acts as a particle, as in string theory (Sirag, 2016, Rauscher, 1981, 1982b, 1982c).

Some physicists, such as Eugene Wigner (1967), this author and others, have examined the possibility that maybe there are viable nonlinear quantum theories. (See Fig. 7c.) Perhaps the "Standard quantum theory" is only an approximation in a given domain to a larger "truth" or theory. Indeed and if, conscious observation is necessary to determine the collapse of the wave function to a particular state of a system then in a sense the quantum theory implies consciousness exists and is necessary to the quantum formalism! Maybe in a somewhat nonlinear quantum series, a collection of a more global state of consciousness determines the final outcome or state of a system. These nonlinear theories, though not well accepted usually involve additional nonlinear terms in quantum wave equations such as the Schrödinger equation (Rauscher, 2010), the Dirac equation (Rauscher, *et. al.,* 2015), the Klein-Gordon equation, etc. The issue of local, nonlocal and global action of consciousness may be addressed by these considerations. Both the Dirac and Klein-Gordon equations are relativistically incorrect (See Rauscher and Amoroso, 2011). We have derived the Schrödinger equation in the complex eight space and also the Dirac equation (Rauscher and Amoroso, 2009). (See Fig. 7c).

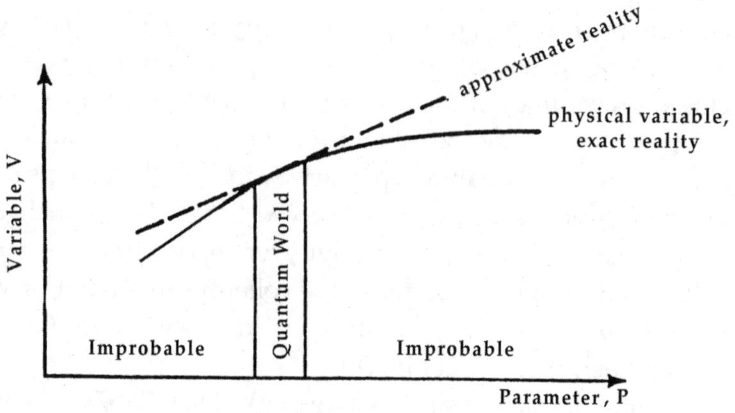

Figure 7c We approximate the quantum domain as a linear variable, V, dependent on a parameter, P. The full "space" of exact reality is nonlinear. We may be able to consider a limited domain of reality as linear.

How well does the quantum theory really describe the micro domain? We discussed completeness, that is the quantum theory is universal; for example the Heisenberg Principle always applies, but is the quantum theory really an exact theory? In the case of the Niels Bohr hydrogen atom description utilizing the quantum principle of discreteness formulated by Max Planck terms of h or $\hbar = h/2\pi$, Planck's constant and the de Broglie relation $p = \hbar / \lambda$, the excitation and emission spectrum of hydrogen, the two body system of a proton and electron, are well described by the Rydberg constant, R. Note that Newton's universal gravitational theory also has a constant, G the universal constant which occurs in his two body interaction law of the force of gravitational attraction between two massive bodies.

In many body mechanical theories are quantum theories for more than two interacting bodies or systems, and approximations have to be made. This is true for calculating orbits of planets in the solar system in which other planets produce perturbations on a planet's orbit about the sun. In atomic, as well as in nuclear physics, where the quantum formalism applies, again multi-particle systems for greater than two particles or a particle and a field require that approximations and additional terms are required, for example, to calculate the emission spectrum of the sodium atom. Note also that the law of the electric charge between two charge particles is exact by a constant

$$ke = \frac{1}{\sqrt{4\pi\epsilon_o}} \quad \text{for} \quad F = k_e \frac{q_1 q_2}{r^2}$$

where ϵ_0 is the value of the permittivity vacuum. The Coulomb force between two particles of charge q_1 and q_2 separated by distance, r is given by the above equation. More detailed analysis on these constants such as e, the charge on a single electron, proton, etc., G, R, $\hbar$, c, as fundamental universal constants is in my book on General Relativity and quantum gravity (Rauscher

1971a) which further utilizes a ten dimensional geometric model. When we discuss the nature of quantum completeness and quantum exactness, this applies to the two body problem. Only here do we have exact quantum solutions. A classical analogy is Newton's Universal Law of gravitational attractions between two masses m_1 and m_2 separated by a distance, r. The gravitation between the two bodies is $F = G/2\pi\ m_1m_2/r^2$ where G is the universal gravitational constant. This formulism has a similar structure to Coulomb's law between two charged bodies.

In the case of the hydrogen atom, consisting of a central nuclear proton and electrically attracted "orbital" electron with the quantum principle, the Bohr orbital electron moves in a fuzzy wavy path and is a two body problem. If we have a Helium atom with a nucleus of four nucleons, two protons and two neutrons and orbiting are two electrons, the nucleus acts as one particle, the nucleus and then the electrons act as two other bodies. This is the classic three body problem. However, in both classical and quantum mechanics the three body problem cannot be solved with an exact solution. We have explored a number of different solutions to the three body or multibody problem in atomic physics but all involve approximations (Bruch, *et.al.*, 1994; Amusia, *et.al.*, 1993).

It is vitally important to examine the applicability, universality and implications of various significant theories and their relevance to psi phenomena and vice versa. In general the formulation of physics and psi both involve the correlation of local and nonlocal events in space and time. We address some of these issues in Chapter 5, but let us return to quantum theory since it may have an inherent role for the consciousness formulated in it. In general all of physics, engineering (theory and application) and science in general are formulated to exclude psi and most systems, physical, equipment, etc. are "hardened against" the action of consciousness and conscious intention so that exact reproducibility is possible and so is reliability. To construct a system that is conducive to intentional intervention one must deal with nonlinear, metastable systems to enhance that ability to observe psi effects. Such systems have been constructed by a number of researchers including Rauscher, van Bise, (van Bise and Rauscher, 1990; Schmidt, 1976) and others, who have demonstrated the correlation of intention or *will* and effect or *result*. Various methods to enhance the correlation and magnitude of the effect are being developed. Some involve effects that are quantum mechanical in nature.

Consciousness nonlocality in spacetime and/or psi has both macroscopic, quantum domain consequences. It can be argued that macro-events can be made up of a group or series of (atomic) micro events or that a series of micro events "add up" to macro events. This is an issue to be debated and hence leads to the fact that the quantum domain alone cannot explain consciousness as it has both microscopic and macroscopic effects and consequences. (See Chapter 5.)

The two major key elements in the case of the possible relevance of the quantum theory to psi are (1) how an observation may select or determine a specific state of a system i.e. relate observation and state selection to consciousness, and (2) inherent, fundamental theoretical description and experimental verification and determination of nonlocality at the quantum level. Furthermore we need to examine more deeply the implications of a conscious observer collapsing a wave function and whether mind-matter interactions or psychokinetics are involved in all measurements.

We can argue that in the photoelectric effect, photons, some in the optical region and some in the x-ray region, produce a change in the system upon which they impinge. Optics and more complex systems of visible light and electrons, in electron microscopes, x-rays and x-ray film, and rays (which are modified) make systems visible to the human eye and to electronic systems and hence are measurable. Electromagnetic waves of sufficient energy, even infrared, IR, heated surfaces, excite atoms, make changes in the systems so that we may ultimately view them and/or measure them — this is the key to observation. The process of observation requires an effect on the system such as shining light on the system.

5. The Schrödinger Cat Paradox and the Particle Wave Paradox and their Implications for Nonlocality: The Observer as a Conscious Intentive Observer

What constitutes an observer, particularly in the quantum sense? A recording instrument can be designed to record the state of a system, for example, one of two states of the system as in the Schrödinger equation in the "Schrödinger cat paradox." Is the point at which the knowledge of the state of the cat is known only when a human observer makes the observation and determination?

The so termed Schrödinger cat paradox arises out of the linear properties of the structure of the quantum theory. Basically, all quantum processes are considered to be linear and obey linear superposition. This is stated that all quantum wave functions are constructed out of a linear sum over a basis set vector space. The case of the Schrödinger cat paradox is a hypothetical experiment thought up by Schrödinger (or perhaps his dog).

We discussed the Schrödinger cat paradox in detail at the November 1977 Iceland conference and its implications for consciousness and its effect and causal intent on the physical world (Rauscher, 1979). The cat paradox involves the "Gedanken" or thought experiment in which a cat is enclosed in an airtight cage with a cyanide pellet and a means to break it such as a hammer poised on a lever. The possibility of activating the hammer to break the pellet is "chosen" by the quantum randomness of the decay of a radioactivity element. A proper connection is made so that the emission of a radioactive particle is detected and then transmitted to a system to activate the hammer mechanism to crush the cyanide capsule. It is assumed there is enough oxygen to keep the cat alive if the pellet remains intact. The state of affairs depends on two factors (1) the probability of the decay of the radioactive element (or some other random event generation), (2) the actuality of the event i.e., its actual occurrence.

The system is set up so that the experiment remains behind a curtain unobserved by a *human* observer. The wave function, using linear superposition, is given as $\Psi = a\Psi_{alive} + b\Psi_{dead}$ where a and b are normalization constants. This wave function is a solution to the Schrödinger wave equation. If the curtain is removed then the observer collapses the wave function to one of two states, either cat Ψ_{alive} or cat Ψ_{dead}. The paradox arises out of the fact that the fate of the cat is (presumably) determined by the act of removing the curtain and observing the state of the cat, alive *or* dead (not alive and dead).

A facetious part of the argument in Iceland turned to the desire not to kill a cat so that the rat and even the gnat paradox was addressed. In fact there is an important issue to be addressed that is, the cat knows its state or at least that it is alive, Ψ_{alive} (and if there is life after death, the cat may also perceive the dead cat state, Ψ_{dead}). A central issue then is whose consciousness perceives what? Richard Amoroso modified my cat paradox Fig. 7d(a). He substituted a bat for a rat. Ok, Richard! See Figs. 7d(b) and (c).

The Everett-Graham-Wheeler (EGW) model attempts to resolve the cat paradox by suggesting that at each instant in forward time an infinite set of possibilities exists or in a sense an infinite number of Universes, two of which contain a cat alive Ψ and a cat dead Ψ, or if you prefer a rat alive and rat dead Universe. The observer then just finds himself in one of these Universes (DeWitt and Graham, 1973). The multiverse concept has gained popularity in recent years (Rauscher and Amoroso, 2009).

In this type of picture, a PK event becomes acausal or a synchronicity. The PK event occurs and the human "agent" then just happens to be near by. In the pure EGW model there is no "communication" between the various universes and hence there is no way to detect any other possible state of a system to exist so the existence of these other universes becomes a moot point i.e. immaterial since one cannot have knowledge of them.

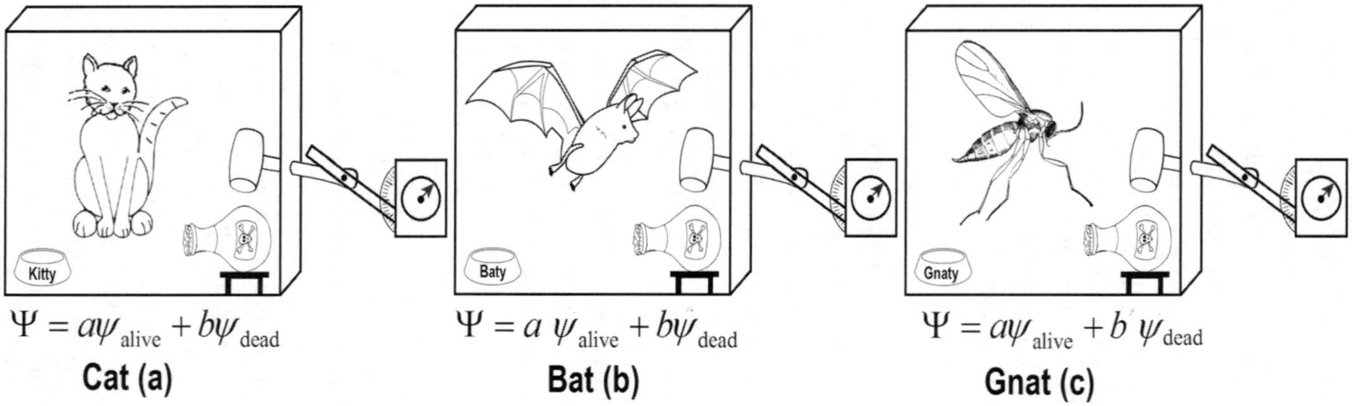

Figure 7d Letter to me by Richard Amoroso of November 30, 2010. "In a new paper I'm writing I made a hierarchical diagram from your CAT, didn't mean to use BAT instead of RAT but realized after. The unobserved system has a probability at any time, *t* of 50% that the cat is dead or alive." (Courtesy of Richard Amoroso.)

The central issue of the Schrödinger cat paradox is: who causes what? How is the state of a system determined and the wave function collapsed to a particular single valued state!? Actually, the paradox embodies the issue of who or what is conscious, is it the wave function for the whole universe or all the universes that determine the state of each and all systems? Is (are) the universe/s conscious? Can we deny consciousness to a cat, a rat, a bat and how about a gnat?

Central to the operation of the scientific method is causality and objectivity. In classical physics, it is believed processes occur and all things go about their business without a human observer. A human observer enters the screen and the processes continue, although some animals can be affected by the observer i.e., as they observe the observer and make a choice about their observation. Plants may be affected by humans who water them or cut them down, etc. This involves observation and interaction.

What is the role of a passive human observer? Can the observation be made completely without interaction? Probably not in the true sense of air molecules and other physiological processes — the universe is changed at each instant by some degree by one's very state of being Ψ alive, human or otherwise.

Our question centers on, besides physical effects, what about mental intent and thought transference between the human observer/participator/interactor with animals, plants, the physical states of systems and other humans. At the other end of the spectrum of thought is Rene Descartes and George Berkeley's view paraphrasing his statement that "I think therefore I am" and "I cannot prove anything else exists but me," according to Descartes. It may all be a total illusion of my mind! This view has shades of Jean Paul Sartre's "it's all an illusion."

Actually, Rene Descartes' argument was a syllogistic one (1) "I think therefore I am", (2) "I did not create myself'," (3) "therefore God did it." Philosophical arguments in Descartes' day were often concerned with developing a logical and scientific *proof* of God's existence. It appears that Descartes neglected to consider the act of his parents in his existence but then perhaps he could argue about the existence of his parents.

These paradoxes, Schrödinger's cat, Descartes' existence, the multi-universe EGW notion and formalism express ignorance as to what consciousness is, what is intentional will (and responsibility), etc. Essentially a paradox expresses our ignorance of a particular understanding or lack thereof of our conceptual framework and its descriptive value in comprehending *Reality*. (See Fig. 7e).

It appears that the resolution of the Schrödinger cat paradox lies in how the possible becomes actualized in time and hyperdimensional geometrics. (See Chapter 5.) And what is time? (See Fig. 7d) With the linear superposition principle, the paradox remains and it may require a nonlinear quantum theory which may be only slightly nonlinear to select a preferred state, perhaps by the action of consciousness. Before we turn to another related quantum paradox, to quote Erwin Schrödinger (1887-1961) on the cat paradox, "I don't like it, and I'm sorry I ever had anything to do with it" (Schrödinger, 1926a, 1926b, 1926c).

Another much discussed, and this author believes, related paradox is the particle-wave paradox. Is light or electromagnetic energy a particle or a wave? Sir Isaac Newton (1642-1727) believed that light was corpuscular in nature, that is, particle-like. His experiment with prisms and light spectrum, in which white light passing through a prism creates the band of colors of the rainbow by internal refraction, appears to indicate light is wave-like.

The Schrödinger cat paradox exists because of the linear superposition of quantum mechanics. It appears that the state of the system is determined by the act of observing and recording observational data and the result depends on *when* one looks. In the case of the particle-wave paradox, the results of which depend on *what* experiment is performed on photons, of light or light waves (and equivalently via the de Broglie relation) thus depends on the *way* one looks, i.e. what experiment is performed.

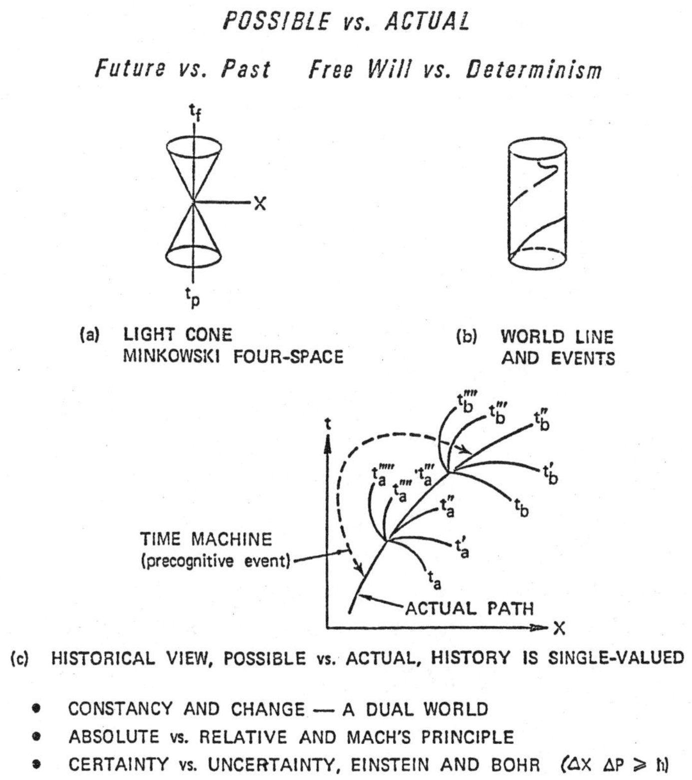

Figure 7e Possible versus actual

Several types of world lines are depicted. Figure 7e(a) depicts a worldline with a single-valued "now," but Figures 7e (b) and (c) depict a multi-valued present. As we move through space and time, Figure c, at each point we are confronted with various possible cases of action and each point we chose the most probable one but not always! There is a dual world: constancy and change, absolute versus relativistic and Mach's Principle and certainty versus uncertainty in terms of Einstein and Bohr ($\Delta x, \Delta p \geq \hbar$).

In a sense, the Schrödinger cat paradox violates Aristotelian logic. After the cat is observed, the state of the cat is determined to be (1) dead *or* (2) alive but before the moment the cat is dead and/or alive or neither or both for $\Psi = a\Psi_{alive} \pm \Psi_{dead}$. Where the case corresponds to a linear relation of (-) and both to a linear superposition (+). The formulation of the cat paradox is usually formulated as a symmetric superposition or (+) not an antisymmetric superposition (-) (See Table 1 and Fig. 7f.).

In a sense Zen four "logic" is non-Aristotelian four logic, that is, contains the group of operators of *neither and both* (Targ and Hurtak, 2006). Since Aristotelian logic of either/or, is the dominant logic form of western European/American culture of *either/or,* that is why the cat paradox or the meaning and interpretation of quantum measurement is considered a paradox according to this author.

Nature does not admit to paradoxes as they only arise out of the ignorance of human interpretation. The resolution of the paradox is well within the understanding of the where and what of human consciousness and other consciousness (Targ, 2004).

Figure 7f This is my original cat paradox drawing I made that includes the curtain. A schematic representation of the Schrödinger cat paradox $\Psi = a\Psi_{alive} + b\,\Psi_{dead}$. In the Schrödinger cat in a box thought experiment there is a *50%* probability at any time, t that the cat is dead or alive when the curtain is closed.

6. The Schrödinger Cat Paradox Explained

The Schrödinger cat paradox is hypothetical but does demonstrate that the linear superposition principle may not fit the "real world" in which most actual processes are nonlinear. It appears that biological systems are more nonlinear than chemical or physical but Galileo's, Newton's and Einstein's theoretical models of the gravitational field formulate in terms of very nonlinear formalisms, as the gravitational field is a very nonlinear field. Certainly one of the major difficulties in developing a study of quantum gravity arises out of the linear model of quantum processes and the nonlinear properties of the gravitational field (Rauscher, 1971a, 1972c, 2005).

If we are to attempt to reconcile the physics of quantum mechanics (and physics in general) with consciousness, perhaps we must deduce from quantum theory and experiments a role demanded for consciousness in the physical world, at least in part, in the micro domain. If this approach is a viable one, we need to examine in detail which of the quantum formalisms are most relevant to relating physics and consciousness. The Schrödinger equation applies to non-relativistic systems, but is descriptive of many quantum systems.

The Dirac equation is relativistic, but primarily applied to electron theory. The Klein-Gorden equation is also relativistic and the modification of the Klein-Gorden equation as the nonlinear form is the Klein-Gorden equation, having solitary wave or soliton solutions is relevant to the description of phenomena involving nonlocality (Rauscher, 1982a). Since nonlinearity or nonlocality are properties of consciousness, this fact leads us to consider the Klein-Gorden equation as a fruitful area of physics to examine, relevant to describing the properties of consciousness. Remote intentional perceptional communication and interaction may be well described and fit with the nonlocality described by the coherent collective nonlinear soliton solutions that can represent a signal, which remains coherent over distances. We have also determined that one can formulate nonlinear forms of the Schrödinger equation which as soliton solutions have both relativistic and non-relativistic quantum formalisms that can relate to remote connectedness phenomena, i.e. such as an observer and the observed (or perceived) and its physically remote cause (Rauscher and Amoroso, 2006).

The reason to consider a relativistic quantum theory is not related to the fact that relativistic phenomena occurs near to the velocity of light but the relativity theory formally formulates the correlation of events in space and time. Since essentially we argue that the existence of psi and the causal effects of psi are determined or measured by the correlation of events in space and time, then we may argue that we should concentrate on the Klein-Gorden equation.

When we deeply and truly examine the nature of what we term real, there is plenty of "room" for psi, consciousness and many dimensions of existence for future generations to discover, for it is certainly true that there is no illusion more dangerous than the belief that the progress in the advancement of science is predictable! Certainly nonlocality is a great surprise in the form of interconnectedness associated with Bell's theorem and the EPR paradox (which was resolved by the formulation of Bell's theorem and its many subsequent tests). It is as if a spider in its web feels each disturbance in the web's far reaches as it sits at the web's center (Rauscher, 1971b, See Table 1).

"The world thus appears as a complicated tissue of events in which connections of different kinds alternate or overlap or combine and thereby determine the texture of the whole," from *Physics and Philosophy* by Werner Heisenberg, (1938).

We can form an analogy to attempt to resolve the particle/wave duality and the mind/body duality: the specific experiment one conducts makes light or particles act and "look like" a particle or a wave. The perceptual experiment about our view of reality determines how we perceive reality to be in terms of

Table 1
Philosophical Viewpoints
or
"Who Killed Schrödinger's Cat?"

Listed are some of the philosophical views that relate to the interpretation of quantum mechanics and the so termed Schrödinger cat paradox.

1. It's the view of positivism "Everything" is considered as a series of experiences and observations, in quantum mechanics, the observer does not participate.

2. Innate knowledge as it relates to epistemology in Emmanuel Kant's view of innate categorization and causality.

3. Ontology, that is what exists as fundamentals being as perceived reality, connected to or unconnected to conscious perception. Conscious perception of existence "brings it into being or existence," for example, Wheeler's concept "The unobserved universe would not exist."

4. Structuralists, particularly in biology "Survival of the *fittest*" as Darwinian evolutionary concept, space-time evolves out of the biological evolutionary process so the space and time are not external constructs. This may be compatible with quantum theory in that integral time does not exist in the microcosmos. Issues of casualty come to the fore such as "what causes what" in some nuclear processes and in the case of precognition.

5. Time and causality are intimately connected; time seems so exact and it's fundamental nature yet so illusive time itself, at least in the microdomain may be quantized, which Rauscher and Prigogine formulated (Rauscher, 1971a). To quote one of Albert Einstein's thoughts in 1941 "time and space are modes by which we think and not conditions in which we live." Also Sir Arthur S. Eddington in 1923 suggested that "time is a mental construct of our private conscious-

ness...physicist construct the concept of a world wide time from a string of subjective instances." (Rauscher, 1993a, 1993b).

6. Discrete states of reality, includes the self organizing principle of Ilya Prigogine, (Prigogine, 1997) where systems act as macroscopic "quantum" or discrete processes under the influence of an energy *flux*. State changes occur in discrete catastrophic steps for nonlinear, non equilibrium open systems.

7. Mutogenic, metabolic processes in which specialization and diversification occurs, expressible in terms of energy, entropy and information processes. We can consider such a system as dynamic or process oriented on its structural level and energy properties may give rise to a concept of time. These processes can be microscopic or quantum in nature or macroscopic in biological and cosmological in nature. Issues related to point 6 and 7 may involve a Lamarckian modification of the Darwinian model of evaluation which is currently termed epigenetics (Rauscher, 1971c).

8. Dualistic concepts such as mind/body duality, cause effect pairs of action and effect, paired variables in physical theory and conceptual opposites. Dual concepts have been put forward for centuries, such as the Chinese Yin-Yang each carrying seeds of the opposite. Dual concepts lead to unity attempts such as those of Leibniz mind/matter monad model. The Heisenberg uncertainty principle results from the relationship of paired variables which is at the foundation of the structure of the Hamilton-Jacobi classical mechanics and the foundation of quantum theory.

the mind/body or mind/brain issue. Assumption of the purely mechanistic view will imply that brain/body dominates, or the assumption of the non-mechanistic view gives more credence to the mind or conscious spirit as the dominate entity.

Each fundamental assumption about reality further reinforces what reality is to be to each individual perceiver. We emphasize our beliefs and exclude contradictory perceptions. To quote Wolfgang Pauli on the topic of quantum mechanics and the mind/body duality problem, "the deeper the physicist intruded into the realms of the subatomic and supergalactic dimensions, the more intensely he was made aware of their paradoxical and common sense-defying structure, and the more open-minded he became toward the possibility of the seemingly impossible." The psychological parallelism envisioned in the last century will not account for the general problem posed by the relationships of mind/body.

7. Comments on the Work of E.A. Rauscher, Ph.D.

In 1982 this author addressed a conference on consciousness at the University of Philadelphia, Pennsylvania, in which many physics' luminaries were present. After my talk and panel presentation, Eugene Wigner of Princeton University, New Jersey, commented on my implication for the complex eight dimensional geometry, superluminal information transmission, Bell's Theorem and consciousness. He commented as follows:

"I would like to point out that the possibility of transluminal (superluminal) information transmission has been essentially experimentally demonstrated. J.S. Bell formulated a theorem in 1964 which involves a correlation function which describes remote connectedness of correlated events—consider two particles, which have opposite spin, for example, in the ground state of a hydrogen atom. The measurement of the spin of one electron, determines the spin observed in the other electron. These probability measurements indicate that information can be transmitted transluminally. I'll also mention that the quantum mechanics of the J.S. Bell experiment was questioned, but in a couple of years it was very well confirmed.

"There is one other thing that I can mention in this connection. A space-time point cannot be defined in quantum mechanics, because suppose you construct a state of a particle which exists at a certain time at this point. In other words, that state is different from, perpendicular to, a state which is displaced from it. Then this is not relativistical invariance, it will not be orthogonal to the initial state. It is easy to prove that the wave function spreads out with greater than light velocity. That means that space-time concept, in my opinion, will have to be reviewed in quantum mechanics. Whether the proposal which you (E.A.R.) make is the best one, I don't know, but the mathematical description of something can be modified terribly much. I could construct a quantum mechanics, which is not complex, and I could construct a quantum mechanics which is quaternionic, but how I describe things mathematically is not uniquely prescribed. Maybe what you propose is the best thing, but maybe it isn't." (The issue of complex space and quaternions is addressed in Rauscher and Amoroso, 2011.)

Table 2
Some Quantum Mechanical Attributes and Evaluations

1. "Two paths to the same place," Young's double slit experiment implies connectedness by a multidimensional space.
2. "Microscopic indeterminacy" or quantum uncertainty—the Heisenberg and Compton Effects appear to be due to scale differences of the observer and the observed.
3. "Photonic measurement" or "seeing with light"; (observation) most measurements involve visible frequency electromagnetic interactions in the initial, immediate and final analysis.
4. "Remote connection" in three spaces as explained by John S. Bell's theorem and the John Clauser and later Alan Aspect Experiments and N. Gisin (connected by a multidimensional space, see Rauscher, 2014).
5. "Discreteness or particle nature of the 'Photon of Light' and matter," e.g. grainy nature of substance and the fundamental nature of identity of substance.
6. "Relationship of 'particle' and 'wave,'" i.e. the manner in which one examines Nature and determines what on "sees" (observes), the de Broglie relation, $P=\hbar/\lambda$.

8. Quantum Measurement and the Collapse of the Wave Function, ψ or 'Psi'

The interpretation of quantum mechanics and its formalism is very much affected and changed by the assumption of the "universe as a whole hypotheses," that all existence is alive and conscious. Let us consider, who "collapses the wave function, i.e., who can make, or is making, a quantum measurement? Is it humans only (plus a meter); is it man and animals? Consider the Schrödinger cat paradox in which a cat is an external stimulus to us humans, or what about the cat's observations; what about plant observations, or rock observations?

Let us consider the system that responds to remote mental influence, such a system in which current flow depends on intentional volitional intervention and interaction between observer and a system (that is observed). This system, in this case, is defined as inorganic or apparently nonliving, and yet this system responds as if to be in an open specific state or another living system. Is this not similar to one state or another chosen by a cat, rat, or gnat in the "cat paradox?" What about the states of existence and changes that affect plants, rocks, etc.? This brings us to the "Gaia hypotheses" that the Earth itself is a living organism since it gives rise to life, although not quite of the same kind as itself, but it supports life. Then the planet as a whole is observed, but can observe and hence, choose, to a lawful degree (science Law), its state of existence (van Bise and Rauscher, 1990, 2004; see also Schmidt, 1976).

The elements, moving, changing, and giving rise to new states of existence, give rise to weather changes and matter's dynamical process. In all cases of existence, consciousness plus the system, is all that can be perceived and observed, and the system itself may be generated by another aspect of consciousness.

John Wheeler has spoken of some of the fundamental aspects of the quantum measurement process, stating "the quantum principle tells us that the observer is more than an observer, he is a participator. In some strange sense, this is a participatory universe."

Eugene P. Wigner, in his classic book, *Symmetries and Reflections,* Scientific Essays, from Indiana University Press, (Wigner, 1967) discusses the implications of a nonlinear quantum theory and the role of an active observer and for the nature of life itself. He expands the vector space to include a matrix form that allows a method to analyze the effect of one or more observers (i.e. perhaps a human and a cat) and or multiple humans. In this book Wigner discusses parity and other symmetries.

A discussion of the implications of Wigner's work by William van Bise is useful at this point. This discussion is taken from his 1975 essay on his research on low intensity, electromagnetic effects of VHF and MW on the human brain. Essentially this discourse relates to all effects of or by human (and possibly other) consciousness to quote van Bise, "a quote from Eugene P. Wigner seems appropriate—'Every phenomenon is unexpected and most unlikely until it has been discovered—and some of them remain unreasonable for a long time after they have been discovered'" (van Bise, 1978a, 1978b).

The arguments used in Wigner's essay on *The Mind Body Question,* evolved in the language of quantum mechanics in which he pointed out that physicists possibly learned "that the principal problem was no longer the fight with the adversities of nature, but the difficulties of understanding ourselves and nature if we want to survive" (van Bise, quoting Wigner, 1978a). If more than one conscious observer enters into a system of measurement this joint system cannot be described by a wave function Ψ after the interaction since the result of an observation modifies the wave function of the system. A proper description of their quantum state is a mixture. (Wigner, 1967). The wave function is,

$$\frac{\alpha}{2}\Psi_1^2 \, x \, \chi_1$$

with a probability $\alpha/2$ or; it is

$$\frac{\beta}{2}\Psi_2^2 \times \chi_2$$

with a probability of $\beta/2$.

To continue the quote of van Bise's, "Philosophically this implies that if an observer of one group of experiments asks another observer of the same experiments about his feeling *before* he observed the results, his answer, whether or not it agrees with the questioning observer's conclusions, shows that the question was already decided in his mind before he was asked. In order to avoid this difficulty, it is necessary to postulate that the equations of motion of quantum mechanics are grossly non-linear when conscious beings with opinions enter into the equations. Here again is a paradox in scientific research.

"Complete objectivity in the real world is only approachable—not attainable. Even the stubborn scientific attitudes and the most carefully contrived and controlled experiments suffer from subtle biases within each of us—in other words we are subject to human emotions and judgments. And if any of us are not human in any way, then the conclusions from non-humans about humans are not applicable to humans."

Eugene Wigner (1967) who, in my opinion, was one of the 20th Century greatest physicists stated: "It is *not* possible to formulate the laws of physics in a fully consistent way without reference to the consciousness of the observer." Before we leave this chapter note the relevant issues in the following Table 3, on the topic of the active observer as a participator.

To conclude we quote Bryce DeWitt (1971) on the reality problem in quantum theory: (Rauscher and Targ, 2001) "No development of modern science has had a more profound impact on human thinking than the advent of quantum mechanics. Wrenched out of centuries old thought patterns, physicists of a generation ago found themselves compelled to which this reorientation caused continues to the present day. Basically physicists have suffered a severe loss of their hold on reality."

Table 3
Tenets of
The Properties of Consciousness and Quantum Measurement

1. Consciousness is involved in all measurement processes and procedures.
2. The greater degree that consciousness is involved, the more nonlinear the system behaves.
3. Consciousness is definable in physical terms, at least in part, because it interacts with physical processes such as the act of measurement or psychokinesis (PK) effects and can interact other consciousness or *mind stuff* such as telepathy, etc.
4. Consciousness can effect micro as well as macroscopic (such as earth size scale) phenomena.
5. Consciousness may act as a conserved entity, that is, have density-like properties and can have volume like spatial, temporal modalities of influence.
6. No observed event occurs without conscious interaction. Each perception that is recordable involved *mind-matter* interaction or *mind-mind* interaction.
7. I'm not sure it is possible *for* any event to occur, no matter how involved with just physical process it is, without conscious intervention or interaction. In fact, the primary substance of the universe, may indeed be what we term consciousness.
8. What we can well formulate in terms of quantum mechanics including the linear superposition principle involves minimal conscious intervention and interaction.

9. A more complete description of a quantum process involving conscious intervention is represented as nonlinear processes in greater than four dimensional space.
10. The usual super-impossible solutions to wave equations are represented in four space (space and time) as a slice through a higher dimensional space (N>4) which contains a domain of action of consciousness.
11. We will represent state vectors as tensors in a complex eight dimensional geometric space.
12. We consider the relationship of this space to other multidimensional spaces.

References

Amusia, M.Ya., E.A. Rauscher, R. Bruch. and S. Fuelling (1993) "Theoretical Analysis of Ionization Plus Excitation of Helium by Fast Electron and Proton Impact," *Nucl. Instrument Methods in Physics Research,* B79, p. 117.

Aspect, A., P. Grangier, and G. Roger (1992) "Experimental Tests of Bell's inequality using time-varying analyzers, " *Phys. Rev. Lett.,* 49, 1804 –1907 and private conversation with Aspect, 1977.

Bell, J.S. (1964) "On the Einstein, Podolsky, Rosen paradox," *Physics* 1, pp. 195-200.

Bell, J.S. (1966) "On the problem of hidden variables in quantum theory," *Review of Modern Physics,* 38, p. 447.

Bruch, R., E.A. Rauscher, S. Fueling, D. Schneider, S. Mannercik and M. Larsson (1994) "Collision Processes of Molecules and Atoms," Ed. Byass, L., *Encyclopedia of Applied Physics,* 10, pp. 437-470.

Chew, G. (1964) *The Analytic S-Matrix, Frontiers of Physics,* Benjamin and Co.; and private communication.

Clauser, J.F. and W.A. Horne (1974) "Experimental consequences of objective local theories," *Phys. Rev.* 10D, 526, and private conversations with Clauser.

DeWitt, B.S. and N. Graham (Eds.) (1973*) The many worlds interpretation of Quantum Mechanics,* Princeton: Princeton Univ. Press and private conversation with B.S. DeWitt.

Einstein, A., B. Podolsky and N. Rosen (1935) "Can quantum-mechanical descriptions of physical reality be considered complete?" *Physical Review* 47, p. 777.

F"F"G (the Fundamental "Fysiks" Group) (1975-1978) The purpose of this group was to explore the meanings and foundations of quantum mechanics, Bell's Nonlocality Theorem and its test, Relativity and multi-dimensional geometries and the nature and properties of consciousness. We also conducted research on remote viewing of replication studies of the SRI International, Palo Alto, CA.

Gisin, N., W. Tittel, J. Brendel and H. Zbinden (1998a) "Violation of Bell's inequalities by photons more than 10 km apart" *Physical Review Letters*, 81, pp. 3563-3566.

Gisin, N., W. Tittel, J. Brendel and H. Zbinden (1998b) "Quantum correlation over more than 10 km," *Optics and Photonics News*, 9, p. 41.

Heisenberg, W. (1938) *Physics and Philosophy*; and private conversation at UC , Berkeley the year before he died.

Kaiser, D. (2011) *How the Hippies Saved Physics: Science, Countercultures and the Quantum Revival*, New York: W.W. Norton and Co.

Prigogine, I. (1997) *The End of Certainty*, New York: The Free Press. Prigogine, I. 1992 Private communication, The University of Nevada, Reno, Nevada.

Rauscher, E.A. (1968) "Collective Electron Interactions and Quantum Plasma Physics," *J. Plasma Phys.* 2, p. 517.

Rauscher, E.A. (1971a) *A Unifying Theory of Fundamental Processes* in UCB/LBNL, UCRL-20808, Lawrence Berkeley Laboratory also a in *Bull. of Amer. Phys. Soc.* 13, 1643 (1968).

Rauscher, E.A. (1971b) "*The Philosophy of Science*," text, taught at UC Berkeley, Stanford SLAC and J.F. Kennedy University, CA 1971 to 1975.

Rauscher, E.A. (1971c) "Geometric Constraints on Biologic Evolution and Repeated Segments of DNA," Space-Science Laboratory, UC Berkeley, Preprint September.

Rauscher, E.A. (1972a) "A Set of Generalized Heisenberg Relations and a Possible New form of Quantization, Lett. AL. *Nuovo Cimento* 4, p. 757.

Rauscher, E.A. (1972b) "A Group Theoretical Representation of the Generalized Heisenberg Relations," Lett. AL. *Nuovo Cimento* 5, p. 925.

Rauscher, E.A. (1972c) "Closed Cosmological Solutions to Einstein's Field Equations," Lett. AL. *Nuovo Cimento* 3, p. 661.

Rauscher, E.A. (August, 1979) "Some physical models applicable to remote perception," in *The Iceland Papers: Frontiers of Physics*. Select papers on experimental and theoretical research on the physics of consciousness; foreword by B.D. Josephson, Edited by A. Puharich. Assentia Research Associates, Amherst, Wisconsin 54406, pp. 50-93. and in PACE, Ottawa, Ont., Canada (1996).

Rauscher, E.A. (1981) "Conceptual Changes in Reality from the New Physics," Vol. II, 31, ICF Press, New York, pp. 1407-14.

Rauscher, E.A. (1982a) "Application of Solition Physics to Plasma – MHD and Superconductivity-BCS," Tecnic Research Laboratory contract report to PET Corp, PSRL-3107, November.

Rauscher, E.A. (1982b) "Solitary Waves, Coherent Non-Dispersive Solutions in Complex Minkowski Spaces," *Bull. Amer. Phys. Soc.* 27, p. 35.

Rauscher, E.A. (1982c) *"Conceptual Changes in Reality Models from New Discoveries in Physics,"* PSRL-1976, Preprint, September 1981. Published in Proceedings of the First International Symposium on Non-Conventional Energy and Technology; pg. 114, October 1981, University of Toronto, Ontario, Canada and Bulletin Amer. Phys., Soc., 35.

Rauscher, E.A. (1993a) "A Theoretical Model of the Remote-Perception Phenomenon," *Silver Threads: 25 Years of Parapsychology Research*, London: Praeger, pp.141-150.

Rauscher, E.A. (1993b) "Longitudinal Comparison of Local and Long Distance Remote Perception Phenomena," *Silver Threads: 25 Years of Parapsychology Research*, London: Praeger, pp. 64-77.

Rauscher, E.A. (2005) "Cosmogenesis and Quantum Gravity," *Beyond the Standard Model: Searching For Unity in Physics,* Eds. Amoroso, B. Lehnert, J. and Vigier, P., The Noetic Press, Inc., Orinda, CA.

Rauscher, E.A. (2010) "Quantum Mechanics and the Effect of Intentional Will," *Complementarity of Mind and Body: Realizing the Dream of Descartes, Einstein and Eccles,* Ed. R.L. Amoroso, Nova Science Publishing, Inc., New York, pp. 36-63.

Rauscher, E.A. (2014) The Formulation of Bell's Theorem in Complex Eight Space, (in progress).

Rauscher, E.A., P. Rowlands and R. Amoroso (2015) "Dirac Equations in Nilpotent Quaternionic Space-Antispace and Eight Dimensional

(8D) Complex Minkowski Space" in Unified Field Mechanics: Natural Science Beyond the Veil of Spacetime Eds. R.L. Amoroso, L. Kaufman, and P. Rowlands, World Scientific.

Rauscher, E.A. and R.L. Amoroso (2006) "The Physical Implications of Multi-dimensional Geometries and Measurement," *CASYS, International Journal of Computing Anticipatory Systems*, Ed., Dubois, D.M., Vol. 19, CHAOS Pub., Institute of Mathematics, B37, University of Liege, Belgium, pp. 161-177.

Rauscher, E.A. and R.L. Amoroso (2008) "The Schrödinger Equation in Complex Minkowski Space, Nonlocality and Anticipatory Systems," Ed. D.M. Dubois, *CASYS, International Journal of Compelling Anticipatory Systems*, Vol. 22, CHAOS, Pub., Institute of Mathematics, B37, University of Liege, Belgium, pp. 370-388.

Rauscher, E.A. and R.L. Amoroso (2009) "Relativistic Physics in Complex Minkowski Space, Nonlocality, Ether Model and Quantum Physics," *Ether Spacetime and Cosmology*, Vol. 3 Physical Vacuum, Relativity and Quantum Physics, Eds. Duffy, M.C. and Levy, J. Apeiron Montreal, Canada, pp. 23-47.

Rauscher, E.A. and R.L. Amoroso (2011) *Orbiting the Moons of Pluto: Complex Solution to Einstein, Maxwell, Schrödinger, and Dirac Equations*, World Scientific.

Rauscher, E.A. and R. Targ (2001) "The Speed of Thought, Investigation of a Complex Spacetime metric to describe psychic phenomena. *J. Scientific Exploration*, 15, p. 331.

Rauscher, E.A. and R. Targ (2002) "Why Only Four Dimensions will not Explain the Relationship of the Perceived and Perceiver in Precognition," *J. Scientific Exploration*, 16, pp. 655-658.

Rauscher, E.A. and W. van Bise (2002) "Harnessing Earth-Ionosphere Cavity Energy for Wireless Transmission," *Harnessing the Wheelwork of Nature: Tesla's Science of Energy*, Ed. Valone, T., Adventures Unlimited Press, pp. 233-268.

Renshaw, K. (2009) *Beyond Einstein's Horizon: Science, Remote Viewing*. Constellation Press, CA and references therein.

Schrödinger, E. (1926a) *Ann. Physik* 79, 361.

Schrödinger, E. (1926b) *Ann. Physik* 79, 489.

Schrödinger, E. (1926c) *Ann. Physik* 80, 437.

Schrödinger, E. (1926d) *Ann. Physik* 81, 109.

Schmidt, H. (1976) "PK Effect on Prerecorded Targets," *J. Am. Soc. Psychical Research* 70, 267; and private communication.

Sirag, S.P. (2016) "ADEX Theory: How Coxeter's Unify Mathematics Physics," World Scientific and private communications.

Targ, R. (2004) *Limitless Mind: A Guide to Remote Viewing and Transformation of Consciousness.* New World Library: California.

Targ, R. and J. Hurtak (2006) *The End of Suffering*. Charlottesville: Hampton Rhodes.

Wigner, E.P. (1967) "Remarks on the Mind-Body Question," *Symmetries and Reflections, Scientific Essays,"* Bloomington: Indiana Univ. Press; and private communication.

Wigner, E.P. (1982) Comments on the work of E.A. Rauscher, page 1479, *Absolute Values and the Creation of a New World,* Vol. II, ICF Press, Philadelphia, Pennsylvania, New York.

van Bise, W.L. (1978a) "Very High Frequency and Microwave Frequency and Dependent Effects of Non Ionizing Radiation on the Human Organism; a Compilation of Man and His Electrical World," Report from NW Center for Study of Ionizing Radiation, Portland, OR.

van Bise, W.L. (1978b) *Physiological Chemistry & Physics* 10, 387.

van Bise, W.L. and E.A. Rauscher (1990) "Theoretical Models and Experimental Data Concerning the Space=Time Properties of Consciousness and Remote Mental Influence," Buck Fine Arts and Science Grant, 1988-1990, p. 222.

van Bise, W.I. and E.A. Rauscher (2004) *Quantum Mechanics and the Role of Action for Intentional Will, Abstracts, Towards a Science of Consciousness, Consciousness Res.,* Tucson: Univ. of Arizona, p. 73.

Chapter 8

The Relationship Of Complex Eight Space, The Kaluza -Klein Model And The Properties Of PSI To The Current Physics And Unified Theories

by

Elizabeth A. Rauscher, Ph.D.

"What we observe as material bodies and forces are nothing but shapes and variations in the structure of space."

— Erwin Schrodinger

Table of Contents

Introduction 481
1. The Observer in The Quest for Truth 484
2. GUT, TOE and Supersymmetry Models and The Complex Spacetime and The Kaluza-Klein Theory 488
3. Some Concluding Remarks About the Current State of Physics 500
References 503

List of Tables

Table 1: Forces and Relative Strength 482
Table 2: Group Theories and GUT Theories 491
Table 3: Schematic of the Strategy for Relating the Superstring Theory and Models of Reality 494
Table 4: The Essential Aspects of the Theory of Everything...... 496
Table 5: Elements that relate to the Development of a Unified Physics Theory 498
Table 6: Experiment and Theory 502

List of Figures

Figure 8a Subjective Verses Objective Reality 487
Figure 8b Unification Schemes 492

Introduction

Speculation on a Unified Field Theory (UFT) and Grand Unification Theories (GUT)

TOE, a theory of everything or a comprehensive theory of the Universe, has been the goal of much of scientific endeavor throughout history. Instead of attempting to give a comprehensive description of the efforts to develop a TOE, or a unified field theory, we will present my perspective of some highlights from my days at Lawrence Berkeley National Laboratory (LBNL) as a graduate student and later as a staff member in the Nuclear Science and the Theoretical Physics departments including updates of current advancements.

Most staff members were interested in particle physics but only very few were interested in general relativity, astrophysics and cosmology, and I was one of the few! I was interested in and researched both particle physics and cosmology. My passion was to understand the Universe, which clearly includes conscious sentient beings.

My motivation was to develop a unified field theory in terms of multidimensional geometries and their relationship to describing nonlocal, nonlinear phenomena, including a domain for the action and participation of the conscious observer in physical process and consciousness in general. Scientific discovery is a process of observation, data systemization, and theoretical hypothesis and formulation about the observed data. Scientific rules or laws are developed from the process of experimental examination and theoretical hypothesis, and the further testing of these concepts.

We demonstrate the manner in which the complex eight space and the Kaluza-Klein geometries relate to current unification programs in current unified field physics. Albert Einstein spent his whole life in the quest to find a unified theory of the four forces: the strong nuclear force, the electromag-

Table 1 Forces and Relative Strength:

The relative magnitude and range of the four major forces in Nature are given.

They are: (1) Nuclear-Strong and (2) Weak Decay, (3) Electromagnetic and (4) Gravitational (Geometric). The electroweak mediator is U(1) x SU(2) with intermediate vector $W^{\pm}$, Z^{O}; the strong force composed of eight gluons, SU3; electromagneticmediated by the photon, the gravitational field mediated by the spin 2 graviton.

	FORCE	COUPING CONSTANT OR RELATIVE STRENGTH	RANGE (fm)	INTERACTION TIME (sec)
8 SU(3)	STRONG (nuclear)	1 TO 10	1 fm	10^{-23}
1 U(1)	ELECTROMAGNETIC	10^{-2} (or 1/137)	∞	10^{-21}
2 SU(2)	WEAK (decay)	10^{-11} to 10^{-14}	SHORT RANGE	10^{-6} to 10^{-9}
G(2)	GRAVITATIONAL	10^{-39}	∞	∞
11 dm				

netic force, the weak nuclear decay force, and the gravitational force. These forces are listed in terms of their strength, range of effect and fundamental interaction times. (See Table 1).

The purpose of the discussion in this chapter is to (1) demonstrate that our theory that accommodates psi is an integral part of modern physics, as well as making new testable predictions; (2) provide a summary of the striving to develop a complete picture of reality; and (3) give an overview of current attempts to develop a unified theory of "everything." The physics approach is constructed to exclude consciousness. But a domain for action of consciousness creeps in by the inclusion of quantum nonlocality and the complex eight space, which I have extended to accommodate the quantum Schrödinger and Dirac theories (Rauscher and Amoroso, 2008, 2011; Rauscher, 2015) and Maxwell's equations (Rauscher and Amoroso, 2011) which lead to new physics and (4) demonstrate the fundamental mathematics and physics that not only accommodate consciousness and that aspect of psi in physical theory but demonstrates it is fundamental to it. This chapter contains mathematics for completeness and for the mathematically inclined. For those who are not so inclined, they can skip this chapter. It is important to note that the theory that accommodates psi phenomenon is an integral part of modern physics.

The Standard Model (SM) involves the strong and weak nuclear interactions and electromagnetic field. This model has good theoretical and experimental predictions and verifications, but does not include the gravitational field and, hence, is not a TOE theory. Sometimes, the SM is called "a theory of almost everything!" Quantum electrodynamics of electromagnetism is incorporated into chromodynamics of quarks and gluons, and the electromagnetic and weak interactions are incorporated as the electroweak force. (See Table 1).

The Standard Model may act as a basis for other models with multidimensional geometries with symmetries such as supersymmetry. Supersymmetry (SUSY) is a type of spacetime symmetry that relates to basic classes of elementary particles, bosons (integer spin) and fermions (half integer spin). Each boson and fermion particle has a superpartner that has the same mass and internal quantum numbers and differs by a spin by a half integer. However, to date no superpartners have been observed (Boerner, 1963).

One of the spontaneously broken supersymmetries is the minimal supersymmetric Standard Model (MSSM), a model beyond the Standard Model. Such particles have not been observed in the CERN—Large Hadron Collider (LHC). The Higgs mass is related to supersymmetry at the TeV (trillion electron volts) mass scale.

It is hypothesized in the SUSY model that each "bosonic Hamiltonian" with basic eigenstate has a SUSY partner which would be "fermionic" with fermion eigenstates (Rothe, 2012).

1. The Observer in the Quest for Truth

It is evident to us that in any unified field theory the observer must be included. Therefore, are observation and perception prerequisites for existence as in Descartes' and Wheeler's views? Does this mean that the unobserved universe does not exist? What is the connection between the observer and observed or between what is observed, and how is it observed? What role does the observer/participator have in the collapse of the wave function in linear quantum theory as exemplified in the Schrödinger's cat paradox? Of course the SUSY picture is quantum mechanics. (See Chapter 7).

A comprehension of physical reality involves the scale from the mini black hole to the size of the Universe and all in between. In Figure 1a (Chapter 1), we present a scale from the size of the Universe, as it is conceived in current physical theories. If the Universe is $r_u=10^{28}$ cm in size with a mass of 10^{56} gms, it fits the Schwarzschild condition of $r_s = 2Gm/c^2$ where G is the gravitational constant, for a mass *m* undergoing gravitational collapse. In this sense, even though the Schwarzschild solution is an exterior solution, the Universe, fits the Schwarzschild condition (Rauscher, 2005; Rauscher and Amoroso 2011).

If the quantum form of space has a lower limit of a mini Planck black hole of

$$\ell = (\hbar G½/c3)½$$

it also fits the Schwarzschild condition. The length ℓ is 10^{-33} cm (Rauscher, 1971; Rauscher, 1972; Rauscher, 2005; Rauscher, Hurtak, and Hurtak, 2013). The smallest thing in the Universe is the mini black hole with a radius of ~10^{-33}. Interestingly humans on this scale lie at about $10^{2.5}$ cm; a good vantage point from which to look at the larger and smaller scales of the Cosmos thought to be ~10^{28} cm.

Physics is assumed to be the most fundamental of all the sciences and its body of knowledge is the most comprehensive. Using the precise and logical language of mathematics, it is perhaps the basis for all human knowledge. As we accumulated knowledge through a succession of inductive and deductive inferences which were derived from observation and theoretical hypothesis and theoretical explanation, and prediction and experimental confirmation, our attempts to understand physics which was originally called natural philosophy, the workings of the natural world, led to our current understanding of physics. The concept of a unified theory of physics or a theory of everything (TOE) assumes that the origin of everything is explained and also that it can be explained in terms of a single obvious source. When one does not know all "things," knowledge and learning can occur, for we can only learn what we do not already know or think we know. Therefore, if learning is an ongoing process, is a "final theory of everything" even possible?

The word 'objectivity', for the past several hundred years, has been used to define what one knows. As all one knows is what is in one's mind, external reality is thus subjective reality, i.e. the subject of one's study. The current definition of objective reality is what is "out there" (external) as something fixed and immutable and that what one knows is subjective, incomplete and inaccurate knowledge of the objective reality of physics, biology, etc. However, consider the mind/brain issue. Is consciousness simply an epi-phenomenon of brain neuronal activity or, as I believe, is it something more? (Eccles, 1952). There is evidence to support our belief that it is more than just collective neuronal, glial cell activity. (Rauscher, 2010). Some features of conscious effects act nonlocally, one of the many attributes of consciousness, together with doing math, physics, science, art, poetry and creating civilization, that leads one to the inevitable and reasonable conclusion that there is more to consciousness than the firing of a set of neurons (Bohm and Hiley,1993).

We represent the objective view of reality as a "contour integral" of which the inside contains objective reality. In most current thinking the reality of the mind is excluded. It is seen as some subjective entity not fully describable by that which lies within the contour integral. In our complex hyper dimensional space, the contour integral includes the mind:

- What we perceive as real depends on our state of consciousness.
- Barriers to new knowledge are artificial constructs of mind.
- What is real must necessarily include that aspect called mind reality to be complete or unified.

Note that in physics, the couture integral is given as

$$ds^2 = 16\pi i \oint \frac{(dz)^2}{2\Omega} d\Omega$$

where $d\Omega$ is the double line integral over two complex dimensional spaces Z_{Re} and Z_{Im^*} where Z and Z^* stand for spacetime.

SUBJECTIVE VERSES OBJECTIVE REALITY

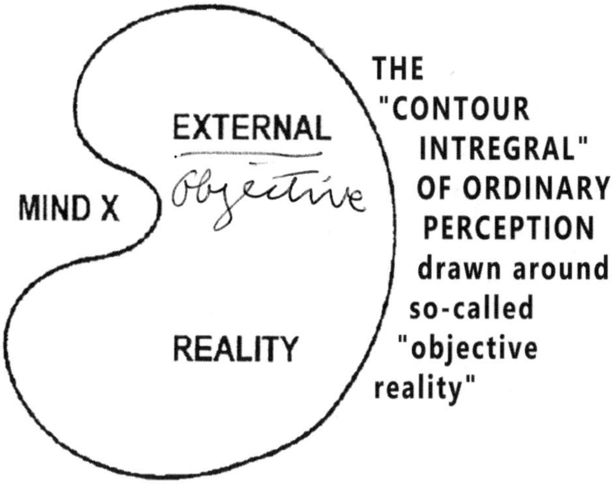

Contour Integral Model

1.—What we perceive as real depends on our state of consciousness

2.—Barriers are artificial mental constructs

3.—What is real must necessarily include that aspect called mind for reality to be complete and unified

Figure 8a

Subjective versus objective reality in the contour integral model. The contour model is based on a least action principle in the complex plane. The contour integral depicted is the current standard approach to science but we need to include mind, represented by Mind X.

Global causality and path integral method relate to the least action principle of physics and perhaps the Tao of life! (See Fig. 8a).

2. GUT, TOE, Supersymmetry Models and the Complex Spacetime and The Kaluza-Klein Theory

We describe the manner in which my complex eight space theory fits with the current physics Standard Model (SM) and the Theory of Everything (TOE), in this section. This is an important point as it demonstrates the fact that indeed psychic phenomena and the nature of consciousness does not lie outside of physics and may be an integral part of it through quantum theory and other aspects of physical theory, that puts the mind, X in the whole of reality. (See Fig. 8a).

Basic to current physics is group theory which will be presented here. This discussion involves advanced mathematics and may be unfamiliar to some readers, but this is for those who may just want to see, in a general sense, the manner in which the current picture of physics can accommodate remote viewing and precognition. This section is not a comprehensive discourse on group theory nor a detailed formulation of the foundations of physics. Our purpose is to present enough background to the current approaches to fundamental physics and to demonstrate the manner in which the complex eight space and the Kaluza-Klein geometry, as well as spinors and twistors, occupy a basic role in the foundations of physics. (See also Sirag, 2016). Twistor theory has been introduced as an approach to the unification of quantum theory and general relativity by Penrose (Penrose and Rindler, 2008).

Group theory comprises a powerful tool for codifying the basic symmetry observed in physics from elementary particle interactions to crystals (Rothe, 2012). Unified theories have their expression in group theoretical terms. The basis of physical law is the formulation, in terms of variables and constants of the relationship, constancy (conservation), and symmetry (order) of the physical universe. Both finite groups with infinite algebraic generators of the group and Lie groups with infinitesimal generators of the group, which comprise the algebra are extremely useful mathematical tools (Lie, 1893; Gilmore, 1974; Boerner, 1963; Coxeter, 1991).

The mathematical model involving partial group symmetries leads to an eleven dimensional space in the Grand Unification Theory (GUT) scheme, combined with the gravitational force, as defined by some current supersymmetry models. The foundation of the Standard Model (SM) is group theory and, in the context of this approach, that of the supersymmetry models, has evolved our knowledge based on our understanding of the "zoo" of particle data which has become numerous through the evidence of vast accelerator particle physics (Hofman, *et. al.*, 2002; Melissios, 2012).

The supersymmetry models include gravity and comprise the TOE approach. In some models, scientists consider a 24-element group in terms of spacetime and strong and weak interactions and the electromagnetic fields. The supersymmetry models and superstring theory were developed in an attempt to include gravity in the GUT theories (Green, Schwarz and Witton (1987); Hall, 2005; Witton, 2003). The so termed Standard Model involves the three stronger forces, the strong, electromagnetic and weak forces of SU_3, U_1 and SU_2 respectively.

The Kaluza-Klein theory includes five dimensions and with additional dimensions may allow us to incorporate gravity in the Standard Model in order to develop a Unified Field Theory (UFT) or Theory of Everything (TOE). Unified theories involve multidimensional geometries, but first and foremost, physicists are attempting to develop a unified theory of the four major force fields, strong nuclear force, electromagnetic force, weak nuclear decay force, and the gravitational force.

Particles are split by their quantum number properties, energy (n), angular momentum (ℓ), magnetic moment (m_ℓ), and spin (m_s). A change in these numbers is called symmetry breaking whose effects are those that violate the invariance of a given symmetry scheme causing changes just as the petals on a flower or snowflake symmetries are not exact. An example is caused by an independent strong force which is broken by the electromagnetic and weak (electroweak) interactions of $SU_2 \times U_1$ charge. Electric and magnetic forces were unified by James Clerk Maxwell (Georgi, 1982; Hofman, Bleicher, Garland, Hoffelder, Chwake and Stocker, 2002).

The GUT (grand unification theory) includes the strong, electromagnetic, and weak forces, and also involves ten or more vector bosons exchanged as a subset of the superstring model as $SU_2 \times U(1)$ and SU_3 where U(1) is the group of electromagnetic interactions producing electrons, positrons, quark and neutrinos after the exchange of a photon and electroweak interactions. The transition from the neutrino or quark requires an exchange of the three vector bosons $W^{\pm}$, Z^0 and the eight gluons (for the strong nuclear force that holds nucleons together), for the group SU_3. Together, the group of elements of 1 of U(1), 2 of SU_2, and 8 for SU_3 allows for 1+2+8 which comprises 11 dimensions of the GUT theory (involving all three universal forces except gravity) (Randall, 2005; Rauscher and Amoroso, 2011; Duff, 1986).

Additional dimensions can also be included in the supersymmetry structure. In Table 2 is a list of the various current formulations. Of particular interest are the four space-time dimensions of $U_2 x U_2$ or U_4 for the complexification of four dimensional Minkowski space (M_4). The additional U_2 group, thus, works with the four dimensional real spacetime and U_2 constitutes the imaginary four dimensional spacetime which comprises our complex eight space $\mathbb{C}_4$, which is a subset of the GUT scheme (Ramon and Rauscher, 1980; Rauscher, 2001; Penrose and Rindler, 2008).

Rauscher (Rauscher and Targ, 2001, 2003) and Newman (1973, 1976) have constructed a complex space identifiable with the real four and four imaginary dimensions. We express the complex eight space metric within M_4 because it represents the

Table 2
Group Theories and GUT Theories:

We present some different Group Theories and their relationship to the Standard Model (SM) and ultimately a GUT Theory. Complex eight space and the Kaluza-Klein Model are subset groups of the SM.

- The GUT Theory unifies standard gauge groups
- $S_4 = U(1) \otimes U(1) \otimes SU(2) \otimes SU(3) \otimes SU(3) = 11$
- $SU(5) = SU(2) \otimes SU(3) \otimes U(1)$
- M-Theory is an 11D theory and contains a 5D membrane. The 11D supergravity theory which is a point particle theory is not a string theory
- 25-1 = 254 Permutations in Eddington-Klein Group
- $\overline{S_4} = U_2 \otimes \bar{U}_2 \otimes U(4)$ AND 24 = 4 +4 + 16
- $\overline{S_4} = SU(2, 2/1)$ Penrose Twistor and Supergravity Matter Fields
- The $U(4)$ are 4-Space and Time $U(2) \otimes \bar{U}(2)$ for the Complexification of 4-Space as an 8D space

  U(2): 4 Real Space and Times
  $\bar{U}(2)$: 4 Imaginary Space and Times
  ] Complex Space as / A Penrose Twistor

- Kaluza-Klein 5-space, U(1) Relates to SO_3 + Electromagnetic and Gravitational Fields and the Spinor Calculus
- The 8-Space Twistor Algebra is Mapable to the Spinor Calculus of the 5D Space of the Kaluza-Klein geometry.

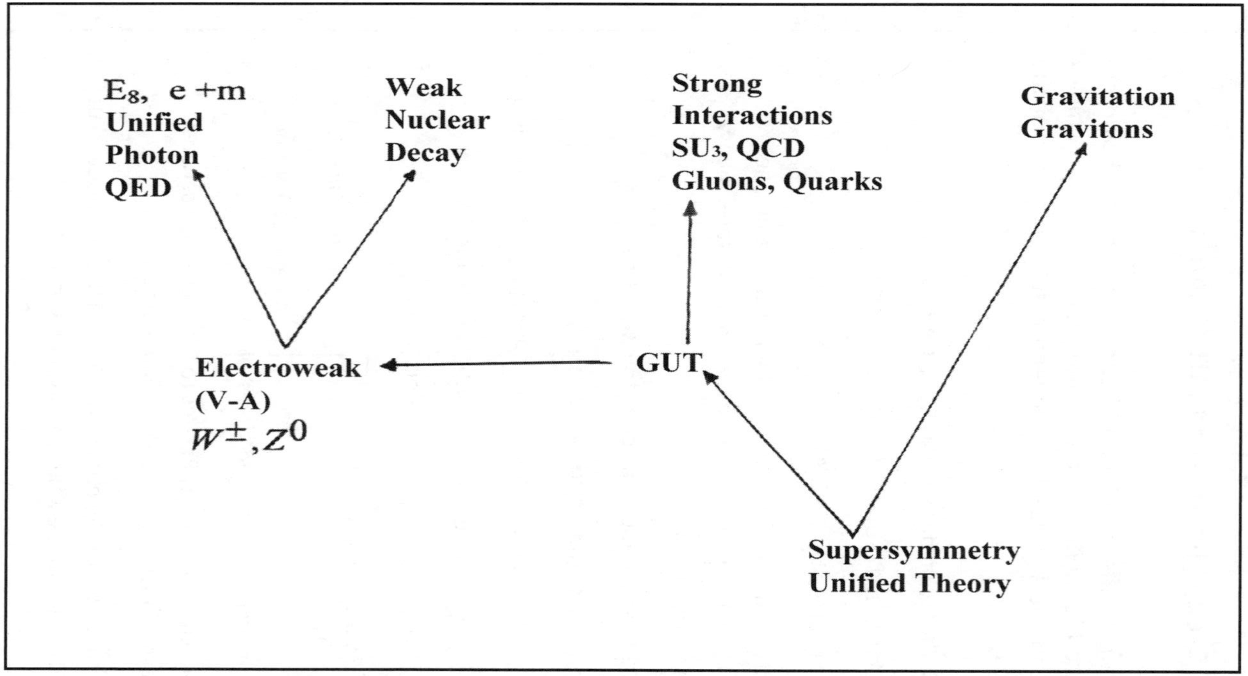

Figure 8b

Unification Schemes: The strong color gauge is $SU(10)_C$ which can be decomposed into $U(9)_C$ symmetries associated with conserved color components of the electric charge of fermions. The term QED is quantum electrodynamics and QCD is quantum chromodynamics and V-A is the vector-axial vector of the electroweak force.

complexification of four spacetime dimensions. The complex space is expressed in real (Re) and imaginary (Im) terms of the complex eight space as variable Z^{μ}, where $Z^{\mu}=Z^{\mu}_{Re} + iX^{\mu}_{Im}$ and where $Z^{*\nu}$ is the complex conjugate of Z^{μ} so that $Z^{\nu}=Z^{\nu}_{Re} + iX\nu_{Im}$. We now form the complex eight space differential line element in deSitter space as $dS^2=\eta_{\mu\nu}dZ^{\mu}dZ^{*\nu}$ where the indices run 1 to 8 instead of 1 to 4 as in the case of the usual Minkowski space. In our formalism, we proceed by extending the usual four dimensional Minkowski space (M_4) into a four complex dimensional spacetime ($\mathbb{C}_4$). This new manifold (or spacetime structure) is analytically expressed in the complexified eight space (Rauscher, 1979; Rauscher and Targ, 2001).

For the five dimensional Kaluza-Klein geometry the electromagnetic four space dimensions are related to the fifth proper orthogonal matrix or group of rotations SO_3^+ as a rolled up dimension of the order the Planck length (Planck, 1897), where $\ell = (\hbar G/c^3)^{1/2} \sim 10^{-33}$ cm. The complex $\mathbb{C}_4$ space and Kaluza-Klein and twistor spaces can be seen as subsets of the GUT and TOE theories (Newman, 1973; Hansen and Newman, 1975).

Table 2, lists also additional permutations of symmetry in the approach of various researchers to unify the four force fields, which has lead to the GUT and TOE theories and other group theories. Again, the supersymmetry models can be applied also to eleven dimensional space as needed to unify the four force fields (the *strong force* with SU_3 symmetry of the gluons of eight dimensions and strongly interacting particles, the *electromagnetic force* with U_1 symmetry of one dimension and the *weak force* nuclear decay symmetry of SU_2 symmetry with two dimensions which comprises the eleven dimensional SM and ultimately *gravity*) in the Grand Unification Theory (GUT). The three first forces are the easiest to unify, but several of these multidimensional theories are also an attempt to develop a theory that includes quantum gravity (Rauscher, 1971, 2005) and unify it with the three SM forces (Wigner, 1967; Wheeler, 1978; Weinberg, 1995; Rauscher, 1971, 2015). Since the quantum theory of the strong force and weak forces and electromag-

Table 3
Schematic of the Strategy for Relating the Superstring Theory and Gravitation and GUT

1. The superstring in 11 dimensions (4 non-compactified and 7 compartified) relates the strong, electroweak and gravitational forces.
2. The 11 dimensional supergravity involves the compactification (on a Calabi-Yau manifold) which is triple torus, $U_2 \times U_2 \times U_2$.
3. The 4-dimensional "no-scale" supergravity and the Gauge group $\subseteq E_6$ predict the "Gaugino" – (relating to the gravitational field) condensation in "hidden" vector space.
4. Local Supersymmetry, that is, broken gavitino rest mass $\neq 0$ and the rest mass $\neq 0$ produced by quantum vacuum state polarization corrections.
5. Effective low-energy theory in which Supersymmetric Gauge Theory yields non-zero particle masses, i.e., having gravitational effects which would require an expansion of Gauge conditions.
6. Additional neutral currents and additional matter particles may require additional dimensions.

netism in terms of QED (Quantum Electrodynamics) are primarily linear superposition, it is difficult to formulate a resolution of these pictures of reality with the structure of gravitational fields (Eddington, 1922; Rauscher,1981; Rauscher and Amoroso, 2008; Rauscher, 2010).

It would be necessary to include gravity if one was to construct a theory of everything (TOE). It becomes even more important with the recent finding of gravitational waves detected on September 14, 2015 through the Laser Interferometer Gravitational-wave Observatory (LIGO) detectors, located in Livingston, Louisiana, and Hanford, Washington. The development of superstring theory is an attempt to expand on the Venaziano Model (dual model describing the scattering amplitude of strings).

The string theory model, although far from complete, is encouraging in that it replaces the corpuscle-particle concept with vibrating strings, that are more like waves, in order to avoid the infinities in the equations that arise from the consideration of point particles (Witten, 2003).

In Table 3, we present some of the recent approaches of superstring theories and models of reality. We examined the relationship the four force fields (FFF) and the manner in which they can be unified into a Supersymmetry Unified Field theory. Their interrelationship is denoted relevant to the current understanding of physics that is under the supersymmetry scheme. The QED, electroweak, and strong forces are unified under the GUT scheme. The QCD (Quantum Chromodynamics) formalism is a strong force theory which allows the GUT theory to be combined with gravitation, leading to the supersymmetry unified theory. (See Fig. 8b and Table 1, see also Muta, 1987.) These approaches are related to those of Sirag (Sirag, 1983), and Penrose (Penrose and Rindler, 2008; Gerock, *et.al.*, 1973), as well as the complex Minkowski space of Hansen and Newman (Hansen and Newman, 1975; Kozamah and Newman, 1983) and Rauscher (Rauscher, 1979; Rauscher, 1983; Ramon and Rauscher, 1980; and Rauscher, 1996). It is interesting to note

Table 4

The essential aspects of the TOE theory are:

1. Kaluza-Klein (KK) geometry is a unified field theory of gravity and electromagnetics incorporating the fifth dimension. The fifth dimension is considered a circular in terms of space which can be seen as a unitary group U(1). Therefore, one dimension is for the electromagnetic field and the other four is for the gravitational Minkowski field. In this way the 5th dimensional acts to create a charge, for a clockwise loop as a plus charge and counter clock wise a minus charge.

2. In superstring theory which has expanded on the KK Theory to 11 dimensions, the weak force involves the exchange of intermediate vector bosons $W^{\pm}$ and Z^0 in the vector minus axial vector theory having two dimensions. The strong nuclear force has eight charge particles for the quark and eight dimension for the 8 gluons.

3. Hence, the total dimensions is one dimension for the U_1 (electromagnetism), two dimensions for the SU_2 (weak interactions), and eight dimensions (gluons and quarks for the octet and triplet of SU_3) which are eleven dimensions, that is, seven dimensions plus space-time for the four forces. In the GUT, the scheme implies a 10 or more vector bosons exchanged which is a subset of superstring theory.

that the triple torus, which comes out of the Calabi-Yau string theory, can also be constructed from the Penrose model (Weinberg, 1995; Georgi, 1982; Green, Schwarz and Witton, 1987; Rauscher, 1983; and Rauscher and Amoroso, 2011; Newman, *et.al.*, 1978).

I have investigated the relationship between Kaluza-Klein geometry and the complex eight space, which is related to the twistor algebra of the complex eight space to the spinor calculus of the Kaluza-Klein geometry (and other spinor models). This helps to demonstrate how our model fits into the GUT scheme through a multidimensional model which comes out of the Calabi-Yau string theory, which includes the Penrose model of twistors (Gerock, Heldand and Penrose, 1973, Penrose and Rindler, 2008). The lowest number of dimensions that have the property of nonlocality and which is consistent with Poincaré invariance or Lorentz invariance is eight dimensions. In this space, each physical spatial distance has an imaginary temporal counterpart, such that there is a zero spatial separation in higher dimensional space. We can, thus, hypothesize that this path is what awareness accesses in realtime remote viewing (Rauscher and Targ, 2001). Likewise for every real (Re) physically temporal separation, there is a counterpart imaginary (Im) spatial separation that subtracts to zero on the metric, allowing awareness to access precognitive information. "Eight space" becomes the minimal space needed for remote consciousness connection. (See Table 4).

When Einstein attempted to unify gravity and quantum mechanics, his concept, and those of others, was to find a unique set of equations with a unique solution. However, string theory allows 10^{100} or so possible vacuum solutions. So why does it appear we "live in" a unique universe? Maybe we do not according to some superstring models incorporating the multiverse concept (Green, Schwarz and Witton, 1987, Hurtak, Hurtak and Rauscher, 2015). Some string theories have trouble maintaining a classical Lorentz symmetry. Tachyonic signaling, however, is sometimes being associated with certain string theory solutions.

Table 5
Elements that relate to the Development of a Unified Physics Theory

In this table are listed some of the elements that relate to the development of a unified physics theory. Note some terms such as up, down, top and color are acronyms for quantum symmetry quantum number properties and are not to be taken literally.

1. The properties and characteristics of the four force fields.

2. Strong nuclear processes that involve strongly interacting hadrons (Baryons) with substructure, quarks and near massless gluons which transmit hadronic energy between the quarks.

3. Symmetry triplet of quark, color SU_3. From the SU_3 type model, five flavors, three families are given as:

a. Up (u) and down (d)

b. Charm (c), strangeness (s)

c. Top (t), and bottom (b)

d. Left (L) and Right (R) or dextral.

4. Quark confinement in quantum chromodynamics (QCD), white color singlets are found in independent particles entities.

5. Three primary color values of quarks which represent hadronic charge, threefold, triplet, R (red), G (green), and B (blue) and anti color counterparts, $\bar{R}$, $\bar{G}$ and $\bar{B}$. The three quarks make up white particles or baryons as R, G, B and mesons are made up of quark — anti-quark pairs.

6. Photons act as the transmitters of electromagnetic energy; the symmetry group is U_1 where all phase factors, that is, complex numbers of unit magnitude, and we have electric charge.

7. Spin 2 graviton, mediator of the gravitational force which is a tensor force; this involves the TOE Theory.

Physicist are not new to the development of multidimensional geometries. Such concepts have become prominent only in the last thirty years or so. Previously, it took Einstein and Minkowski to expand the concept of Newtonian three dimensions and then Kaluza and Klein in the 1930s to five dimensions and next, this author and others, to eight and eleven dimensions in the early 1970s. Hyper-dimensional geometries, in the main physics community became wide spread in the early 1980s. We must distinguish between an extended dimension such as space and time, my complex eight space (Rauscher, 1979) and eleven dimensional Descartes space with ten extended dimensions and one rotational dimensions (Rauscher, 1971) and the rolled up additional seven dimensions of the eleven dimensional Standard Model of the GUT scheme. Dimensionality represents degrees of freedom so that there is the movement in space. The distinction of dimensional type is made clear in Lisa Randall's book (Randall, 2005).

In Table 3 we present some models of superstring theory that include the gravitational field. In Table 5, we present a detailed summery of a TOE theory, including quarks, gravity and the FFF or four force fields. The dimensionality of E_8 dimensions is 248 and the full symmetry group of the standard superstring theory a product of two E_8's as $E_8 \times E_8$ with a dimensionality double that of E_8 or 496 dimensions. Note that in forming a product, the dimensions of the space add. Multidimensional geometries have become an integral part of modern physics. Our complex eight space can be expanded to twelve dimensions or more (Ramon and Rauscher, 1980; Amoroso and Rauscher, 2009; Rauscher and Amoroso, 2011), but eight is the least number of dimensions to accommodate the proper symmetry principles and nonlocality so we proceed using Occam's Razor.

3. Some Concluding Remarks About the Current State of Physics

There are many conceptual and mathematical issues to be resolved before we will be able to form a final Theory of Everything. Sudden awakenings to new knowledge have been experienced and wondrous new discoveries made in many periods throughout history, sometimes producing rude awakenings. The search for knowledge and truth is an ongoing process! Despite those within society who frequently believe that they know all they need to know, there are fortunately always knowledge seekers who look beyond and search for the deeper meaning, interpretation of observations and data gathering and its organization into theory. An expansion of our view and understanding of ourselves and the Universe is brought about by these seekers and listeners to the heartbeat of nature. It is fortunate that much more is to be learned so we can find positive changes to make in the world from a philosophical point of view.

The expansion of scientific exploration and knowledge is not an orderly process. In 1899, the Commissioner of Patents suggested that the Patent Office be closed because almost everything had already been invented! Despite this pronouncement, many more inventions were made and patented, some by Elizabeth Rauscher! Even Lord Kelvin, after an illustrious career in science, announced in the 1880's that students should not go into physics as "There is nothing new to be discovered in physics now. All that remains is more and more precise measurement" (Kelvin, 1900). Furthermore, in his opinion there were two dark clouds on the horizon of physics. One was the interpretation of the Michelson-Morley experiment (Michelson and Morley, 1887) and the other was the problem of the fit of the Rayleigh-Jeans law of black body radiation, known as the ultraviolet catastrophe (Planck, 1897). The first of Kelvin's so-called blots led to the theory of relativity and the second to the quantum theory through Max Planck's correct fit with the introduction of Planck's constant, $\hbar$ to the equation to fit the black body spectrum.

It is never wise to claim that we almost know everything as such a position almost inevitably seems to be a gateway to a new scientific revolution! Major changes in thinking such as the Copernican revolution and Galileo's proof of the Heliocentric Universe, as well as the advent of quantum mechanics and relativity have not only scientific effects but also philosophical effects, and create a paradigm shift in thinking. I believe we may be heading for such a crisis and hence a revolution in physics. Certain concepts, for example the little understood hypothesis of dark matter and dark energy, the role of the Higgs particles and mini black holes, indicate that a deeper, more thorough, reexamination of physical theory is required. But through crises and their resolution comes new and deeper knowledge of ourselves, life and truth. We hope that our work with remote viewing and nonlocality is another step towards a new and viable approach that, by discovering and formulating another truth, in some manner incorporates the observer and observed in our ongoing process of discovery (Bohm and Hiley, 1993; Wigner, 1967). (See Table 6).

Progress to a TOE, as desirable as it may be, needs to be undertaken with caution as it appears that knowledge is ever expanding. We are all on a path to new expanded knowledge. The fundamental question is whether we can find "the truth of everything" or only relative truths. New knowledge and new data may take us from what was true for us yesterday in an entirely new direction today and tomorrow. We are traveling towards a rainbow that continually retreats as we approach! We are on a wonderful vast frontier of new knowledge which brings the principles of physics, science and the properties of consciousness together.

Table 6

Experiment and Theory

1. Experiment without theory is like seeing the craters on the moon in Galileo's time; how were they formed: Volcanoes? Impact craters? The fact of their existence? The fact of their existence was not well accepted without a theory. New knowledge often lies counter to accepted current ideas.
2. The theory acts as a coherent agent to put isolated experimental data together and yield it to comprehension.
3. Theory without experiment is idle chit-chat, speculations and religion.

References

Boerner, H. (1963) *Representation of Groups*, John Wiley and Sons.

Bohm, D. and B.J. Hiley (1993) *The Undivided Universe*, Routledge. And Private communication with Bohm (1977-1983) and Hiley (1977).

Coxeter, H.S.M. (1991) *Complex Ragulor Polytopes*, 2nd ed., Cambridge U. Press.

Duff, M.J. (1986) "Recent Results in Extra Dimensions," Eds. I. Piran and S. Weinberg, *Physics of Higher Dimensions*, London: World Scientific.

Eccles, J.C. (1952) *The Neurophysiological Basis of The Mind*, Oxford: Oxford University Press.

Eddington, A. (1922) "The Mathematical Theory of Relativity," New York: Chelsea.

Georgi, H. (1982) Lie Algebras in Particle Physics, Benjamin Cummings.

Gerock, R., A. Heldand, R. Penrose (1973) *J. Math. Phys.* 14, p. 874.

Gilmore, R. (1974) *Lie Groups, Lie Algebras and Some of Their Applications,* Wiley Interscience.

Green, M.B., J.H. Schwarz and E. Witton (1987) *Superstring Theory*, Cambridge University Press.

Hall, G.M. (2005) "A Geometry for Non Geometric String Backgrounds," arXiv Archive, hep-th/0406102, v.3.

Hansen, R.O. and E.T. Newman (1975) *General Relativity and Gravitation*, 6, p. 216.

Hofman, S., M. Bleicher, I. Garland, S. Hoffelder, S. Chwake and H. Stocker (2002) *High Energy Physics*, Phenomology Hep—Ph/0111002.

Hurtak, J., D. E. Hurtak, E.A. Rauscher (2015) "Examining the

Existence of the Multiverse." *Quantum Biosystems*. 6(1) 115-130.

Kelvin, W.T. (1900) Lecture given entitled "Nineteenth Century Clouds over the Dynamical Theory of Heat and Light" London: Royal Institution.

Kozamah, C.N. and E.T. Newman (1983) A non-local variable for General Relativity. Ed. Nig. H., *Proceedings of the Third Marcel Grossman Meeting on General Relativity*, New York: Science Press and North Holland, pp. 51-55.

Lie, S. (1893) *Vorlesungen Uber Kontinulerliche Grupper mit geometuschen und onderen Anwendungen*. Ed. G. Scheffer, Teubneir, Leipzig.

Melissios, A. (2012) *"Reminisces: A Journey Through Particle Physics,"* London: World Scientific.

Michelson, A.A. and F.W. Morley (1887) *Am. J. Science* 34, p. 333.

Muta, T. (1987) *Foundations of Quantum Chromodynamics,* London: World Scientific.

Newman, E.T. (1973) "Maxwell's Equations in Complex Minkowski Space." *Journal of Math and Physics*, 14, pp. 202-203.

Newman, E.T. (1976) "H-Space and its properties," in *Gen. Rel. and Grav. 7*, pp. 107-111.

Newman, E.T., R.O. Hansen, R. Penrose, and K.P. Thorn (1978) "The Metric and Curvature Properties of H-space," *Proceedings of the Royal Society of London*, A363, pp. 445-468.

Penrose, R. and W. Rindler (2008) *Spinor and Twistor Methods in Spinors and Spacetime,* Cambridge, Cambridge University Press,

Planck, M. (1897) *Verlesungen Uber Thermodynamik,* Berlin: Veit and Co.

Ramon, C. and E.A. Rauscher (1980) "Superluminal Transformations in Complex Minkowski Spaces," *Foundations in Physics*, 10, Nos. 7 and 8 (August): pp. 661-669.

Randall, L (2005) *"Warped Passages: Unraveling the Mysteries of the Universe's Hidden Dimensions,"* San Fran: Harper Collins Pub.

Rauscher, E.A. (1970) *Bootstrap and a Uniform Formalism of the Four Force Fields,* LBNL, UCRL—10068.

Rauscher, E.A. (1971) *A Unifying Theory of Fundamental Processes,* LBNL/UCB book, USRL-20808.

Rauscher, E.A. (1972) "A Group Theoretical Representation of the Generalized Heisenberg Relations," *Lett. AL Nuovo Cimento,* 5, p. 925.

Rauscher, E.A. (1979) Some Physical Models Potentially Applicable to Remote Perception. *The Iceland Papers: Frontiers of Physics Conference.* Amherst, WI: *Essentia Research Assocs.,* pp. 50-93.

Rauscher, E.A. (1981) Coherent Solutions of the Schrödinger Equation in Complex Eight Space, *Proceedings of the Tenth International Conference on the Science, Vol. II,* New York: ICF Press, pp. 1407-1731.

Rauscher, E.A. (1983) *Electromagnetic Phenomena in Complex Geometries and Nonlinear, Non-Hertzian Waves.* Millbrae, CA: Tesla Book Co.

Rauscher, E.A. (1996) Some Models Potentially Applicable to Remote Perception, Eds. A. Puharich, B.D. Josephson, *The Iceland Papers, Select Papers on Experimental and Theoretical Research on the Physics of Consciousness,* 2nd edition, PACE Ottawa, Ontario, Canada.

Rauscher, E.A. (2001) "Non-Abelian Gauge Groups for Real and Complex Amended Maxwell's Equations," Vigier 2000 Symposium, Vigier 3, Berkeley, CA: Kluwer Press.

Rauscher, E.A. (2005) "Cosmogenesis and Quantum Gravity," Eds. R.L. Amoroso, B. Lehnert and J.P. Vigier, *Beyond the Standard Model: Searching for Unity in Physics,* Orinda, CA: Noetic Press, Inc.

Rauscher, E.A. (2010) "Quantum Mechanics and the Role for Consciousness in the Physical World," Ed. R.L. Amoroso, *Complementarity of Mind and Body: Realizing the Dream of Descartes, Einstein and Eccles,* Nova Science Publication.

Rauscher, E.A. and R.L. Amoroso (2008) "The Schrödinger Equation in Complex Minkowski Space, Nonlocality and Anticipatory Systems," CASYS, *International Journal of Computing Anticipatory Systems:* Ed. D. M. Dubois, Vol. 22, CHAOS Pub., Institute of Mathematics, B37 Belgium: University of Liege.

Rauscher, E.A. and R.L. Amoroso (2011) *Orbiting the Moons of*

Pluto: Solving Einstein's, Maxwell's, the Schrödinger Equation and Dirac Equations in Complex Space, London: World Scientific.

Rauscher, E.A., J.J. Hurtak and D.H. Hurtak (2013) "Universal Scaling Laws in Quantum Theory and Cosmology," pp. 376-387. Ed. R.L. Amoroso, L.H. Kaufman and P. Rowlands, *The Physics of Reality, Space, Time, Matter, Cosmos,* World Scientific:.

Rauscher, E.A., P. Rowlands and R. Amoroso (2015) "Dirac Equation in Nilpotent Quaternionic Space—Anti Space and Complex Eight Space." R. Amoroso, L.H. Kaufman and P. Rowlands, *Unified Field Mechanics, Natural Beyond the Vale of Time,* London: World Scientific.

Rauscher, E.A. and R. Targ (2001) Investigation of a Complex Space-Time Metric to Describe Precognition of the Future. *Journal of Scientific Exploration,* 15, 4, pp. 331-54.

Rauscher, E.A. and R. Targ (2003) "The Speed of Thought: Investigation of a Complex Space-time Metric to Describe Psychic Phenomena," *Journal of Scientific Investigation,* 15, p. 331.

Rothe, H.J. (2012) *"Lattice Gauge Theories,"* London, World Scientific.

Sirag, S.P. (1983) *International Journal of Theoretical Physics,* 22, p. 1067.

Sirag, S.P. (2016) "ADEX Theory: How Coxeter's Unify Mathematics Physics," World Scientific and private communications.

Weinberg, S. (1995) *The Quantum Theory of Fields,* Cambridge University Press and private communication at LBNL.

Wells, H.G. (1920) *Outline of History,* McMillian and Co.

Wheeler, J.A. (1978) *Mathematical Foundations of Quantum Mechanics,* Ed. A.R. Marlow, Academic Press, pp. 9-48.

Wigner, E. (1967) *Symmetries and Reflections,* University of Indiana and private communication.

Witten, E. (2003) "Perturbative Gauge Theory as a String Theory in Twistor Space," arXiv:hep-th/0312155.

Chapter 9
Concluding Remarks
by
Elizabeth A. Rauscher, Ph.D.

"Sit down before fact like a little child, and be prepared to give up every preconceived notion. Follow humbly whenever and to whatever abyss nature leads, or you should learn nothing."

—Thomas H. Huxley

Table of Contents

1. Some Concluding Results 509
2. Foretelling, Planning, "luck" or use of psi 510
3. What I Have Learned 513
4. A Word Apart and A World of Unity 521
5. The Scientific Method, Consciousness, Psi and Life Processes 521
6. References 530
7. Acknowledgements 531

List of Tables

Table 1: List of Some Basic Concepts 520

Table 2: Some Attributes of Consciousness 525

Table 3: Some Conclusions About the Remote Perception Phenomenon 526

Table 4: States of Consciousness that Lead to Success 527

Table 5: Some Implications of Psi For Our Personal Lives and Global Interconnection 528

List of Figures

Figure 9 The Universal or Remote Connection 529

1. Some Concluding Remarks

"We are both spectators and actors in the great drama of existence." Niels Bohr, (the father of the modern atomic concept).

We have made giant advancements in our understanding of the nature and properties of consciousness by applying the scientific method. Revolutions occur in cycles and this one began in the early 1970s. I believe we are on the threshold of another great advancement in psi research that utilizes the scientific method, with personal applications of the methodologies described herein and this both combines the powerful scientific method with the study of the properties of consciousness. I also believe that the advancement of this knowledge at a personal level, as well as a global level, will create a new spiritual health and new valuable traditions. Psi is as old as human kind and beyond, extending to animals and plants. We are in a new and exciting era of a deeper discovery, which we are privileged to experience as we seek the scientific exploration of psi (Kuhn, 1962).

In the next section, I outline some areas of my own research, conducted with my colleagues. Maybe my success in these areas was because of intention or was psychic, or luck or maybe precognition or destined as spiritual development, but it all has been a great adventure for sure. I might also add a lot of work, perseverance, determination and not following the status quo along with the many wonderful people I mention in my acknowledgements.

2. Foretelling, Planning, "luck," or Use of Psi

Here I list some of the things, that I "guessed right," foresaw and/or created in my areas of interest and research that lead to my success.

First, I became interested in cosmology and astrophysics when I was eight, spurred on by meeting an astronomer who talked about billions of stars and galaxies, etc. I studied relativity and wrote a series of papers on cosmology, which I developed and published in a series of papers and a book including a scaling law in terms of black hole physics in the early 1970s. This included fundamental work on black holes and more recently I expanded this work. Of course, now, black hole physics is a mainstream of modern astronomy and they appear to be ubiquitous throughout the universe.

Second, related to this work was my development of a multidimensional geometry to demonstrate a unified field theory concept and an attempt to create a quantum gravity theory. The idea originated when I was fifteen. I had been given a Dover book, by a UC Berkeley physics graduate student which laid out the fundamental papers by Einstein and others on the foundations of the relativity theory, including Minkowski's work on four space of space and time (Lorentz, H.A., A. Einstein, H. Minkowski and H. Weyl, 1923). It seemed to me that Einstein's $E = mc^2$ should be connected in some manner to $s^2 = X^2 - c^2t^2$, the invariant line element in Minkowski's four space. I intuited that there was a fundamental force that connected these concepts in a hyperdimensional space consisting of at least five dimensions. This led to my development of a tenth and eleventh dimensional geometry which I expanded on in the book I wrote in 1971 and also in a series of published papers from 1972 to present which helped kick start my career. The connecting force I determined from the stress energy term $T_{\mu\nu} = G/8\pi c^4$ in Einstein's field equations or $F = c^4/G$, where c is velocity of light and G is the universal gravitational constant. It was fun driving around with these insights, giving them birth and, sometimes, being the only one having them.

The third area of research and investigation was on some of the nature and properties of consciousness. Since, I was a child and planned to study nature and the physical universe; my ultimate plan was to study the nature and ultimately properties of consciousness. I pondered the question about the reality of thoughts. This interest and my concepts about it led me to the work described in this book. This work led to new truths and great adventures.

The fourth area, that got my interest, was that of quantum nonlocality and quantum entanglement. Although nonlocal information acquisition was associated with a quantum phenomenon, I believed that I could construct a macro spacetime nonlocality formalism to accommodate the nonlocal aspect of consciousness, the psi aspect and maybe the general properties of consciousness itself as a ubiquitous phenomenon.

I developed a multidimensional complex geometry which appears to reconcile the main body of physics with psi phenomena. I published a number of books and papers on this work and it is part of the current Standard Model of physics. I also started, organized and chaired the Fundamental "Fysiks" group at LBNL, when I was there on staff of the Theoretical Physics group to explore quantum nonlocality and quantum entanglement and to replicate the remote viewing research at SRI, in the early 1970s to mid 1980s (David Kaiser, 2011). Now quantum entanglement has become "big business" in quantum computer algorithms and in the forefront of quantum physics taking us out of the domain of "just calculate and don't question" back to the 1930s of the Schrödinger's cat paradox where the foundation of quantum theory was greatly discussed.

As before mentioned, as a student at UC Berkeley, taking a junior level quantum theory course, I raised my hand and said, "what does all this mean?" and I got the Copenhagen response, "shut up and just calculate!" So I reopened that Philosophical Pandora's box to question and search for a philosophical basis and meaning of the quantum theory and all theory, all science and all endeavors!

The fifth area of research occurred in the early 1970s. I got interested in wound healing and electromagnetic field effects enhancing biological tissue. Here, again, I started as a skeptic but open minded with a lot of "prove it to me" attitude. I was more open minded to psi but, of course, started as a skeptic. I think that the "prove it to me" does not work well on psi research but it was not a problem for electromagnetic effects on biologic tissue. With over thirty-five years of research, I can definitively say there are profound effects! Some fields are benign, some can produce profound positive effects and also as with any chemical, biological or electromagnetic effects there can be a down side or detrimental effects. I and my colleagues William van Bise and Mark Busier were interested in the positive, life enhancing effects and this led to clinical, FDA trials and patents! I have felt that for over forty years, we are on a threshold of a new medicine, a gentler, less invasive medicine to complement useful surgery, pharmaceuticals and other treatment modalities.

I have been interested in other endeavors such as the inventions, ideas and work of Nikola Tesla and Leonardo de Vinci, the ancient Egyptians, Greeks, Ionians, indigenous people and many others. I enjoyed exploring the archeological wonders of Egypt with Drs. Hurtak through remote viewing. (See Chapter 12.)

Key to all my research was perseverance, dedication, hard work, and persistence in the face of 'no-sayers.' You learn to dream your dream and create it!

3. What I have Learned About A Life of Observation, Contemplation, Investigation and Meditation

I have learned many things and had many experiences in my life. Some of these life lessons I summarize here. I hope some of these lessons and adventures are of value to the reader. The following are some interesting things I have learned in this life. Wow! It's all magic anyway and I do love the scientific method as it is a great tool to move in a viable manner in the search for truth.

1. Psi exists; direct knowing exists. Thoughts are real and have real consequences.

[Note: I have conducted over 80 remote viewing experiments achieving a success of several million-to-one odds against chance for one tailed statistical analysis.]

2. The past affects the future and the future affects the past.

[Note: In life it appears that there is not only a nonlocality in space but also a nonlocality in time. See my and Richard Amoroso's book *"Orbiting the Moons of Pluto: Solving Einstein's, Maxwell's, Schrödinger's, and Dirac's Equations in Complex Eight Space,"* World Scientific, 2011. Also, there are apparently five or more moons of Pluto.]

3. Truth can be hard to come by and requires hard work.

[Note: The key is to *"work like Hell and advertise"* which is a quote from my uncle, Alfred Mitchell, a well known California fine artist. He and his wife, Dorothea were Theosophists who believed thought forms were real. I worked for many years and did a lot of "all-nighters," studying, writing and working hard to gain and disseminate knowledge, hopefully to better the world. Actually, I really worked hard, but some of it was fun, and I enjoy creating new ideas.]

4. In many cases, most of what is said to be true is not and many elements of what is said to be myth are true.

[Note: One needs to examine what is considered *known* and *true* but one also needs to look at what is called *myth*. There is accepted truth, there are unaccepted truths, there are accepted falsehoods, and unaccepted falsehoods. It takes a great deal of examination to discern the best current knowledge of reality. Just remember the process is always ongoing and appears never to end.]

5. The *"blue pearl of spiritual wisdom"* exists and is observed in meditation.

[Note: After many years of daily meditation, I came to see a blue glowing speckled pattern somewhat like a laser pattern in my field of vision in a dark room, sometimes after many hours with my eyes closed. It has been called the blue pearl of spiritual wisdom but I am not sure what it is. It looked the color of Cherenkov radiation in a nuclear reactor so I was going to take an East Indian guru who said he saw it too, to check out whether what he saw matched the radiation in a water-cooled reactor. Never got him to the reactor but sometimes, objective and subjective experiences become blended beyond the so-called distinction between internal and external states of reality.]

6. The eye of god exists, God exists? The observer and observed.

[Note: I was visiting a friend on a cattle ranch, and sitting on a nice bench. I closed my eyes to meditate a bit. In my vision I saw an eye scanning back and forth, like some sort of cosmic observer. I have seen this a number of times since and sometimes, the eye is blue and sometimes brown—very detailed. I have talked to others who say they have had a similar image. Is it the ultimate observer, God?]

7. One can do the firewalk.

[Note: I did the firewalk and I am definitely cautious

about fire. The video tape of me shows that I am in a trance like state. I felt no heat at all and felt the ground in the fire pit was cool like the grass around the fire pit. It was not just hot coals, there were 6-inch-high flames. When I got to the end of the walk, I had a coal stuck between my big toe and the next one, and shook it out. When I got back to my lodge room, I had a big water blister there, and I said: *"Oh, shucks, I just did the firewalk, I don't need this blister!"* And it went away very soon thereafter. I still might have been in a different state of consciousness to some degree, as I cannot always, on demand, get instantaneous healing!]

8. One can communicate with animals and plants.

[Note: When I would hike alone in the woods, or swim in the ocean alone, I noticed that when one is alone and maybe not giving off "human vibes," animals behave differently than when they are around a lot of people. I had a great number of interesting and profound experiences with curious animals who weren't sure what I was. Also, they transmitted love. There is a lot more to say about some of these experiences. My neighbors noticed I would grow enormous plants with leaves as much as six-times normal size. I was called a farmer by my neighbors and I sometimes grew plants that made headlines in newspapers when they were grown in the San Francisco Arboretum. Heck, I just grew 'em outside and watered 'em!

Bill van Bise, my late husband, and I fed two pairs of quail outside of our lab/house in the Sierra Nevada's which was near BLM land. We fed the quail (within a short time we had 200 quail) and the blue jays, who played with us, along with the bunny rabbits, jack rabbits, and coyotes. The coyotes would come by and show themselves off. After six years, we had to leave. The quail stood like sentries on the rocks in a formation we had never seen before—they knew we were leaving that place forever. This still is a moment that makes me very sad, yet happy, at their companionship.

What's interesting is that the birds and other animals

would know when we were driving up with food in our van and rush up to greet us. If we had no food, and drove up, they would not rush up to the van but would come out to see us when we fed them. The birds would call the bunnies, and types of birds that were worm eaters would knock on our window when the *seed* eaters wanted some food. What communication!

I always wanted to swim with the dolphins and I went out with people that had swum with them before, off the west coast of the Big Island of Hawaii with skin-diving gear. We swam out several miles and I saw a pod of spinner dolphins about 80 feet down. I thought I'd like to see them up closer so I said in my mind: *"I love you, I love you, I love you, and can I see you up close,"* three times and almost immediately, two came up jumping and breaching right in front of me, just a few feet away. Wow! Love is universal.]

9. Open your crown chakra to receive "all knowledge or the Akashic records," *Kings and Queens wear crowns of gold.*

[Note: I have found that one has to learn as much as one can and really work at it, day and night, and sometimes deny themselves sleep and going out and having a *"good time"* because one can get profound information from other dimensions from the spiritual world. You need a lot of knowledge and information to translate the incoming information into something useful on the physical plane. To bridge the spiritual and the physical requires one to be able to translate the information that is given. I think the information wants to be *explicate* (in David Bohm's terms of the *implicate* and *explicate* order) on the physical plane. This is the key to creating new useful knowledge on the physical plane. This may, in fact, be one of our duties in life.]

10. Extremely low and RF frequencies at very low intensity with specific wave forms, duty cycles, etc., can have *profound* effects on biological systems.

[Note: Bill van Bise and I studied the effects of various kinds of electromagnetic and magnetic signatures on biological systems. Bill began these studies in the 1970's. He set up an experiment to measure possible electromagnetic influences with medical volunteers at the Oregon State Graduate School of Medicine and to look at possible corresponding changes in EEG and EKG. The purpose of his experiment was to *disprove*, to his (then) wife that there were any changes that could possibly exist. Boy, did he prove himself wrong! There were profound changes.

When I met Bill in 1979, after his divorce, I thought there could not be any effects of low intensity and low frequency electromagnetic fields, but boy was I wrong! It is easier to find detrimental effects, but one can find life-saving and life-enhancing positive effects. Bill and I spent 30 years researching these and developing medical devices to enhance life. We have a number of issued patents. This work continues with Mark Busier.]

11. Solar activity affects our brain waves and us.

[Note: The heavy particle interaction from solar coronal mass ejections drives a person's brain into the Alpha frequency of brain wave activity, which is a state where we can relax, sleep and meditate and also comprehend the subtler aspects of reality. I believe that the Sun god is talking to us and we should listen. It was fortuitous that 2012 and 2013 were periods of high solar activity which correspond to the hope and expectation many people have of the Mayan prophesy of a new era (not the end of the world). My meeting with Mayan elders was a *"love fest"* and I think the prophecy is still being fulfilled, along with change and new hope.]

12. One can solve problems in one's sleep and dreams including mathematical problems.

[Note: In high school I had a lucid dream about a trigonometry problem which was assigned for homework that I had trouble solving. I woke up the next day with the thought 550 feet and looked up the answer in the back of the book and this was it! I reconstructed my dream and solved the problem. I realized what a "problem solver" dreams were, they could solve analytic problems, as well as general problems. I keep pen and paper by my bed. I had two dreams that led to two books and a number of referred papers. I was on a close-up photographic field trip while studying general relativity and cosmological models for a decade; I dreamed up an equation $F = c^4/G$ which is a fundamental force in Einstein's stress energy tensor! It is also related to the force of universal expansion. In the lucid dream I wrote the equation and then tried to "plug in" the constants, speed of light, c and gravitational constant G. I must have made an arithmetic error as a "big red error bar", like on the old classic HP calculator came up in my dream and I woke up! I wrote the equation on my note pad. I "plugged in" the constants and got the answer! Also, a key dream on higher dimensional geometries depicted in Figure 5b in Chapter 5, came in a dream and clarified and led to the theory in this book, three other books and published papers. One has a vast personal problem solver in dreams to yield wonderful solutions.]

13. Ghosts are real. P298

[Note: Bill and I saw the same black ghost who we thought was just *"out for a float."* It saw us, and it looked *surprised* that *we* saw it, I think. It had its *"cloaking device"* off and then slowly it cloaked from the bottom up.]

14. *"Life"* after death appears to exist.

[Note: I have felt the strong presence of my Mother's mother, who was very kind to me and after she died, I seem to feel her presence. Also, after my late husband Bill died, I asked him about some of the circuit diagrams on our inventions. It was a few weeks after he passed and he said: *"Don't bother me, I'm very busy!"* After about 6 months, he let me ask him questions. I don't know what he was doing, but he was in great pain before he died. A psychic told me what day and hour he would die, and he was correct! I felt great peace from Bill all that evening after he died. I didn't want to go to bed and lose that feeling, it made me so happy since he was out of great pain as he was dying and in a new peace. Of course, I went to bed eventually. I have attempted to make contact with other people who are deceased that I felt close to, but I got no answers. Was it a busy signal? Or what were they doing? I don't know. It is obviously a two-way communication!]

15. The Sun, the son of God, and Sun god of Egypt, which Imhotep or Akhenaton worshipped, may have involved a spelling error of the word Sun or Son. This was pointed out by Bill van Bise to me (when he was embodied).

16. One event can be found true, such as one's birth.

17. Evil is *live* spelled backward.

[Note: I don't know why this is so.]

18. What about UFOs and ET's?

[UFO-ologists please note: I don't know about the ET's yet so you'll have to cut me some slack on that. I have studied some material from some sightings, one of which was scoriated metal sample and appeared to be burned by going through the atmosphere. It smelled and tasted like iron oxide. With neutron activation analysis at LLNL, it was determined to be FeO_2, primarily but with 10% *molybdenum*. Was it a structural member of a satellite? The Canadian government asked me to do this study. The sighting was made by a Royal Canadian Mounted policeman who stated that he saw two cylinders on fire descending from the sky. This was in about 1970.]

Table 1
List of Some Basic Concepts

1. All is a web of interconnection.
2. All is change, with some constancy.
3. Mind, body and spirit act in unity.
4. There is complete freedom and choice of thought and action but only at the spiritual level.
5. There is compassion and interdependence in the web of all life, and all existence.
6. Humans are keepers and humble caretakers of life and the world.
7. It is all science, it is all belief because it is *all*.
8. We are unifying the spiritual and the physical, as two paths to the same "*place*."
9. **Think Thoughts! And Be and Do!**

4. A World Apart And A World of Unity

Some of my thoughts and suggestions about life involve the following list. Thoughts are real and have real consequences and I suggest one creates good ones! If there was a universal understanding about life that respected the principles of the interconnected whole—that what you think determines what you experience and how you carry out your actions, i.e. with consideration and respect for all, we would have a very different direction for humanity. These are the teachings of the ancient ones and are incorporated into many of the world's religions. One must be, and do, to the best of our capabilities for the sake of each other and for all of existence. (See Table 1.)

5. The Scientific Method Consciousness, Psi and Life Processes

If one diligently attempts replication of someone else's experiment one may or not find the same results. This can occur in particle physics, chemistry, or biology, psychology or any field of research. I have found in the replication of other's work that it is best to observe them conducting the experiment, make careful observations, ask questions and read their protocols in detail and, if they will let you, examine their laboratory note books. I have observed cases where students had difficulty and could not replicate simple chemistry and physics experiments even with reasonable instructions. I have also observed researchers' difficulties in replicating complex particle accelerator experiments. It requires good communication, cooperation and team effort and perhaps some psi. If one is not able to replicate a complex experiment, this means that one did not find the phenomena, but it does not mean the phenomena does not exist. I have observed and participated in physics which involved conducting acceleration particle experiments with various results. As Charles Tart suggests there is "state specific science" and I have observed tired, arguing scientists get poor results and make errors in data collection and its interpretation. I present an example here:

In the 1970s, during a "run" at the Bevatron Proton accelerator, which usually lasted for up to 72 hours of beam time, a calibration source was left in the beam line and some of the physicists interpreted the data as a new resonance of the excitation of the target material. I noted that it looked like the resonance of the decay of a known element in one of the calibration sources. I had the experiment closed down and we looked in the cave where the particle beams collide with the target and there, on the floor was the calibration source! In any experiment one must use care and question one's interpretation of results and have extensive knowledge and experience.

As we before stated the scientific method is marked by the following features:

(1) Careful and accurate classification of facts and observation of their correlation and sequence,

(2) Discovery of scientific laws by aid of the creative imagination, and intuition, and

(3) Self-criticism and the final touchstone of equal validity for all normally constituted minds.

The concept of pragmatism represents the carrying over of the scientific method into the domain of philosophy. A relaxed, alert state, without judgment of the mind and intuition is key to psi research and good science practice also requires these states. Experimentation requires a more alert, active state of mind and action.

We must examine and reexamine our assumptions. For example, we can consider three major conceptual frameworks of life:

(1) The Mechanistic view—it is all matter and neural physiology, mechanistic psychology and the endo-

crine system that can explain all of consciousness,

(2) Mind/Body duality in which there is a dualism of mind and body, and

(3) The Spiritualistic View in which most of reality is spirit and some is condensed out as matter.

We can form an analogy for resolution of the particle/wave duality in quantum theory to the mind/body duality. In the case of the particle/wave paradox, is light a particle or a wave? The specific experiment one conducts makes light behave and "look like" a particle or a wave. The perceptual stand point about our perceptions of reality determines how we perceive reality to be in terms of the mind/body duality paradox or other issues. One can assume the purely mechanistic view or that brain/body issues dominate the reality. Another possibility is the non-mechanistic view which gives more credence to the mind or spiritual point of view. Our fundamental assumptions about reality further reinforces what reality is and what it is to be for us. We can emphasize our beliefs and hence exclude contradictory perceptions and lose valuable information and points of view!

How we "look" determines what we "see," that is, light is both a particle and a wave, or neither of these as we said. This is termed four logic as opposed to the "either or" logic of Aristotelian Logic (Targ and Hurtak, 2006). Four logic also has neither and both which fits well with the particle-wave and may resolve other paradoxes as well.

In Table 2, I present some of the general attributes of conscious awareness reference points we started from. In Table 3, I enumerate some of the conclusions of psi and in Table 4 some states of consciousness that lead to success.

It is important to consider the moral implications of using psi functioning in daily life. I feel there are many useful purposes for the ability to "tune into" scenes across space and time. We have spent a great deal of time considering the practical applications of the various abilities that we find emerging among people connected with our psi research. This immediately brings us to the matter of the morality of the use to which these human capabilities might be put. This is an important consideration in our research. How can this capacity be used for good? How can we avoid a future in which it could, or would, be used for harm? Knowledge and morality must go hand in hand. (See Table 5).

Certainly our world is not in optimum condition now, man pitted against man, man destroying much of nature. We believe our experiments, as well as all others of this kind, show the interconnectedness of man with man and all aspects of his and her environment everywhere. How easily we can influence each other, share thoughts, perceptions, feelings! We are intimately connected to our environment and able to perceive it accurately at great distances.

We base our experimental procedures on personal interrelationships. We believe that the research should be enjoyable, where people continue to want to come back in order to learn new things about themselves and reality. We believe that the best research can be conducted where there is a sense of sharing, so we ask for input from all who take part in our studies. All are part of the team. It is important that there is caring, not competition. Perceptions are a major consideration and they are taken into account in all of our work including research that is considered non-psychic, such as particle physics, but then this researcher believes some amount of psi may enter all research.

I believe that each decision one makes is not just with one or a few individuals but involves the fundamental laws of the universe. These laws involve the manner in which thought transforms and moves into action. In fact, each decision involves a multitude of aspects of the universe, each act involves the whole of what underlies our experience of reality, this is the origin of moral judgment. Psi tells us to tell the truth as we know it. In Table 5, we list some of the implications from the existence of psi in our personal lives and for the world at large. (See Fig. 9).

Table 2
Some Attributes of Consciousness

Where do thoughts come from? We delineate aspects of consciousness as:

- Sensations, reactions to stimuli,
- Perceptions, awareness of sensations,
- Emotions, experiences as responses to perception,
- Situational emotions, positive or negative judgment about emotions,
- Cognition, conceptualization or reflections,
- Intuition, A-logical as logical or non-logical (four logic),
- Roles of consciousness, introspection, observation and measurement,
- Self-Awareness, "objective," sense of self,
- Unity, oneness, whole, boundlessness.

Table 3
Some Conclusions About the Remote Perception Phenomenon

1. Remote perception is a very strong phenomena.

2. The main constraints on the phenomena are psychological rather than restricted by physical process.

3. It is difficult to design experiments to separate different types of psychic modalities which may involve artificial definitions.

4. Space and time are not restrictions on the access of remote information.

5. Transitory motion at the site can be but not often remotely perceived by the subject in the laboratory room.

6. Analytical comparison of subject meditation and target location can be made by persons or computer analysis.

7. Learning to access one's psychic impressions has the potential for improving the quality of one's life.

8. Psychic phenomena and other life processes involves carrying a thought or thought concept into a final result.

9. Psychic phenomena, as well as other life processes involves goal orientation. A thought is created as to what one desires to achieve, a process is devised to achieve the goal and a choice is made and action is taken (or not taken) to create the desired outcome.

Table 4
States of Consciousness that Lead to Success,
Fluid Peak Performances,
State of Mind to be "in the zone,"
Create and Disseminate Knowledge

1. A driving focus or ordering.
2. A feeling of making a contribution.
3. An element of risk or challenge.
4. A sense of not knowing but knowing all the same that things will turn out well.
5. A sense of destiny, of doing the work one is meant to do.
6. A look for the whole or oneness.

Table 5
Some Implications of Psi
For Our Personal Lives
and Global Interconnection

1. Optimize personal psi phenomena for self understanding and improving life for all.
2. Social implications of psi for truthfulness and sincerity to oneself and others.
3. Use of psi for better comprehension of the relationship of mind, body and spirit.
4. Psi in self healing and as a medicine for the healing of others.
5. Implications of psi for education, health, creativity, philosophy, and society and a new peaceful, joyful vision of life.

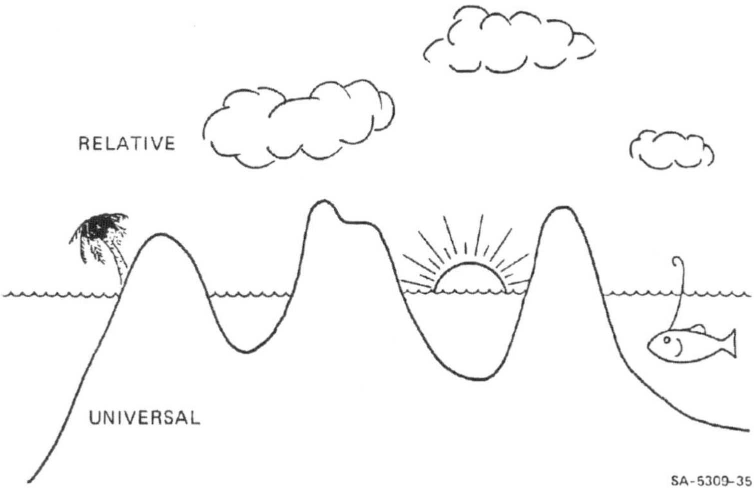

Figure 9

The Universal or Remote Contiguous Connection

I will conclude with thoughts about interconnectedness of the web of reality, see my drawing Fig. 9.

> *"That discoveries are made by not just seeing individual Islands above the surface of the sea but looking deeper to see the interconnections of these Islands and to attempt to understand this deeper connection of the relative to the absolute. This is the way nature works; it is the universal or remote contiguous connection that binds us all and all existence into the interwoven fabric of the whole?"*

Quote and drawing by Elizabeth Rauscher, 1973.

References

Kaiser, D. (2011) *How the Hippies Saved Physics,* New York: Norton and Co. Publisher.

Kuhn, T. (1962) *The Structure of Scientific Revolutions,* Chicago: University of Chicago Press.

Lorentz, H.A., A. Einstein, H. Minkowski and H. Weyl (1923) *The Principles of Relativity,* New York: Dover Publisher.

Targ, R. and J. Hurtak (2006) *The End of Suffering*. Charlottesville: Hampton Rhodes.

Acknowledgements

PSI Research

By

Elizabeth A. Rauscher, Ph.D.

First Row: 1. Unknown; 2. Stephan Schwartz, Ph.D.; 3. Russell Targ

Second Row: 4. Judy Tart; 5. Robert Morris, Ph.D.; 6. Elizabeth Rauscher, Ph.D.; 7. Elisabeth Targ, M.D.; 8. Unknown; 9. Charles Honorton; 10. Charles Tart, Ph.D.; 11. Marilyn Schlitz, Ph. D.; 12. Unknown; 13. Keith Harrey; 14. Hella Hammid.

Acknowledgements

This researcher wishes to acknowledge the assistance of the Parapsychology Foundation of New York, the Orb Foundation of London, England, Essentia Research Associates of Amherst, Wisconsin, SRI International of California, and for the assistance of the Lawrence Berkeley National Laboratory in supplying facilities for the operation of the "Fundamental 'Fysiks' Group" during part of my employment at Lawrence Berkeley Lab and University of California Berkeley.

I acknowledge some of the wonderful innovative and profound leaders that I met and worked with in my life. Many other's influenced my thinking as did my observations of and communication with Nature and the profound beauty of the Universe. Some taught me gifts such as modes of thought and others taught me modes of action and still others spurred my interest, others became like long friends, some supplied useful input and still others became colleagues and friends and one became my husband.

As a child growing up with experience of living in the California Woods on Witton Indian land in Napa County, I felt that all of nature and its beauty is interwoven, interconnected, nature and that all is consciousness! This is not a view held by anyone in my immediate family or acquaintances, particularly teachers! I did not speak about my early thoughts and experiences, such as a profound OBE (out of body experience).

When I was nine years old, I got to get together with my aunt, Dorothea (my father's older sister) and her husband, Alfred R. Mitchell and well-known California landscape artist. I started drawing from an early age and he encouraged my artwork. I heard them talk about the reality of the effect and meaning of thoughts. I had thought a lot about thoughts, including human to animal and plant inter-communication!

Also, Dorothea told some great ghost stories and ideas about "life" after death and mostly "life" before life.

The Mitchells had driven up to the San Francisco Bay area, where we were living in Berkeley (in sight of the UC Berkeley Campus Campanile Bell Tower). I diligently worked to persuade the Mitchells to allow me to ride back to their lovely home in San Diego in order to learn more about the properties and nature of thought and in general about ideas about consciousness that they talked about from their interest and reading in Theosophy.

I had "hit" it off with Fred and Dorothea in part due to my ability in art and interest in consciousness! It was a great trip. It opened doors to writings about consciousness and my interest in Eastern Mysticism and meditation practices. I noted that Dorothea tried to control my reading of the Theosophical literature, "you are not old enough" but they went to bed early and I did not and read their books at night. I also often flew back alone by airplane. Scary but fun. I later took flying lessons in a Cessna 150 and 175. I love flying. Later, I inherited the Mitchell's Theosophical Library. Yes, it was great to have someone to talk with over the years and would visit them often. I found that meditation had a great positive effect on my life's work!

Earlier, when I was about seven years old, my parents attended a party with their friends, with me in toe. The place was beautiful, with an stream in their backyard. Everyone seemed elegant, refined and well traveled all over the world, having great stories and travel artifacts. I remember this couple's books, particularly, the wife who took an interest in me and gave me a blue covered book entitled *"Man's Right to Knowledge."* This made me assume a "person's right to knowledge." I do not remember their names but they had a definite positive influence on me and I felt one should be a world citizen and travel and connect with people all over the world, and gain and disseminate knowledge! This I did.

At eight, I met an astrophysicist at my school one day. He spoke of billion billions of stars, and galaxies and that we live in a marvelous universe. I do not remember his name but I acknowledge him. Being out in the country, I had seen the beautiful glowing stars and the Milky Way in the woods where we lived in Napa country. I wanted to study the very small, and the very large, the universe and use this knowledge as a foundation to study consciousness!

From the age of nine to thirteen I designed and built six telescopes, five refractors and one reflector. I kept one refractor and gave the reflector to my son, Brent Rauscher. In actuality, I did not have all six at a time, as I used parts, lenses, and took parts from some to build others. I got the parts because of my mother, who introduced me to the "Edmond Scientific" catalogue, where she got some photographic equipment and my father, who was in charge of land and water resources for the seven Western States and had many maps and many sturdy map tubes to use; just right to build telescopes with! I acknowledge the astrophysicist for helping stir my interest in the cosmos!

As a freshman in physics and chemistry at The University of California Berkeley, my introductory physics classes were taught by Luis Alvarez, Ph.D., Nobel Prize winner. He was great fun and was supportive of me and treated me equally as the one and only woman in a sea of over 400 male students. For the first three weeks, Luis spoke of the world of atoms, quantum physics and relativity theory, what a blast! Then after three weeks, he said "well a third of you dropped out and now its time to get down to business." Well, then it was the physics of ladders and pulleys. After all, it was a course in classical mechanics! I have applied the laws of pulleys later for the change of direction and for mechanical advantage, so maybe some of the knowledge was useful.

As a undergraduate student in physics and chemistry, I found that, as an honor student, it was fun and useful to conduct special projects, research projects and honors seminars from my sophomore to senior year. In my senior year, I conducted a theoretical study of alpha decay and wrote my second research paper which ended up as a footnote. The first paper I wrote in my junior year on plasma physics and it was published. My research on alpha decay was conducted under the guidance of John O. Rasmussen, Ph.D. From him, I learned to refine my research methods and reference searches. He was also my masters degree adviser in Nuclear Physics and also was a student of Glen T. Seaborg, Ph.D., Nobel Prize winner, who served as my Ph.D. adviser in Nuclear Science all at UC Berkeley. Seaborg had more honors degrees than anyone on the planet and he was great to talk to, with a fantastic memory and so was the past head of LBNL (Lawrence Berkeley National Laboratory), as was Edwin McMillan, Ph.D., Nobel Prize winner. He and I loved to talk about the past history of the laboratory; more down to earth, great communications. Seaborg along with David Rockefeller helped assemble and put together a traveling museum exhibit on psi research, that traveled the United States in the early 1970s and he was aware of my interest in consciousness and psi.

I met John A. Wheeler, Ph.D., Nobel Prize winner, at NASA Ames in California and he was one of my great advisers, mentors and encouraged my work on multidimensional Descartes Spaces and black hole physics, partly based on an extension of his work in "Geometrodynamics," New York, Academic Press (1962).

Later Brian Josephson, Ph.D., Nobel Prize winner inspired me in his open minded pursuit of physics and consciousness. Eugene Wigner, Ph.D., Nobel Prize winner, was a great supporter of my research in psi and my theoretical model presented in the science community.

I also had an opportunity to work with Edward Teller, Ph.D., Nobel Prize winner, on the theory of Quasi Stellar Radio Sources (QASARS), at the Lawrence Livermore National Laboratory and later at the Hoover Institute Stanford University. He sure did know his physics! It was quite an experience! At LLNL, I also researched Nuclear and Plasma physics. I met some great friends, particularly Bobbie Balanda and her husband John. We went skin and scuba diving together and I taught diving classes and discussed spiritual matters.

Paul Lieber, Ph.D., UC Berkeley professor of Mechanical Engineering, gave me the opportunity to work with him on a Navy ONR grant through UCB for five years (1969-1974) on General Relativity. In those years, Navy grants were given for non-military research. We talked physics and philosophy. I also had a Navy grant with Eldon Byrd Ph.D. to work on the mechanism of electromagnetic effects on biological tissues (1982-1983) and later, two Navy grants on environmental natural earth-ionosphere electromagnetic resonant fields (1991-1993).

Through Paul Lieber, I met John Clauser, Ph.D. at his UC Berkeley Laboratory, in 1971, where he and W.A. Horne were graduate students conducting the test of Bell's Theorem and the EPR Paradox Quantum Non-locality Entanglement experiment. At this time, I was on the staff of the theoretical physics department where Geoffrey Chew, Ph.D. was chairman and worked with him and learned a great deal from him about the foundations of physics. I was working on Multi-dimensional Geometries in Quantum Theory and General Relativity. There I met George Weismann, Ph.D., at that time a student of Chew's and I had met Henry Stapp, Ph.D. earlier in 1964 at LBNL. Geoffrey Chew gave me a paper by Fritjof Capra, Ph.D. in which was a chapter from his later book *The Tao of Physics*, by Shambhala Press, Berkeley (1975) and Geoff said to me as we passed each other in the Bldg. 50A halls, "Hey, I think this is some of your kinda stuff." I read the preprint and corresponded with Fritjof. I found out he was also interested in Chew's S-Matrix and got Chew to invite him to the theory group from University of Vienna, where Jack Sarfatti, Ph.D. was also. Correspondence with Jack introduced me to Nick Herbert, Ph.D. and Saul Paul Sirag and later Gary Zukav, *The Dancing Wu Li Master*, by William Marrow publisher and Co., Inc. New York (1974).

Then, I met Beverly Rubik, Ph.D. who later worked with me on the healing effect of Olga Worrell on a model bacterial system. This group became the core group of the Fundamental "Fysiks" Group which I named, started and chaired with up to forty attendees in E.O. Lawrence's old office which he had when he was director of LBNL. George and I assembled the initial group and the Fundamental "Fysiks" group ran from 1975-1979 with weekly meetings I arranged and chaired.

Fred Allan Wolf, Ph.D. was also part of these meetings as was Philippe Eberhard, Ph.D. and Henry Stapp, Ph.D. as was John Clauser, Ph.D.. The inspiration for the group was two -fold, first, the interpretation of the foundations of quantum non-locality, and quantum entanglement and second, the replication of the Stanford Research Institute (SRI) Remote Viewing psi perception research (see David Keiser's *"How the Hippies Saved Physics"*, New York, W.W. Norton, 2011).

To digress to the early 1970's, I had met Edgar D. Mitchell the Apollo 14 astronaut who walked on the moon and started the Noetic Institute. Yes, I was impressed, the guy walked on the moon and was instrumental in conducting and promoting psi research! Also, about the same time I met Henry Dakin of the Washington Research Center in San Francisco, which he started and ran. We all exchanged information and names of people interested in the nature of consciousness.

In about 1973, I met with Ingo Swann, who coined the term remote viewing, (See I. Swann (1975) *"To Kiss the Earth Goodbye,"* his autobiography, Hawthorn, New York), Russell Targ Ph.D. and Harold Puthoff Ph.D. (1977, *Mind-Research: Scientists Look at Psychic Ability"* Delacorte Press), at SRI for lunch and began my collaboration with the masters of Remote Perception (RV). I took my book "A *Unifying Theory of Fundamental Processes,"* LBNL, UCRL—20808, July 1971 on Multidimensional Descartes Spaces, with me and I was hired to work on a theory of RV at SRI. I knew somehow, the remote perception properties had to do with a multidimensional complex geometry and both Hal and I met with Gerald "Gary" Feinberg, Ph.D. from the Columbia University. By then I had drafted my initial calculations on my complex eight space, which demonstrated the possibilities of nonlocality and RV macrocosmic spacetime, a counterpart work of Bell's quantum non-locality (E.A. Rauscher and Richard L. Amoroso (2011) *"Orbiting the Moons of Pluto,"* World Scientific). I learned the trade, i.e. how to conduct RV experiments from the masters at SRI and Feinberg encouraged my approach to complex eight space. I conducted RV experiments with the SRI group, the F"F" Group and with the Berkeley Research Group (BRG) which I also set up, 1975-1983. I conducted RV experiments with subject participants, such as Ingo Swann, Gary O. Langford, Hella Hammid, Susan Harris and Ray Miller. This research included outbound experimenters, besides me, such as Jeffrey Michlove, Ph.D., Saul Paul Sirag, Beverly Rubik, Ph.D. and A.J. (Hope) Mullins, B.S. who also conducted useful subject and outbound target experimental transcript, descriptions and comparisons for the BRG grants and SRI reports.

I further conducted a series of long distance experiments with Jack Houck formally of Douglas Aircraft and Shumway Pool who was the RV perception receiver. Houck popularized the "spoon bending parties" and conducted almost one hundred of them! This started with a visit to my laboratory by Irwin Weisberg who started to bend my cutlery. Jack Houck and I and Jessica Haynes got together for dinner in which Jessica started to bend spoons after seeing Weisberg do it.

I found that when Irwin Weisberg said "it is ready to bend" it was soft and easy to bend. When I started I bent, manually, a spoon handle, it was hard to do as the bend was a loose loop. Later I found that I could rub the metal item (spoon, fork, metal bars) and then it felt soft and ready to bend. I could wrap up a handle of a spoon tightly, all the way to the end, and bend the bowl of a spoon as well. I also bent a 3 degrees 6" long brass bar that was 3/4" in diameter —it rolled smoothly but bumpy on the table before I bent it and then it did not roll smoothly but bumpy afterwards. Does this outdo Arnold Schwarzenegger? Afterwards I learned some martial arts and I think they also use mind over matter.

Others who contributed to my work on the psi aspects of consciousness were, Charles T. Tart, Ph.D., (1973, *"States of Consciousness,"* E.P. Dutton and Co., Inc., New York), Stanley Krippner, Ph.D., Evan Harris Walker, M.S., Helmut Schmidt, Ph.D., Montagne Ullman, Ph.D., Keith Harry, Willis W. Harmon, Ph.D. (who was on the Regents of UCB, who I read about in high school), Charles Honorton, Edward May and many others.

In the early 1970's through Jeff Mishlove, I met Uri Geller and then Andrija Puharich, Ph.D. (A. Puharich (1973) *"Beyond Telepathy,"* Anchor Press/Doubleday, New York), who brought Uri over to the United States from Israel. Uri's stage performance at UCB in 1972 caught the attention of people who later became members of the F "F" Group (Rauscher, E.A., 1978, *"Exploration Experiments in Psychokinesis with Subject Uri Geller,"* Psi Realite' (French), Vol 7, p. 34-38; Rauscher, E.A., *"Psychokinetic Introduction with Laboratory Prepared Materials: A Prototype Experimental Design,"* 1984, Vol 3, p. 26-41; U. Geller, (1975) *"Uri Geller: My Story,"* Warner Books, New York). Later I conducted controlled Laboratory experiments on psychokinesis with Uri with sealed laboratory grown crystals and also with John Hasted, Ph.D. and with Steven North who affected and sometimes broke materials without touching them with very interesting results using strain gages attached to the crystals! I also met David Bohm, Ph.D., Nobel Prize Winner, and Basil Hiley Ph.D. at the University of London, Birkbeck College who also spoke to my F "F" Group and shared my interest in Theosophy.

I was on a lecture tour of the East Coast and got together with Uri in his New York apartment with friends. I also met Andrija Puharich, M.D. in his Ossining, New York home. We arrived late at night and a colleague of Andrija answered the door. As we entered, Andrija came "gliding" down the stairs in a black cloak with stars and half moons on it. I thought "what have I gotten myself into?" He sure had a flair for the dramatic! I slept on his couch with a little white cat by my head. What a great experience and a good influence and a great beginning for someone who became a good friend.

Through Andrija, I met Josh (R.J.R. III) Reynolds of Devotion at Southern Pines, North Carolina. He was a good friend to me and my late husband, William van Bise, MD (Hon.) and we took care of Andrija at Josh's request when he was ailing and later died at the Devotion Estate.

My appreciation is also expressed to William A. Tiller, Ph.D. for the opportunity he gave William van Bise, M.D. (Hon) and me to work with him, 1997-2002. I especially enjoyed my NASA contract with James B. Beal at the Michoud Lockheed-Martin (then Martin Marietta) Aerospace Plant in New Orleans, LA to increase the weldments on the space shuttles main Hydrogen-Oxygen tank (1983-1985) which lead to a patented process.

I shall mention several other people who contributed to my work. My mother, Claire E. Soderblom Webster, M.S., encouraged my interest in science and shared my love of nature and father Philip J. Webster, Ph.D. from who I gained strength to pursue my goals with perseverance by his model of action, even though we did not get along.

My son, Brent A. Rauscher, B.S. and his family and grandchildren have been a love in my life. I acknowledge especially my late husband of many years. I give great thanks to him, William L. van Bise, M.D. (Hon.), who traveled the road as a scientific explorer and adventurer with me, sharing together love, respect, joy, work, collaboration and yes, hardships. We conducted extensive work on biological effects of electromagnetic fields, obtaining measurements of electromagnetic fields vital to life on this planet. I have carried on this vital research with my good friend and colleague, Mark Busier. This work lead to five patents issued and patent pendings. He is a great contributor to furthering this work.

I especially wish to give my special thanks to James J. Hurtak, Ph.D., Ph.D. and Desiree E. Hurtak, Ph.D., founders of The Academy For Future Science, an international organization, for contributing their great insights, talents and efforts to this project and for making this book possible.

All these wonderful special people have contributed in their own way to the world. Two other people who greatly influenced me, who I never met were Albert Einstein, Ph.D. and Nikola Tesla.

A comprehensive collection of this author's work is available at the University of California at Berkeley in the Bancroft, UC Berkeley Library; there is a good sampling of my physics, biomedical, engineering, geophysical, philosophical and consciousness research work, as well as my poetry and sampling of my art.

Chapter 10:
Mind Dynamics Unfolded

by

J.J. Hurtak, Ph.D., Ph.D. and Desiree Hurtak, Ph.D.

"Science cannot solve the ultimate mystery of nature. And that is because, in the last analysis, we ourselves are a part of the mystery that we are trying to solve."

— Max Planck

Table of Contents

Introduction 545

Scientific Theory and RV 548

Conclusions 554

References 555

Introduction

Utilizing the discipline of Remote Viewing (RV), we along with Dr. Elizabeth Rauscher have discovered new relationships of mind-body, mind-consciousness development. This development reveals how Remote Viewing can bring forth a greater comprehension of the unconscious side of life. It is normally the utterly pervasive side of unconsciousness in human life that disrupts the even flow of energy within the human system. Remote Viewing pierces the undercurrents and the limitations formerly attributed to the unconscious mind allowing for the achievement of a higher creative consciousness. Consequently, bringing awareness to the unconscious mind alters forgetfulness, brings about harmony, and allows one insight into the true purpose of human existence, which is to integrate, to wholify, and to comprehend oneself within the cosmos around us.

In seeking answers to the dilemma of human identity with its "trickle of consciousness," we begin to understand how to ride upon the ocean of unconscious reality. The theory of Elizabeth Rauscher and her colleagues in studying Remote Viewing advances the remarkable conclusion that the human mind has the triggering mechanisms for an uninhibited global reach in a nonlocal, especially global correspondence. The hidden nature of consciousness is beginning to be understood and it does not appear to be the act of sending and receiving information, but an intended movement of a mind-reach of "being there" at different geographic locations.

The underlying hypothesis of this book is that "Remote Viewing" is a legitimate tool for "information gathering." It offers an explanation of the reception of information without violating physical conservation laws. Outside the use of our five senses, information can be perceived well beyond the audio and visual brain perceptions, to help professionals who operate in well-defined areas of problem solving.

It has been shown over the past forty years by experiments with Remote Perception that practical insights can be obtained from target locations. Consequently, all 'secret' or 'hidden knowledge behind closed doors' is theoretically eliminated. Governments accepting this, have sought to use Remote Viewing, as during the Cold War, to seek out various targets. For example, secret installations were detected with great accuracy in the former Soviet Union (Targ and Hurtak, 2006). The acquired information was used for problem solving with far-reaching implications for predicting and observing socio-political activities that could be considered harmful or dangerous.

Our work [Drs. Hurtak] has been to use psi as a tool to overcome, correct, or alert us to occurring changes. We have applied it to the arena of social and political events seeking to instill positive results through the mental transmission of peaceful ideas, as detailed in our work with Dr. Andrija Puharich in the Middle East (Puharich, 1976, Hurtak and Puharich, 1976). (See Chapter 11.)

One should also recognize that a lifetime of learning and the carrying out of paranormal studies using mental powers for global surveying can also be directed to other areas of consciousness awareness. Psi has, thus, also been applied not only by governments and research scientists, but by those seeking the detection of illness, life enhancement, and good health through avenues of remote healing (Schlitz, *et. al.*, 2000).

Rauscher's model accounts for actions and applications that can be applied across a broad spectrum in a variety of areas of learning. How is this accomplished? *Mind Dynamics of Space and Time* details how, but in brief the unitary All-Space hypothesis suggested by Rauscher's research is to relax and diminish the "intellectual chatter" of the mind and to develop a new awareness which transforms mental perception and brings into focus a universal understanding of reality.

We are at a time when environmental and economic crises have changed life styles and the information revolution has shifted the learning paradigms from a carbon-base to a silicon-base quest for knowledge. A new wave of self rediscovery has occurred along with the advances in cognitive studies, multidisciplinary programs and other discoveries that are showing us an expanded frontier of self-realization.

A new roadmap for humanity is appearing as we begin to see ourselves and humanity as "cosmo-planetary-quantum beings." There is an excitement of life with the rediscovery of our expanded abilities from the very best research communities. Ongoing information from university and research institutes looking deeper for answers has resulted in new insights into our human identity.

Research scientists working with Rauscher and her colleagues at SRI (i.e., Russell Targ and Harold Puthoff) built the first major worldwide database for demonstrating the nonlocality of consciousness! Consequently, even within the greatest conservative institutions there are shifts in the human intellect taking place introducing a new horizon where virtual reality and the psi brain nature begin to contribute in unique ways to transform the human intellect. The brain is beginning to be seen as the instrument for consciousness and not the generator of consciousness.

It is the premise of this book to demonstrate that the natural intelligence of the human conscious nervous systems is vastly more versatile and competent when we include Remote Viewing. In fact, this is where we show we are more efficient than any artificial intelligence or digital computers.

At this historic point of global consciousness awareness and development through the "remote information" revolution, the possibility of training people to use Remote Viewing or the power of mind assumes a deeper significance. RV can lead to key mental insights, which can support conflict resolution, global stability (see Chapter 11), as well as personal balance.

Rauscher (1979) and colleagues have postulated a "new physics" which is an extension of known physics with the power of psi. The implications of using psi or the paranormal are pushing the envelop of scientific and humanitarian exploration. We each need to look at positive ways of using this method of knowledge acquisition to help humanity.

However, we also need to continue to define the manner in which it works. The new neurophysiology and neuropsychology models must account for the fact of the brain's morphology, mind dynamics, and the vast retrieving of information beyond the level of simple brain chemistry. Remote Viewing helps us principally to understand the interplay between micro- and macrostructures in both the psi and physical worlds of nonlocal events. Specifically, we are creating a big picture of quantum mechanical and relativistic metric space with implications for mind-body research. This stands in contrast to the human mind seen by neuroscientists as following the actions of only a series of pyramidal or Purkinje cells and other neurons causing electrochemical transmissions in the brain. The brain's microstructures do involve synaptic membranes and microtubules (Hurtak, 1973; Hameroff and Penrose, 1996), nerve impulses propagating along nerve cells, which are always present and constituting a noisy dynamic background in the brain, but which also involve both classical and quantum physics.

Scientific Theory and RV

Our research leads to new ideas of what consciousness is in connection with "brain dynamics," where the mind is freed from imposed linear reality by merging with important 'eureka' discoveries. This leads us to four significant bench-marks which are the foundation for our model of a global mind reach:

i. The Heisenberg Uncertainty Principle. Werner Heisenberg's masterful insight into the indeterminacy of any quantum object being studied earned him the Nobel prize in physics in 1932. Specifically, it states that the position and momentum of a particle (or energy and time) cannot be simultaneously measured with high precision. This is not due to the inaccuracy of measurements or our inability to measure particles; it arises from quantum mechanical description of wave particles in nature. Considering the wave-particle duality, a wave exists in all of space at the same time. The uncertainty of finding its position is possibly infinite. Examining the particle, it would seem to jump or tunnel from one place to another without moving through the space in-between. This principle was the first foundational step to a new reality of the less than deterministic world of physics that includes instead many or even infinite possibilities (Rauscher met with Heisenberg at University of California, Berkeley in 1975 one year before his death).

ii. Einstein-Podolsky-Rosen Paradox in 1935 postulated possibilities for a scientific acceptance of 'nonlocal' physical realities sharing the same signal range at different physical distances. It was this indication of nonlocality or "spooky" interconnectedness by Einstein that carries consequences for both the macroscopic order and the microscopic (or atomic) order which could be applied to brain dynamics with time scales in the milliseconds, and down to the nanosecond range.

iii. J.S. Bell's work in 1963 (Bell, 1964) has allowed for the testing of predetermined statistical distribution of quantum processes demonstrating, in repeated laboratory instances, quantum interconnectedness or nonlocality (Salart, 2008).

iv. Schrödinger was in the middle between classical and quantum physics and wrote his equation which predicts what the probability distributions are for waves, particles and even quantum tunneling. There are many observables that can be measured, called "operators," that satisfy the generalized Schrödinger equation form. All of this was seeking to quantify quantum mechanics in the light of the "Copenhagen Interpretation" which said that a quantum system remained in this superposition until it interacted with the observer, at which time the superposition collapses into one of many measurable states, where the "observer" determines the outcome, as in Schrödinger's cat experiment to deduce a single classic macroscopic state.

We would now add a fifth benchmark and that is an understanding that we live in a multidimensional reality and behind that may be a consciousness field. The multidimensional universe has only been theorized, the most popular of which is the many interpretations of string theory. The eight-dimensional model of spacetime, called "eight-space," proposed by Rauscher suggests that soliton waves in a complex multidimensional space might serve to establish possible psi mediating nonlocal connections, and, hence, are behind Remote Viewing. (See Chapter 5.) This suggests mental access is available through events in a relativistic hyperspace, multidimensional reality. We agree with her model and propose that behind the many dimensions is a consciousness field that is not limited to the third and fourth dimensions and yet is present in all dimensions.

The processes of expanding consciousness appears to come from a mind shift that leads to holonomic operations in moving from simple Euclidian geometry or viewing a scene in two-dimensions to viewing reality in three, four, five or eight dimensions. Essays into such hyperspaces are now being explored (e.g. *Hyperspace*, by Micho Kaku, 1994) in physics, but had not been applied to understanding the variety of frames of reference in our conscious perceptual experience and the relation to one another, until others like Rauscher's Fundamental "Fysiks" Group came along. They were known as part of the Berkeley 'hippies who saved physics' by changing the way we see life through expanded consciousness (see Kaiser, 2011).

These benchmarks, including the four listed above, allow for the notion that reality is determined or influenced by the observer. The influence of the observer is presented in various PK (psychokinesis, the ability to move objects without touching them) experiments, as seen mainly in Russian psi research, but the ability to touch nonlocal reality has been confirmed by remote viewers, such as Ingo Swann and others.

The acquired body of information over the last 50 years seeks to establish a quantum mechanical and general relativity unity within the human mind itself. This allows for realities that are not found or localized in any of the neuro-circuits of the brain's 'wetware,' but transcend the mechanisms of the synaptic regulators of the brain. The hardware of the brain becomes a biotransducer for coherent consciousness existence which is nonlocal while its neural net also functions within the realm of classical physics (Rauscher, Hurtak and Hurtak, 2013)!

The situation is analogous to the studies by neuroscientists on the all-important question of how long a quantum state can live before it loses its coherence. Other researchers have come to investigate aspects of quantum brain dynamics which attribute long range coherence in the neuronal network to macroscopic quantum states.

Yet, there are other aspects of how this reality comes into awareness in the brain and one interesting approach has been presented by Hameroff and Penrose (1996). Hameroff and Penrose (1996) propose that the coherent coupling of neural synapses takes place via microtubular connections, where quantum coherence (macroscopic quantum state) is used to couple micro-sites in the brain (e.g., microtubules). (See Chapter 13.) Here the brain exhibits quantum transitions to produce spatio-temporal patterns. Working at the Planck scale, Hameroff and Penrose postulate that there are superpositions and that the brain is interacting directly with these quantum states. This leads to an emergent property (a patterned organization) of brain processes.

Taking this one step further, this implies that synapses act as resonant cavities within such structures as microtubules (Hurtak, 1973; Hameroff and Penrose, 1996) which are a type of hexagonal hololattice, that will on neural firing expel a single quantum, probabilistically.

Realistically, we would not stop at the microtubules, but consider the whole body as a living bio-transducer of energy and information. The quantum trigger through RV can further initialize transitions between different macroscopic modes (stochastic limit cycles, Grifoni and Hänggi, 1996).

There are other models being examined which involve apparent macroscopic and microscopic nonlocal consciousness worlds. For example, qubits (the quantum mechanical generalized computational analogue of bits) are also incorporated by Hameroff and Penrose (1996) simply to account for data and to make the data exchange realizable.

Pushing a little further, we add that these contents of consciousness are composed of nonlocal quantum bits that actually exist throughout the cosmos, including in other dimensions, and that our perceptions resonate with them (in some way match them). Accessing the quantum bits was historically called the mystical experience, but there may not be anything mystical about it.

However, one can also introduce a more mystical definition of consciousness held by many philosophers and others. We express this as tapping into a cosmic consciousness. Clearly many efforts have been made to understand how our consciousness can encompass the whole, including seeing the planet itself as a type of neural network where we become conscious of the consciousness of others.

With the expanded tools at hand, we seek to define what is life and where we go from here with a new approach to expanded consciousness. For some like Rauscher, this can all be successfully scientifically defined, whereby the consciousness experience as a product of our brain interacts with other dimensional fields (containing both human and cosmoplanetary realities) through a Rauscher "eight-space" reality. This model is developed in terms of the least number of additional dimensions which are required to be consistent with the main body of physics.

It may be our "mind reaches" into an expanded awareness of the universal cosmic consciousness that exists in an All-space reality that is beyond the distractions of the local environment. It may also be a state of spiritual tranquility with the All or Divine Space of which the ancient mystics spoke.

We must embrace the fact that nature is orderly and not just random and even within chaos theory there seems to be some order. If there is an order to the cosmos, there may even be a hidden matrix. Whatever it is, it is not static and, thus, we begin to understand Gödel's theorem (Gödel, 1931) on the limits of logic theory and mathematical formalism, as well as the difficulties of devising functional algorithms for psi.

The adaptions of quantum and spacetime physics into the expanded awareness of psi research go back to 1979 when prominent psi researchers met in Iceland, including Rauscher and Puharich (1976) (Rauscher, 1979, 1995) to share what they were working on connected with something analogous to the relativistic quantum holographic model of the brain/mind, that included, but was not limited by, phase conjugate adaptive resonance (Pribram, 1999). Rauscher shared the fact that human brains can be so much more versatile, competent, and efficient than their digital information processing counterparts, in relation to perception, cognition, language and intelligence.

We have asked the readers of this text to take a step forward and expand their mind into a consciously controlled exploration of the world beyond one's normal field of reflection. We are asserting that a unity of the left-side and right-side of the human brain brings about a top down (encoding) and a bottom up (decoding) approach to three dimensional pattern recognition. Remote Viewing may be a fundamental part of the latent power of the higher mind of consciousness that everyone can access.

We personally support the quantum nonlocal model along with a notion of Mind-2. We define the Mind-2 model of consciousness much as Rauscher's "eight space," where our existence reaches into a hyperspace consciousness existence. There our brains as Mind-1 (earthly existence) can connect with Mind-2 (hyperdimensional existence), in unifying or in tandem to create a mind-to-mind basis, where normal consciousness can fully interplay within a larger hyperspace reality. The mind can also work with advanced events preceding the world of physical form while making simultaneous connection on many knowledge-based levels (psychology, physics, linguistics, mathematics, micro-technology, etc.). Brains connected through consciousness expansion begin to work as not only global mind, having effective insights and patterning, but as Mind-2 that includes hyperawareness and advanced "time flow" information data.

Conclusions

A major shift has taken place since the 1990's among cognitive studies and the philosophy of science. A new information paradigm is now at hand, where the recent experimental validation of not only general relativity, but also quantum physics is starting, in terms of theory, to unify. Quantum teleportation (Bouwmeester, *et. al.*, 1998) is a striking affirmation of the holistic nature of our physical reality. We are connecting with a wholly quantum world operating over all macroscopic general relativity in geometric scales (not merely the microscopic). In this context, Remote Viewing expresses a modern form of the quantum gravity principle, which has been historically used to construct quantum mechanical models to include their classical general relativity counterparts. We are adapting it to, ultimately, being aware of omni-consciousness of what has traditionally been called the Universal Mind.

The loss of scientific and spiritual dialogue by neglecting the extended powers of the mind is a heavy price to pay, if we ignore it, especially as we transition into the future. In addition, there are many ways, both in the East and in the West, by which consciousness expansion is being experienced, through meditation of various methods, synergy of various disciplines, scientific work in parapsychology and paraphysics, life styles of numerous cultures, as well as innumerable systems of applying psi in individual interventions and post-intervention procedures and successes.

Consciousness development is a key part of a convergent network for the increasing of intelligence on planet Earth. As an increase of information is obtained, a new reality emerges that is the inclusion of information from consciousness, sub-consciousness and global consciousness pathways. Let us help future generations triumph and expand their abilities through the science of consciousness. May we be able to see nature not as the old nature — *sub-species aeternitatis* — but as supernature, recognizing Creation by pure thought and as the Divine spark within us. As creation expands through us, this pure thought cascades and models itself in the meta-redesign of the universe. In effect, re-creation by pure thought ultimately comes into reach, here and now, through humanity.

In the end, our primary objective should be the advancement of all life and education in the full awakening of human consciousness. This leads to a complete evolution of humanity into the wholeness of being, with the awareness of a greater potential of the human Mind. It is here that we rediscover the Path of the Eternal Being existing as "Consciousness Being," in between physical Being and Becoming.

References

Bell, J.S. (1964) "On the Einstein Podolsky Rosen paradox," *Physics* 1, p. 195.

Bouwmeester, D. *et.al.* (1998) Experimental Quantum Teleportation, *Nature*, 390, pp. 575-579.

Gödel, K. (1931) "Ueber formal unentscheidbare." *Monatshafte fuer Mathematif und Physik*, p. 38.

Grifoni, M. and P. Hänggi (1996) "Coherent and Incoherent Quantum stochastic resonance." *Physical Review Letters*, 76, pp. 1611-1614.

Hameroff, S.R. and R. Penrose (1996) Conscious events as orchestrated space-time selections. *Journal of Consciousness Studies* 3(1): 36-53. Orchestrated reduction of quantum coherence in brain microtubules: A model for consciousness. In *Toward a Science of Consciousness*. Hameroff, S.R., Kaszniak, A. and Scott, A.C. (Eds.), Cambridge, MA: MIT Press, pp. 507-540.

Hurtak, J.J. (1973) *The Book of Knowledge: The Keys of Enoch®,* Los Gatos, CA: Academy for Future Science.

Hurtak, J.J. and A. Puharich (1976) Non-local Experiments. A JPL presentation, Pasadena California (private).

Kaku, M. (1994) *Hyperspace: A Scientific Odyssey Through Parallel Universes, Time Warp, and the Tenth Dimension,* Oxford: Oxford University Press.

Kaiser, D. (2011) *How a Group of Hippies changed Physics: Science, Counterculture and the Quantum Revival,* New York: W.W. Norton & Co.

Pribram, K.H. (1999) "Quantum holography: Is it relevant to brain function?" *Information Sciences,* 115(1-4), pp. 97–102.

Puharich, A. (1976) "Conference on Higher Intelligence" Masonic Auditorium, Lecture with Dr. J.J. Hurtak, Oakland, California.

Rauscher, E.A. (1979, 1995) *The Iceland Papers: Frontiers of Physics,* Coeditor and contributor, foreword by B.D. Josephson and E.A Rauscher, Editor A. Puharich, Essentia Research Associates, Amherst, WI and PACE, Ottawa, Canada.

Rauscher, E.A., J.J. Hurtak and D.H. Hurtak (2013) "The Role of Consciousness in Modern Physics" Ed. Deepak Chopra *Brain, Mind, Cosmos: The Nature of Our Existence and the Universe*, Sages and Scientists, 1, Chapt. 24.

Salart, D., Baas, A., , J. A. W. van Houwelingen, N. Gisin and H. Zbinden (2008)"Spacelike Separation in a Bell Test Assuming Gravitationally Induced Collapses." *Physical Review Letters,* 100, 220404.

Schlitz, M., *et.al.* (2000) "Distant Healing Intention: Definitions and Evolving Guidelines for Laboratory Studies," *Alternative Therapies,* Vol. 9, No. 3 (May-June), pp. A31-A42.

Targ, R. and J. Hurtak (2006) *The End of Suffering, Fearless Living in Troubled Times.* Charlottesville, VA: Hampton Roads.

Chapter 11:

Experimental Programs in Paraphysical Communication and Remote Viewing with Dr. A. Puharich at Lab Nine, Ossining, New York 1974-1975

by

J.J. Hurtak, Ph.D., Ph.D. and

Desiree Hurtak, Ph.D.

"A person starts to live when he can live outside himself."

— Albert Einstein

Table of Contents

Introduction 559

1. The Timing of the Experiment 561

2. The Faraday Cage 565

3. The Pre-selection Period 568

4. The Remote Viewing Participants/Experimenters 571

5. Protocols: The Basic Experimental Format

   A. The Structure 572
   B. Hours of Operation 573
   C. The Protocols 573

6. Visualization Techniques 576

7. Target Venues 578

8. Examples of what we saw 579

9. Reviewing our Experiences 582

10. Results 583

Conclusions 585

References 588

List of Figures:

Figure 1. Distant Viewing: Faraday Cage Research 566

Introduction

The experimental programs of Remote Viewing (RV) in the early-1970s mainly functioned as government research in the USA, Israel and Russia (Kaznacheev and Trofimov, 2008). However, other privately funded RV studies were underway. This report is regarding one of the studies which concerns a mind-to-mind communications study utilizing a Faraday Cage and a companion operation's room at Lab Nine in Ossining, New York. Initially, the core team gathered in November 1974 to coordinate the experiment which officially began in February 1975 and ended in April 1975, covering a period of three months.

The authors (Hurtak and Hurtak) were part of this study and the experimental work involved two aspects: 1) A general period of training volunteers to work together with Remote Viewing; and 2) a core team trained in parapsychology which would confirm or deny RV "hits" of targets, human movements at the targets, and details of the distant areas.

The preliminary consideration for the working group was the ability to bring principal personnel and scientists together. This involved personal and travel commitments for a long period of time. The time period was one in which events in several Middle Eastern countries were politically degenerating and a need was felt by those who sought to participate to assist in neutralizing this escalating situation to prevent war, but from a distance.

Therefore, beginning in early February 1975, in an attempt to view and neutralize the specific "build up" of cultural violence and thoughts of war in the Middle East, our goal was to insert thoughts of peace and to support and strengthen all Middle East peace efforts.

The principal research began by setting protocols and identifying subjects. Many of those who participated were professionals and had backgrounds from leading universities or were working in technology industries, including satellite communications.

The results of our experiments during this period were repeatedly confirmed by real events in the days and also years following this experiment which showed that the information acquisition and other work accomplished by the RV were successful. The information received was also verified by scientists and other sources from several major governments around the world.

Since the early 1970s, the receiving of information remote viewed from distant geographical localities even several thousand kilometers apart, without using conventional technical facilities, had been growing in acceptability in the scientific literature (Rauscher, 1982; Puthoff and Targ, 1977; Kaznacheev, 2008; and Targ and Hurtak, 2006). It had also been demonstrated that any person can remote view, if they seriously make the effort (Targ, 2012), although some are still more accurate than others. It had also been proposed that enhancements of remote viewings could be made when subjects were placed in a Faraday Cage (Puharich, 1974). In our research, we worked as teams of outbound and inbound senders and participants to compare data from feedback, after the completion of our experimental runs. During our remote viewing sessions, which will be described, background music was added to induce a visualization soundscape to help focus the mental journey into the targeted areas.

For the remote viewing experiments, we participated in at Lab Nine, New York, during the early months of 1975, we defined our protocol through collaboration with Dr. Andrija Puharich, a medical doctor and leading parapsychologist. I (Dr. Hurtak), a social scientist and linguist, created specific research protocols with Dr. Puharich to demonstrate how we process information, "send and receive" remote data, etc., beyond the normal five sensory channels. These protocols were especially designed for this experimental project.

The experiments were directed by Dr. A. Puharich and Dr. J.J. Hurtak, with Desiree Hurtak joining in. We created a communications network to collectively confirm details of sites and events taking place on a daily basis. We maintained a minimum of twelve participants at all times in Ossining, New York. The larger group transmitted information from Ossining to "remote viewed" weapons sites and other potential areas of conflict. A team of engineers, writers, and sensitives perceived and recorded details of events taking place in the Middle East by building a mental "television screen." Dr. Puharich's house and his neighboring buildings called Lab Nine in Ossining, New York were utilized. This was a large three building complex.

The intention of our practice was to evaluate the accuracy of the remote viewed details which led to the detection of unauthorized military and terrorist activity. This was conducted by participants who were open to psychic ability, with a desire to seek peace in the Middle East.

1. The Timing of the Experiment

The authors had initiated previous work and studies in several countries in the Middle East and were aware of the need to work for conflict resolution and peace. In early 1975, the crisis generated by geopolitical events in the region was escalating. The specific period in early 1975 was a time when Dr. Henry Kissinger's diplomatic strategy was failing.

Specifically, after the end of the 1973 "Yom Kippur" or October war, Kissinger began a series of shuttle diplomacy missions. Technically, the end of the war was never official as it was stopped by a temporary cease fire agreement which shortly thereafter developed into several "disengagement agreements" that later were more fully secured. The first agreement was in January 1974 between Egypt and Israel and some months later in May 1974 between Syria and Israel. In September 1975, Israel and Egypt signed another disengagement treaty, or "Interim Agreement." (*www.fordlibrary museum.gov/library/*)

Between November 1973 and September 1975, Kissinger made eleven Middle East peace negotiation trips. As part of the official disengagement agreements, The United Nations established buffer zones and took over the military outposts in many of the areas of conflict. It was exactly at the end of November 1974, that we began our plans to meet and seek to encourage further peace agreements, accomplishing our most extensive work from February to April 1975.

It is important to note that all the participants were not taking a bias on either side of the political argument, but were simply trying to prevent another war from occurring in the region. Hostilities were still flourishing on both sides and the reports being shared with us by various sources were that anger was building on all sides involving Israel, Egypt, Lebanon, Syria and Jordan.

In fact, in Nov. 13, 1974 Yasser Arafat spoke for the first time to the UN General Assembly (UNGA) on the Palestinian question, by invitation (Oct 14 - GAR 3210; vote: 105-4). The UNGA in Nov. 1974 recognized Palestinians' right to sovereignty (GAR 3236) and granted PLO observer status (GAR 3237; 22 Nov 1974).

It was at this point that tensions were high. This was the setting in which we came together to try to attempt to neutralize the build up to war and to establish peace. Were we successful? We concluded a positive turn of events began to take place on June 2, 1975 when President Ford met Egyptian President Anwar Sadat, in Salzburg, Austria. Although US President Gerald Ford insisted that these talks did not "represent the beginnings of a new American-led negotiation in the Middle East," (Ford, 1975) they were being regarded with intense interest by all parties to the Arab-Israeli conflict. Kissinger's "step-by-step" strategy was moving positively ahead behind the scenes immediately after we stopped our sessions in April 1975. Thus, we collectively concluded that our work was, in part, successful in moving the negotiations forward and diminishing the tensions and terrorist operations, thus, increasing the chances of peace.

The second series of disengagement agreements called officially the "Sinai Interim Agreement" or Sinai II (signed September 4, 1975) was also an important land-for-peace agreement between Israel and Egypt where they created a 20-mile north-south line on the east side of the Suez Canal and the Israeli forces withdrew a few miles to the east. According to the United Nations summary, the agreement provided for the Israeli withdrawal within Sinai to the eastern ends of the Mitla and Gidi Passes. It also created a UN-monitored buffer zone in the evacuated area and changed the previous buffer zone into Egyptian territories. It also provided for the Israeli's withdrawal from the oil fields at Abu Rudeis and Ras Sudar (UN Peacemaker, 1975). Egypt also agreed to open the Suez Canal to Israeli non-military cargo ships and to establish American early-warning stations in the area of the geographic Passes. The agreement was perceived as an important step towards reaching a comprehensive understanding in accordance with UN Security Council Resolution 338. Overall, it also brought about a real strengthening of Egypt, Israeli and US negotiations for peace.

Arafat, late in 1974, was calling for the world community to decide between what he called an "olive branch or a freedom fighter's gun." He declared:

> "The chairman of the PLO and leader of the Palestinian revolution appeals to the General Assembly to accompany the Palestinian people in its struggle to attain its right of self-determination...I have come bearing an olive branch and a freedom fighter's gun. Do not let the olive branch fall from my hand." (Arafat, Nov. 13, 1974)

In all of these speeches and negotiations there was ample information from various sources that activities involving weapons were taking place in Lebanon, Syria, Jordan, Egypt and Israel, with the specific aim of causing massive destruction to industrial capabilities and producing (or harboring) a secret Israeli nuclear storage area. Stuart Holroyd's (1977) book hints at this series of private sessions that we will detail here, as well as the dangers the Western world was facing.

Specifically, it was in the midst of this 1975 shuttle diplomacy, that a remarkable series of tests of mind-over-matter, Remote Viewing, psychokinesis (ability to move objects at a distance) and nonlocal mind-to-abstract or "tele-thought" experiments were carried out. This involved J.J. Hurtak, social scientist and linguist and Andrija Puharich, medical doctor and leading parapsychologist at his own laboratory (Lab Nine) in Ossining, New York along with others such as Desiree Hurtak, Sir John Whitmore, Phyllis Schlemmer, Fred Alan Wolf, Beardsley Graham, Lyle Watson and many more. Their goal was to neutralize any military and terrorist activity aimed at civilian populations through a daily survey by remote viewing activities of geographical locations in the Middle East mainly from North America.

The group divided into two and Dr. Puharich, Schlemmer and Whitmore traveled outbound to several areas in the Middle East, while in New York, Dr. J.J. Hurtak mentally led the group to focus on the region. The nature and thoughts of this experimental program were to send mental language composed of constructed mental pictures from the inbound senders which included both authors and other well-trained or uniquely gifted participants to change events into peaceful occurrences in the Middle East. Each human was to act as a "biotransducer" to "receive and transmit" data streams of information (Puharich, 1974; Hurtak and Hurtak 2007a and Vogel, 1975).

2. The Faraday Cage

Initial plans were discussed at the site of Puharich's Lab Nine house in Ossining, New York. In fact, Dr. Andrija Puharich, M.D. had a large, but personal Faraday Cage in his house. This inner room, or "screen room," rested on rubber cushions to filter and disperse mechanical vibrations. In order to create an environment of physical and electromagnetic isolation, the Faraday Cage (Fig. 1), constructed by Puharich, was according to specifications of his previous work with the US Army. It was both soundproof and contained a significant amount of copper layers to create an electromagnetically shielded room.

A Faraday Cage works like any hollow conductor which is given a charge on the inside. The charge spreads over the outside surface of the conductor in such a manner that no electric fields arrive inside. In Puharich's design, inner and outer copper cages were fitted together: a thin copper metal cage reinforced by another set of copper walls created a three inch thick structure.

Puharich had been a consultant with the US Army in the field of telepathic investigation. He designed and built the Faraday cage for purposes of his own investigations. He believed that remote viewing signals were not connected with electrostatic or mid-range electromagnetic wave propagation, but maintained that the consciousness field in a Faraday Cage was present and that the cage helped to filter electromagnetic "noise" that might disrupt psi abilities. The solid copper shielding and sound-proof nature of the Faraday Cage blocked sound and specifically radio frequencies, protecting those inside from mid-range electromagnetic fields, while allowing ELF (extremely low frequency) waves to enter. That is, the rigorous environment of the Cage eliminates all electrostatic and certain electromagnetic waves which might interfere with RV. The key to the non-interference of mind-to-mind signaling by electromagnetic and magnetic radio fre-

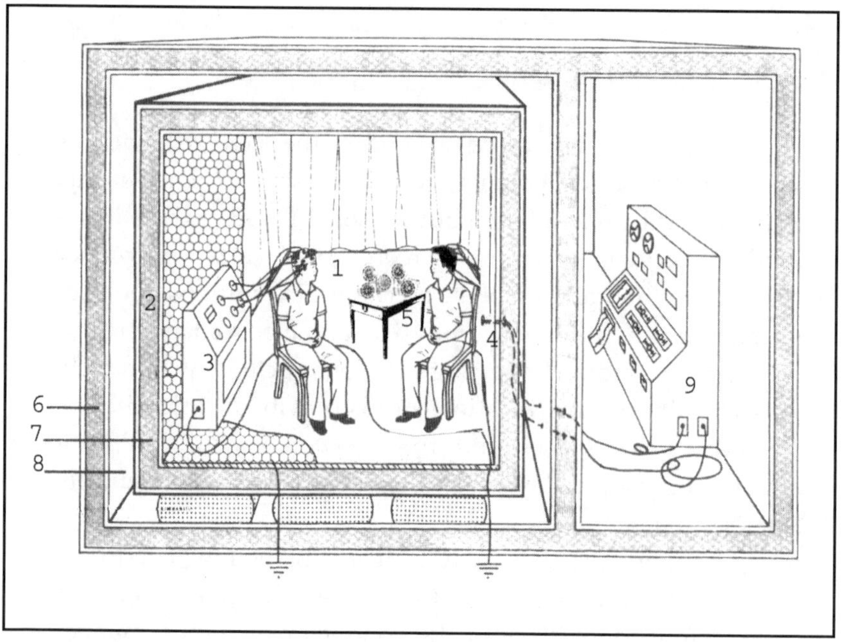

Figure 1 *Distant Viewing: Faraday Cage Research*
FARADAY CAGE MODEL 1. Metal Box 2. Faraday Cage
3. EEG Monitors 4. Transducer 5. Equipment 6. Outside Wall
7. Inside Wall 8. Air Chamber 9. Data Collection
© 2003 J.J. Hurtak (*Future History ~ Spring 2003, p. 12)*

quency fields was the use of the heavy copper-plating throughout the walls. Puharich found that the Faraday Cage enhanced RV communication signals and results showed that human-to-human communication over vast distances could be better established.

According to Puharich, in the Faraday Cage since it allows extremely low frequency waves, voltage can be applied by means of a Van de Graaff generator electrostatic device. From the theory and design, it is hypothesized that psi is enhanced by being inside the cage.

The Ossining Faraday Cage was only used by those who had several years or more of parapsychological research. In the 1970s, Andrija Puharich, M.D. conducted many experiments within his Faraday Cage to investigate methods of how to improve and verify the psi phenomena on the basis of intentionality and the possible significance of viewing at a distance. Puharich's investigations were to experimentally demonstrate that a change in brain wave pattern coherence was correlated to positive psi responses. He tested this by using EEG equipment within the cage (Hurtak, 1995).

Testing of the subject's brain signals with an EEG apparatus in the Ossining Faraday Cage recorded signal frequencies of approximately 8 Hertz power spectrum peaking during transmittal sessions. To generate 8 Hertz waves in the brain one must be almost in a meditative-like state (bordering the alpha and theta states) removed from physical disturbances (Hurtak and Hurtak, 2009). In studying ELF (extremely low frequency), Puharich also believed that rates of 6.6 Hz could cause depression while 7.83 Hertz makes the subject feel good (connected with the so-called Schumann Resonance, the earth's pulse rate).

In synergistic terms, this means that one neuronal field of high coherence (high synergy) power spectrum of low frequency alpha EEG is capable of changing the organization of another neuronal field. This may explain how a human mediator affects the state of mind of other subjects (Hurtak, 2008).

Thus, Puharich designed his experiments with various methodologies to explain the simulation of what could be called *direct communication* between subjects in order to also analyze changes in brain activity.

Puharich performed many experiment in his Faraday Cage. In one, pairs of subjects were allowed to interact together in a Faraday Cage and were then separated with the RV in the Cage and the associate outside. Once separated into the two locations, the outside subject was stimulated with flashes of light and sound until evoked brain potentials were produced. At the same time, the other subject inside the Cage showed a continued mutual "handshake" with the other subject knowing when the flashes were invoked and when they were not, despite being in two different locations.

Puharich believed that remote communication was directly related to the correlation of inter-hemispheric coherence and he made electroencephalograms of his subject's brains at different stages to test his theory. These are just a few of the experiments that Puharich performed at his home in Ossining (Hurtak, 1995).

In the early Ossining tests, people with remote viewing abilities were placed in the Faraday Cage with the intention of transmitting signals to human biological targets, first in New York City (37 miles distant). Later this was expanded to human targets stationed in major cities around the world and especially the Middle East, some 5,700 miles away. In all he sought to create a model showing what occurred in the brain when remote viewing occurred in real time as two subjects entered into direct communication, and their individual inter-hemispheric correlation patterns underwent a modification to become similar to one another in what could be called a *harmonic operating mode* (Puharich and Hurtak, 1976).*

Dr. Puharich performed a variety of experiments in his own Faraday Cage laboratory. The authors participated mainly as observers or monitors in his Faraday experiments. However, we were encouraged by the preliminary paraphysical experiments established by Dr. Puharich within the Faraday Cage (Vogel, 1975; Hurtak and Hurtak, 2008).

3. The Pre-selection Period

As a research scientist, Dr. Puharich made assessments as to how to develop the protocols for many of his ideas. One was to create a team of participants who would mentally try to help ensure peace and not war in the Middle East. Along with Dr. J.J. Hurtak, he developed the following guidelines to establish a three-month experiment at Lab Nine (Feb. to April, 1975). It began when A. Puharich and J.J. Hurtak were enclosed in the

---

* Unfortunately, Puharich's house was destroyed in a fire so his results unless published are no longer available.

Faraday Cage for the preliminary discussions, while the larger group worked on creating an operation's room (Schlemmer, 1993) in the largest room in his house.

Logistically the concept was to create remote, distant communications between a larger group of experimenters in Ossining while a smaller group would be sent to the Middle East. Assembling a group for the purpose of distant communication, first required gathering the right individuals. The project first sought to acquire key individuals from communication experts, former government officials, cultural anthropologists and others who assembled because they understood a "Situation of Peril" was building aimed at disrupting Middle East peace. Indeed, peace in the Middle East was the underlying purpose of these experiments (Holroyd, 1977).

A second consideration was the possibility of amplified thought on objects. Some of the participants (B. Graham, L. Watson, F.A. Wolf and J. Hurtak) knew that Heisenberg's Uncertainty Principle predicts that in the scientific measurement of physical reality, pairs of particles can affect each other. According to Schrödinger, the revolutionary consequence of the discovery was that the act of observing actually sometimes can correlate from one state to another, which brings us to the scientific reality of the observer affecting and creating measurable evidence. In concept, we consider the power of the mind can produce nonlocal effects. Therefore, our work with Dr. Puharich was based upon this theoretical research and its inquiry into the interconnectedness of physical reality as formulated through Bell's Theorem (Bell, 1964).

First and foremost, it was important to choose people who had a desire and enthusiasm for peace and a positive attitude without a negative agenda. It was believed that the experiment would be much more successful when carried out with subjects who were interested in a positive outcome, rather than with people who were experienced, but uninterested in the results. For example, running ESP experiments in a classroom of moderately bored students will rarely show any kind of success, but people keep doing it, none the less. Furthermore, participants who are enthusiastic about the experiment are the most successful in the remote viewing and precognition studies, whether or not they have any experience (Kaznacheev, 2008). Subsequently, individuals were sought out who had not only the ability to remain focused, but also a desire to conduct the experiment. A talent for performing RV work was not required, but some individuals had this talent.

Second, it was also important that those who were selected wanted to remain low-profile. For this reason, the preselection and selection process of the people used both knowledge and integrity.

It was determined by Drs. Puharich and Hurtak that all participants spend one week together to establish a sense of awareness and connection amongst all of the participants. A connection or mental linkage could be established first together and secondly at a ~ 5700 miles / 9175 km distance, between New York and the Middle East, so that information could be coherently transmitted back and forth.

The team was mainly comprised of top-level scientists, as well as managers. Some could not remain for the entire three months, so schedules to come and go with replacement subjects were established for a few. Most subjects were committed for the entire three months. Some additional advanced testings were conducted to coordinate the remote communication by making sure inbound senders (i.e., those in Ossining) were also able to receive their images and record or draw on paper the mental picture or symbolic code they perceived from those who were the outbound participants. In the week prior to the experiment, there were some selected experiments conducted for training the mind to perform actions at a distance. A few examples are as follows: a) Projecting to remote places, evaluating the environment, and returning with expanded mental pictures; b) trials of PK (psychokinesis) of small physical objects, that is, changing an object's position without manual contact; c) drawing or sketching a person or object seen through Remote Viewing. We found when using multiple targets, responsibility requires emotional balance to mentally score with long-distance outbound participants at targets.

Finally, the team was assembled representing individuals who were considered eager, but also confident in using their own innate abilities. They understood that complex bioenergetic effects involved the use of a good laboratory environment, but also felt within themselves the global need to use their RV abilities.

4. The Remote Viewing Participants and Experimenters

Dr. J.J. Hurtak, as director and monitor of the tests in Ossining, was 'second in command' and took care of all of the preparation work, which encompassed directing the sessions, using music, vocalizations and direct guidance during the remote viewing sessions. Some of the participants included: Dr. J.J. Hurtak, Ph.D., and Desiree E. Hurtak, Ph.D. both social scientists and futurists. Also Beardsley Graham, a former SRI manager and a former incorporator of COMSAT, Glenn Olds, Ph.D. former president of Kent State University and a consultant to President John F. Kennedy on the creation of the Peace Corps), Lyle Watson, Ph.D. South African biologist and author of *Romeo Error*, Fred Alan Wolf, Ph.D., a theoretical physicist (also a member of Rauscher's Fundamental "Fysiks" Group) and others. The outbound subject participants operated primarily as "receivers" (but also as "senders") and included: Dr. Andrija Puharich, M.D. specialist in parapsychology and paraphysics; Phyllis Schlemmer, noted American sensitive (Schlemmer, 1993), and Sir John Whitmore, explorer of consciousness development and supporter of the annual May Day Medical Healing Conference in London in the 1970s, and currently well known for his work in corporate coaching.

5. Protocols: The Basic Experimental Format

A. The Structure:

The process we utilized was somewhat reversed from the normal remote viewing process at other laboratories, where the inbound individuals in Ossining were both the remote viewer and the "senders" of the images they mentally saw. After remote viewing the target, they were to resend what they had gathered out to the "outbound" three individuals. The outbound individuals were generally considered as "receivers" of information from the Ossining participants, but they were also senders of information and sometimes were used to confirm the information sent from the larger group of participants.

The experiments included an initial period of telepathic orientation of various target locations during which a communication protocol was established. As in any remote viewing experiment, the senders from Ossining did not know where the three receivers were, so each participant had to find their own perception of the target locations.

As before stated, Dr. J.J. Hurtak was based at Lab Nine as the principal monitor for the "inbound senders", while Puharich was one of three overseas receivers. Hurtak's group was to have a minimum of twelve people that were always situated at Lab Nine in Ossining, but back-up subjects could be used to sit in for the main principals. Hurtak was in charge of keeping the Lab Nine team together for around-the-clock 24/7 operations that ran for three months while Dr. Puharich, Phyllis Schlemmer, and Sir John Whitmore operated as a three-fold team of "receivers" moving around to critical targets in the Middle East. The goal was to prevent any large military exercise from being initiated and, if possible, also smaller terrorist attacks from occurring in the Middle East by the applied use of psi perception.

The groups received phone calls at least three times a week from each other during a twelve week period. During the calls, notes and activities were compared on a formal content-basis of the various target areas viewed. The purpose was to observe and map ground topologies in space and time for the diagnosis of a targeted area. Once an area was selected, it was concentrated on or visualized to observe and neutralize any weapons or hostilities that were felt to be present.

B. Hours of Operation:

When we describe these Lab Nine experiments as "formal studies", we are indicating that they had predetermined starting times and a fixed number of trials per day, although on some occasions, the participants were called to work at any time of the day or night, depending on information needs. Agreement was made between senders and receivers for the time of transmission, with the prearranged times set every three normal working hours (East Coast Time) starting at 9:00 AM, then noon, then 3:00 PM, then 6:00 PM and, finally, 9:00 PM. Each of these sessions was initiated by Dr. J.J. Hurtak. The experiments were started sharply on the hour with an audio recording of the sessions. The tapes were destroyed in a house fire at the Ossining Laboratory in the 1980s, but Dr. Hurtak retained a few recordings for his own archives.)

C. The Protocols:

The Lab Nine participants in both the USA and in the Middle East used pre-determined protocols. The protocols were a set of instructions, of how to process information and a means to analyze the data that they mentally received. They knew these signals were not spatially or temporally dependent, but only dependent on mental intention. The selection processes of the target site and information in order to address all major events were taken into consideration. As before stated, it is important to note that all participants were not to take sides on the political issues. The remote viewer was to seek to neutralize any military build up and/or terrorist events in the areas that were perceived, regardless of who initiated it.

We timed our sessions with Puharich and the other two outbound receivers, as in previous remote viewing experiments. In some cases, specific questions and answers regarding distant targets were considered in the Faraday Cage. No beverage, food or smoking was allowed. The sessions began and ended with vocal affirmations and visualizations.

The inbound team's visualizations were designed to focus mental images to the outbound senders. We, as "inbound senders," used verbal sounds to maintain mental focus as an aid to help remote view specific target points. The program design was to assist the human biotransducer to visualize potentially unstable areas (Mattuck and Walker, 1979).

The experiments specifically followed these basic protocols, some of which we have mentioned before:

1) Participants first remote viewed the target area. Then they focused on their own mental images to send long distance mind-to-mind and mind-to-target contact to the outbound team or to target areas at certain times of the day. Generally, the group collectively shared notes at the end of the session and put together the images they remote viewed from the session. They collectively then could resend the images in the next session to balance or neutralize the specific remote viewed area through visualizations. Thus, our signals went to not only the three individuals in the Middle East, but also to any region the mind remote viewed and considered as an area of potential weapons "build up."

2) The guidance leader or monitor of the group, Dr. J.J. Hurtak, located at Lab Nine in Ossining, NY, assisted the individuals in the group to record their data. In our experiment, the three other individuals in the outbound region, (or outbound 'receivers/transmitters') were receiving and confirming images, in their targeted time zones.

3) The guidance leader (Hurtak) further provided both the visualization of the place(s), as well as sacred tones usually utilizing music and spoken words, generally, in Hebrew-Aramaic-Egyptian, sometimes in a chant form for the kindling of energy. The verbal visualization and the voice signals were to trigger the minds of the participants into higher states of consciousness for longer periods of concentration and to help in the sending of energy signals.

4) The work of all participants began on a designated hour and continued for one hour. Sometimes additional times were added according to instructions previously mapped from coordinates.

5) Mica crystals were gathered from the hill behind Puharich's Lab Nine property. The area was the site of the first musical transmission over wireless telephone by Robert Gowen of the De Forest Radio Telephone and Telegraph Company in the early 20th century. Each participant was instructed by Puharich to find a mica piece from behind the house to leave at the place where they sat during the sessions.

6) Two rooms were used for communication: the special Faraday Cage (2 x 3 meters) and the central group living room (6 x 5 meters). First for coordination while in New York, Puharich, Schlemmer and Whitmore and J.J. Hurtak used the Faraday Cage. Once the project was underway and Puharich, Schlemmer, and Whitmore went outbound, the large living room (6 x 5 meters) was used by a minimum of twelve participants and their back-ups for round-the-clock periods which extended to 90 days.

7) Telephones were generally turned off (except on a few occasions) and removed from the main room at Lab Nine, although a tape recorder was allowed.

8) One person (with backup) was selected to keep a record (written protocol and audio cassette) of each of the sessions which sometimes included discussion of the mental pictures and guided visualizations (Rauscher, Hurtak and Hurtak, 2011).

9) The three principal outbound senders and 'receivers' (Puharich, Schlemmer and Whitmore) were to tap into the non-verbal communication signals and remote-viewing pictures being sent to them, generally of both positive targets, as well as critical or dangerous situations. Unless otherwise deemed necessary, a phone call was exchanged three times a week which provided additional information and coordinates.

During the experiment, verbal recordings of events or target descriptions made on a small tape recorder at the time of the RV event, were checked with the outbound team during the phone conversations.

The matching of the distant targets by the observers was made by comparing hand drawings or notes after the remote viewing sessions were completed. Notebook sketches made on a specific day were later compared to the outbound team's notes and sketches upon their return from the Middle East. Puharich told Hurtak in private conversations, that in his own calculations [not provided] there was a 72% overall success rate in the received information both in form and content.

6. Visualization Techniques

To detail the protocol, in addition to times of silence, Dr. J.J. Hurtak would occasionally insert certain ancient sacred words to resonate with the local area. The sounds were said out loud by the group which generated a whole series of lower overtones or sub-harmonics which created a type of tone of mathematical ratios which varied in wavelength and frequency. It was thought that there is a natural musical modality connected with different states of consciousness that actually leads to paranormal experiences or higher states of consciousness.

The techniques come out of Dr. Hurtak's earlier work inspired by the legendary Nam June Paik and noted composer and music synthesizer inventor Morton Subotnik. The "Buchla music synthesizer" used in training sessions and bio-feedback sessions showed that there can be cognitive enhancements and creative levels of bio-feedback stimulated by certain types of music entrainment which lead to creative consciousness and higher states of awareness. For example, Sitar musician, Ravi Shankar, claimed to be "sitting outside his body" during his concerts (Shankar, 1970).

Music also allowed the group to continue their focus during the long sitting, remote viewing sessions. So along with periods of silence and guided visualizations of target sites from earlier sessions or discussions, music was also used to enhance the participants' focus. All Remote Viewers were encouraged to concentrate on peace and the neutralization of tensions.

The visualizations helped to maintain a positive feeling of being in close human relations although some were thousands of kilometers apart. The voice-tones and music used in the sessions were thought to increase brain wave coherence. In ancient meditation traditions, one tunes into the internal OM vibration which is called listening to the internal sound current (*nadam*), which is clairaudiently registered directly by the brain and the subtle bodies (with variations such as *Shalom*). This mental practice is based on the principles of using the fundamental carrier frequencies which are then applied to consciousness expansion.

In summary, the RV team in Ossining used a methodology that was aided by the concentrated use of collective vocals and background music which helped sustain concentration. As the sessions were long and several times a day, this kept concentration high. The technique would not be needed for a short experiment with a single location target. It was understood that the goal of most RV experiments is to use silence or to ask the remote viewer questions during a single laboratory session.

7. Target Venues

During the visualization or remote viewing sessions, Dr. J.J. Hurtak guided the participants to send mental images not only to the outbound receivers but also:

1) To look at human targets and movements of militants poised for combat in the Middle East so as to detect unusual movements of personnel from one country to another, particularly concerning the dangerous borders of Israel, Egypt, Lebanon, Jordan and Syria.

2) To look at technologies being assembled to see if there were any supported by military operations. To look at unusual movements of high and low profile persons around alleged facilities of high technology or energy.

3) To look for various movements of troops anywhere in the vicinity of the Middle East. To see if any boat or craft was ferrying unusual personnel or unusual arms. To detect an armament strike or series of operations that was considered dangerous and could result in larger acts of destruction.

4) To focus on the three outbound receivers and help them to accomplish their tasks by focusing and remote viewing their present locations, which often were completely unknown.

The methodology was based on Dr. Puharich and Dr. Hurtak's understanding that a body of dedicated and focused sensitives could describe any distant location through remote viewing, given only its coordinates. Then mental PK (psychokinesis, that is moving of objects by the power of mind) could be used to create changes in the remote area (Rauscher,

1982). In each case they were to report what they saw to the group.

In most cases, especially where more than a single participant agreed on their perception, that target area was singled out for several sessions to focus on that site for the "neutralization" of hostilities. The remote viewers would visualize images of, for example, ways to neutralize bombs, send images into the minds of those there to create peaceful changes in whatever scenario they saw. In special cases, it was shared with the three outbound receivers who could often move into the area for confirmation.

After about one month of positive hits on target areas, we were intrigued by what we were experiencing, and so we asked others who were living in other parts of the world including Canada and Europe to join and coordinate with us remotely. Additionally, friends who were familiar with the territory and events in the Middle East were called in to provide geographical coordinates of something interesting which became the remote viewing targets that our Middle East team could then further investigate (Holroyd, 1977).

8. Examples of what we saw

These are some confirmations we had of our RV sessions:

1) When we began to focus our attention on other surrounding missile sites in southern Lebanon, we (Drs. Hurtak) remember the words of Dr. Glenn Olds (inbound sender) viewing Russian activity on the southern Lebanese front: "There's a lot of activity. They're trying to make a big splash with these missiles on cities in northern Israel. It looks like this area will be a tough area for years to come, but for the Russians it is not going well, because of the lack of proper technicians on the ground."

We were unaware that some of these missiles would be used for an ensuing civil war that was building in Lebanon. Dr.

Puharich was able to state, upon his return to the United States: "We were happy to receive this confirmation through remote viewing of Soviet military operation in Lebanon." There was, thus, a strong confirmation between the two groups of what was being viewed in Lebanon.

2) Because of at least two confirmations regarding Lebanon, we performed another special viewing. We sat with Beardsley Graham, an electrical engineer who had consulted with President John F. Kennedy and many of the luminaries in the American space program. He went into Andrija's copper-screened, electrically shielded Faraday Cage and we asked him to pick up on his "mental television" screen details of a Soviet Sam missile on its launching pad in southern Lebanon. As he psychically projected his mind to the missile site, he said, "I see the truck that carried the missiles." Beardsley was able to view and scan southern Lebanon for the target. Beardsley was attentive to the details by using remote viewing of the side of the missile and the tubing within it. Using remote viewing and psychokinesis he sought to neutralize the missile. A few hours later, he added, "the missile is now neutralized on its launching pad." He mentally short circuited the wires with his mind so that the missile would not operate and would be aborted.

We felt this was successful as several weeks later after days of remote viewing we heard from one of our correspondents in Lebanon that a missile in the perceived location had blown up on its launching pad. Whether this was coincidental or the result of paraphysical interaction cannot be established.

3) On another occasion, our group using remote viewing techniques saw people planning to blow up the Great Pyramid with some type of dynamite explosives hidden in their backpacks and mentally warned the officials in Egypt near Giza who intervened to stop the crime against the Seventh Wonder of the ancient world. This was later confirmed by governmental intelligence sources and news agencies.

4) Another striking result came in the form of the remote viewers in Ossining seeing various agreements being signed, literally, the signing of documents between high officials. This was not confirmed completely at the time, but later it was shown that these were the dates when Kissinger began diplomatic talks with President Assad of Syria and King Hussein of Jordan. Jordan and Syria strengthened their own alliances with certain agreements and shortly thereafter (April 30 – May 1st) Kissinger began talks with Egypt which later resulted in Sinai II.

5) A small event occurred during one of the RV sessions, when someone inadvertently left the telephone in the room, although it was normally off or out of the room. There were no plans to talk to the three outbound receivers. However, during the visualization when Dr. Hurtak was directly guiding the group, he stated the words, "We now see Andrija, Phyllis, and John." Immediately, the phone rang and it was them. This was a confirmation for all of us that we were mentally in "synchronization."

Although it is difficult to confirm each of these events some 40 years later, it is sufficient to note that only one terrorist attack took place during the time of our visualization and that was an attack by terrorists who landed from Lebanon on the beaches of one of the hotels in Tel Aviv called the Savoy Hotel (4-5 March, 1975). It became a hostage situation where in the end, two soldiers, eight civilians (five were freed), and seven terrorists were killed (one captured). Later that year there were two more terrorist attacks in Jerusalem and one near the Lebanese border.

The other exception was on April 13, 1975, when Christian and Muslim sects started a civil war in Lebanon that lasted 16 years. As an addition, the Lebanese civil war (1975-1990) although a tragedy, did take pressure off the possibility of an international conflict. The next trans-border conflict was in June 1976 when Syria became involved in Lebanon. We did feel that more tragic events could have taken place had we not been involved, and that many more terrorist activities would have taken place during this stressful time. Our main focus was to stop large military exercises that would lead to large scale military attacks between countries, which did not take place during that time.

In the end, the Arab-Israeli Dispute which Henry Kissinger had focused on solving between 1974–1975, was at least temporarily solved with the final signing of the September 1975 Sinai II agreement. This did bring a sense of stability to all local countries surrounding Israel with the exception of Lebanon that was experiencing its own civil war.

9. Reviewing our Experiences

During a very short period, a highly reliable non-local biofeedback network was created amongst the subjects operating from North America to targets in the Middle East and from the Middle East to North America. Our purpose in working for peace was not to only visualize, but also to neutralize any cross -border or terrorist violence that was escalating in the Middle East. The purpose was to remote view and access the target and neutralize the negative thoughts, intentions and if possible the technology. The project was an independently funded project with mainly scientists and university associates who volunteered their time in this historic project.

Some of the subjects reported that they experienced physical sensations (e.g., smell, sounds, etc.) of being in the Middle East; others stated that they had tapped into images and thoughts of the local people at the target site or near the RV locations. With psycho-linguistic preparation and meditation, the human subjects operated more as human biotransducers than passive individuals.

The results supported the concept of direct interactions between human awareness in unique environments. We are suggesting that a larger Mind-2 (see Chapter 10) or Rauscher's Eight-Space (Rauscher and Targ, 2006) was nonlocally experienced whereby both the senders and receivers could meld into a common state of synergistic awareness (Hurtak, 1973, 1975).

10. Results

All participants felt we had achieved positive results from our work. Newspaper reports appear to confirm our results and the very fact that no cross-border war ensued during this time period seems to confirm that something was accomplished. The most significant effect may be that the Sinai II or "Sinai Interim Agreement," signed on September 4, 1975 in Geneva. The agreement stated that the conflicts between the countries "shall not be resolved by military force but by peaceful means" (United Nations Peacemaker, 1975). This was exactly what we were encouraging to take place. Of course negotiations leading up to this agreement were emerging during the time that we did our remote viewing work. Also direct meetings between Sadat and Ford, and shortly thereafter, Rabin and Ford were arranged later in 1975 and although it took another US presidency to sign the famous 1979 accord between Egypt and Israel, historians would have to admit that it went back to the early meetings in 1974-1976 when peace negotiations and meetings were taking place.

If we follow the United Nations Security Council Resolutions we see the turning of events beginning with Resolution 368 (April 17, 1975) which called on the parties involved in the prevailing state of tension in the Middle East to immediately implement Resolution 338 (the cease-fire resolution which had been initiated October 22, 1973). This was followed by a similar resolution, Resolution 369 (May 28, 1975), which expressed concern over the prevailing state of tension in the Middle East. Finally, in Resolution 381 on the 30th of November 1975, the

United Nations asked to extend the mandate of the United Nations Disengagement Observer Force, which was a big step towards maintaining ongoing peace. Also, Resolution 381 stated that the UN would reconvene on January 12, 1976, to continue the debate on the Middle East problem including the Palestinian question. The Council, consequently, decided to invite the PLO to participate at the meeting on January 12, 1976; the Council decided, by eleven votes in favor to one against, with 3 abstentions.

Additionally, on November 10, 1975, there was the General Assembly United Nations Resolution 3379 that stated the need to end racism and the discrimination against the Palestinian peoples, as well as other peoples around the world. The UN Security Council considered peace and security in the Middle East, including the Palestinian question under these agenda items, in several meetings during the next years.

When the representative Yasser Arafat of the PLO first spoke to the United Nations (November 13, 1974), he stated that the willingness of the Security Council specifically to consider the Palestinian question was a welcome sign for the Palestinian people who sought a widespread understanding of their predicament. He submitted that had there not been a question of Palestine there would not have been what was mistakenly termed "the Middle East crisis." The representative of the PLO stressed that the Palestinian people wanted peace for themselves and for the Jews and appealed to the Security Council to bring about forceful measures that would promote the hopes of the Palestinian people for peace with justice for the whole Middle East (Arafat, 1975).

Arafat's 1974 United Nations appearance was the initiation of this process and emphasized its importance for the world community. But still it took another year before the United States and other powerful nations were willing to recognize the existence of the Palestinian people. Specifically, on November 12, 1975, Deputy Assistant Secretary of State for the Near East and South Asian Affairs, Harold H. Saunders, testified before the House Foreign Affairs Subcommittee on the Middle East and stated that the Palestinians collectively are a political factor (Rabinovich, 2001).

Regardless of the reader's political viewpoint, 1975 became an important turning point for peace because negotiations were opened to both sides of the issue and no war ensued after the 1973 Yom Kippur war and these agreements and all of these efforts led to the 1979 Peace Treaty between Egypt and Israel. Excepts for attacks from Syria and Israel on Lebanese soil during their civil war, real violence directed at Israel did not ensue again until the 1987 Intifada some twelve years later.

Conclusions

The special experiments of Lab Nine on the East Coast, carried out between 1974-75, and specifically from February to April 1975, explored the nature and power of consciousness. The experiments were privately funded, mainly by Sir John Whitmore from the United Kingdom, and involved volunteers who gave freely of their time out of a concern for seeking positive solutions to problems in the Middle East. There were also other privately funded university projects that supported the effort at a distance.

Previous laboratory research in this field suggests that remote viewing effects, which could be expanded to remote healing, warrant serious study, but most scientists and funding agencies are unaware of the evidence in the relevant literature (Rauscher, Hurtak and Hurtak, 2011). By following the work of Lab Nine and other projects on remote viewing, a greater work for peace can be accomplished.

Our work with The Academy For Future Science has continued to focus on ways to maintain a peaceful focus in the world and especially in areas of contention. This is critically

Phyllis Schlemmer Carmel, Andrija Puharich, and
J.J. Hurtak at Megiddo, Israel
Photo: Desiree Hurtak, 1983.

important for alternative paraphysical research, in general, and for distant communication tools, in particular (Kupperschmidt, 2012). It is apparent that the phenomenon of remote viewing means there are no more secrets and one should tell the truth. It can no longer be seen as simply a local process, but rather as our inherent nonlocal ability to expand our mind into a greater knowledge of spacetime and matter-energy.

Human intelligence exists in several continuums, some can transcend space and time. It may appear that human consciousness processes represent a true view of the universe where balance and order appears out of chaos through mind-setting processes. Hence, it follows that humanity on Earth and humanity as a whole are not an entirely isolated phenomena, but a very complicated combination of various integrated properties of intelligence that can be awakened by new forms of consciousness scripting. Perhaps this is the reason Dr. Puharich later became involved with the well-known script writer and producer, Gene Rodenberry (Hurtak and Hurtak, 1978) who was also influenced by the work at Lab Nine and began to see the cosmic frontier and the ultimate quest to push the envelop of research for future inhabitants in space.

We believe the human mind penetrated distant fields, while on another level, human intelligence projected enormous peaceful and humanitarian understanding to change what could have been disastrous circumstances. The ultimate goal is not only peace, but to show that every person has the ability to stimulate their inherent ability. From some forty years of research by Puharich, Drs. Hurtak and Rauscher, it is clear that the human body is a biotransducer with distant viewing capabilities.

We are living at a time when the concepts of information transfer and ordering, entropy and centropy, are being seen as reflecting the interconnection between cosmophysical and biological processes. It is also here that we should concentrate on using these innate skills for practical, preventive, and peaceful solutions in order to avoid conflict and increase longevity of humans on planet Earth.

Based on the fundamental conclusions of our RV, paraphysical tests of mind over distance, we infer that the structure of life is open to vast changes and what we do here is of critical significance. We have a set of diminishing natural resources and we have ways of using advanced technology to help or to hurt. We ask everyone to use a positive psychology confirmed by research scientists to create a "future science," or science guided by consciousness that can help re-balance planetary and personal issues of life. This basic proposition requires further development and respective studies that are crucially important for the planet's future! We conclude that humanity is discovering that we can play an intricate role through the background Plenum of the universe and tapping into it brings us into a state of consciousness and personal/planetary transformation. We invite you to try it!

References

Arafat, Y. (1975) "Palestine at the United Nations," *Journal of Palestine Studies*, Winter 1975, pp. 181-92.

Bell, J.S. (1964) "On the Einstein Podolsky Rosen paradox," *Physics* 1, p. 195.

Ford, G. (1975) 243 - The President's News Conference May 6, 1975. *www.presidency.ucsb.edu/ws/?pid=4898*

Holroyd, S. (1977) *Prelude to the Landing on Planet Earth*, London: W.H. Allen Publishers. (Paperback title: *Briefing to the Landing on Planet Earth*) by Stuart (1977) Some of the procedures and findings that follow were described and offer a popular description of our early remote viewing and remote communication research.

Hurtak, J.J. (1973) *The Book of Knowledge: The Keys of Enoch*. Los Gatos: Academy for Future Science.

Hurtak, J.J. (1975) "The Mind as Microcosm," in S. Krippner and

D. Rubin, *Energies of Consciousness*, New York: Gordon and Breech.

Hurtak, J.J. (1995) "Andrija Puharich: A Legacy to the Plan of Cosmic Birthrights," *Future History*, Series l, vol. 8, pp. 10-14.

Hurtak, J.J. (2004) "Introduction to Contemporary Russian Biophysical and Bioparaphysical Studies," in *Reflections on Life and Intelligence on Planet Earth* by V. Kaznacheev and A. Tromifov, Wasserburg, Bodensee, Germany: Academy for Future Science, Europe.

Hurtak, J.J. (2008) "Bioluminescence: the Inner Light" *Future History* (English edition), Series 5, Vol. 9, pp. 2-6.

Hurtak, J.J. and Desiree Hurtak (1978) Personal conversations with A. Puharich, Tepotzlan, Mexico.

Hurtak, J.J. and Desiree Hurtak (2007a) "Consciousness, Coherence and Quantum Entanglement," *Future History,* 5, Vol.5, pp. 7-10.

Hurtak, J.J. and Desiree Hurtak, (2007b) "Climate Change and Consciousness Change," *Future History,* Series 5, Vol. 6, pp.7-10.

Hurtak, J.J. and Desiree Hurtak (2008) "Expanding the Body Electric," *Future History,* Series 5, vol. 7, pp. 11-14.

Hurtak, J.J. and Desiree Hurtak (2009) "Understanding the Consciousness Field," *Future History* Series 6, Vol. 1, pp. 9-14.

Hurtak, J.J. and Desiree Hurtak (2012) Conversation with Phyllis Schlemmer, Flagler Beach, Fl. Unpublished mss. Los Gatos, CA: The Academy for Future Science.

Hurtak, J.J. and Desiree Hurtak (2013) "Consciousness Awareness and The Near Death Experience," *Future History,* Series 7, Vol. 2, pp.7-10.

Kaznacheev, V.P. and A. Tromifov (2008) *Reflections on Life and Intelligence on Planet Earth,* J.J. Hurtak (General Editor), Wasserburg, Germany: The Academy for Future Science, Europe.

Kupperschmidt, K. (2012) "Concentrating on Kindness", *Science* Vol. 341, pp. 1336-1939.

Mattuck, R.D. and E.H. Walker (1979)"The Action of Consciousness on Matter–a Quantum Mechanical Theory of Psychokinesis". *The Iceland Papers*. Amherst, WI.: Essentia, pp. 131-139.

Puharich, A. and J.J. Hurtak (1976) *Conference on Higher Intelligence*. Berkeley, 4 CDs., Los Gatos, CA. Academy for Future Science.

Puharich, A. (1974) Private conversations between the authors and Dr. A. Puharich, Ossining, NY

Rabinovich, I. (2001) "The Palestinian Issue: Changing Israeli Perspectives" in *Global Politics: Essays in Honor of David Vital*, eds. David Vital, Abraham Ben-Zvi, Aaron S. Klieman London: Frank Cass, p. 127.

Rauscher, E.A. (1982) "Conceptual Changes in Reality Models from New Discoveries in Physics," PSRL-1976. Also in *Bulletin Amer. Phys., Soc.*, 35, 1982.

Rauscher, E.A. and R. Targ (2006) *Investigation of a Complex Space-Time Metric to Describe the Precognition of the Future.* Apache Junction, AZ: Tecnic Research Lab.

Rauscher, E.A., J.J. Hurtak and Desiree Hurtak (2011) Personal correspondence. Rauscher was a neighbor of Puharich in North Carolina.

Schlemmer, P. (1993) *Only Planet of Choice*, London: Turnstone.

Shankar, R. (1970) Personal conversations with Dr. J.J. Hurtak, School of Music, at California Institute of the Arts, Burbank, CA.

Sinatra, S. (2010) *The Sinatra Solution: Metabolic Cardiology*. Amazon.

Targ, R. and H. Puthoff (1977) *Mind-Reach*. New York: Delacorte.

Targ, R. and J.J. Hurtak (2006) *The End of Suffering*, Hampton Roads: Charlottesville: VA.

Targ, R. (2007) Personal discussions with J.J. Hurtak and Desiree Hurtak, Palo Alto, CA.

Targ, R. (2012) *The Reality of ESP. A Physicist's Proof of Psychic Abilities*. Wheaton, Il.: Quest Books.

United Nations Peacemaker (1975) "Interim Agreement between Israel and Egypt, 4 September 1975, *http://peacemaker.un.org/egyptisrael-interimagreement75.*

Vogel, M. (1975) Personal conversations with J.J. Hurtak at IBM, San Jose, California.

Chapter 12
Remote Viewing Experiments Between Dr. Elizabeth Rauscher and Drs. J.J. and Desiree Hurtak,
by
J.J. Hurtak, Ph.D., Ph.D. and Desiree Hurtak, Ph.D.

"Quantum physics thus reveals a basic oneness of the universe. "

— Erwin Schrödinger

Table of Contents

Introduction 595
1. Remote Viewing Region #1. Cairo, EGYPT 596
Results of Egyptian RV tests 614
Conclusion 616
2. Remote Viewing Region #2. Bimini, BAHAMAS 617
Experimental Design 626
Results 627
Conclusion 629
3. Remote Viewing Region #3. ISRAEL-GOLAN 630
Experiments: A Brief Travelogue 632
Results 648
Conclusion 650
References 651

List of Tables

Table 1: Remote Viewing Experiment in Egypt 599
Table 2: RV tests in the Bahamas off the coast of Florida 619
Table 3: Hurtak-Rauscher RV Test in the Near East 635

List of Targets/Figures

Egypt Target 1 — Photo: Hawara 600
Egypt Target 1 — RV Drawing 601
Egypt Target 2 — Photo: A University in Cairo 602
Egypt Target 2 — RV Drawing 603
Egypt Target 3a — Photo: University Complex 604
Egypt Target 3b — RV Drawing 605
Egypt Target 3c — RV Drawing 605
Egypt Target 3d — Photo: University Complex 606
Egypt Target 3e — Photo: University Complex 606
Egypt Target 4a — Photo: Giza Plateau 607
Egypt Target 4b — Photo: Giza Plateau 608
Egypt Target 4c — RV Drawing 609
Egypt Target 5 — Photo: Giza 610
Egypt Target 5 — RV Drawing 611
Egypt Target 6a — Photo: Giza Plateau....................612
Egypt Target 6b —Photo: Giza Plateau 612
Egypt Target 6 — RV Drawing 613

Bimini Target 1-2 — Photo: Waters off Bimini 621
Bimini Target 1-3 — RV Drawing 622
Bimini Target 3 — Photo: Boat Anchor....................623
Bimini Target 4 — Photo: View of rocks from Boat 624
Bimini Target 4 — RV Drawing 625

Israel Target 1 — Photo: Mt Herman, Golan 636
Israel Target 1 — RV Drawing 637
Israel Target 2 — Photo: Tiberius 638
Israel Target 2 — RV Drawing 639
Israel Target 3a & 3b — Photo: Rujum al-Hiri 640
Israel Target 3 — RV Drawing 641
Israel Target 4 — Photo: The Dan Hotel Lobby 642
Israel Target 4 — RV Drawing 643
Israel Target 5 — Notre Dame Hotel Restaurant 644
Israel Target 5 — RV Drawing 645
Israel Target 6a & 6b — Photo: Temple Tunnel 646
Israel Target 6 — RV Drawing 647

I. Background Details of Remote Viewing Experiments with Elizabeth Rauscher (2012-2013)

Introduction

The following pages reflect Remote Viewing work we experimented with in three different locations around the world with Elizabeth Rauscher from 2012-2013. The Remote Viewing included the gathering and recording of information about terrain and ocean subsurfaces without predetermined knowledge of the object or area being investigated.

We felt that since the experiments in the past were so definitive that we would also show some that were contemporary. Therefore, we followed the same protocols as used in earlier experiments with SRI, Fundamental "Fysiks" Group (F"F"G) and Lab Nine. Although it was not our intention to make this a "scientific" experiment, we, (Drs. J.J. and Desiree Hurtak) were the outbound senders and Dr. Elizabeth Rauscher was the inbound receiver. We did not tell Rauscher specifics of what we were doing nor the city, only the country, we were traveling to. We gave only a time period, generally her morning and no specific date. We did not use phones or any written or electronic input for immediate verification. Finally, we compared drawings and matched photographs of where we traveled directly with Elizabeth only later when we returned to the USA. It should be further noted that Rauscher never had personally visited any of the three locations we were visiting in our experiments.

The testing started in Egypt and then eight months later, on the other side of the Atlantic Ocean, a small group of islands in the Bahamas and finally the Golan-Israel region. One can argue that the international experiments should have been conducted at fairly regular intervals, and not at widely spaced intervals, because the viewer(s) get(s) out of practice. One could also argue that the countries we were visiting should not have been revealed to prevent any analytical overlay. Again this chapter is not for scientists trying to scrutinize how the experiment was done as it was not based on stringent laboratory conditions as those described in Chapter 3 and Chapter 4 were. Nevertheless, the knowledge base that was acquired through the international team continued to show the paraphysical ability of Remote Viewing. The experiments were created also to show that people, themselves, could try this amongst friends around the world. Using RV amongst friends allows us to begin to expand our ability to use the powers of mind over matter.

Remote Viewing Region #1
Hurtak, Hurtak and Rauscher RV tests in the area of Cairo Egypt – March 2012

THE EGYPT EXPEDITION USING RV WITH
DR. RAUSCHER AND DRS. HURTAK
IN PROBING THE COUNTRY OF EGYPT AND OTHER
DETAILS OF POSSIBLE TRACES OF
EARLIER CIVILIZATION.

Before traveling to Egypt, we contacted our colleague, Dr. Elizabeth A. Rauscher, in order to investigate the possibility to RV this foreign location. Only one general telephone call was made between the principals a week before an airplane was boarded for the Near East with no specific longitudinal, latitudinal details or hotel location given. Rauscher did not know the locations we would be visiting while in Egypt. For example, she did not know we would be visiting a University in Cairo. She only knew the general dates we were to be in Egypt. Even the time of remote viewing was left up to her each day. She was going to remote view based on her schedule since a 10 hour time change existed between us and her. It was roughly understood she was going to remote view in the morning her time, and she was going to Remote View what we did that day.

The project would involve sketches from Rauscher and photographs from the Hurtaks. A general overview of the experiment was collected and later (upon return) given to the outbound experimenters (Drs. J.J. and Desiree Hurtak) to match and come to general conclusions regarding the accuracy and the possibility of ongoing work.

This section includes a target-by-target comparison of the free-style response drawings, sketches and descriptive statements by the inbound principal, with the pictures of the actual targets recorded by the outbound experimenters working between Egypt and the United States.

It is important to note that these RV trials were conducted during an expeditionary week in Egypt amid the post-revolutionary 2011 turmoil and during the interim government. There were issues of safety and security for us working as visitors in sensitive areas. We were given the highest accord and acceptance by members of the Egyptian university community and visited a University in Cairo during our short visit unbeknownst to Rauscher (see photos this chapter).

Towards the end of January 2011, we (Drs. J.J. and Desiree Hurtak) had received an invitation to a special university talk and an investigation of the Hawara Pyramid (Egypt) "unbeknownst" to Rauscher. The Hawara Pyramid area is believed to contain the legendary Labyrinth of ancient Egypt mentioned by Herodotus. This news was also important because we had been looking forward to future "excavation" work at the site, so the preliminary arrangement now defined was important.

During our travels we stayed at the El Mercure Hotel near to the Mena House in the larger Giza-Cairo area. As noted in our notebooks, the first day was a planning day for our travel to the core area of the Hawara Pyramid (a few hours drive from Giza). This was the area that we believe Rauscher chose to draw for that day as our thoughts were there. The second day was at the University in Cairo, where she did accurate drawings although she knew nothing of the event, and then a brief tour of the Giza Plateau on March 21st, followed by our journey another day to Hawara. Our timetables were as follows:

Table 1:
Hurtak(s)/Rauscher Remote Viewing Experiment in Egypt

Target Egypt	Date	Location	Outbound Target
1	March 19, 2012	Giza/Fayyum, Egypt	Planning day for El Fayyum, with the Hawara pyramid where the Labyrinth search begins. (We were located in Giza at our hotel.)
2	March 20, 2012	Cairo, Egypt	Friends walk on side area at the University in Cairo. We are headed to the intercourt of University.
3a	March 20, 2012	Cairo, Egypt	We walk past pillars to a meeting at the University.
3b	March 20, 2012	Cairo, Egypt	Desiree and J.J. pose with scholars at University in Cairo.
4a	March 21, 2012	Giza, Egypt	Inspector's tent near to the Pyramids/Sphinx.
4b	March 21, 2012	Giza, Egypt	Antiquities Office for Giza-Pyramid.
5	March 23, 2012	Giza, Egypt	Looking at Giza Plateau from a high building (heading to Fayyum).
6a & b	March 25, 2012	Giza, Egypt	Discussions of a different Sphinx-Like structure on the Giza Plateau and traffic.

Egypt Target #1 Photo: Dr. J.J. Hurtak and Dr. Desiree Hurtak at Hawara, EGYPT, in March, 2012 on Exploration.
(See round depression in the center in front of cleaved pyramid.)

Egypt Target #1 RV Drawing: Rauscher's Remote Viewing of Drs. Hurtak. Her handwriting says: "talking to each other" "Desiree pointing," "keep getting water," "hesitate to say fountain," "circular motion."

Egypt Target #2 Photo: Rendezvous with scholars at a University in Cairo walking towards conference hall. Note the side wall as a tall structure protruding with columns to hold the roof's edge and the walkway with people and shrubs as seen by Rauscher. There was a flat plate on the roadway which she may have taken as a vendor cart. Several cars were in the area as well as a delivery van which may have caused some confusion. The balloons may be the air-conditioning units seen in the second floor In fact, three are clearly seen in this picture and three are seen in the distance.

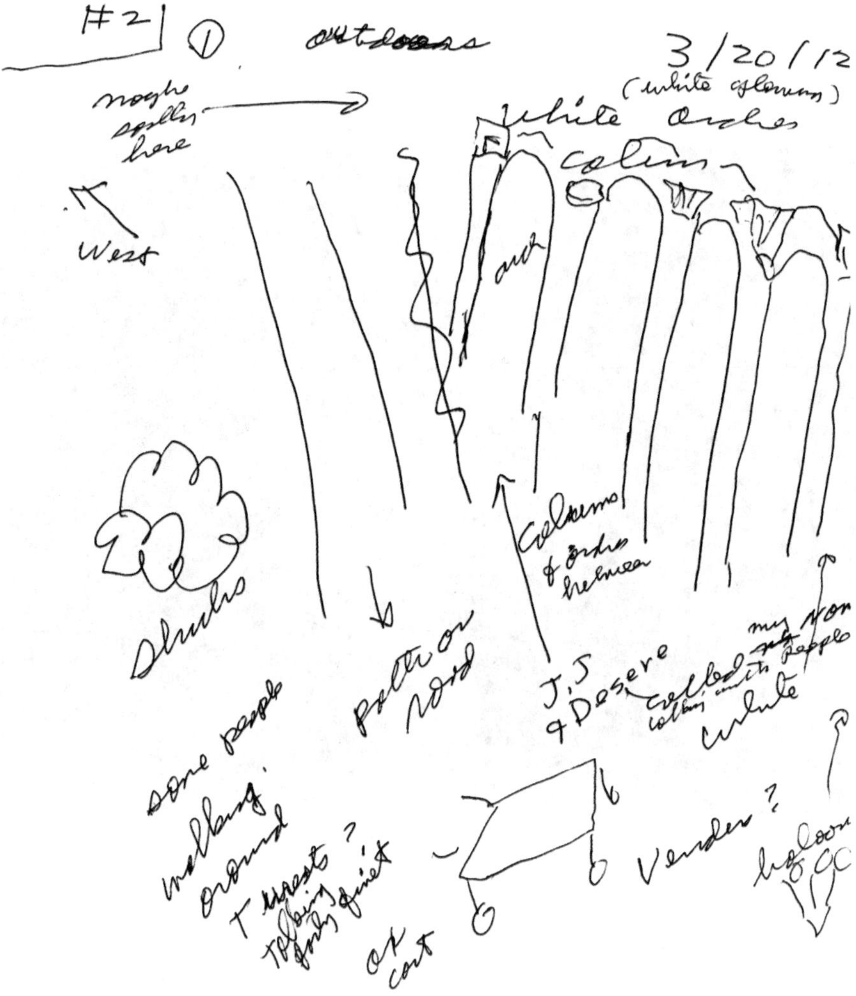

Egypt Target #2 RV Drawing: Remote Viewing by Rauscher during the time Drs. Hurtak were visiting the university. Note the building, the pathways and the shrubs which existed at the site.

Rauscher's handwriting says: "outdoors," "maybe smaller here," "shrubs," "some people walking around," "tourists?" "talking fairly quiet," "vendor," "ox-cart," "path or road," "balloon," "white arches, columns (white glowing)," "columns and orders between," "J.J. and Desiree called my name, walking with people." The balloons could be the three circular objects in the background.

Egypt Target #3a Photo: Drs. Hurtak walking with scholars towards conference hall at the University in Cairo. Note the unusual light fixtures with the round ball on the top and the embellishments on the bottom of the pole, as remote viewed by Rauscher. Note also "people looking" at the entourage as noted. The cobalt blue is on the door to the facility in front of us.

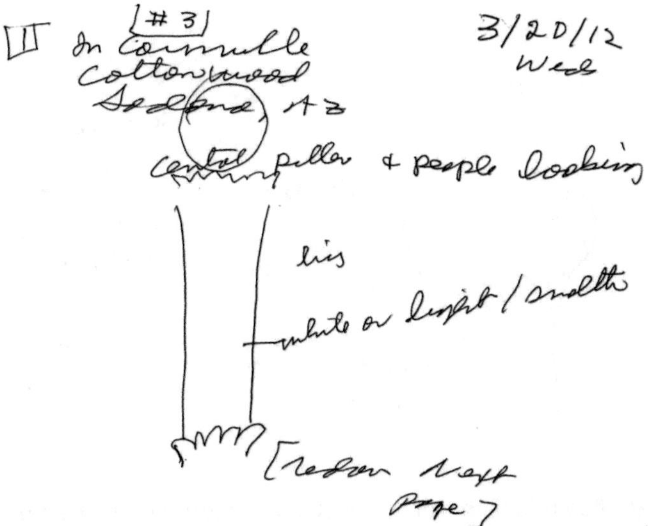

Egypt Target #3b Drawing: Rauscher's third remote viewing showing an unusual pillar which we see as a light post in the actual experience. She also writes "people looking" and "cobalt blue" both of which were true. Rauscher's handwriting says: "sending this from Cornville, Cottonwood, Sedona," "central pillar and people looking," "big" "white of light/ smooth," and "redraw next page."

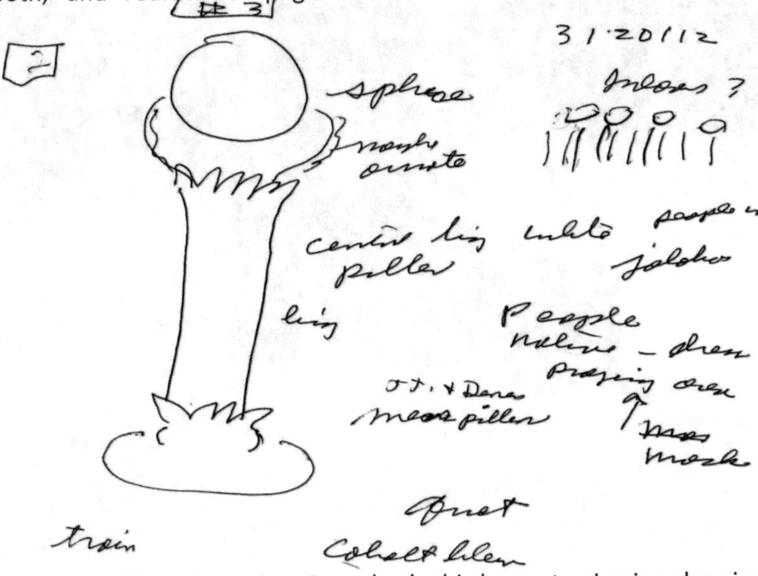

Egypt Target #3c RV Drawing: Rauscher's third remote viewing showing an unusual pillar. Rauscher writes in her handwriting: "sphere at top," "sphere rough ornate," "central big white pillar," "JJ and Desiree near pillar," "quiet," "indoors?," "people in jackets," "people Muslim dress praying over mosque," "train," "quiet," and "cobalt blue."

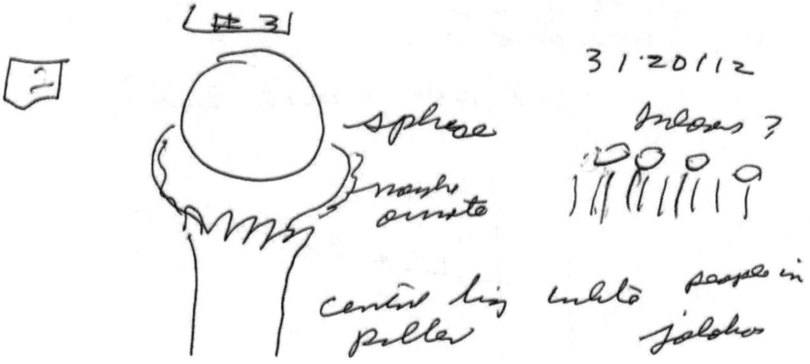

Giza Target #3d (blow up from previous page) Remote Viewing by E.A. Rauscher showing the 4 figures standing at the University in Cairo.

Giza Target #3e Photo: Note another representation of the group of four, not indoors but in a courtyard.

Egypt Target #4a Photo Drs. Hurtak on the Giza Plateau near the pyramids, sitting in the only tent of the plateau used by one of the inspectors. Dr. Hurtak has a cup of coffee. They are joined by their colleague Andrzej Wojcikiewicz on the sandy floor. Note that the top of the tent is pyramidal shaped as indicated in the drawing.

Egypt Target 4b. Photo: Drs. J.J. and Desiree Hurtak visiting the Antiquities Office at the Giza Plateau. You can see the rectangular-type building that is picked up by the remote viewing.

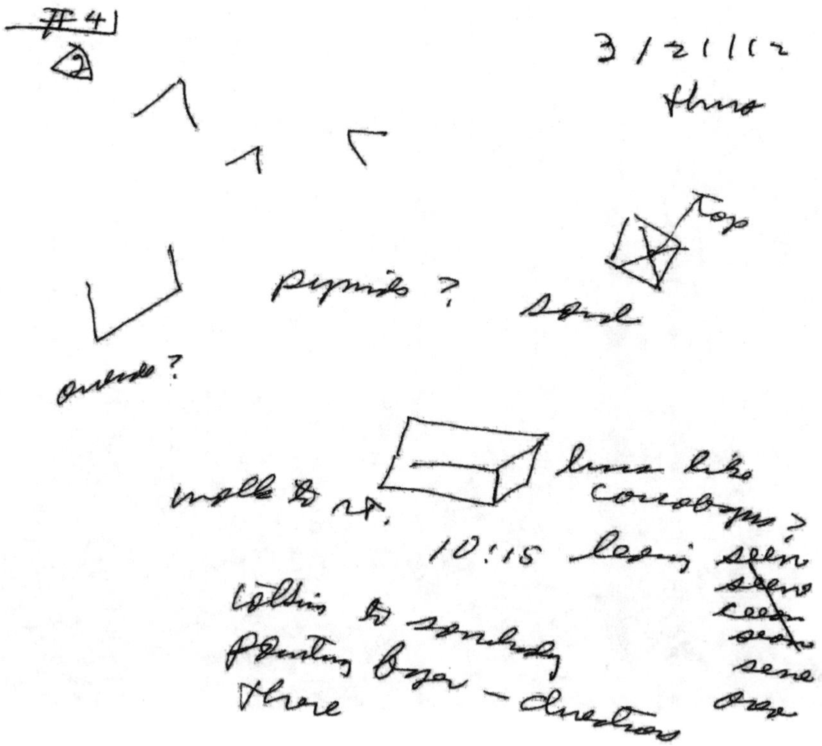

Egypt Target #4c RV Drawing: Remote viewing of a tent-like structure. Note that the top of the tent is pyramidal shaped as indicated in the drawing. There is also a nearby long rectangular building that is the field office for the head inspector working with the Supreme Antiquities Council (formerly used by Dr. Zahi Hawass). So both structures actually are on either sides (although at a distance) from the three Great Pyramids we visited.

Rauscher's handwriting says: "top," "outside," "pyramids?," "sand," "walk to right," "talking to somebody pointing finger—directions there," "10:15 AM leaving," "lines like cornerfigures ... scene area."

Egypt Target #5 Photo: Drs. Hurtak view looking out from a high building next to the Giza Plateau where you can see the multi-storied light color building and a busy street, actually a highway at the ground level. Although the road does not look busy, it is in fact a major roadway into and out of the Giza area. Markets for food are in the area behind the building as noted in Rauscher's RV drawing notes (see Egypt Target #5).

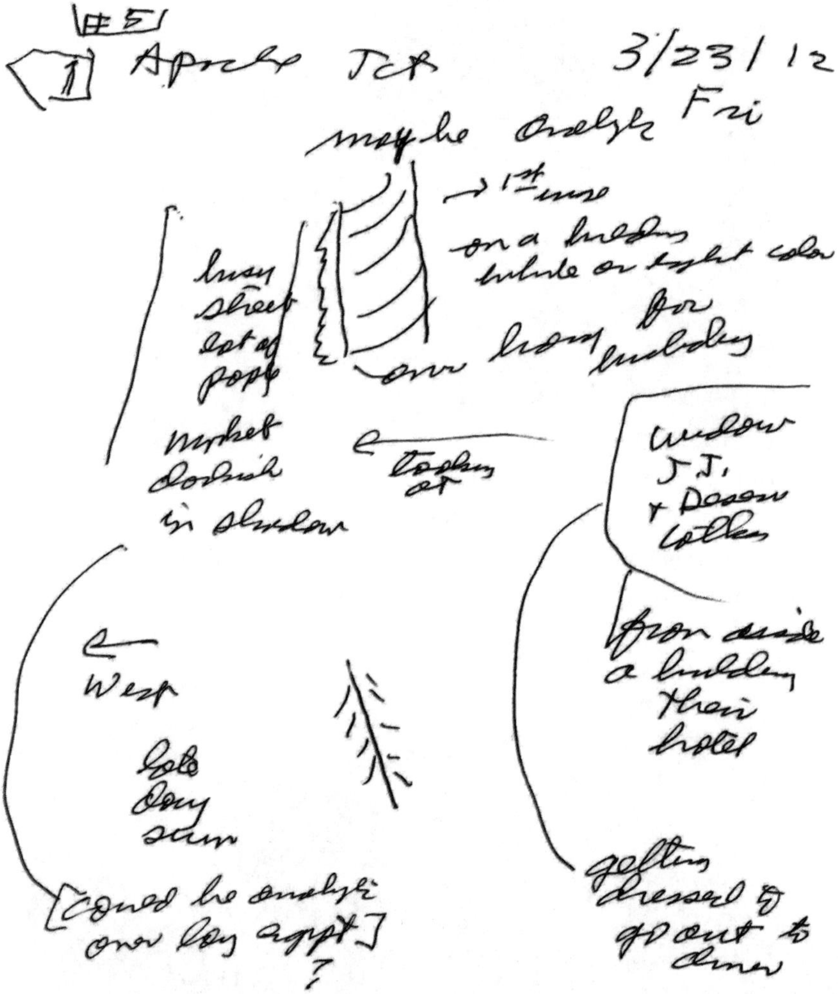

Egypt Target #5 RV Drawing: Remote viewing of a high building where Drs. Hurtak are looking out at distant Giza. Rauscher points out both a light color building and a busy street both of which are true. She also notes a market in the area which is also true. Rauscher's handwriting notes say: "Apache Junction (Rauscher's location)," "busy street a lot of people," "market district in shadow," "west," "late day sun," "could be analytical overlay Egypt," "maybe analytic," "1st sense on a building, white or bright color," "from inside the building, their hotel," "window J.J. and Desiree talking," and "getting dressed to go out to dinner."

Egypt Target #6a Photo: Although most people only recognize one main Sphinx on the Giza plateau, it is the belief of some archeologists that there is a double lion, or "second Sphinx". Drs. Hurtak visited this second sphinx at the time of the remote viewing experiments.

Egypt Target #6b Photo: There is lots of traffic in the area. Even over by the Sphinx there is also a road for cars to travel. Although we did not take a picture of traffic on the road next to the Sphinx — we did take pictures of the traffic. We even crossed this road on foot without a crosswalk, with the help of our Egyptian associate. We think Elizabeth picked up on that as it was hair-raising and in the early evening.

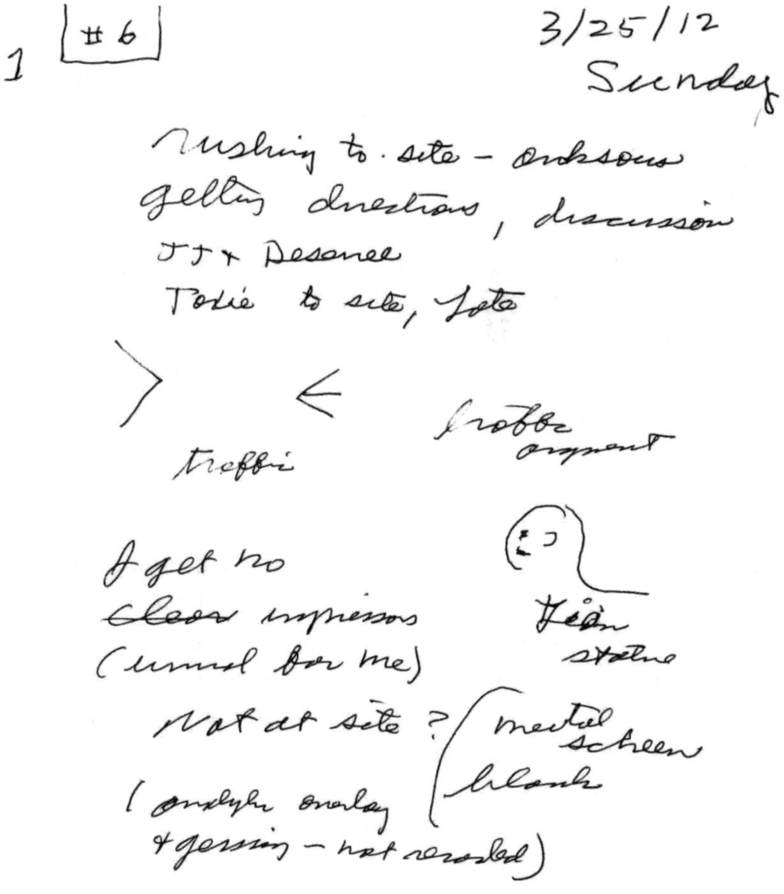

Egypt Target #6 RV Drawing: During Rauscher's remote viewing she sees a Sphinx-like structure, yet she gets no impressions perhaps because there is no real face, just the body and head of the lion form. Rauscher's handwriting says: "rushing to site," "anxious getting directions, discussion J.J. and Desiree," "taxi to site," "late," "traffic," "I get no clear impressions (unusual for me)," "not at site?," "(analytic overlay and guessing—not recorded)" "traffic arrangement," "lion statute," and "(mental screen blank)."

Results of Egyptian RV Tests

Egypt Target #1: We did not travel out, but we were discussing, "talking to each other" about our future plans to journey to the area of El Fayyum. So on this day we were busy looking over maps and pictures of the site, and "pointing" to the towering, now "rounded" pyramid of Hawara. On this occasion, we (Drs. Hurtak) began to use our paraphysical abilities to tune into Dr. E.A. Rauscher and also to look for the possibilities of an underground location of the Great Labyrinth near to the Bahr Yussef Canal. It is important to note that Rauscher saw and indicated the presence of water in her drawings. This area has one of the most interesting waterways (Bahr) of the region; one that is attributed to the ancient biblical figure of Joseph (Yussef). We took this as accurate read.

Rauscher's note on the circular mound was, we believe, clearly the Hawara pyramid ('sugar-loaf like') which you can see behind us in the photograph and the canal of water is behind it. The water "leaks" under the pyramid which may be a unique type of circular water system or aquafer. Also large piles of dirt, as well as small mounds can be seen in the background on three of the four sides of the pyramid. "Water" was present and the rounded depressions were obvious. How the two come together are still unknown so her questioning (note question mark) was correct.

Once there, towards the end of the trip, the principals walked around the towering pyramid of Hawara in search of the best position for ground penetrating radar to map out the underground basement complex of the labyrinth and took the photograph.

Egypt Target #2: The second day, as we parked our car and headed to the University meeting room, Desiree took this picture. We walked on a small private road (really a stone path) on the way to the far side of the intercourt of the University. There are small shrubs on the left side and students are walking by, many in head scarfs, etc. Although there was no oxcart, there were a few small cars in the area and a metal rectangular plate in front on the ground. A food place was nearby (out of the photograph). The arches were not white, but the sun was bright, perhaps giving the appearance.

Egypt Target #3: After our talk to faculty colleagues at the University in Cairo, we went back outside into the intercourt to have coffee with colleagues. As we were walking, we passed unusual light posts on the campus. Desiree walks behind the group to take their picture. Although there was not a lot of talking, as we neared the building, I (J.J.) am talking to the university colleagues who point out the need to help restore the central faculty building we are walking by, and one can notice the beautiful ramp that connects with an exquisite set of doors. The doors have blue color because they are metal and oxidizing. They are not cobalt blue but nevertheless a unique blue color. There is no train nearby as far as we know, but there may have been public transportation in the area. Girls were sitting at the base of the lamps which are clearly remote viewed by Rauscher. Discussions on strategy and common goals to map out future areas of archeological research were followed by lunch at the University.

Egypt Target #4: On the next day, we made a brief journey to the famous Giza Plateau. We (Drs. Hurtak) stop at the inspector's office to meet the new team and to discuss future plans. We meet at the official office complex assigned to the Dept. of Antiquities which is an adobe type of long rectangular structure at the Giza site, that most tourists never see.

Therefore, one of the images on the fourth target seems to be that we have identified ourselves with the Office of the Supreme Antiquities Head (formerly the office of Zahi Hawass) which we visited in order to talk about future permits for exploration. So Rauscher's RV is true. Next we walked on the Plateau past the three pyramids to see the sites and our colleagues invited us to sit with them in the inspector's tent on the Giza Plateau. This tent is on the opposite side of the Giza Plateau not far from the Sphinx. The coffee is good but it is even more interesting that Rauscher picked up on the two structures we visited, the one-story enlongated "office" building on the plateau and the tent. Neither structure is well known to normal tourists who visit the Plateau.

Giza Target #5: We were in a high story building looking out at a distance to the Giza Plateau. We could also see other nearby buildings that are similar to ours. Something that the RV has clearly drawn. This day we also journeyed to El Fayyum and captured the picture used in Target #1. Between us and the three Pyramids is a major roadway. Although you do not see the market, it is nearby.

Giza Target #6: We did not journey out this day as we were preparing to leave the area. Since our hotel was adjacent to the Giza Plateau, we could see the Pyramids from our balcony and we were in discussion with noted Egyptologists speaking about previous excavations and the new confirmations. In our conversations we were discussing the possibility of a "Double Sphinx" on the Giza Plateau and noting the rock formation (see photograph taken March 21, 2012) that may be the counterpart to the historic Great Sphinx. As the double lion and the Hawara Pyramid were our two main focal points, it was interesting that Rauscher picked up on both of these at the beginning and end of our travels. Traffic was also a major issue. There were lines for gasoline all the time and coming back the last day, we crossed a major street (seen in the picture) in Giza on foot in the early evening without a crosswalk. We could only do it with the help of our Egyptian friend. An older Egyptian lady joined us in our crossing and greatly appreciated the help of our friend to make it across the busy road. To an untrained American this was an impossible feat as no cars were stopping as we crossed. Although we were not taking pictures while we did it, we did take a picture of the road. There is also a road next to the Sphinx which we drove on (but no pictures were taken).

Conclusion

Overall, there generally were good matches made by Elizabeth Rauscher (when comparing her drawings with our photographs) over the brief time period. The exhibits drawn by Rauscher through Remote Viewing were reflective of good correspondence without too much analytical overlay.

Remote Viewing Region #2
Hurtak, Hurtak and Rauscher RV tests in Bimini, Bahamas — November 2012

USING RV BETWEEN DR. RAUSCHER AND DRS. HURTAK IN PROBING THE AREA OF BIMINI AND THE WESTERN ATLANTIC REGION

The legendary stories about sunken roads off the coast of Florida in the Bimini Islands were part of a story we had discussed with the late anthropologist Manson Valentine in Miami in the 1970s (Valentine, 1974). There, it is said, existed forgotten cities, ancient roads and a Caribbean Atlantis now sunk according to Valentine. In fact, Valentine claimed it was part of an ancient sailing route across the Atlantic that was followed by successive waves of explorers connected with copper trade.

The western Caribbean around Bimini is one vast area where probes have been made by various divers working formerly with the American intelligence like Colonel John Alexander and explorer Pino Turolla, to name a few. Shallow dives sometimes don't feel like real dives with gear. There's not the sense of challenge, that frisson of danger, that a diver gets when he or she is down there in deep water. Less than 5 meters below the surface, Bimini is a gentle and kindly place to be underwater. The greatest danger is the occasional nurse shark skulking in the nearby area.

The typical bottom of the sea floor near Bimini is mainly sand. Of course there are some rocks under the water, but they are few and of irregular shapes. Yet, on occasion an ancient underwater roadway that was composed of man-made shaped stones is known to appear.

In late November 2012, we (Drs. J.J. and Desiree Hurtak) embarked upon an expedition to look at the waters off Bimini as part of a larger sailing route system across the Atlantic Ocean. We asked Dr. Rauscher to use her power of RV and join us on certain days without telling her where we were located. We beamed mental pictures to Elizabeth at a specific time we had arranged without telling her whether we were on land or in a boat.

Contrary to the National Geographic Society's research report that downplayed the size of the stones off the island of Bimini in the Western Atlantic, our late colleague Pino Turolla, underwater diver, shared with us, photographs of what he said were blocks in the 1-5 ton range. He concluded they were from a time when the sea level was lower and so these "man-placed" blocks were from a previous, perhaps Atlantean era. I (Desiree) roughly measured some blocks that appeared to be part of the ancient roadway but the stones were only about 1 meter across, nevertheless we felt they were part of the so-called Bimini Road. Turolla also spoke of how the stones seemed elevated as if they were lifted up by blocks underneath, so that you could easily confirm the underwater roadway (Turolla, 1978).

The ancient roadway now submerged suggests that the islands of Bimini, if more contemporary than the Atlantean legends, could have served as an ocean port for pre-European merchants, that is, earlier Phoenician ships looking for precious minerals along the American coastal frontier as early as 2,000 to 1,500 BC. The possibility of artifacts from ancient places such as Egypt and Phoenicia being smelted in North America as part of their ocean trade system has been theorized by some American anthropologists in the first decade of the 21st century (Wakefield 2013). But on a practical level, for the ocean levels to be that much lower, it must have occurred perhaps as much as 10,000 to 12,000 years ago, around the time of the Quaternary Extinction when a possible comet hit the area of Eastern Canada or Greenland and abrupt climate change occurred.

TABLE 2: Hurtak-Rauscher RV tests in the Bahamas off the coast of Florida. Note that the RV covered only one day because Rauscher was busy with her holiday schedule.

Region 2	Date	Location	Outbound Target
Target 1	Nov. 24, 2012	Bimini, Bahamas	Rocks filmed with an underwater camera by Desiree of what appears to be an underwater roadway.
Target 2a	Nov. 24, 2012	Bimini, Bahamas	Rocks filmed with an underwater camera by Desiree of what appears to be an underwater roadway.
Target 2b	Nov. 24, 2012	Bimini, Bahamas	Rocks filmed with an underwater camera by Desiree of what appears to be an underwater roadway.
Target 3	Nov. 24, 2012	Bimini, Bahamas	J.J. examines special underwater equipment and anchor line of boat.
Target 4	Nov. 24, 2012	Bimini, Bahamas	J.J. looking overboard with a blue-bucket to see smooth stones.

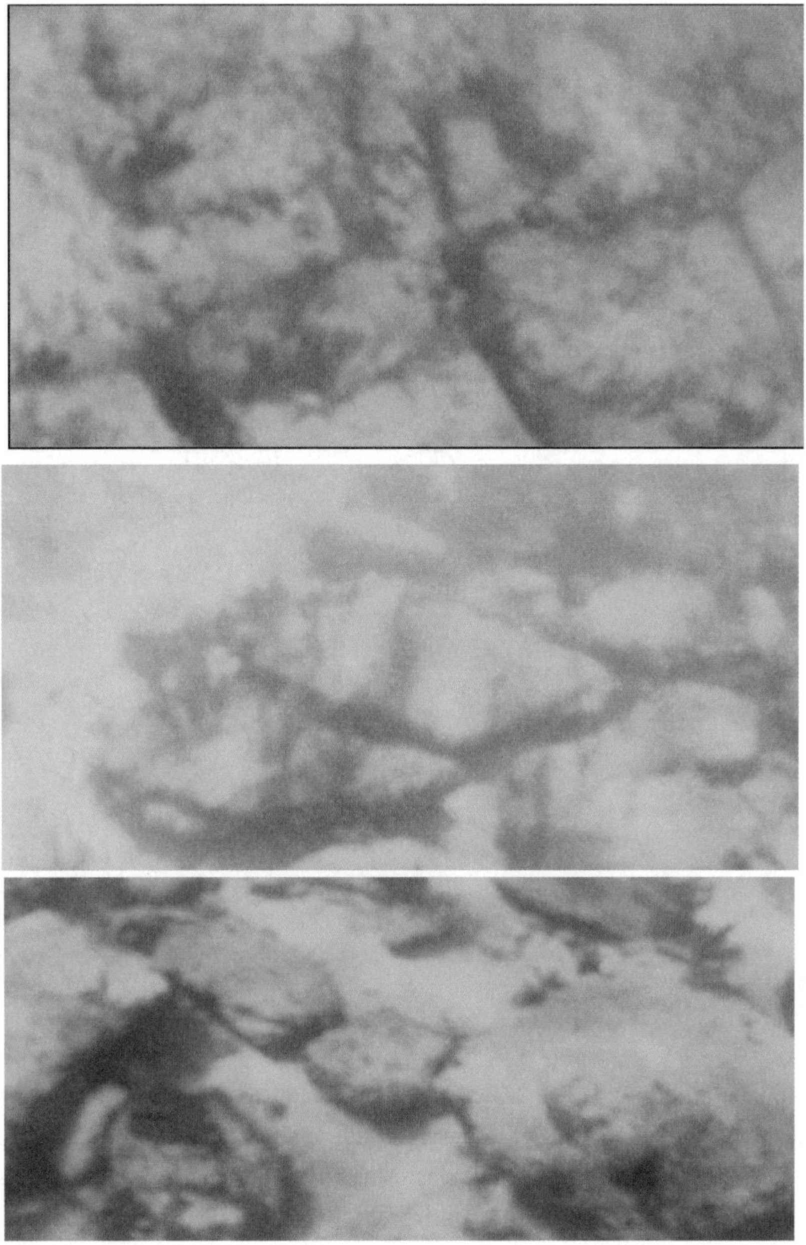

Bimini Target #1, Target #2a and Target #2b Photo: Where there normally is just a sandy underwater sea floor, in a unique area on the Western side of the Island is an area that has interesting interlocking blocks which Drs. Hurtak were able to dive and capture on film.

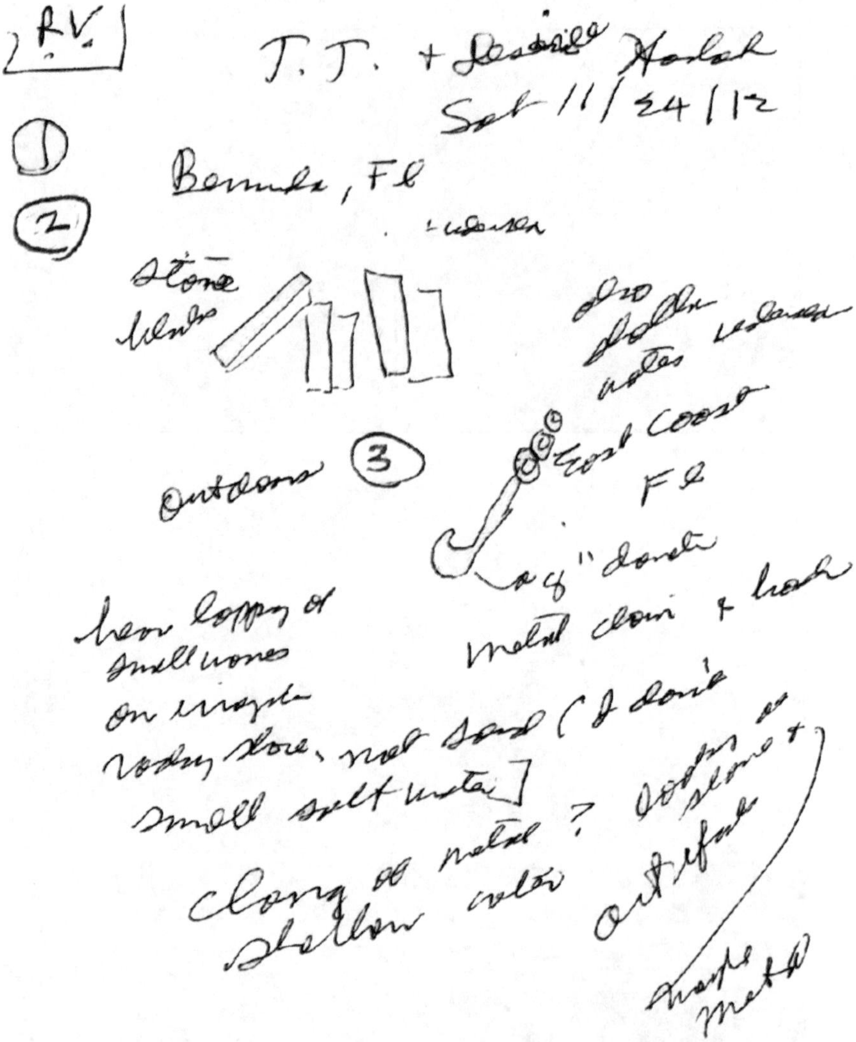

Bimini Target RV: 1–3, Drawing: Elizabeth Rauscher's remote viewing skills pick up on a series of underwater stone slabs, as well as the special anchor system that Dr. Hurtak was using to anchor the boat. Rauscher's handwriting says: "J.J. and Desiree," "Bermuda, FL," "stone slabs," "underwater," "under sea," "outdoors," "hear flapping of small waves on a regular rocky shore, not sand (I don't smell salt water)," "long or metal, shallow water," "an 8 inch metal chain and hooks" and "looks as chain and hook artifacts, maybe metal."

Bimini Target #3, Photo: The images that Rauscher describes are accurate in both the observation of what was underwater from the boat and even the anchor chain and anchor itself can be seen in the photograph to the right as mentioned by Rauscher. Dr. J.J. Hurtak is attending to the gear of the underwater probe. Elizabeth looks at the special equipment and the chain that are behind the oval shaped motor.

Bimini Target #4 Photo: Dr. J.J. Hurtak looking down from the boat using a plastic bucket with a glass bottom, to see the cut, smooth stones which could prove a theory of Atlantis. This scene seems to have been confirmed in the RV.

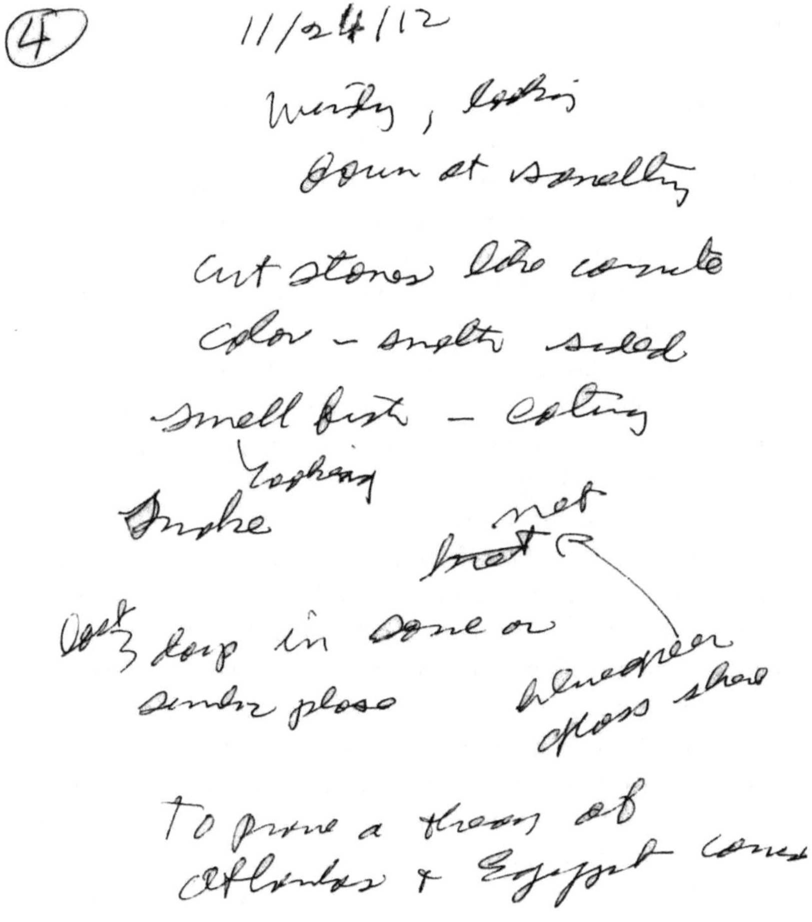
4

11/24/12

windy, looking
down at something

cut stones like coral
color - smooth sided
smell fish - eating
looking
smoke
net
3 days in some or
another place
blue green
glass sphere

To prove a theory of
Atlantis & Egypt correct

Bimini Target #4 RV Drawing: Elizabeth Rauscher who has never been to the area of Bimini scans the bottom of the ocean with her remote viewing ability and sees a pattern of cut stones suggesting the fingerprints of an earlier civilization like Atlantis.

Rauscher's handwriting says: "windy, looking down at something, cut stones like coral color, smooth sided," "smell fish-eating," "smoke looking," "3 days in some or another place," "blue green net— glass sphere," and "to prove a theory of Atlantis and Egypt correct."

Experimental Design

We spent a single day diving and doing RV work, trying to expand our thoughts to Elizabeth Rauscher who was on the other side of the North American continent (a three-hour time change) and was not given any clues to our location except for our general location. Another day we joined a friend for bone-fishing, but Rauscher did not RV that day to our surprise due to other commitments.

The question has always been whether the neatly placed horizontal stones were just bits of loose rock that had been lying around on the sea-bed and that had been washed up naturally by tides or storm swells. But if so, why were they only in one location like a roadway albeit, short.

What we saw both from the boat and in the water were blocks of stone in a recurrent pattern. Blocks were arranged in straight paths, with groups of blocks of different shapes combined to form a walkway. We were not far off shore, so theoretically at one time, if the ocean levels were lower, Bimini could have been a much larger island and we were seeing the remnants of that earlier era near the western end of the shore line on one side of the island. This was interesting because Rauscher thought we were in Bermuda, but it was Bimini so not sure if that was a plus for her ability to view an area accurately but not consider with accuracy the name of the country. We were technically in the area of the Bermuda Triangle so that might part of the confusion.

In all locations of Bimini, we were trying to get our bearings on the underwater roadway and to figure out what it was. Around noon with the sun almost directly overhead and the underwater visibility at its best, the long straight avenues of blocks seemed to show some evidence of having been a man-made artifact. It is said that they sometimes would disappear completely under sand drifts, only to reappear from time to time.

The natives on Bimini speak of several sunken ceremonial centers of an ancient culture without providing details. Rauscher was able to pick up on our dives and the film work done by Desiree.

Our archaeological expedition team had been unsure which day of the week we would go to explore this ancient roadway because of the weather. We were very interested in navigating between the small island clusters and wanted to briefly follow the earlier leads of underwater explorers Pino Turolla and Dimitri Ribikov. Therefore, the specific date and time were unknown to the inbound experimenter. Nevertheless, the inbound experimenter E.A. Rauscher had a remarkably good penetrating vision of the data which proved to be correct, especially because it was during the holiday season and she gave this RV only a short portion of her time.

Results

BIMINI-BAHAMAS: Hurtak, Hurtak and Rauscher Remote Viewing Experiments on the Island of Bimini in the Bahamas. It was not Bermuda, but we did leave the mainland from Florida which was 53 miles away.

Bimini Target #1 - 2: J.J. and Desiree at an unknown location off the coast of Bimini Island.

The first target was to identify J.J. and Desiree who with associates were in a rented boat off the shores of Bimini. Rauscher writes "Bermuda FL" which is not correct. Bimini is off the coast of FL (Florida) in the Bahamas. The population on this island is small, only about 2,000 people. It is located in the Bermuda Triangle so that is another possibility and then would be accurate.

Desiree was in the shallow water, just near the boat, filming what looked like a group of stones that were placed uniquely next to each other and what could be the ancient "Bimini Road." So "stone slabs," "underwater," "under sea," "outdoors" are all accurate viewing.

The second target provides a larger view where Target's 1 and 3 were focused more on the rock formations. Rauscher's viewing said "hear flapping of small waves on a regular rocky shore, not sand (I don't smell salt water)," "long or metal, shallow water," The water was shallow. The air was fresh (not smelly) maybe because it was winter and had just rained. Desiree was able to explore the contours of the so-called Bimini road, mentioned earlier to us by Manson Valentine and Pino Turolla who considered that these may be the remains of a previous cycle of life connected with the Florida shoreline. The rocks, mentioned by Rauscher, could be the shore or the rocks beneath us.

Bimini Target #3: Dr. J.J. Hurtak with equipment at a location showing the boat off Bimini Island.

The third target identifies the boat with special equipment and especially the anchor that is drawn by Rauscher's RV. The boat was anchored about 1 kilometer from the shore, and the anchor chain can be seen in the drawing and on the right side of the photograph which corresponds to the viewing of an "8 inch metal chain and hooks" and "looks as chain and hook artifacts, maybe metal."

Bimini Target #4: This is a continuation of the other Bimini Targets.

Here Dr. J.J. Hurtak is looking over the boat with a blue bucket. The remote viewing mentioned a blue-green color; note the water is blue-green. He is looking at the unusual stones in the area on the seafloor, which is a confirmation of what Rauscher describes. She also sites "smell fish-eating," "smoke looking," "3 days in some or another place," "blue green net—glass sphere," and "to prove a theory of Atlantis and Egypt correct." We did spend 3 days on land and only the one day on the water. We ate fish and were interesting in exploring the legends of the area.

Conclusion

Elizabeth saw what we transmitted to her at our location which was about 1 kilometer off the island of Bimini. We were not able to find the large 'pillars' mentioned personally to us by Pino Turolla in the 1970s, but we found unmistakable man-made patterns indicating a roadway and the unusual placement of stones side-by-side that looked man-made, but clearly a smaller arrangement when compared to our research in Yonaguni, Japan, in 1998 (DeMauro, 2002).

We considered this accurate RV correspondence with good information on the general subsurface artifacts of Bimini with relatively little incorrect information. However, one day, in a known area, does not make for an extremely objective confirmation. Nevertheless we felt there was good accuracy of the details drawn by Rauscher in her Remote Viewing, although we would not consider this a "scientifically based experiment" as it could have analytical overlays and was not done in a controlled laboratory environment.

Remote Viewing Region #3
Hurtak, Hurtak and Rauscher RV tests in the area in Israel including the Golan–June 2013

III. HURTAK-RAUSCHER RV EXPERIMENTS IN THE GOLAN HEIGHTS OF NORTHERN ISRAEL, THE SEA OF GALILEE AND JERUSALEM

This was our third RV experiment together with Elizabeth Rauscher and Drs. J.J. and Desiree Hurtak. This Hurtak-Hurtak-Rauscher Remote Viewing Experiment (June 2013) was between Phoenix, Arizona and the Golan-Israel: A distance covering approximately 11,900 kilometers. Arizona had also a 10 hour time difference during the summer months. This area is well regarded around the world as a place that brings together peoples of all backgrounds (e.g., Israeli Jews, Palestinians, Syrian Christians, Druze, Lebanese Muslims) through ancient culture, archaeology and now through Remote Viewing.

Our work in 2013 was to film and document several places in the area of Golan and Israel. However, we only mentioned the area of Israel to Dr. Rauscher. She did not know we were going to stay in the area of Mt. Hermon, the highest mountain in the Near East, nor visit Rujum al-Hiri, also in the Golan.

In fact, the major focus of our stay was within the area of the Golan Heights. Specifically, our research was centered in the region of what scholars call the Anti-Lebanon where Lebanon, Israel and southern Syria come together. The importance of the region is its unique history. From the late Archaic period (1,500 BC) and in the following centuries, the Golan Heights changed hands incessantly, enduring brief bouts of occupation by everyone from Alexander the Great to the Roman Empire. The history of the rocky, Los Angeles-sized plateau called Golan, strategically nestled between Lebanon, Syria, Israel and Jordan, traces back its importance to biblical times. From 953-596 BC the Golan Heights was both a buffer zone and a contested area for the ancient Kingdom of Israel and the Aramean Kingdom in Damascus. Proto-biblical texts have been found that record the names of rulers in the region that go back to a time when the pre-biblical Ebla texts were written. Their king lists are revealed in the book of Genesis.

Our work was close to the critical areas of renewed strife and war in Syria and we carefully chose our targets as the ground work and objective of some RV exchanges with Elizabeth without explaining to her details of our location or our interest in ancient archeology in Golan. Additionally, we visited massive and unusual land forms called "Rujum al-Hiri" that I (Dr. J.J. Hurtak) wrote about in 1973, which showed an earlier strata of society that had the mathematical skills to devise a computer-calendar-like system made up of stone circles. My writing on the site was significantly before Israeli and Arab scholars reported it as an historic area of interest.

"Rujum al-Hiri" (also spelled Rujm el-Hiri) is located in the lower Golan and served as a type of Stonehenge in this part of the world. It may have been a cipher for sophisticated star alignments. In brief, we believe this area served as some type of early astrophysical computer for astronomers and magi in the ancient Near East.

The Golan, throughout history, has revealed many interesting and important traditions. It has often been a key point for stability for all countries of the Near East and so we also used our time to focus on peace in all of the Near East, which was of paramount importance at that time.

Experiments: A Brief Travelogue

Our first point of departure was the cool waters of Banias where early Christians gathered and where we also gathered with old friends to renew our purpose of prayers for peace. Launching from the historic place of the waters of Banias, in the early morning, we were able to see ruins of an earlier culture within the hillside. The same area has the famous Nimrod's Castle at a high point in the mountainous region of the Golan Height, directly south of Mt. Hermon. Nimrod was the great grandson of Noah and the one often associated with the Tower of Babel.

We made our way up from the floor of the Jordan Valley in northern Israel. Nimrod's Castle is not quite megalithic in the strict sense of the term, but very close to it, as the massive structure overlooked important roadways going north to the City of Damascus in the early biblical period.

After this gathering point in the morning, we journeyed to Mt. Hermon the highest point in the Near East. It is also known as *Jabal al-Skaykh*, the Mount of the Chief, located in the Anti-Lebanon summit region. Its summit reaches 2814 meters (9232 feet). On its very top is the Qasr Antar, one of the highest temples of the world, and it is also known as the Mt. of the Oath associated with the ancient *Book of Enoch*.

We explored the area of Mt. Hermon where the three countries of Lebanon, Syria and Israel come together. This is the historic area according to the (first) *Book of Enoch* where the fallen angel, Semjaze, came down to teach humankind in the ancient Near East how to use the weapons of war. This is also the place, some believe, was the true Mt. of Transfiguration. Traditionally this is considered to be Mt. Tabor, near Nazareth. However, the Bible said that shortly before this, Jesus was at Cesaresa Philippi, and that from there he went to a lonely place, which best describes Mt. Hermon.

We sat and meditated and visualized Dr. Rauscher. It is here where we came together for peace that we also took a picture of a small circular pool of water near the top of the mount. Other hikers would sometimes walk by.

The day after, we made a short journey from our locale to the Sea of Galilee to visit our associates' relatives. We stopped in Tiberius, and had fish at the seaside. Tiberius is a place of many cultures, since many diverse invaders had ruled the city throughout the ages. Desiree took a picture of al-Amari Mosque near the sea.

After a stay at the area of Nazareth-Tiberius, we returned to where we were staying in a small village called Majdal-Shams on the border with Syria, where fighting between Syrian factions was heard in the distance. The next day, we used a four-wheel drive vehicle in following our mental map towards a key place in the Golan, the place I (J.J.) had written about in my earlier research, called 'Rujum al-Hiri.' (Hurtak, 1973) This was also near the border with Syria and Jordon proper.

We set our GPS (ground positioning system) units to look for a rugged course of stones in an elevated field that had been assembled in megalithic times into a series of very large concentric circles that interlocked like a Swiss watch. Rujum al-Hiri is a series of concentric circles each having a multitude of stones around a central circle, probably an ancient dome-like observatory structure. At some time in the distant past these stones were standing walls and were thought to have been used as measuring points for the interconnecting motions of both lunar and solar movements through the use of sacred geometry. The larger area also has additional interesting formations when seen from space.

The unusual series of circles was calibrated to work like one of the world's oldest manmade computers somewhat akin to what Gerald Hawkins had speculated about when he examined the circular majesty of Stonehenge and called it a computer. The same architectural principle had been used in the massive curved patterns that were interconnected in a unique and perfect way so at the center, nexus point, of the innermost circle, that was once a dome, still exist underground rooms. Actually, trapped amongst the rubble of the ancient rock formations there were still a number of passageways that met at points that would align with solar and celestial patterns that would form throughout the year.

The vast display of the concentric patterns indicates a high culture that had, as in other places of the world, mastered several disciplines of geophysical and astrophysical mappings, linked to recognizable constellations that were behind folk mythology at a very early period. Having time for a mind link, we tuned into Rauscher at a precise time of the day to establish ourselves and to, hopefully, convey a schematic on a nexus point of Near Eastern cultural history. Next we spent the rest of our journey in Jerusalem, and had a most exciting time under the Temple Mount which Dr. Rauscher also seemed to view.

TABLE 3: Hurtak-Rauscher RV tests in the Near East, including Golan Heights, Sea of Galilee and Jerusalem. Note that the RV covered only seven days.

Region 3	Date	Location	Outbound Target
1	June 1, 2013	Mt Hermon, Golan Heights	Water Pond on the slope of Mt Her-mon.
2	June 2, 2013	Tiberius, Israel	Sea of Galilee town with both Christian and Muslim inhabitant's influences.
3	June 3, 2013	Rujum al-Hiri, Golan	Ancient Archeolog-ical zone.
4	June 5, 2013	Jerusalem, Israel	Interior of Dan Hotel showing geometries and interior lights.
5	June 6, 2013	Jerusalem, Israel	Notre Dame Hotel at the top Restau-rant overlooking the city.
6	June 7, 2013	Jerusalem, Israel	Under the Temple Mount.

Israel Target #1 Photo: Taken by Drs. Hurtak while traveling to the top of Mt Hermon, this picture shows the highest mountain in the Near East in the Golan Heights. Rauscher seems to be able to accurately remote view the area by her statement of the hill or mountain and the strange circular structure in the area with a tan yellowish color water. People do walk or hike in the area but are not seen in the photograph.

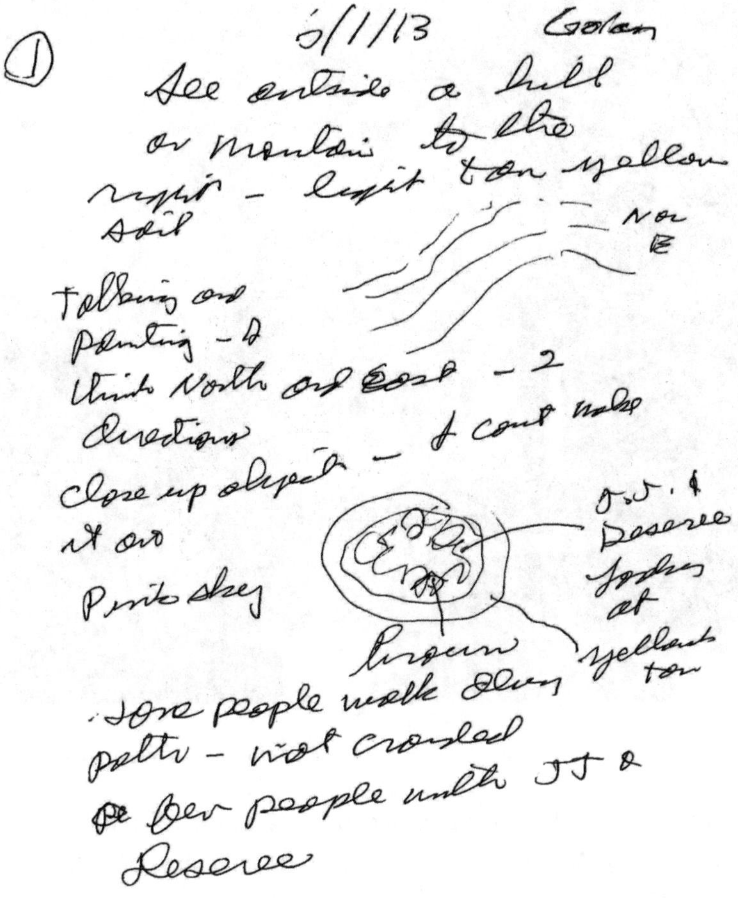

Israel Target #1, RV Drawing: Elizabeth Rauscher who has never been to Israel and Syria, picks up on the unique land feature, a round pool near the top of Mt. Hermon, the highest mountain in the Middle East. People normally hike the area.

Rauscher's handwriting says: "see outside a hill or mountain to the right soil," "light tan yellow ," "talking and pointing—I think North and East directions," "close up object—I can't make it out," "pink sky," "J.J, and Desiree looking at yellowish tan brown [circular area]," "some people walk along path—not crowded, few people with JJ and Desiree."

Israel Target #2 Photo: A photograph taken of the town of Tiberius of the al-Amari Mosque. Upon the mosque are many large archways, especially on the front (not seen in this photograph). This mosque is just a few blocks from the Sea of Galilee. It shows an arch/dome as Rauscher describes and a minaret tower. What is not seen is the Sea of Galilee which is within a few blocks of the building. In fact, Drs. Hurtak took this picture right after eating at the seaside and while they were walking back to their car.

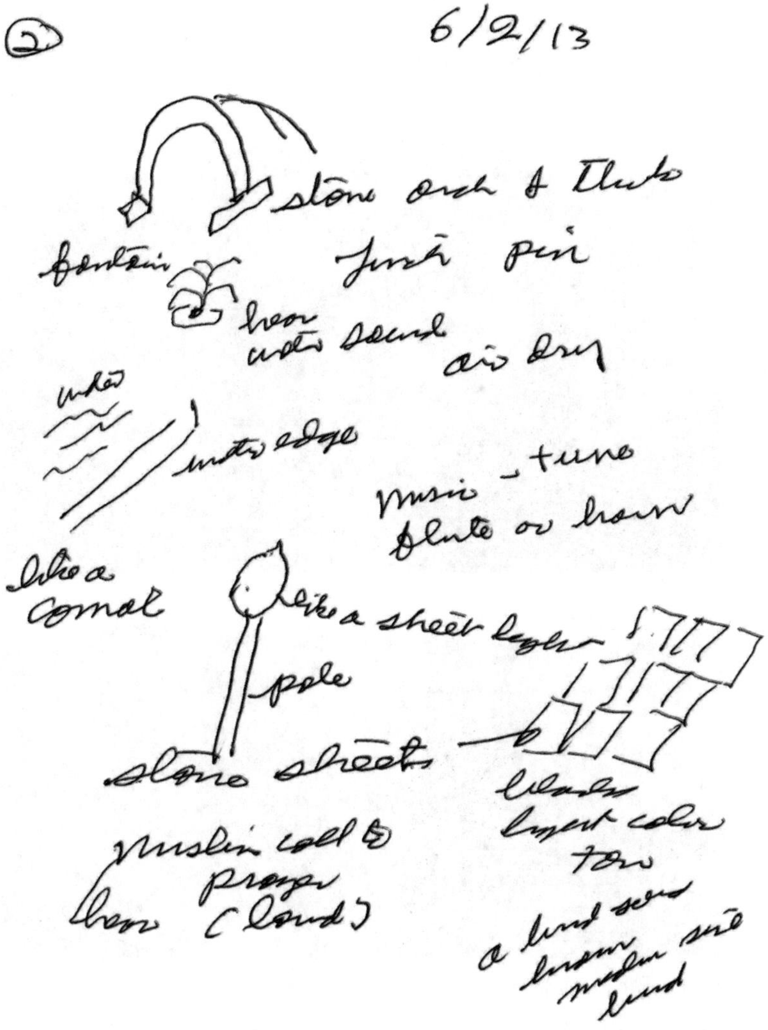

Israel Target #2, RV Drawing: Rauscher remote viewed a scene of an archway and the Muslim call to prayer tower. She also saw water nearby. Rauscher's handwriting says: "stone arch," "I think linchpin," "fountain far left," "hear water sounds," "air dry," "water," "water edge," "like a canal," "music tune," "flute or horn," "like a street light," "pole," "stone streets," "hear Muslim call to prayers (loud)," "blocks light color tan," and "a loud sound, brown medium size building."

Israel Target #3a and 3b Photo: Drs. Hurtak at Rujum al-Hiri, Golan. The original structure had a stone dome at the center in pre-Christian times. It is now in ruins but accessible. On the bottom picture you can see the main structure to the left of Drs. Hurtak as they prepare to leave the site somewhat in a hurry to get back before dark, but willing to take a final picture. There are many strange shaped stones that confirm Rauscher's strange images. It is also the Hurtaks' belief that this was an ancient calendar of circular stone rings, better viewed from above. Desiree is also wearing a beige hat. There are others with them but not currently in the pictures.

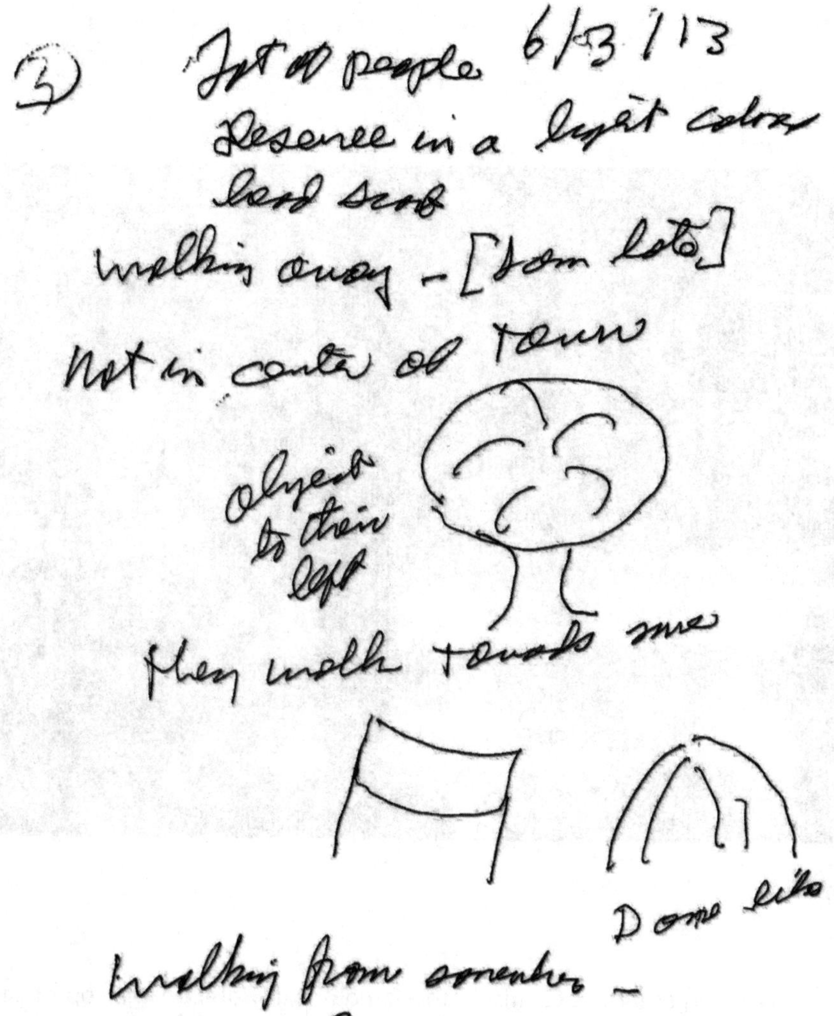

Israel Targets #3 RV Drawing: Remote Viewing by Rauscher of a dome -like structure in a rural archaeological area. She sees Desiree wearing something light colored on her hair and the object radiating energy. Rauscher's handwriting says: "Desiree in a light color head scarf walking away (I AM late)," "not in center of town," "object to their left, they walk towards me," "walking from somewhere—an event," and "Dome like."

Israel Target #4 Photo: Inside the famous Dan Hotel on the top of the Mt. of Olives in Jerusalem. Here we see the reflecting lights mirrored off the large glass walls and open levels that were connected with a magnificent lobby. Elizabeth Rauscher was accurate in viewing J.J. and Desiree Hurtak moving through walls of lights that had certain symbol designs (see near the legs of Dr. Hurtak). There are dark tables with people having coffee also in front of where Dr. Hurtak is standing.

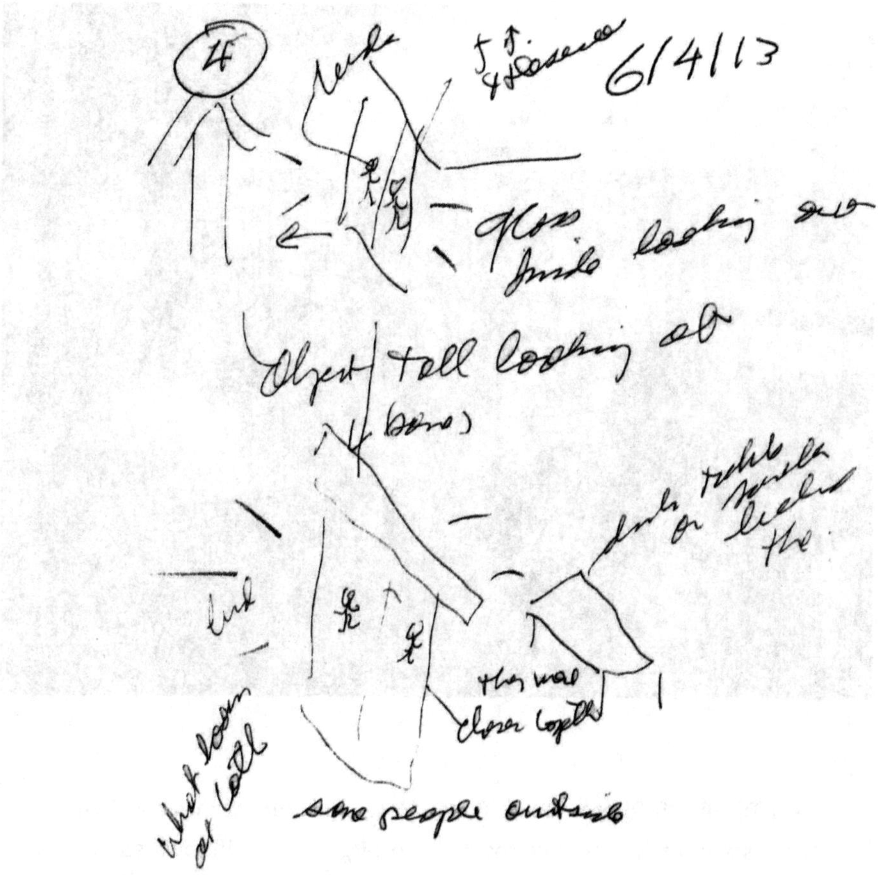

Israel Target #4 RV Drawing: Elizabeth's remote viewing and drawing picks up on unique stair levels with Dr. Hurtak inside a Hotel with the lights and glass. Rauscher's handwriting says: "J.J. and Desiree," "glass inside looking out," "object tall looking at (some)," "What looking at tall," "Dark tables or something behind," "they were closer together," and "some people outside."

Israel Target #5 Photo: Notre Dame Hotel Restaurant in Jerusalem. This restaurant has seating inside with large glass windows so you can see the Old Jerusalem City. It also has wooded beams as its structure which can be seen in the photograph.

There is an equal series of tables and chairs inside. The brown beams can be see in the railing that Desiree is sitting next to (which is made of wood), as are the window frames, and wooden floor planks (out of the picture). No fish tank .

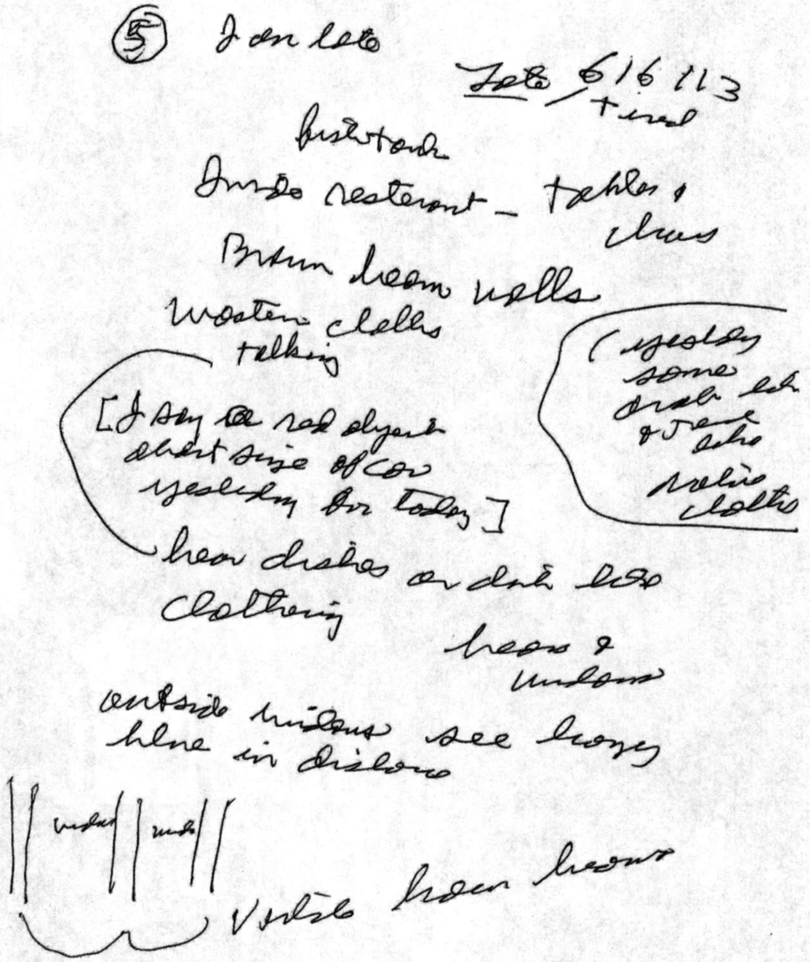

Golan-Israel Target #5, RV Drawing: Remote Viewing of Restaurant with noise of dishes and view with large glass windows around table on porch. Wooden beams are noted. Rauscher's handwriting says: "late time," "fish tank," "inside restaurant," "tables and chairs," "brown beam walls," "western clothes," "talking," "hear dishes or dish like clattering," "beams and windows," "I say red object, about size of car yesterday for today]," "yesterday some Arab-like and Jewish-like native clothes," "beams and windows," "outside windows see hazy blue in distance," "window, window," and "vertical brown beams."

Israel Target 6a and 6b, Photo: On one of our last days we were able to go under the Temple Mount. The archways are all underground, and therefore throughout there are square direction signs as location notifications and in case of emergencies. These signs have Hebrew and also English on them. The walls are also light colored natural stone as described by E.A. Rauscher. The tile of the danger sign is white with a blue hue as she also describes. This was a place of prayer for the local peoples and also there is a mosque above.

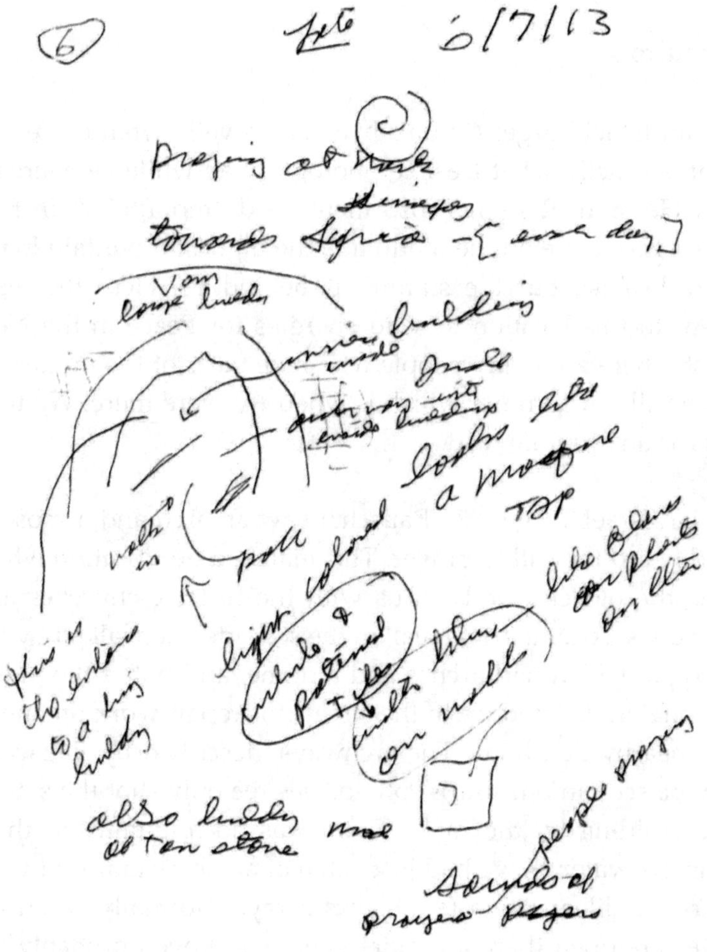

Golan-Israel Target 6, RV Drawing: Rauscher's Remote Viewing reveals the following in her handwriting: "praying at mosque," "towards Syria [each day]," "large building," "inside building made," "archway inside inner building," "looks like a mosque top," "this is the entrance to large building," "walk in," "path," "light colored," "also building made of tan stone," "white and patterned tiles with blue on walls, like flowers or plants on altar," and "sounds of prayer people praying."

Results

Golan-Israel Target #1: Elizabeth saw a yellow/tan circle and that is exactly what Desiree photographed while we were on Mt. Hermon. Rauscher also mentioned "mountain." In fact, Drs. Hurtak are on the mountain, the highest mountain in the Middle East, but the summit is behind us. Here the team went to this location to send energies for Peace in the Near East. There are many people who hike parts of the mountain, especially in summer which is when we were there. We took this as an accurate read.

Golan-Israel Target #2: Rauscher saw an arch and a mosque and heard the call to prayer. This matched our location which was the old city of Tiberius with the historic churches and mosques. After a brief meal on the sea side, we walked by the mosque which had arches and a dome, and noted the building materials lined up in the streets for repair work on one of the nearby buildings. The archways, described by Rauscher, can be seen in our tourist photo. Desiree only shot the side of the building by the café. There was no fountain but there was the water as we had just eaten at a fish restaurant by the Sea of Galilee only a few blocks away. Normally when the cafés are open there are more people and even probably the sound of music.

Golan-Israel Target #3: We journeyed to the lower Golan to an energy point that served as a type of Stonehenge in this part of the world which may have also acted as a cipher for sophisticated star alignments. Here we probed the integrated structure of concentric circles that represent, perhaps, the first man-made computer in stone.

Rauscher picked up on the circular form and clearly there were massive and unusual stones in a circular formation which I (Dr. J.J. Hurtak, see photo) disclosed in my earlier book *The Keys of Enoch*® as a series of computer-calendar-like stone circles.

In brief, the area known in Arabic as 'Rujum al-Hiri' served as some type of early astrophysical computer for astronomers in the ancient Near East. Rauscher seemed to have viewed us walking with a few people near a circular structure. She seems to have focused on the central dome (now collapsed) structure and then outwards towards the concentric circles. When we left it was "late" in the afternoon, as Rauscher accurately states, one of the people needed to return before dinner to her family so we were in a rush to leave.

Golan-Israel Target #4: Inside the Dan Hotel on the Mt. of Olives overlooking the Temple Mount. This is where we stayed while in Jerusalem, and as we walked up and down the spacious stairs of the hotel, Rauscher viewed the balcony that had large glass windows. Although we did not take a photograph of the balcony, we do have a photograph of the inside multi-floor lobby and the amount of glass that is present inside is clearly visible. Elizabeth Rauscher was able to use her RV ability to see Drs. Hurtak walking around the huge walls, stairways and glass decor. In the public lounge at Dan Hotel, Jerusalem, Dr. J.J. Hurtak is standing in a place where you see the amount of glass in the inner balconies of this ultra-modern hotel, but behind the camera are many sitting places to eat and drink. The main view of the old city of Jerusalem is also just behind the camera on an outside balcony.

Golan-Israel Target #5: Dinner at the Notre Dame Hotel Restaurant, managed by the Pontifical Institute Notre Dame. The facilities hold precious Christian artifacts and the restored church-hotel was redesigned by one of our colleague's relatives who is a leading Christian architect in Israel.

The visit to the top of the restaurant at Notre Dame

overlooking the city of Jerusalem allowed for a view in three different directions. Here we prayed for peace and the preservation of all holy places connected with the children of Abraham, as the location is adjacent to the walls of the Old City.

Rauscher notes the tables and chairs, the wooden, brown beams and also the large windows of the facility. She notes a "fish tank" which to our recollection does not exist. But the majority of her notes are accurate.

The location is within a walkable distance to the historic Wailing Wall and The Temple Mount.

Golan-Israel Target #6: Under the Temple Mount. Rauscher's eye remote viewed the arch-like patterns that walk you down the long corridors of this underground structure where archaeologists are uncovering the true foundation of the world's most remarkable temple connected with Western civilization. The square natural tiles are broken in their symmetry by exit and warnings that are present throughout, written on glass with white etched Hebrew (and also secondarily English), giving a bluish hue to the image. There are people who enter these chambers just to say special prayers for peace. There are some unique stones in this area which are estimated to weigh several hundred tons.

Conclusion

Overall Elizabeth Rauscher was accurate in identifying the locations from the concentric circle patterns of Rujum al-Hiri and the other places that we had travelled to in the Holy Land and Golan. This is truly a place of historic significance. The locations that we visited, like those in Egypt, are not the most common areas that a tourist would visit and so we gave her a high accuracy in her remote viewing abilities.

Overall there was good correspondence on her drawings in Golan (Syria) and Israel with matchable elements intermixed with correct information.

References

DeMauro, Iris (2002) *Temple of Mu* documentary, Australian Fox Television, 2000. IMD Films .

Hurtak, J.J. (1973) *The Book of Knowledge: The Keys of Enoch.®* Los Gatos: The Academy for Future Science.

Turolla, Pino (1978) Discussions between J.J. and Desiree Hurtak and Pino Turolla at his home in Miami Beach, Florida.

Valentine, Mason (1974) Discussions between J.J. and Desiree Hurtak and Mason Valentine at his home in Miami, Florida.

Wakefield, Jay (2013) Discussions between J.J. and Desiree Hurtak and in Saravejo, Bosnia, Sept. 2013.

Chapter 13:
The Nature
and
Properties of Consciousness
by
J.J. Hurtak, Ph.D., Ph.D. and
Desiree Hurtak, Ph.D.

"The evolution of consciousness has a quality impossible to describe."

— Pierre Teilhard de Chardin

Table of Contents

Introduction 655

1. Theories of Remote Viewing 656

2. Biological functions and
   Remote Viewing..664

3. Local and Nonlocal Spacetime
   and Remote Viewing..675

Conclusions 678

References 680

Introduction

Scientists have devoted much effort to understanding various aspects of quantum physics, specifically where one particle of nature can directly link with another particle at a distance as if they were connected. This phenomenon appears to indicate that the universe has a larger intercorrelated relationship which we are now beginning to comprehend. Called "nonlocality" in quantum physics, this phenomenon, we believe, directly relates to the science of Remote Viewing (Walker, 1975; Rauscher and Amoroso, 2011).

We have examined the manner in which "Remote Viewing" developed into a study of distant objects or events that are beyond the scope of the usual five senses. As in "nonlocality," we contend that Remote Viewing is not a matter of sending and receiving signals or information, although we sometimes use that terminology, but of becoming aware of how we are functioning within a greater domain of consciousness.

From a physics point of view, the puzzling feature of Remote Viewing is that there is no evidence that its performance declines with distance between receiver and target, including up to several thousand kilometers distant (Puthoff and Targ, 1976). Rauscher has clearly demonstrated this ability (Rauscher and Targ, 2001).

Regardless of the terminology, we have presented evidence that we can capture events outside the five senses, which we believe requires a hyperdimensional access by the mind. It is worth noting that individuality is not lost during the "sending-receiving" of a signal, but becomes transpersonal.

Scientists like Hal Puthoff and Russell Targ, in their studies of Remote Viewing (Targ and Puthoff, 1977) and E.A. Rauscher (Rauscher and Targ, 2001), have found that there is a remarkable information flow into human consciousness that occurs immediately from distant parts of the world without "any" delay in time. Research from Targ and Puthoff also indicates that consciousness is not localized in the brain (Targ and Puthoff, 1977). If the perception of unity between the sender and the target is real, then there must be reliable neurophysiological techniques that could be used to activate both the perception (Remote Viewing) and the state of unity (nonlocality). In this chapter we analyze the great territory of cross-disciplinary methodologies associated with both.

It is important to state that after seeing the posting of millions of internet pages of documentation on Remote Viewing, we encounter: a) confirmation of Remote Viewing of distant targets; b) the possibility of precognition and retrocognition of human activities; and c) the ability to create a consciousness change in our reality such as promoting peace. The question is how does this take place?

1. Theories of Remote Viewing

In 1995, comprehensive studies in remote viewing were declassified by the CIA and released to the public. Not only is this research providing accurate results, in terms of images transferred across long distances of space, but it is also demonstrating non-degradation of information retrieved instantaneously from over thousands of kilometers away (Rauscher and Targ, 2001).

It is intriguing that those conducting Remote Viewing experiments were able to see objects inside buildings even when the outbound sender could not access them. Even more intriguing is that Remote Viewing is not just a spatial phenomenon of viewing objects at a greater distance (such as New York) from a research location in California, but one that can predict near-future events as well (Targ, 2012). These events, or "occasions of experience," may, in some models, be considered as quantum state reductions of events in physical reality that are accessible (Hurtak, 2007). This suggests that we may exist in a type of wave field or holographic geometry (Hogan and Jackson, 2009), that relates to both general relativity and quantum mechanics. One could call this the "consciousness field" that may involve quantum state reductions, where the larger mind functions like an *encyclopedia galactica* in the universe (Hurtak, 2004).

Although everyone has the ability to Remote View, numerous individuals have demonstrated the potential for vast mental capabilities as they investigate their own minds to the very depths of their being. According to Henry Stapp (2007), there is no system in the present understanding of the electromagnetic body that can account for the activity of Remote Viewing and distance communications, although it accurately occurs as detailed in this book and at Stanford Research Institute (Targ and Puthoff, 1977; Targ and Hurtak, 2006).

In this section, we propose some additional concepts regarding the mechanism of RV that complement Rauscher's "eight space" model. We also propose that thoughts and images are an integral part of what we term the "consciousness/quantum field," which may relate directly to the macrocosm of relativity or Minkowski space, although the nature of these interactions is not yet fully comprehended. What we term a "field" in this context is an extended and, perhaps, global domain for consciousness and consciousness effects. How does RV work? Rauscher (1979) proposes that the unity of the field "exists in Eight Space" (Rauscher and Targ, 2001) which is a type of hyperdimensional, minimally eight-dimensional space in accordance with Lorentz conditions. More dimensions are possible for this model. This implies that we can function in a multidimensional reality where conscious awareness is affected and brought into "sympathetic vibrational resonance" through a connection of dimensions.

"Eight space" opens up a bridge between our local spacetime location in terms of such concepts as frequency, wavelength, amplitude, phase, and others that are formulated in the physical sciences. Today, we are beginning to understand this through String Theory, where all particles operate in multiple dimensions. Einstein considered this view in his unified field theory, where the particle is simply a singularity or discreteness as a very high spacetime concentration that bends the spacetime of a nonlinear field. Louis De Broglie and David Bohm (1980) took this another step forward. Bohm called his concept the Implicate Order behind our ordinary reality, which he called the Explicate Order. The Implicate Order being "the field" that provides order to our reality.

De Broglie conceived of a particle as a "singularity" in a wave or field in which particles are guided by a wave field. Together they created the De Broglie-Bohm theory which can be applied to the entirety of the universe. They put forward the concept that one particle depends on the position of all other particles in the universe. In fact, the very concept of a particle took into consideration the particle-wave duality. So there is an interactive wave function that guides the universe.

Until recently, the tendency in quantum mechanics, as well as in neuroscientific circles, has been to ignore the phase of the de Broglie wave. The Iceland Conference, however, brought together Rauscher (1979), Brian Josephson, Andrija Puharich and other participants to create *The Iceland Papers* that attributed significance to the frequency, wavelength, and the non-negative square of the de Broglie wave amplitude. A few great physicists such as Born, Dirac and Feynman, countered the common attitude of dismissing the de Broglie wave as a mathematical tool by claiming it did have possible fundamental significance.

Although Rauscher and Targ (2012) consider Remote Viewing to be juxtaposed with multidimensional space, the theory of an "interactive wave function" can help explain the process of Remote Viewing in spacetime. Here the condition is given whereby the object wave in real or virtual form, interacts or coincides with the brain. Puharich considered RV to be based on the electron and on some quantum particle transfer. He considered it was based on a two-state quantum trigger established by a quantum tunneling to other consciousness connections, establishing proto-communication (Puharich, 1973).

In Russia, similar research into the nature of wave and brain interactions with outside influences, was investigated by Vlail Kaznacheev whose experiments were conducted to analyze how the human mind was influenced by surrounding fields, specifically the electromagnetic field. He further examined how the mind can influence the chemistry of reactions in a petri dish thousands of kilometers away. Kaznacheev also agreed that cognition is a process of events occurring in an overarching field of consciousness experience (Kaznacheev and Trofimov, 2008).

Kaznacheev and Trofimov explored helicoidal anisotropic structures and gave us critically important insights into what underlies the self-organizing properties of all living systems at the atomic and molecular level. Although some of the methodology of the Russian researchers is not well defined, their ability to determine the biological mechanism of remote effects is notable. It is their understanding that the planet's electromagnetic field blocks the consciousness field and acts as a filter for time and space enabling us to have this experience in linear time (Kaznacheev and Trofimov, 2008), although there is the ability to influence or override the local field.

The Russian influence on this ability to affect fields may follow recent studies that show that local sidereal time (LST) may be significant in enhancing or overriding the normal fields. The effect of Remote Viewing seems to occur more easily at certain times of the day or night cycle. According to Spottiswoode (1997), energy fields permit a more effective signal for 8 minute periods, depending on the local sidereal time (LST). Spottiswoode gathered data on 1,468 published ESP trials and calculated that the effect more than tripled when the LST was near 13:30.

Spottiswoode questioned his own research but in another analysis he tested his findings by collecting an additional 1,015 trials from different experiments, i.e., which validated his previous findings. The peak of his validation set occurred at the same time. Coordinating the data revealed that anomalous cognition is more than three or four times as effective in a rather narrow window that rises and falls near 13.5hr LST (Spottiswoode, 1997). The results from several research groups from Europe and the USA were reported in the study made by Spottiswoode (1997). This included Stanford Research Institute and PEAR (Princeton Engineering Anomalies Research, Dept. of Engineering, Princeton University) (Jahn and Dunne, 1986).

We conclude that there is more to the *external* and remote *operating mode* relationship than has previously been investigated and it may be influenced by the solar cycle, but it is not the principle cause. Rauscher and Busier (2015), also demonstrated that certain specific frequencies generated by solar coronal ejections affect human brains, enhancing EEG alpha.

The effects on RV related to solar frequencies do not disavow the multidimensional aspect of "eight space" (Rauscher and Targ, 2012) nor Mind-2 (Hurtak, 1973). They only indicate that the mind is sensitive to many external, currently unacknowledged, fields.

All these theories do not exclude a "consciousness/ quantum field" that could extend into other dimensions as "eight space." Tests and analyses by Roger Nelson which originated at Princeton University under the title "Global Consciousness Project (GCP)" have used RNGs (random number generators) to show that consciousness can influence matter. RNGs were deployed worldwide, called EGGs. The hypothesis is that a physical system, which is a well-defined part of the material world, can exhibit anomalous behavior when correlating with "global" human mental activity (Bancel and Nelson, 2008).

The stated goal of the GCP is to detect the possible emergence of non-random number effects during important global events, and data continues to be acquired and analyzed. The project has found correlations that reflect the presence, activity and influence of consciousness on random numbers during real-time events as an indicator of global consciousness coherence. Several events of global significance have been clearly identified by the project team. Their results show that out of an aggregate deviation of data during 236 registered *formal events,* there were significant 4.5 standard deviations (Bancel and Nelson, 2008, Radin, 2009). Events, such as 9/11 or other disasters like a train crash that caused major loss of life in India, appear to impact the "consciousness field", which is immediately registered through clear changes to the RNGs with sensor analysis.

Roger Nelson's research from PEAR (Princeton Engineering Anomalies Research) has demonstrated that the human "biocomputer" influences the RNG showing some connection of consciousness on real events. We propose that the "consciousness field" is not limited to 3-4 dimensional space, but works with a higher dimensional connection, which we call Mind-2 (Hurtak, 1973), that functions in an unbounded four-dimensional space and beyond (Rauscher and Amoroso, 2011). In fact, our entire universe may be arranged holographically, where the expanded concepts of the hologram exist as a continuous field in multidimensions and every part is part of every part. Here we also expand the concept of Pribram's holonomic brain (1991), where our brain functions more as a holographic storage network using wave oscillation which creates wave inference patterns in which memory is naturally encoded.

Although the holographic model may not be completely accepted, that is to say that everyone stems from a two-dimensional reality (Hogan and Jackson, 2009), but we may be from an eight dimensional reality or greater. Nevertheless, it is easy to see how the mind is part of the field of information flow which we (Drs. Hurtak) call Mind-1 or brain consciousness, that comes into a full interplay via its nonlocal ability through experiences with other hyperdimensional spaces and beyond ($N > 4$) as Mind-2 (Hurtak, 1973). This may relate to how, with Remote Viewing, one can record images of an object being observed where the whole of Mind-2 experiences the target. Imaging the target may correspond to a type of coherent wave reconstruction from the multidimensional reality of the original object with all its imagery.

Specifically, Mind-2 is the consciousness field existing in the unified space, which for Rauscher is "eight space" (Rauscher and Targ, 2001). With Mind-2 one can anticipate events and perceive any subject in any area of the world and create an objective map of information by accessing space beyond conventional space and time beyond conventional time. In fact, in "eight space" there may be time, just not linear time (i.e., past, present and future) but our complete timeline.

What we demonstrated in our studies from Lab Nine and from others, such as Roger Nelson's Princeton University studies (Bancel and Nelson, 2008) and Rauscher (1979), Targ and Puthoff (1977) at SRI, may be confirming the existence of a multidimensional "consciousness quantum field". The field is not that of primary matter in the substratum of nature, but a wave-type function that relates to multidimensional realms and is a type of ordering that exits beyond our 3-4 dimensional ordinary space to bring order and harmony to living systems.

A scientifically based remote viewing theory should describe, scientifically, what is conventionally considered to be the province of the paranormal (Mitchell, 1999). The fundamental perspective arising from this consideration of the emerging physics of quantum mechanics is that matter arises as a dynamic modification of the forces and fields that are the very substance of space, but not limited by 4-dimensional spacetime (e.g., String Theory and M-Theory).

The use of Remote Viewing opens a new understanding of how the human brain can act in the greater domain of multidimensional processes and is capable of operating on many levels of local and nonlocal activities. This led several leading psychologists and scientists (Pribram, 2005) to suggest that the brain operates as a collective 'global mind.' This has furthermore enabled some researchers to think of the brain as having a superior 'wetware'. When the outbound experimenters focus their thoughts (as described in Chapters 3, 4, 11 and 12) for the purposes of remote cognition, the properties of multidimensional Mind-2 become enhanced. Here intention seems to play a role.

It is important to understand that new concepts detailing how particles interact in the universe are changing rapidly. Bell's theorem of nonlocality has now been confirmed by Gisin in 1997 (reported on by Tittel, et. al. 1997) and other experiments with Salart, *et. al.* (2008). These experiments have confirmed the measurements of entangled pairs interacting in a continuous measurable correlation at a distance (an 18km distance, Salart *et. al.*, 2008). In fact, researchers in both Russia and the West have confirmed that quantum mechanical forces "transmit" information between photons faster than the speed of light (Tittel, *et. al.*, 1997, Salart *et. al.*, 2008) which is believed to be related to the quantum field. We are claiming the same process operates where the quantum field is interrelated to the "Psi" field (Puharich, 1973), but that the fields are not limited to 3-4 dimensional space, but operate in "All-Space".

Some term this the Noosphere (Teillard de Chardin, 1975, Vernadsky, 1967) while for others it is the *Logos*-sphere (Gangadean, 1998). To Rauscher and Targ it is "eight space" or "All-Space" creating a unity that acts upon the usual 3-dimensions. For us it is our connection with Mind-2 (Hurtak, 1973) that is the interaction with the All-Space and where the quantum processes allow Mind-1 to receive the information. We believe quantum electrodynamics (QED) and biology interact with Mind-2 to interpenetrate our quantum/consciousness field, influencing the physical substrate as well.

Another way to describe this connection is to consider the "neurosynergistic" fields in the human brain coherence as Mind-1, and the ability to conceive of human brain—universal mind field interactions as Mind-2. Expanded consciousness supports the existence of a greater Mind-2 (Hurtak, 2004) dimensional field or Rauscher's eight space (Rauscher and Targ, 2001; Rauscher and Amoroso, 2011) and its possible interaction with the synergistic continuum of infinite possibilities, where consciousness, thus, emerges as the dominant part of the field.

More importantly, the very concept of consciousness and remote viewing changes the separation between the 'I' and the collective. One thing is becoming clear, humanity is more than neuron nets, but is a continuous transducer or "biotransducer" of energies and information which correlate with our thoughts and our experience of reality.

Why is any of this important? Understanding our interconnectedness releases us from our limitations and makes us part of the greater collective totality. This collective is understood to operate as a dynamic fractal-like process, or like a growing tree with its extensions becoming a living process (in unbounded four-dimensional space and beyond) that includes the human mind-body. However, the choices we make in the reduction of information from the consciousness field as the observer create both positive and negative events in our lives. So it is up to us to comprehend the schema, the energy pathways, as libraries within our brain and to make the greater choices.

2. Biological functions and Remote Viewing

Given that we are unable to directly perceive the neuronal or atomic processes responsible for the creation of the remote visual images recorded by our perceptual apparatus, it becomes difficult to analyze how we obtain the source or the properties of the data. Some of the same limitations happen when we think of how we perceive our exterior environment, which is separate from us. We have to admit that what we observe is the product of our perceptional interpretation of an exterior world to which we also have no actual direct access. This "myopia" is responsible for our emphasis on our immediate material world and our possible misperception in subjective levels of experience. The existence of the extraocular visual phenomenon cautions against this deception and illusion, in the same manner that retinal vision should.

If the brain and consciousness occupy an entangled whole, as revealed in quantum brain dynamics (QBD) the brain is constantly entangled with the consciousness field through a resonance and coherence (Jibu and Yasue, 1995). This gives rise to not only a nonlocal correlation in space, but also in time. For example, when we are observing a car on the road, the state of our nervous system is 'entangled' with the state of the car. Here the concept of entanglement can be defined as a continual relationship between two separated particles, where even at a distance of space there is a correlation of states of matter. How is it that we can connect with an external object which becomes part of 'my' perception? It may be through the field relationship that consciousness and the brain establish a connection of entanglement across what is considered a temporal divide of distant realities so that their states remain correlated.

Another perspective is that we need not ponder over the classical "origins" of atoms so much as the resonance or quantum "coherence" of fields. This allows the measurement of one of the quantum particles or fields in the "consciousness field" to determine the quantum state, itself.

Considered as passive or Remote Viewing, the same principles can be applied to "intentional" viewing for purposes of affecting outbound experimenters at a distant target. A neurophysiological-like component of the state of unity and remote perception appears to exist outside neurological functions, but at some time perception is coupled to it. For the remote perceiver, the physical brain is the encoder/decoder equipment for the intention through remote signals acting like a receiver or transceiver mechanism.

It is proposed that what we call the "remote viewing experience" is the interaction between our neuronal system and the synergistic organization of events in space and time, which are outside our normal perception. Reciprocal influences are postulated in that a single neuron could affect and be affected by the morphology and informational organization in which it interacts like a micro-physiological antenna connected with the wetware of the brain.

The illusive nature of consciousness, once a matter of philosophical speculation, has established an important presence in the field of quantum physics through the scientific field of Remote Viewing (Rauscher and Targ, 2001). Consequently, taking quantum physics into account, it appears that the consciousness of the "observer" is what collapses the wave function, at least within our own field of consciousness (Hameroff and Penrose, 1996). The patterns are "harmonically" reflected to the physical nervous system of the intended recipient through the intermediate harmonic levels of the existing "energy fields," which we propose interact with all-space. This can explain the process of remote healing (Targ, 2002).

Of course, the perceptual field of the remote viewer is not the norm within our cultural environment and claims of visualizing distant targets are usually ignored. It should be mentioned that not all brain functions are exclusively from the consciousness field, for the physical brain, with its neuronal cells, also functions with memory and automatic responses, such as heartbeat signals, etc. (which may be quantum mechanical, but are not directed from that field).

Nevertheless those who are trained in Remote Viewing, may have enhanced abilities for "distant intentionality." In addition to perceiving a nonlocal target, perceivers can affect the target at a distant location. For example, one may produce a healing effect on the target, by visualizing the balancing of proper functioning of human organs. This is performed through the establishment of an integration process that the healer is visualizing. Carefully defining the intentions of the sender is crucial. Intentions should be specific, such as that of holding an intention to "lower blood pressure," "reduce tumor size," "decrease anxiety" or even "increase emotional and physical well-being."*

The process of "distant intentionality" may be inter-

*We suggest this only be added to any traditional allopathic medicine or physician intervention.

preted as an interaction of neuronal processes with the occurrences in spacetime at any location, that is, local (less than a meter) to distant (several thousand kilometers)—with no degradation of acquired information. In working with traditional healers in different cultures throughout the world over the last forty years, we have observed that they utilize an *"external operating mode,"* that is the ability to visualize, from a transpersonal perspective, a different aspect of reality through a type of "Remote Viewing." The *external operating mode* does not require a "gift," although some have the ability to heal without any training. Historically, those who pray for others visualize the intended subject and by attaining certain mental states establish expanded neurosynergistic modalities.

It is known that complex electromagnetic vibrations move in and out of the cellular and skeletal structures. Our bodies are constantly exposed to infrared, microwave, radio and other invisible frequencies from remote phones, computer systems and even cosmically-derived extremely low frequencies. Cells are known to react to electrical pulses, stimulating glands, triggering the heart muscles, or sending out biologic signals (Hurtak and Hurtak, 2008; Sinatra, 2011). The bioelectrical condition of the body is really just a part of a larger biophysical energy system that is in continual dynamic interaction. Each molecule is engaged in a constant vibratory energy exchange between three separate, interacting energy systems: kinetic, electromagnetic, and nonlinear (non-Hertzian) fields (Rauscher, 1983).

Achieving coherence requires establishing a harmonic resonance between three levels of bio-energy: 1) Kinetic-acoustic or kinetic-mechanical vibratory energy fields; 2) the electromagnetic fields (electrical and magnetic fields, and electromagnetic radiation), and 3) other fields which are nonlinear, nonlocal, non-Hertzian (electromagnetic), hyperdimensional, perhaps also superluminal, and supra-temporal (Vind, 2004, Rauscher and Amoroso, 2011). It may be the latter fields (points 2 and 3) that are being "affected" by the thoughts of the sender.

Substantial data has been reported that changes can occur within the human cells of a person who is exposed to remote healing (Targ, 2002). We use the concept of energies that may be activated by the sender's *remote operating mode*. The capacity for the remote focusing of mental images at the target can be called the *directionality factor*, connecting the morphology of interacting "energy fields" through what had historically been called the all-encompassing presence of a Universal Mind (Hurtak, 1996, Hurtak and Hurtak, 2011).

Does remote healing violate personal space or is there a general public space that all thinkers use that includes the possible branches of "observation?" One should always create positive input within the "consciousness field" with no harm wished on any individual. However, remote healing, like remote communications, simply places thoughts into the field to make the "possibility of transformation" possible, the choice of thought still belongs to the "observer/receiver."

Consequently, the larger consciousness field seems to have the ability to provide the information, but it is the brain's action according to will and thought that makes the reduction or determination. This implies that a major role of the brain is the retrieving and disseminating of specific desired information from the consciousness field. For the remote viewer, the brain is much more than rote memory, data storage and retrieval, and the assembly of stored data placed into logical patterns. Knowledge is part of a complex process beyond the internal color patterns, and phosphene explosions.

In the larger roadmap of consciousness evolution, there are literally millions of ways that the external consciousness field can be perceived and processed by human beings. The processes of human thought, prior to extension of thought processes, may occur within the minute crystalline-magnetic domains (Coetzee, 2000), operating in a manner somewhat similar to magnetic bubble networks that were developed for advanced computer systems. Recent investigations of the brain suggest that the neural net stays close to instability, and in this way, can be switched by minute action between different states (Freeman, 1996).

We are proposing that consciousness exists as a multi-dimensional field that works through quantum mechanical properties. It interacts with the internal structure of the brain and cellular components such as pyramidal brain cells, but also mirror neurons, blood cells, and on a smaller micro scale, ATP, in such a way that it is able to manage, as well as be influenced by the physiological cellular structure.

The work of Roger Penrose and Stuart Hameroff may demonstrate one possible "receptor" vehicle which is the microtubule structural geometry within cells that reacts to the reduction of thought (Hameroff, 2001). While microtubules have traditionally been considered as purely structural components, recent evidence has demonstrated mechanical signaling and communication functions (Vernon and Wooley, 1995) and they may be an additional receptor site for consciousness activities.

Stuart Hameroff, at the Center for Consciousness Studies at the University of Arizona (Tucson), collaborating with quantum physicist Roger Penrose, has advanced his theory that examines an extensive network of intracellular microtubules to explain the remarkable ability of our brain to perform incredibly complex functions and to reach into realms of consciousness. As an anesthesiologist, Hameroff identifies microtubules as being related to the conscious and unconscious states.

Microtubules are inelastic tube-like polymers, assembled from molecular filaments. They form tiny tubes of uniform diameter (25nm) from two complementary protein subunits (alpha and beta tubulin). These tubulin heterodimers are joined end-to-end to form protofilaments. These in turn are assembled into 13 protofilaments that create a helical arrangement with GTP (Guanosine triphosphate) and GDP (guanosine diphosphate) present (Hameroff, 2001).

Microtubules are basically self-assembling hollow crystalline cylinders whose walls are hexagonal lattices. They exist in various types of human cells and those of other life forms. As hollow crystalline cylinders, they exist in the cytoplasm of the cell and are a key part of the cellular structure (Hurtak, 1973). Microtubules also exist in neurons. In neurons, they self-assemble to extend axons and dendrites and form synaptic connections; microtubules then help maintain and regulate synaptic strengths responsible for learning and cognitive functions (Hameroff and Penrose 1996).

What is unique is that microtubules have plus and negative charged ends. Usually, the negative ends are within the center of the cell's cytoplasm and the plus ends extend towards the cell walls, i.e., all axonal microtubules have plus-end-out orientation. However, in proximal dendrites in neurons, most of dendritic microtubules are oriented with minus ends distal to the cell body.

Hameroff and Watt (1982) outline the cellular mechanism for coupling to some form of higher level functioning in which microtubules appear to form a biomolecular quantum-level coupling within every cell, which may allow for what we call the *external operating mode* between fields of consciousness and the cells in our body (Vind, 2004). It is interesting that microtubules are bioactive in the range of acoustic frequencies (Sahu, *et. al.,* 2013).

Hameroff proposes that tubulins, the subunits of the microtubules, undergo coherent excitations, for example, in the gigahertz range by a mechanism suggested by Fröhlich (1975) where excitations of tubulin support computation and information processing (e.g. Hameroff and Watt, 1982; Rasmussen, *et. al.,* 1992).

Neurobiologist, Alexander Bandyopadhyay (2014) discovered quantum resonance at gigahertz, megahertz and kilohertz during excitations in single microtubulins. He found coherence resonance peaks ranging from 12 kilohertz to 8 megahertz. Microtubule coherence connected with quantum vibrations appear to resonate over different scales, to generate various 'beat frequencies,' where megahertz frequencies may change with the processing of information. Through coherent excitations, computations may take place between neighboring tubulins causing cells to act as "cellular automata" (Penrose and Hameroff, 2011).

The microtubule structures may not be alone in playing a key role in interaction with the consciousness field. There is also over 70 years of research on the numerous pyramidal cells within the different laminations of the cerebral cortex. The greatest concentration of pyramidal cells is in the frontal lobe region between the eyebrows and the occipital lobe near the brain stem at the back of the head. They principally reside in the forebrain structures such as the cerebral cortex, hippocampus, and amygdala. They are large cells with pyramidal-shaped cell bodies (*soma*), having an apical dendrite (emerging from the top) and a long axon. The complexity varies depending upon their position in the various layers in the brain and their spinous structure varies also amongst species with the human having larger and more complex structures (Elston, 2003). It is now known that the axons of certain pyramidal cells in the hippocampus CA1 region are able to process information via the dendrites, bypassing the soma region of the cells (Thome, 2014).

The pyramidal cells occupy a critical role in the ability of the brain to integrate information. Recent research has also shown degeneration of the pyramidal cells in Alzheimer's patients (Mann, 1996). Alzheimer's relates directly to information and cognition, but if the consciousness field interacts with the brain via pyramidal cells as a "receiver" device, one can see a connection. Pathological analysis shows that pyramidal cells contain a molecular liquid crystal structure immersed in a lipid. These cells with their dendrites form a system that functions as a non-linear oscillator (Brumberg and Gutkin, 2007) with sensitivity to light. Their communication is bi-directional and functions with other cells, as well as other neurons. Scientists (Elston, *et. al.*, 2001) accept the notion that these cells are designed to carry out some basic computational function in the nervous system, as well as cognitive functions. We believe that the pyramidal cells are an intricate part of tapping into the consciousness field (Hurtak, 1973).

Pyramidal cells are activated by frequency oscillation signaling, but also new research (Johansen, 2010) has shown that optically stimulated lateral amygdala pyramidal cells can produce learning and memory formation. This is perhaps one of the keys to the sending and receiving of an image in connection with Remote Viewing, making the mind-brain matrix in no way magical. Instead, it may be a key piece of the 'wetware', working with the "sending and receiving" of information which is able to go beyond conventional sensory channels, working with interhemispheric actions to tap into the plenum of the surrounding field (Hurtak, 1996).

Thus, pyramidal cells may be another receptor site for the brain-body complex, but it is the cells or what is within the cells that are the receptor points of the quantum field. There is also ATP (adenosine triphosphate) which acts as the body's energy machine, as well as the mitochondria in the cells (Hurtak, 1973). ATP uses electrons to function and when released from neurons, ATP functions as a neurotransmitter and neuromodulator. ATP is co-released with classical neurotransmitters at the brain's synapses. ATP released at synapses is also metabolized extracellularly to adenosine (Zimmermann, 1994).

Electron transport and ATP synthesis occur in the inner membrane of the mitochondria. Mitochondria contain their own DNA or mtDNA. Also, ATP is processed through oxidative phosphorylation in the cell membrane in which the lipoprotein oscillates at 10^{11} Hz. Rauscher and Busier (2012) believe that the ATP process is key to the energetic "life battery" where the "life force" is transduced in part in the human body.

Rauscher and Busier (2012), and Rauscher and van Bise (1988, 1989; van Bise and Rauscher, 1990; van Bise, *et. al.*, 1989) have *in vivo* and *in vitro* evidences that excitation comes through the cerebral Purkinje process and endocardium Purkinje fibers which communicate at a fundamental frequency of 7.6 Hz, which is also the beat frequency of the iliac bifurcation. In the cardiac system, the Purkinje process acts as a step down frequency divider to the pulse rate.

Brain cortical structures perceive images both through the visual cortex and also by synchronizing fields that are associated with stable wave packets. The dendrite rich Purkinje system acts as an I/O system establishing inner body communications which operate through the hypothalamus pituitary axis and through the vagal system. A detailed mechanism described in the research of Rauscher and Busier (2012) discusses the manner in which these mechanisms interface with the ATP process, and the mechanism in which external fields can be utilized to also enhance wound healing, inflammation, as well as pain reduction (Rauscher, 2011).

Rauscher and van Bise (1988, 1989; van Bise and Rauscher, 1990; van Bise, *et. al.* 1989) conducted extensive research and clinical studies on enhancement of biological systems by electromagnetic fields in forty years of research. They propose that we are intimately linked to our environment by a set of fundamental frequencies which is vital to our well being and alters our state of consciousness (Rauscher and Busier, 2015).

We see that the work of many researchers is coming together to point to how we are connected to the consciousness universe. We are, now perhaps, on a threshold of understanding the manner in which inner and outer consciousness meet.

Russian research data also cites a high degree of coherence among the cells and recent research has examined the cellular microtubule structures (Gariev, Hurtak and Hurtak, 2017), as their molecules tend to resonate in harmony with their neighbors, as also the Purkinje process *in vitro* and *in vivo* (van Bise and Rauscher, 1990), that is, every cell operates (resonates) as if it is part of a larger system of cells, and various coherent groups operate within a progressively higher organization of whole organs, and the whole organism. We are taking this one step further to say that everything, from atomic structures to DNA to organs, are part of the greater resonance field. An interconnection could harmonize "discordant and even chaotic" energy patterns to produce a coherence of information in the body.

Coherence can become contagious as it interconnects everything from whole organisms to cell assemblies. This provides an explanation for the rapid operation of the brain with speeds as fast as one ten-thousandth of a second, moving information as fast as 1,000 meters per second (some ten times faster than the fastest neuronal fiber) (Vind, 2004).

Since the late 1960's Fröhlich and colleagues have confirmed collective behavior of assemblies of biomolecules resulting in long-range coherent radiation in the 10^{11} Hz range. The quantum role, itself, is also addressed in the papers of Japanese researchers, Jibu and Yasue (1995), working with Karl Pribram.

Russian researchers' work in paraphysics (Kaznacheev, and Trofimov, 2008) has also shown that both living and inanimate objects (Gariev, 1993) allow for consciousness linkages through wave or field structures. Gariev (1993; Gariev, Hurtak and Hurtak, 2017) has shown this also applies to DNA as a wave frequency. Gariev is not alone as Luc Montagnier, Nobel Price winner for discovering HIV, in his research, even though not accepted by most of his colleagues, has confirmed that DNA has some components that make it like a resonant sender and receiver antenna. Some junk DNA may even be part of the resonator. Montagnier (2011) created experiments where the DNA is placed near pure water via a 7-8 Hz frequency and allowed to remain there for 8-12 hours. The water received the DNA sequence code although no substance of DNA was present. He claims to have been able to send the sequence of the DNA into water and then back to another DNA structure through polymerase chain reaction (PCR). Therefore, the DNA molecule appears to be able to be transferred as a wave field and maintain the code, not the substance, within the water.

Montagnier and Gariev believe that the next phase of medicine will be "wave medicine" or as Gariev calls it "Linguistic wave genetics (LWG)." (Gariev, 2013). All one needs to do is create the right wave frequencies and you can correct the DNA, which could be used for organ regeneration.

For Montagnier, water is fundamental and required for the codes of DNA to be housed. Before that, it was electromagnetic frequencies that coded the information into water as the 7-8 Hz frequency which was required for the transfer. We propose that the transfer of wave potentials from one subject to another makes use of our own cellular structures, as well as an internal software system which utilizes internal "energy states," as well as local fields. Whether it be distant intentionality, or direct encoding, results seem to show that the structure of cells, including neurological cells, allows for the receiving and sending of information, beyond mere chemical signals.

3. Local and Nonlocal Spacetime and Remote Viewing

Accordingly, *Mind Dynamics in Space and Time,* entertains how there is a multidimensionality, i.e., Rauscher's "eight space", with a general relativity and quantum field connection. The biological feasibility for the mind-brain connection relates also to quantum states that exist in and beyond the brain. Quantum approaches can explain enigmatic features of consciousness, but so can general relativity.

Critics of quantum approaches to consciousness (e.g., Nauenberg, 2007) point out that consciousness is not clearly related to quantum states such as nonlocality. In standard quantum mechanics, even the slightest interaction can generate entanglement. The process of entanglement working through superpositions creates an ability to share information across space. More importantly, entanglement may affect the past, present and future, instantaneously. Russell Targ's research also involved Remote Viewing into future events (less than 6 months) which when tested were found to be predictable (Targ and Hurtak, 2012).

It is interesting that in "eight space," according to Rauscher, there would be time, but not in the linear sense. One can consider that time in eight space is a unified field where events past, present and future in third or fourth dimensional space all come together and are known. So can the future be changed? We agree with Rauscher that the answer is yes, but it must occur in the higher dimensional timeline which then changes it on all the dimensional levels.

It is the "communication" or event occurrence across both space, as well as time that is important. Space and time are linked by the Minkowski metric (Rauscher, 1979). However, time perception and the selection of informational possibilities all originate within the consciousness field—which is why we have said that "time is within the consciousness of the species" (Hurtak, 1973).

All this implies that if there were no entanglements in everyday human existence there would be no neural correlates of consciousness across space and time. In a certain sense, we are in energetic flux from the external surrounds, some of which may be part of a larger "entanglement" of energetic quantum processes of the environment. This further implies the possibility of a larger entangled system beyond our own local consciousness field of experience. Therefore, entanglement resides not exclusively in the brain, but as part of a larger expanded network of energy whose nature is that of interconnectedness that may transduce into electrochemically charged processes within the human system. We hypothesize that all life has been entangled at one point or another and therefore has a common origin. This origin may not reside exclusively in the third dimension, but may be from a fifth or higher dimensional reality which according to Rauscher works best with an "eight space" reality, because of the Lorentz symmetry principles (Rauscher and Targ, 2001).

Thus, the senses or sensory apparatus, although functioning by means of the brain/mind, experience the material world as a consequence of the condition of a larger phase conjugation. Here the brain/mind's consciousness perception includes the premise that reality itself must also be describable by creation/annihilation models (and hence) a three-dimensional phase conjugate adaptive resonant stream of consciousness so that 'objects' are seen as located where they actually are (Rauscher, 1978).

From Heisenberg to Rauscher, the phenomenon of consciousness is found in the dynamic process of nature, with interpenetrating fields between nature and supernature acting upon our body as a biotransducer. Some like Shimony (1993) prefer to limit the activity of quantum correlations calling it "passion at a distance." However, research carried out by members of The Academy For Future Science and Lab Nine at Ossining, New York (Chapter 11), since the mid-seventies suggests the existence of a mind-link, global/multidimensional link reality that can be tapped by hyperspace realities or by achieving higher states of consciousness.

We have also considered that the basic structure for information processes in "bioenergy systems", as in a human, operates through intentionality. If the laws governing the quantum nature of this planet are nonlocal as in quantum physics, then "bioenergies" for Remote Viewing and remote healing may also be functioning through "consciousness intention and extension" to any place on the planet. Ingo Swann has demonstrated that off planetary targets such as Mars, Jupiter and beyond can be remote viewed (Swann, 1997). Communication between mind-to-mind or mind-to-target information may occur by tuning the "relay circuits in the mind" which act as storage and operation centers where thought transmission is neither time limited nor space dependent.

The immediate environment may be a slice of a special kind of 'plenum' in an infinite order. It is full of many superpossibilities which are interpenetrated, entangled, and "superposed," and where we have input. According to physicist David Bohm, "Space is not empty. It is a plenum as opposed to a vacuum, and is the ground for the existence of everything, including ourselves. The universe is not separate from this cosmic sea of energy" (Talbot and Bohm, 1991).

The plenum is a superposition of possibilities and part

of the Implicate Order. And we, being part of the plenum, are part of the consciousness field within and around our bodies. We propose that the majority of remote viewers may activate the neuronal field in the brain by a consciousness overlay that is non-linear and allows the viewer to receive the interplay between the cerebral circuits or neuronal fields and the external realities of experience.

What about individual consciousness? There are aspects of Self or "I" within both the Mind-2 and the physical neurological network of the brain, Mind-1. During the life span of an individual, memory is coded within the brain (although it continues with the soul after death), and other computational processes of the mind remain as an aspect of consciousness there. But the true existence of consciousness thought is a "field of resonance" (McTaggart, 2009) that is all-prevalent and used by Mind-2 to identify its own aspects of individual consciousness within the collective consciousness field.

Conclusions

We are living in a consciousness universe. All living beings are part of a larger phenomena that affects them, ranging from Nature to Supernature, or that which is beyond current scientific norms. We propose that the human body operates as a living biotransducer, which is interacting with many aspects of Nature. Since everything that occurs in the living universe is ultimately the result of one or more quantum mechanical event, our universe is inhabited by a greater consciousness field that collectively is within myriad fields that are responsible for the detailed workings of the physical universe. Remote Viewing may be understood to work within the nature of pure consciousness within and beyond time or space.

We believe there are different, but accessible dimensions of consciousness, and what we call Mind-2 is associated with varied strata of the organization of events in spacetime and beyond. Since all neuronal fields may interact with one another and with multidimensional space, the hyperdimensional field interacts with and is utilized by consciousness which can, in turn, be processed by the mind. When the remote viewer identifies with the hyperfield, the personal self becomes transpersonal, reaching out to the target, as Mind-1 reaches out to Mind-2.

After forty years of research, Dr. Elizabeth A. Rauscher has shown her consistent abilities in Remote Viewing, to see and retrieve critical knowledge in support of consciousness studies (see Chapter 12). Now it remains for a new generation of researchers to apply Remote Viewing directly to challenge the dominant paradigm of science.

The course of the new "consciousness universe" requires further acceptance. Because Remote Viewing and Remote Communication (mind-to-mind and mind-to-target without technology) transcend all known sensory cues and expectancy effects, it is important for experiments to continue with rigorous and blind-testing procedures.

Quantum physics, which plays a key role in the consciousness universe, can further be expanded into areas of quantum biology or quantum biophysics as in the study of epigenetics. Yet in all of this, we are to see ourselves as part of a greater living conscious, collective field that moves us beyond our separate selves.

The vast realms of consciousness now are opened to us. This allows us to turn our mind and heart to the great mystery and awesome wonder of universal existence and to feel the profundity of reality that is the majesty of the cosmic domains of life. The future of remote viewing studies must continue with the next step of building a stronger database that might offer a greater perspective of our own reality but also the use of our mind's ability to see beyond. We have the ability to know what has never been known before and understand physical and consciousness reality as one harmonic totality. We are truly universal humans awakening to the great cosmic design as *homo universalis*!

References

Bancel, P. A., R. D. Nelson (2008) "The GCP Event Experiment: Design, Analytical Methods, Results." *Journal of Scientific Exploration*, 22, pp. 309-333.

Bandyopadhyay, A. (2014) "Pandora's Box: Direct Measurement of Microtubule Bundle Resonance in a Live Neuronal Axon Suggests Scale -invariant Brain Dynamics Extends Inside Neurons", Toward a Science of Consciousness, Tucson, AZ.

Bohm, D. (1980) *Wholeness and the Implicate Order*. London: Routledge, ISBN 0-7100-0971-2.

Brumberg J.C. and B.S. Gutkin (2007) "Cortical pyramidal cells as non-linear oscillators: experiment and spike-generation theory." *Brain Res.* 2007 Sep 26;1171:122-37. Epub 2007 Jul 20.

Cassarino, D. S., and J. P. Bennett (1999) An evaluation of the role of mitochondria in neurodegenerative diseases: mitochondrial mutations and oxidative pathology, protective nuclear responses, and cell death in neurodegeneration. *Brain Research Reviews, 29*(1), pp. 1-25.

Coetzee, H. (2000) Memory and the Synaptic Gap. *Future History* Spring 2000, Series 3 Vol. 3.

Elston, G. N. (2003) "Cortex, cognition and the cell: new insights into the pyramidal cell and prefrontal function." *Cereb Cortex* 13, pp. 1124–1138.

Elston, G. N., *el. al.* (2001) "The Pyramidal Cell in Cognition: A Comparative Study in Humanand Monkey," *The Journal of Neuroscience*. Vol. 21 RC163.

Freeman, W.J. (1996) "Random activity at the microscopic neural level in cortex ("noise") sustains and is regulated by low-dimensional dynamics of macroscopic cortical activity ("chaos"), *International Journal of Neural Systems*, 7, pp. 473-480.

Fröhlich, H. (1975) The extraordinary dielectric properties of biological materials and the action of enzymes. Proc. Natl. Acad. Sci. 72, pp. 4211-4215.

Gangadean, A.K. (1998) *Between Worlds: The Emergence of Global Reason*. New York: Peter Lang Publishing.

Gariaev, P.P. (1993) Wave based genome, Depp. VINITI 15:12. 1993, pp. 278.

Gariaev, P.P. (2013) The Principles of Linguistic-Wave Genetics (LWG), Part One , *Future History*, Summer 2013.

Gariaev, P.P. , J. Hurtak and D.E. Hurtak (2017) Linguistic Wave Genetics and the Wave based genome. In progress.

Hameroff, S.R. (2001) "Consciousness, the Brain and Spacetime Geometry, in Cajal and Consciousness: Scientific Approaches to Consciousness on the Centennial of Ramon and Cajal's Textura," Ed. P.C. Marijuan, *Annuals of the New York Academy of Science*, pp. 929.

Hameroff, S.R., and R. Penrose (1996) "Orchestrated reduction of quantum coherence in brain microtubules: A model for consciousness. In: Toward a Science of Consciousness." *The First Tucson Discussions and Debates*, S.R. Hameroff, A. Kaszniak and A.C. Scott (eds.), MIT Press, Cambridge, MA. Also published in Mathematics and Computers in Simulation 40, pp. 453-480.

Hameroff, S. R., and R.C. Watt (1982) "Information processing in microtubules," *Journal of Theoretical Biology*, 98, pp. 549-561.

Hogan, C.J., and M.G. Jackson (2009) "Holographic geometry and noise in matrix theory". *Phys. Rev. D* 79 (12): 124009. June, 2009, arXiv:0812.1285.

Hurtak, J.J. (1973) *The Book of Knowledge: The Keys of Enoch®* Los Gatos: Academy For Future Science.

Hurtak, J.J. (1996) "The Human Body - Its Energy and Resonance Matrix" *Future History*, Spring 1996, Los Gatos: Acad. For Future Science.

Hurtak, J.J. (2004) "The New Physics: A Dialogue with Burkhard Heim" *Future History*, Summer 2004, Los Gatos: Acad. For Future Science.

Hurtak, J.J. (2007) Personal conversations with Henry Stapp, University of Salzberg, Consciousness Conference.

Hurtak, J.J. and D.E. Hurtak (2008) "Expanding The Body Electric" *Future History*, Spring 2008, Los Gatos: Academy For Future Science.

Hurtak, J.J. and D.E. Hurtak (2011) *Overself Awakening, A Guide for the Schoolhouse of the Soul.* Los Gatos: Academy For Future Science.

Jahn, R.G. and B.J. Dunne (1986) "On the Quantum Mechanics of Consciousness with Application to Anomalous Phenomena," *Foundations of Physics* **16** (8): 721–772. doi:10.1007/bf00735378.

Jibu, M. and K. Yasue (1995) Quantum Brain Dynamics: An Introduction. Amsterdam.

Johansen, Joshua P. *et. al.*, (2010) "Optical activation of lateral amygdala pyramidal cells instructs associative fear learning." *Proceedings of the National Academy of Sciences*, 107 (28), 2010, p.12692.

Jou, S.H., *et. al.* (2009) "Mitochondrial dysfunction and psychiatric disorders." Chang *Gung Med J.* Jul-Aug;32, 4, pp. 370-9.

Kaznacheev, V. P. and A.V. Trofimov (2008) *Reflections on Life and Intelligence on Planet Earth.* Ed. JJ Hurtak, Los Gatos: Acad. for Future Sc.

Mann, DM (1996) Pyramidal nerve cell loss in Alzheimer's disease." *Neurodegeneration.* December, 5, 4, pp. 423-427.

McTaggart, Lynne (2009) *The Field: The Quest for the Secret Force of the Universe.* Harper Collins.

Mitchell, E. (1999) Preconference discussion with Dr. JJ Hurtak at Presentation at the World Forum, Sao Paulo, Brazil.

Montagnier, L. *et al.* (2011) "DNA Waves and Water" *J. Phys. Conf. Ser.*, 306, 1, 012007 (DOI: 10.1088/1742-6596/306/1/012007).

Nauenberg, M. (2007) Critique of "Quantum Enigma: Physics Encounters Consciousness," *Foundations of Physics,* November 2007, Volume 37, Issue 11, pp. 1612-1627.

Penrose, R. and S.R. Hameroff (2011) "Consciousness in the Universe: Neuroscience, Quantum Space-Time Geometry and Orch OR Theory." *Journal of Cosmology* 14, *journalofcosmology.com/Consciousness 160.html.*

Pribram, K. (1991) *Brain and perception: holonomy and structure in figural processing.* Hillsdale, N. J.: Lawrence Erlbaum Associates.

Pribram, K. (2005) "Transcending the Mind/Brain Problem" *Journal of Religion and Science,* 15 Dec. 2005, DOI: 10.1111.

Puharich, A. (1973) *Beyond Telepathy.* Garden City, N.Y: Anchor Press.

Puthoff, H.E. and Targ, R. (1976) "A Perceptual Channel for Information Transfer over kilometer distances: Historical perspective and recent research," *Proc. IEEE,* Vol. 64, no. 3, pp. 329-254.

Radin, D. I. (2009) *The conscious universe : the scientific truth of psychic phenomena* (1st HarperCollins ed.) New York: Harper One.

Rasmussen. S, R. Feldberg and C. Knudsen (1992) Self-Programming of Matter and the Evolution of Proto-Biological Organizations. SFI Working paper: 1992-07-035.

Rauscher, E.A. (1978) "Some Physical Models Potentially Applicable to Observed Remote Perception Data," *Bulletin American Physical Society,* 21, 1304, 1976, and E.A. Rauscher, "Complex Coordinate Geometries in General Relativity and Electromagnetism with Applications to Remote Perception," *Bulletin American Physical Society,* 23, 84, 1978.

Rauscher, E.A. (1979) "Some physical models applicable to remote perception," in *The Iceland Papers: Frontiers of Physics. Select papers on experimental and theoretical research on the physics of consciousness;* foreword by B.D. Josephson, edited by A. Puharich. Assentia Research Associates, Amherst, Wisconsin 54406, p. 50.

Rauscher, E.A. (1983) *Electromagnetic Phenomena in Complex Geometries and Non-linear phenomena, Non-Hertzian waves and Magnetic Monopoles,* Millbrae: Tesla Book Co.

Rauscher, E.A. (2011) "Methods and Devices for Measurement and Treatment of Pain and the Treatment of Inflammation and Osteoporosis", November 22, 2011, US Patent 8,062,229.

Rauscher, E.A. and R.L. Amoroso (2011) *Orbiting the Moons of Pluto: Complex Solution to Einstein, Maxwell, Schrödinger, and Dirac Equations.* London: World Scientific.

Rauscher, E.A. and M.J. Busier (2012) "Rhythms of Nature: A New Age of Health and Wellness," *RRD,* Arizona.

Rauscher, E.A. and M. J. Busier (2015) "Enhancement of Biological function by the use of Electromagnetic fields," *RRD,* Arizona, 101941.

Rauscher, E. A. and R. Targ (2001) "The Speed of Thought: Investigation of a Complex Space-Time Metric to Describe Psychic Phenomena," *Journal of Scientific Exploration,* Vol. 15, No. 3, pp. 331–354.

Rauscher, E.A. and R. Targ (2012) "Investigation of a complex Space-time metric to describe Precognition," Ed. I. Fredriksson, *Aspects of Consciousness: Essays on Physics, Death and the Mind,* McFarland and Co., Inc.,pp. 5-26,

Rauscher, E.A. and W.L. van Bise (1988) "External Magnetic Field Impulsed Pacemaker, non-invasive method and apparatus for modulating brain through an external magnetic field to pace the heart and reduce pain", February 9, 1988, US Patent No. 4,723,536.

Rauscher, E.A. and W.L. van Bise (1989) "Non Invasive Method and Apparatus for Modulating Brain Signals Through an External Magnetic or Electric Field to Reduce Pain," US Patent No 4,889,526, December 26, 1989.

Sahu S, Ghosh S, Ghosh B, Aswani K, Hirata K, Fujita D, Bandyopadhyay A (2013) Atomic water channel controlling remarkable properties of a single brain microtubule: correlating single protein to its supramolecular assembly. *Biosens Bioelectron* 2013,47, pp. 141–148.

Salart, D., A. Baas, J.A.W. van Houwelingen, N. Gisin and H. Zbinden (2008) "Spacelike Separation in a Bell Test Assuming Gravitationally Induced Collapses." *Physical Review Letters,* 100, 220404.

Shimony, A. (1993) *Search for a Naturalistic World View.* Cambridge: Cambridge University Press.

Sinatra, S. (2011) *The Sinatra Solution: Metabolic Cardiology.* Basic Health Publications.

Spottiswoode, S.J.P. (1997) "Apparent Association Between Effect Size in Free Response Anomalous Cognition experiments and local Sidereal time," *The Journal of Scientific Exploration,* Vol, 11, No. 2, 1997.

Stapp, H. (2007) Conversation with Dr. JJ Hurtak, Salzburg, Austria.

Swann, Ingo (1997) Conversation with Drs. Hurtak, New York, NY.

Talbot, M. and D. Bohm, (1991) "Chapter 2: The Cosmos as Hologram," *The Holographic Universe,* p. 51.

Targ, E. (2002) "Research methodology for studies of prayer and distant healing" *Complement Theories in Nursing & Midwifery.* Feb,8(1), pp. 29-41.

Targ, R. (2012) *The Reality of ESP: A Physicist's Proof of Psychic Abilities.* Wheaton: Quest Books.

Targ, R. and H. Puthoff (1977) *Mind-reach.* New York, Delacorte.

Targ, R. and J.J. Hurtak (2006) *End of Suffering.* Charlottesville, VA: Hampton Roads Publishing.

Targ, R. and J.J. Hurtak and D.E. Hurtak (2012) Personal conversations with Russell and Drs. Hurtak.

Teilhard De Chardin, P. (1975) *Toward the Future.* New York: Harcourt Brace Jovanovich (original title, French: *La Direction de l'Avenir*).

Thome, C., *et. al.* (2014) "Axon-carrying dendrites convey priv leged synaptic input in hippocampal neurons," *Neuron,* 83, pp. 1418-1430.

Tittel, W., *et. al.* (1997) "Experimental demonstration of quantum-correlations over more than 10 kilometers," *Physical Review A* 57, 3229. arXiv.org/abs/quant-ph/9707042.

van Bise, W.L. and E.A. Rauscher(1990) "Magnetic Flux Control of Low Back Pain" report on formal study at the Sierra Pain Institute, IDE Document G880034, FDA, Silver Spring, Maryland.

van Bise, W.L., E.A. Rauscher and R. Kroening (1989) "Magnetic Control of Low Back Pain", *Bulletin of American Physical Society,* 34, p. 109.

Vernadsky, V.I. (1967) *Biosfera.* (Russian) Moscow: Nauka.

Vernon G.G. and D.M. Woolley (1995) The propagation of a zone of activation along groups of flagellar doublet microtubules. *Experimental Cell Research,* 220, 2, pp. 482-494.

Vind, G. (2004) "Intercellular Foundations of Consciousness, Part 1 & 2) *Future History,* Winter 2004 Series 4 Volume 7, Los Gatos: Academy For Future Science.

Walker, E.H. (1975) "Foundations of Paraphysical and Parapsychological Phenomena," in *Quantum Physics and Parapsychology* (Editor: L. Oteri), Parapsychology Foundation, New York, pp. 1-53.

Westlake, P. R. (1970) "The possibilities of neural holographic processes within the brain," *Kybernetik,* 10/1970; 7(4), pp. 129-53.

Zimmermann, H. (1994) "Signaling via ATP in the nervous system," *Trends Neuroscience,*17, pp. 420-426.

CELEBRATING A FAMILY OF FRIENDSHIP FOR OVER 40 YEARS

DRS. ELIZABETH RAUSCHER, DESIREE HURTAK AND JAMES J. HURTAK

COVERING RESEARCH IN

CONSCIOUSNESS AND THE POWER OF THE MIND.

p 53 Intrinsic + Extrinsic Geometry

p514 blue peare